INTRODUCTION TO LINEAR ALGEBRA

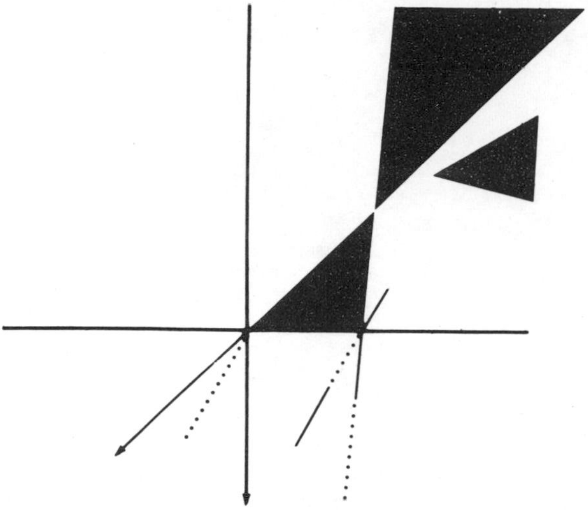

INTRODUCTION TO LINEAR ALGEBRA

PETER J. KAHN,
CORNELL UNIVERSITY

A HARPER INTERNATIONAL EDITION

JOINTLY PUBLISHED BY
HARPER & ROW, NEW YORK, EVANSTON & LONDON
AND JOHN WEATHERHILL, INC., TOKYO

Not for sale in the U.S. or Canada

This Harper International Edition is an unabridged, photo-offset reproduction of the American edition. It is for sale in Japan by JOHN WEATHERHILL, INC., 6-13, Roppongi 7-chome, Minato-ku, Tokyo; in the United Kingdom and on the continent of Europe by HARPER & ROW, LTD., 69 Great Russell Street, London W.C. 1; and in other designated countries by HARPER & ROW, PUBLISHERS, INCORPORATED, 49 East 33rd Street, New York, N.Y. 10016 / For information write Harper & Row at the New York address given above / Library of Congress catalog card number 67-12551 / Printed in Japan / First printing, August, 1967.

To Tania

Trude

Oscar

Jim

Sam

Ed

Wade

John

Bob

"Fuzzy"

CONTENTS

PREFACE

This book is intended as an introduction to linear algebra for the good undergraduate novice mathematics student. It is almost entirely self-contained, including even a rather extensive treatment of elementary set theory. An unimportant assumption is made that the student has some familiarity with elementary differential and integral calculus—unimportant because the only references in the text to this subject appear in illustrative examples and not in the main body.

On the other hand the mathematical viewpoint of the text is basically rather sophisticated and abstract, the underlying philosophy being that this approach is ultimately more meaningful and useful. For example, linear equations are treated near the end of the book rather than near the beginning, the entire machinery of vector spaces and linear transformations having already been established in some detail. For another example, emphasis is placed on the geometric aspects of linear algebra. Thus determinants are introduced as scalar changes in volume effected by linear transformations.

To bridge the gap between the mathematical sophistication of the text and that of the student, a good deal of the text is devoted to motivational exposition. For example, the notion of vector-space isomorphism is heuristically examined in great detail. Or, for another example, before the standard abstract definition of determinant is presented (in terms of alternating n-linear forms), the entire concept is developed on a concrete level in terms of actual oriented area of oriented parallelograms in two-dimensional real Euclidean space. Exercises carry the student further, via oriented volume of oriented parallelepipeds, to three-dimensional real Euclidean space.

One result of this gap-bridging is a text that is, *in toto*, too long for a one-semester course. Nevertheless, by judicious omission of certain sections or portions of sections the numbers of which are indicated by daggers (†), most of the important topics in the text can be covered in one semester. Below we list two possible distributions of course time for text material. The column on the left covers, in one form or another, most of the basic concepts of the text.

The column on the right describes a course of more limited scope, more leisurely in nature, thus permitting the student more time to absorb and explore the elementary linear algebra ideas in greater depth. Needless to say, students with a reasonably good background in set theory may skip Chapter 2, after a cursory reading to acquaint themselves with the notation and terminology used in the text. For such students, a more ambitious program is, of course, possible.

	Number of Weeks	
Chapter	Option 1 (with omissions)	Option 2 (without omissions)
1	$\frac{1}{3}$	—
2	2	3
3	3	4
4	4	4
5	2	4
6	2+	—
7	1+	—

The exercises are designed to be supplementary to text material. Occasionally, an exercise is an important extension of text material, perhaps cited subsequently in the text. In such a case, the exercise is indicated by an asterisk after its number.

At this point I would like to thank Mrs. Ollie Cullers, Mrs. Marjorie Proaper, and Mrs. Ellen Varney for their good typing, and my wife for her help at the final stages of manuscript preparation.

PETER J. KAHN

INTRODUCTION TO LINEAR ALGEBRA

CHAPTER 1 INTRODUCTION TO LINEARITY

It is widely recognized today that the concept of linearity is fundamental to most of modern mathematics, both abstract and applied. This chapter is intended to give the reader some idea of the scope of this concept. We shall avoid precise general definitions here. Instead, we proceed by presenting briefly a number of examples that involve the concept of linearity, pausing now and then to direct the attention of the reader to some of the relevant features of the examples.

There are two equally important ways of looking at linearity. We can think of it as a property of certain *sets*, or as a property of certain *functions*. In Chapter 2 we discuss the abstract notions of sets and functions in detail. For our purpose now, only a rough intuitive understanding of these ideas is necessary. The reader who is totally unfamiliar with them, however, should look at Definitions 2.1 and 2.15 before continuing.

First, we shall look at some examples of *linear sets* (as we shall call them temporarily).

(a) We begin with the set of all real numbers, which, henceforth, we call "**R**." Given any two real numbers x and y, their *sum*, $x + y$, and *product*, xy, are also real numbers. We express these facts by saying that **R** is *closed* with respect to addition and multiplication. Alternatively, we shall say that **R** is a *linear set* (with respect to these operations).

(b) Next, consider a straight line ℓ lying in the Cartesian plane, which we call "$\mathbf{R}^2$," and passing through the origin (see Figure 1). Suppose that ℓ is not vertical. Then, the equation of ℓ is of the form $y = ax$, for some fixed real number a.

The line ℓ consists of all ordered pairs of real numbers of the form (x, ax). Let us agree to define the "sum" of any two ordered pairs of real numbers (x_0, y_0) and (x_1, y_1) to be the ordered pair $(x_0 + x_1, y_0 + y_1)$. That is,

$$(x_0, y_0) + (x_1, y_1) = (x_0 + x_1, y_0 + y_1)$$

Moreover, given any real number r and any ordered pair of real numbers (x, y), let us agree to define the "product" of r and (x, y) to be (rx, ry). That is, $r(x, y = (rx, ry)$.

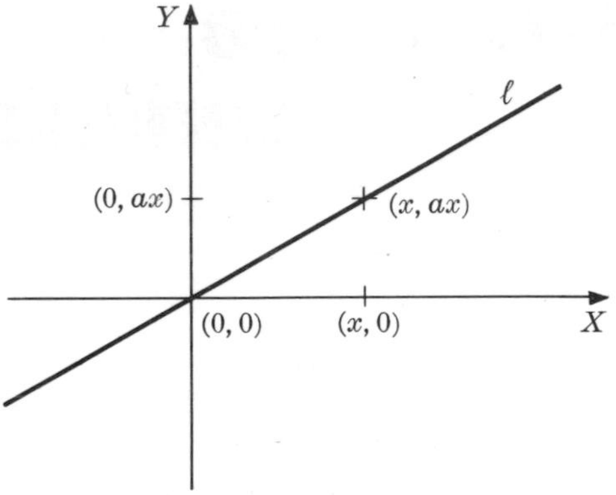

FIGURE 1

With these definitions in mind, it is easy to see that the sum of any two points on ℓ is again a point on ℓ. For

$$(x_0, ax_0) + (x_1, ax_1) = (x_0 + x_1, ax_0 + ax_1) = (x_0 + x_1, a(x_0 + x_1))$$

Moreover, every real multiple of a point on ℓ is again a point on ℓ. For

$$r(x, ax) = (rx, rax) = (rx, a(rx))$$

We express these facts by saying that ℓ is closed with respect to the operations of vector addition (i.e., "addition" of ordered pairs of real numbers) and real multiplication. Again, alternatively, we say that ℓ is a linear set.

(c) The Cartesian plane, $\mathbf{R}^2$, discussed above, is also a linear set. It consists of *all* ordered pairs of real numbers (x, y). In the above discussion, we defined the sum of any two such ordered pairs; it is again an ordered pair (of real numbers). Moreover, every real multiple of an ordered pair of real numbers is again an ordered pair of real numbers, by our definition of "real multiple."

Therefore, the plane is closed with respect to vector addition and real multiplication, and it is, therefore, a linear set.

(d) Let A be any nonvacuous set whatsoever, and let $\mathbf{R}^A$ be the collection of all real-valued functions defined on A. That is, a typical member of $\mathbf{R}^A$ is a function f whose argument, x, ranges over the set A and whose values are real numbers (i.e., $f(x)$ is a real number, for every x in A). To describe in what way $\mathbf{R}^A$ can be considered to be a linear set, we shall describe how to add two members of $\mathbf{R}^A$ and how to multiply a member of $\mathbf{R}^A$ by any real number.

Let f and g be any members of $\mathbf{R}^A$. They are real-valued functions. Therefore, for any x in A, $f(x)$ and $g(x)$ are real numbers, which we know how to add. Put briefly, we shall add f and g by adding their function values $f(x)$ and $g(x)$. In other words, the sum, $f + g$, of the functions f and g is a certain function whose value at any given x in A is given by $f(x) + g(x)$; that is, $(f + g)(x) = f(x) + g(x)$. Similarly, we multiply f by a real number r by multiplying the function values of f by r. That is, rf is a function whose value at x is $rf(x)$ or $(rf)(x) = rf(x)$.

By definition, then, the sum of any two members of $\mathbf{R}^A$, or any real multiple of a member of $\mathbf{R}^A$, is again a member of $\mathbf{R}^A$. Therefore, $\mathbf{R}^A$ has the desired closure property, and, thus, it is a linear set.

(e) This example is similar to the previous one, but slightly more interesting and much more important. Let a and b be any two real numbers, $a < b$. Let $\mathscr{C}[a, b]$ be the set of all continuous, real-valued functions defined on the closed interval $[a, b]$. Define the sum of two such functions and real multiples of such functions as above. It is a well-known fact from elementary calculus that the sum of two continuous functions is continuous and that every real multiple of a continuous function is again continuous. These facts are alternatively expressed by saying that $\mathscr{C}[a, b]$ is closed with respect to addition and real multiplication of functions. Thus, $\mathscr{C}[a, b]$ is a linear set.

(f) Finally, let a, b be as above, and let $\mathscr{D}[a, b]$ be the set of all real-valued functions defined on the closed interval $[a, b]$ and possessing a continuous first-derivative on this interval. Define sums and real multiples of such functions as above. It is, again, a well-known result of elementary calculus that the sum of any two members of $\mathscr{D}[a, b]$ and any real multiple of a member of $\mathscr{D}[a, b]$ is again a member of $\mathscr{D}[a, b]$. Therefore, $\mathscr{D}[a, b]$ is a linear set.

We urge the reader to notice that in all of the above examples, our description did not stop with the specification of such and such a set. Essential to our description was the specification of certain operations, which we called "addition" and "real multiplication" because of their similarity to the usual notions of adding and multiplying real numbers. The set was then shown to be closed *with respect to these particular operations*. Henceforth, we shall never consider the description of a linear set to be complete unless the operations are specified. When referring to the sets $\mathbf{R}$ and $\mathbf{R}^2$, defined above, we shall always think of them as linear sets with respect to the operations defined above in Examples (a) and (c), respectively, unless explicitly stated otherwise.

EXERCISES / 1.1

1. Add the following pairs of real numbers, as prescribed in Example (b), above:

a. (2, 4) and (4, 2)
b. (2, 4) and (−2, −4)
c. (0, 0) and (4, 2)
d. (2, 4) and (3, 6)
e. (2, 4) and (5, 7)

Locate each of the pairs and their sum on the Cartesian plane.

2. Multiply each of the following pairs by 2/3, as prescribed in Example (b), above:

a. (2, 4) **b.** (0, 0) **c.** (3, −7)

Multiply them by 3/2; by −3/2. Locate them and all three of their multiples on the Cartesian plane.

3. Sketch, in the Cartesian plane, the graphs specified by the following equations:

a. $y = 2x + 3$
b. $x = 2 - 3y$
c. $x^2 + y = 4$
d. $y = \sqrt{2 - x^2}$
e. $y = 0$

Each of the above specified graphs is a certain set of ordered pairs of real numbers. Which of these sets is closed with respect to the operations of adding ordered pairs of real numbers and of multiplying them by real numbers, as defined in Example (b)? That is, which of the graphs are linear sets?

4. Consider the case of a vertical line lying in $\mathbf{R}^2$. What is its general equation (using the standard x, y notation)? Describe the ordered pairs of real numbers that lie on such a line. Which vertical lines, if any, are closed with respect to the operations defined in Example (b)?

5.* Show that, if (x_0, y_0) and (x_1, y_1) are any two ordered pairs of real numbers in $\mathbf{R}^2$ not equal to (0, 0) and thought of as opposite vertices of a parallelogram of which another vertex is (0, 0), then the sum $(x_0, y_0) + (x_1, y_1)$ [as defined in Example (b)] is the fourth vertex of the parallelogram. This result provides a geometric interpretation of addition of ordered pairs.

6.* Consider the set of all ordered triples (x, y, z) of real numbers. Define the sum of two triples, (x_0, y_0, z_0) and (x_1, y_1, z_1) by

$$(x_0, y_0, z_0) + (x_1, y_1, z_1) = (x_0 + x_1, y_0 + y_1, z_0 + z_1),$$

and, for any real number r, define the product of r and (x, y, z) by

$$r(x, y, z) = (rx, ry, rz)$$

* An asterisk following an exercise number, here and throughout the book, indicates an exercise that is an important extension of text material (see Preface).

Now, let a, b, c be *any fixed* real numbers and consider the set S of all triples (x, y, z) satisfying the equation

$$ax + by + cz = 0$$

Is S closed with respect to the operations defined above? Justify your answer. Show that the set of all *triples of real numbers is a linear set with respect to the above operations.* Call this set of triples $\mathbf{R}^3$. Henceforth, when we refer to $\mathbf{R}^3$, we shall always think of it as a linear set with respect to the operations defined above.

Now, we look at some examples of *linear functions* (as we shall call them temporarily).

(g) Consider the function given by the equation

$$f(x) = 2x,$$

where the variable x is any real number (that is, any member of $\mathbf{R}$). Let x_0 and x_1 be any given real numbers, and notice that

$$f(x_0 + x_1) = 2(x_0 + x_1) = 2x_0 + 2x_1 = f(x_0 + fx_1)$$

Moreover, for any real numbers r and x,

$$f(rx) = 2rx = r(2x) = rf(x)$$

We express these two properties of f by saying that f respects the operations of addition and real multiplication. This characteristic of f is closely related to the closure property of linear sets. For the graph of f is, of course, just a line through the origin having slope 2. According to Example (b), above, such a line is closed with respect to the operations of adding ordered pairs of real numbers and real multiplication of such ordered pairs. A typical ordered pair on the line is of the form $(x, 2x) = (x, f(x))$. The sum of two ordered pairs of this form is given by

$$\begin{aligned}(x_0, f(x_0)) + (x_1, f(x_1)) &= (x_0, 2x_0) + (x_1, 2x_1)\\ &= (x_0 + x_1, 2x_0 + 2x_1) = (x_0 + x_1, 2(x_0 + x_1))\\ &= (x_0 + x_1, f(x_0 + x_1)),\end{aligned}$$

which is again of the same form. Similarly,

$$r(x, f(x)) = (rx, rf(x)) = (rx, f(rx)),$$

which is, again, on the line, for any r. Thus, the fact that f respects the operations of $\mathbf{R}$ is really the same as the fact that the graph of f is a linear set. We therefore say that f is a *linear function.*

(h) Next, we shall define a real-valued function E whose argument y ranges over the linear set $\mathbf{R}^A$ of Example (d)! That is, for every y in $\mathbf{R}^A$ (i.e., y is a real-valued function of a variable x ranging over the set A), $E(y)$ is going to be a certain real number.

To define E, we choose an arbitrary member a of the set A and hold it fixed throughout the entire discussion. The real number $E(y)$ is then defined to be $y(a)$, the value of y for the argument $x = a$. That is, $E(y) = y(a)$. We chose the letter "E" for this function to emphasize the fact that E is an *evaluation* function: given any y, $E(y)$ is the evaluation of y at a.

Now, let y_0 and y_1 be any two members of $\mathbf{R}^A$. Remember that by the definition in Example (d), the sum $y_0 + y_1$ satisfies

$$(y_0 + y_1)(a) = y_0(a) + y_1(a)$$

In terms of E, this means that $E(y_0 + y_1) = E(y_0) + E(y_1)$. Similarly, for any real number r,

$$(ry)(a) = r(y(a)),$$

so that $E(ry) = rE(y)$.

In this example, the argument of the function E and the values of E lie in different sets, $\mathbf{R}^A$ and $\mathbf{R}$, respectively. In the equation $E(y_0 + y_1) = E(y_0) + E(y_1)$, the "+" on the left denotes the "addition" in $\mathbf{R}^A$, whereas the "+" on the right denotes addition in $\mathbf{R}$. We can summarize the equation verbally by saying that E respects the addition operations of $\mathbf{R}^A$ and $\mathbf{R}$. Similarly, E respects the real multiplication operations of $\mathbf{R}^A$ and $\mathbf{R}$.

Thus, E is a function that takes values in a linear set and whose argument ranges over a linear set. Moreover, E respects the operations of these linear sets. Therefore, we say that E is a linear function.

(i) Consider the linear set $\mathscr{C}[a, b]$ of Example (e). We define a real-valued function $\mathscr{I}$ whose value $\mathscr{I}(f)$, for any given f in $\mathscr{C}[a, b]$, is

$$\int_a^b f(x)\,dx$$

That is,

$$\mathscr{I}(f) = \int_a^b f(x)\,dx,$$

for every continuous, real-valued function f defined on the closed interval $[a, b]$.

Now, let f_0 and f_1 be any two such functions. Then, by definition of $\mathscr{I}$,

$$\begin{aligned}\mathscr{I}(f_0 + f_1) &= \int_a^b (f_0 + f_1)(x)\,dx \\ &= \int_a^b f_0(x)\,dx + \int_a^b f_1(x)\,dx \\ &= \mathscr{I}(f_0) + \mathscr{I}(f_1)\end{aligned}$$

In a similar way, we can show that $\mathscr{I}(rf) = r\mathscr{I}(f)$, for any real number r and any function f in $\mathscr{C}[a, b]$.

Therefore, $\mathscr{I}$ respects the operations of $\mathscr{C}[a, b]$ and **R** so that it is a linear function. This example can be summarized briefly by saying that *the definite integral is a real-valued linear function on* $\mathscr{C}[a, b]$.

(j) We define a function D whose argument ranges over $\mathscr{D}[a, b]$, the linear set of Example (f), and whose values range over the linear set $\mathscr{C}[a, b]$. We shall show that D respects the operations of $\mathscr{D}[a, b]$ and $\mathscr{C}[a, b]$.

Put very simply, for every f in $\mathscr{D}[a, b]$, we let $D(f)$ be the first derivative of f. That is, for every x in $[a, b]$, the value of $D(f)$ at x is $f'(x)$, or $(D(f))(x) = f'(x)$.

We leave it to the reader to show that for any f_0, f_1 and f in $\mathscr{D}[a, b]$, and for any r in **R**,

$$D(f_0 + f_1) = D(f_0) + D(f_1)$$

$$D(rf) = rD(f)$$

This example can be summarized by saying that *differentiation is a linear function on* $\mathscr{D}[a, b]$.

(k) Let f be any real-valued function of a real variable that has a continuous first derivative. Choose any real number x_0, and consider the tangent line to the graph of f at $(x_0, f(x_0))$ (see Figure 2).

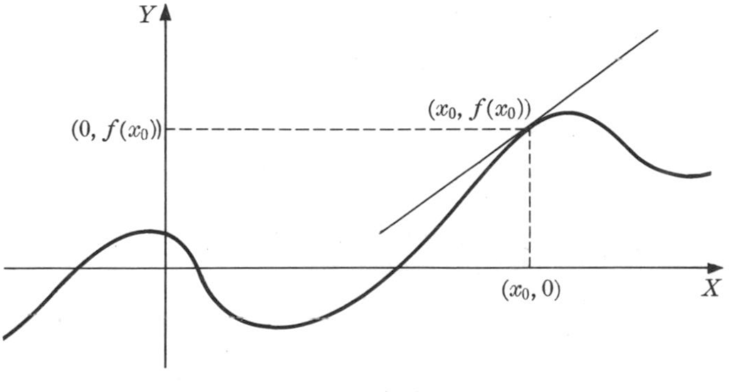

FIGURE 2

The equation of this line is

$$y - f(x_0) = f'(x_0)(x - x_0)$$

It is easy to see (cf. Exercises 1.1. **3a**, **b**) that, unless $f(x_0) = x_0 f'(x_0)$, the tangent line is *not* linear.

However, if we translate the X and Y axes so that (0, 0) goes to $(x_0, f(x_0))$, then the tangent line will go through the origin in the new coordinate system. We shall call the new Y-axis the "dY-axis" and the new X-axis, the "dX-axis." The corresponding variables are called "dy" and "dx," respectively. Actually, we should indicate dependence on x_0 in some way, but to simplify notation we avoid explicit reference to x_0. The situation is illustrated in Figure 3.

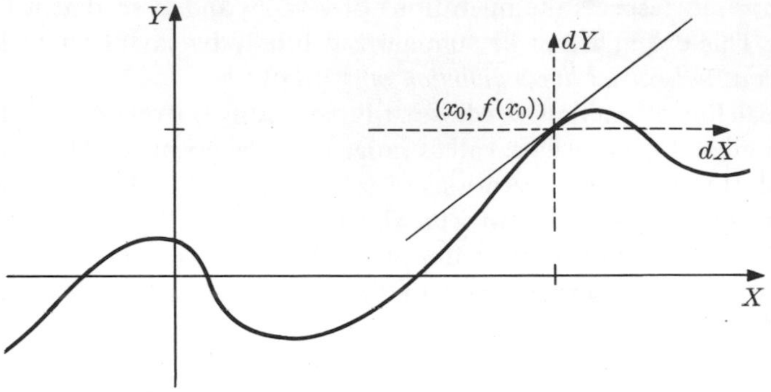

FIGURE 3

The equation of the tangent line in the new coordinate system is

$$dy = f'(x_0)\,dx$$

Viewed as a function of the variable dx, this line is just the *differential of f at x_0*, or df_{x_0}. It is characterized as being the linear function (in the dY–dX system) that best approximates f in the vicinity of the origin. The fact that differentiable functions can be so approximated by linear functions (in the above way) has had a profound effect on large areas of mathematics and accounts for much of the mathematical interest in such functions.

This example may be generalized to three dimensions. For example, let

$$z = f(x, y) = \sqrt{1 - x^2 - y^2}$$

In this case, the graph of f is the top hemisphere of the sphere of radius 1 and center at the origin of three-dimensional space, $\mathbf{R}^3$ (see Figure 4).

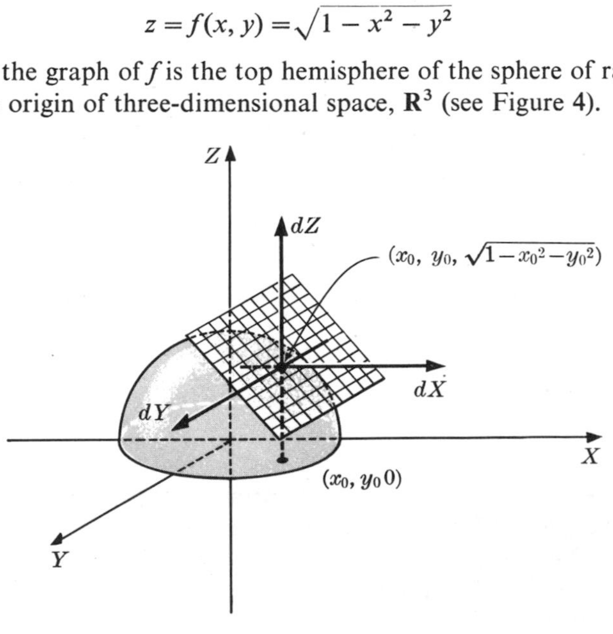

FIGURE 4

This time, instead of a tangent *line* we have a tangent *plane* and new axes, dX, dY, dZ. We shall not go into details here. We just remark that this plane is also a linear set (in the new system) and that it affords the best linear approximation to the hemisphere in the vicinity of the (new) origin. Moreover, the equation of the plane can be expressed in terms of the partial derivatives of f evaluated at (x_0, y_0).

The examples in (i), (j), and (k) indicate that the concept of linearity lies at the heart of much of differential and integral calculus. Linearity plays an even more important role in the more advanced versions of this subject, which we cannot discuss here.

Finally, we note one more feature of the examples in (k). In both examples, we used "variable" coordinate systems. That is, we translated our original system so that the origin went to a point on the graph. If we imagine the point varying continuously along the graph, then we can imagine the coordinate systems "varying continuously" along the graph. Let us think of each of these systems as reproductions of our original (two-dimensional or three-dimensional) linear set, $\mathbf{R}^2$ or $\mathbf{R}^3$. Then, the above examples illustrate the idea of continuously varying linear sets. Such objects (known as "vector bundles") have played a very important role in much of modern mathematics and some modern theoretical physics (namely, relativity theory).

EXERCISES / 1.2

1. Which of the following functions are linear:

a. The real-valued function of a real variable f_1, given by the equation

$$2f_1(x) = x?$$

b. The function of a real variable with values in $\mathbf{R}^3$, given by

$$f_2(x) = (ax, bx, cx),$$

where a, b, c are fixed real numbers?

c. The function f_3 whose argument ranges over $\mathbf{R}^2$, given by

$$f_3(s, t) = (as, bt, cs + dt),$$

where a, b, c, d are fixed real numbers?

d. The function f_4, given by

$$f_4(s, t) = (3st, 1, 2s + 4t),$$

where (s, t) ranges over $\mathbf{R}^2$?

e. The function f_5, given by

$$f_5(s, t) = s^2 + t^2,$$

where (s, t) ranges over $\mathbf{R}^2$?

Justify your answers.

2. Define the function f by

$$f(x, y) = -1/2\,(2/x + y),$$

where (x, y) ranges over $\mathbf{R}^2$.
Draw the graph of f (in $\mathbf{R}^3$). Is the graph a linear set with respect to the operations of $\mathbf{R}^3$? Is f a linear function? Draw the graph of the function g and answer the same questions about it and g, where g is given by

$$g(x, y) = -1/2\,(2x + y),$$

where (x, y) ranges over $\mathbf{R}^2$.

3. Let f be the real-valued function given by $f(x, y, z) = ax + by + cz$, where (x, y, z) ranges over $\mathbf{R}^3$ and where a, b, c are some fixed real numbers. Let d be any real number, and let P_d be the set of all (x, y, z) for which $f(x, y, z) = d$. P_d is called the *level hypersurface of f of height d*. For which heights d is P_d a linear set (with respect to the operations of $\mathbf{R}^3$)?

4. Consider the linear function D defined in Example (j). The argument of D ranges over the linear set $\mathscr{D}[a, b]$ and the values of D range over the linear set $\mathscr{C}[a, b]$. Let h be any function in $\mathscr{C}[a, b]$, and let P_h be the set of all functions f in $\mathscr{D}[a, b]$ such that $D(f) = h$. For which functions h is P_h a linear set (with respect to the operations of $\mathscr{D}[a, b]$)? You do not have to know any calculus to answer this question. You do, however, need some knowledge of calculus to solve the following problems:

Is there an h in $\mathscr{C}[a, b]$ for which there is no f in $\mathscr{D}[a, b]$ satisfying $D(f) = h$? Justify your answer.

Suppose that f_1 and f_2 both belong to P_h. Show that they differ by at most a nonzero constant.

5. Let f be a linear real-valued function of a real variable. Show that the graph of f (in $\mathbf{R}^2$) is a straight line through the origin with slope $f(1)$.

As our final example, we briefly discuss *linear equations*. These equations arise in a wide variety of areas, including abstract mathematics, physics, and the social sciences. Moreover, they furnish a kind of paradigm case for the study of many of the concepts of linear algebra. For these reasons, we discuss this example in somewhat more detail than the others.

A *linear expression in variables* $x_1, \ldots, x_k$ is an expression of the form

$$a_1x_1 + \cdots + a_kx_k,$$

where $a_1, \ldots, a_k$ are some given real numbers. The reader may think of this expression as a first-degree polynomial in the variables $x_1, \ldots, x_k$ with zero constant term. We shall think of the variables as ranging over the set of real numbers $\mathbf{R}$, although any other linear set would do. It is often of interest to determine those values of $x_1, \ldots, x_k$ for which

$$a_1x_1 + \cdots + a_kx_k = b,$$

where b is some given real number. This equation can be thought of as an *actual* equation of certain numbers; that is, we think of $x_1, \ldots, x_k$ as actual numbers. Or we may think of this equation as a shorthand formulation of our interest in determining the appropriate $x_1, \ldots, x_k$. It is usually in this latter sense that the above equation is called a *linear equation in indeterminates* $x_1, \ldots, x_k$.

Suppose, now, that we have a number of such equations and that we are interested in those values of $x_1, \ldots, x_k$ that satisfy all the equations *simultaneously*. We express our interest by referring to these as a *system of linear equations in indeterminates* $x_1, \ldots, x_k$. We now present the usual notation and terminology.

Let a_{ij} and b_i be a given collection of real numbers, where i ranges between the integers 1 and n, and j ranges between 1 and k. These numbers determine the following system of linear equations in indeterminates $x_1, \ldots, x_k$:

$$\begin{array}{ccc} a_{11}x_1 + \cdots + a_{1k}x_k & = & b_1 \\ \vdots \qquad\quad \vdots & & \vdots \\ a_{n1}x_1 + \cdots + a_{nk}x_k & = & b_n \end{array} \tag{1}$$

Closely related to (1) is the following so-called *homogeneous system of linear equations*

$$\begin{array}{ccc} a_{11}x_1 + \cdots a_{1k}x_k & = & 0 \\ \vdots \qquad\quad \vdots & & \vdots \\ a_{n1}x_1 + \cdots a_{nk}x_k & = & 0 \end{array} \tag{2}$$

If system (1) is given first, then we call system (2) the *associated homogeneous system.*

A *solution* to (1) or to (2), respectively, will be thought of as a k-tuple of real numbers, $(c_1, \ldots, c_k)$, such that *when x_j is replaced by c_j in* (1) *or in* (2), *respectively, an actual equation of real numbers is obtained.*

At this point, there are already several manifestations of linearity. For example, we can consider the set of *all* linear expressions in variables $x_1, \ldots, x_k$. Given any two of them,

$$a_1x_1 + \cdots + a_kx_k \quad \text{and} \quad a'_1x_1 + \cdots + a'_kx_k,$$

we define their *sum* to be

$$(a_1 + a'_1)x_1 + \cdots + (a_k + a'_k)x_k$$

Given any real number r, we define the product of r and $a_1x_1 + \cdots + a_kx_k$ to be $(ra_1)x_1 + \cdots + (ra_k)x_k$. With these definitions of addition and real multiplication, the set of all linear expressions in $x_1, \ldots, x_k$ is a linear set.

We may also define addition and real multiplication of k-tuples of real numbers, so that the set of *all* such k-tuples becomes a linear set. The definitions are:

$$(c_1, \ldots, c_k) + (c_1', \ldots, c_k') = (c_1 + c_1', \ldots, c_k + c_k')$$
$$r(c_1, \ldots, c_k) = (rc_1, \ldots, rc_k)$$

We call this linear set $\mathbf{R}^k$.

Of slightly more interest is the set of all solutions of system (2). We call this set S. Since solutions are k-tuples of real numbers, we can add them and multiply them by real numbers, as above. Now, we claim (see Exercise 1.3.**6**) that *the sum of two solutions of* (2) *is again a solution of* (2). *Moreover, every real multiple of a solution of* (2) *is a solution of* (2). Thus, S is closed with respect to these operations; that is, S is a linear set.

These examples show that a number of linear sets are intimately connected with systems of linear equations. We now illustrate how linear functions fit into the picture.

Consider the linear expression $a_1x_1 + \cdots + a_kx_k$. We may consider it as a function of k real variables. Or, to put it another way, the above linear expression determines a real-valued function f of an argument that ranges over $\mathbf{R}^k$; f is defined by the equation

$$f(x_1, \ldots, x_k) = a_1x_1 + \cdots + a_kx_k,$$

for all $(x_1, \ldots, x_k)$ in $\mathbf{R}^k$. The sets $\mathbf{R}^k$ and $\mathbf{R}$ are linear. We show that f is a linear function. Choose any two k-tuples of real numbers $(x_1, \ldots, x_k)$ and $(y_1, \ldots, y_k)$ and any real number r. Then, using the definition of f and the definitions of addition and real multiplication of k-tuples, we get

$$\begin{aligned} f((x_1, \ldots, x_k) + (y_1, \ldots, y_k)) &= f(x_1 + y_1, \ldots, x_k + y_k) \\ &= a_1(x_1 + y_1) + \cdots + a_k(x_k + y_k) \\ &= (a_1x_1 + \cdots + a_kx_k) + (a_1y_1 + \cdots + a_ky_k) \\ &= f(x_1, \ldots, x_k) + f(y_1, \ldots, y_k) \end{aligned}$$

and

$$\begin{aligned} f(r(x_1, \ldots, x_k)) &= f(rx_1, \ldots, rx_k) \\ &= a_1(rx_1) + \cdots + a_k(rx_k) \\ &= r(a_1x_1 + \cdots + a_kx_k) = rf(x_1, \ldots, x_k) \end{aligned}$$

Therefore, f respects the operations of $\mathbf{R}^k$ and $\mathbf{R}$.

Now consider the collection of linear expressions in system (2), above: namely,

$$a_{11}x_1 + \cdots + a_{1k}x_k, \ldots, a_{n1}x_1 + \cdots + a_{nk}x_k$$

For any choice of $x_1, \ldots, x_k$, these expressions together, in order, yield n real numbers as values, say $y_1, \ldots, y_n$, respectively. That is, for every k-tuple $(x_1, \ldots, x_k)$, the expressions in system (2) determine an n-tuple $(y_1, \ldots, y_n)$. More concisely, we say that system (2) determines a function with argument ranging over $\mathbf{R}^k$ and with values in $\mathbf{R}^n$. Call this function A. It is not difficult to show that A respects the operations of $\mathbf{R}^k$ and $\mathbf{R}^n$. For example, let $(x_1, \ldots, x_k)$ and $(x'_1, \ldots, x'_k)$ be any two k-tuples of real numbers. Then,

$$A(x_1, \ldots, x_k) = (y_1, \ldots, y_n) \text{ and } A(x'_1, \ldots, x'_k) = (y'_1, \ldots, y'_n),$$

where

$$y_i = a_{i1}x_1 + \ldots + a_{ik}x_k, \; y'_i = a_{i1}x'_1 + \ldots + a_{ik}x'_k,$$

for every integer i between 1 and n. Notice that

$$y_i + y'_i = a_{i1}(x_1 + x'_1) + \cdots + a_{ik}(x_k + x'_k)$$

Therefore,

$$\begin{aligned} A((x_1, \ldots, x_k) + (x'_1, \ldots, x'_k)) &= A(x_1 + x'_1, \ldots, x_k + x'_k) \\ &= (y_1 + y'_1, \ldots, y_n + y'_n) \\ &= (y_1, \ldots, y_n) + (y'_1, \ldots, y'_n) \\ &= A(x_1, \ldots, x_k) + (A(x'_1, \ldots, x'_k) \end{aligned}$$

Similarly, one can show that $A(r(x_1, \ldots, x_k)) = rA(x_1, \ldots, x_k)$. Therefore, A is a linear function. If we let $x = (x_1, \ldots, x_k)$ and $b = (b_1, \ldots, b_n)$, then system (2) can be written as:

$$A(x) = b$$

This equation, again, is a shorthand (even shorter, this time) expression of our interest in determining those values of the variable $x = (x_1, \ldots, x_k)$ for which equality actually holds.

Thus, a system of linear equations is simply an equation involving a certain linear function.

Certain questions concerning (1) and (2) immediately arise:

1. For which $b = (b_1, \ldots, b_n)$ does system (1) have a solution?

2. Under what circumstances does system (2) have a solution other than $x_1 = 0, x_2 = 0, \ldots, x_k = 0$?

3. What is the relationship between the set of all solutions of (1) and the linear set S of solutions of (2)?

In later chapters, these questions will be reformulated in terms of linear sets and linear functions. This reformulation will clarify the questions to the extent that certain qualitative answers will immediately present themselves.

EXERCISES / 1.3

1.* Consider the systems of equations (1) and (2), where $k = 2$ and $n = 1$. That is, (1) becomes

$$a_{11}x_1 + a_{12}x_2 = b_1,$$

and (2) becomes

$$a_{11}x_1 + a_{12}x_2 = 0$$

Suppose that $a_{12} \neq 0$. Solve for x_2 in terms of x_1. What is the graph of x_2 in terms of x_1 on the Cartesian plane? What are the solutions to (2) in this case? To (1)? How are these two sets of solutions related?

2.* Consider the following system of equations:

$$\begin{aligned} x_1 + 3x_2 &= b_1 \\ 4x_1 + 12x_2 &= b_2 \end{aligned}$$

For what pairs (b_1, b_2) does the system have a solution? Give an example of one pair (b_1, b_2), if such exists, for which the system has no solution. Describe the set of all solutions to the homogeneous system corresponding to the system above.

3.* Consider the linear expressions

$$x_1 + x_2 + x_3,\ 2x_1 + x_3,\ 3x_1 + x_2 - 7x_3$$

For any triple of real numbers (x_1, x_2, x_3), let

$$\begin{aligned} x_1 + x_2 + x_3 &= y_1 \\ 2x_1 \phantom{{}+x_2} + x_3 &= y_2 \\ 3x_1 + x_2 - 7x_3 &= y_3 \end{aligned}$$

Compute (y_1, y_2, y_3) when $(x_1, x_2, x_3) = (0, 0, 0)$, $(1, 1, 1)$, $(-3, 2, 4)$, and $(-2, 3, 5)$.

4. Let A be the linear function determined by the system above. Compute $A(x)$ for $x = (1, 0, 0)$, $(0, 1, 0)$, and $(0, 0, 1)$. Compare these results to the array of numbers

$$\begin{matrix} 1 & 1 & 1 \\ 2 & 0 & 1 \\ 3 & 1 & -7 \end{matrix}$$

obtained from the system above. Is the result a coincidence? Justify your answer.

5. Define the function B as follows:

$$B(x_1, x_2, x_3) = (-2x_1 + 3x_2 + x_3, 10x_2 + 5x_3),$$

for every (x_1, x_2, x_3) in $\mathbf{R}^3$. The values of B are in $\mathbf{R}^2$.

a. Show that B is a linear function.

b. Evaluate $B(1, 0, 0)$, $B(0, 1, 0)$, and $B(0, 0, 1)$ and compare the results to the array of numbers

$$\begin{matrix} -2 & 3 & 1 \\ 0 & 10 & 5 \end{matrix}$$

obtained from the definition of B.

c. Consider the set of 5-tuples of the form

$$(x_1, x_2, x_3, -2x_1 + 3x_2 + x_3, 10x_2 + 5x_3)$$

If we let $x = (x_1, x_2, x_3)$, then such 5-tuples may be more briefly written as $(x, B(x))$. This set is called the *graph of B*. In the discussion above, we showed how to add any two k-tuples of real numbers and how to multiply any k-tuple by a real number. When $k = 5$, this tells us how to add two 5-tuples and multiply a 5-tuple by a real number. Show that the graph of B is closed with respect to these operations; that is, show that the graph of B is a linear set.

6.* Show that the set S of solutions to system (2) in the text is a linear set with respect to the operations of $\mathbf{R}^k$ defined above.

The examples in this chapter should give the reader some idea of the wide applicability of the concept of linearity. This, however, is but one aspect of its usefulness. Another attribute of the concept, which is in some sense complementary to the first, is its extreme simplicity.

The concept is simple, of course, in the sense that it can be described and illustrated relatively briefly. But linearity is simple also in another sense: namely, a linear set or a linear function is completely determined by a very limited amount of information. For example, a straight line through the origin in $\mathbf{R}^2$ is completely determined by one number, its slope. For another example, consider the linear function A in Exercises 1.3.4. A is determined by the system of equations in Exercise 1.3.3, which is determined by the array of numbers (the coefficients of the system)

$$\begin{matrix} 1 & 1 & 1 \\ 2 & 0 & 1 \\ 3 & 1 & -7 \end{matrix}$$

And this array is determined by the values $A(1, 0, 0)$, $A(0, 1, 0)$, and $A(0, 0, 1)$ (the result of Exercise 1.3.4). Thus, A is completely determined by specifying three triples or nine numbers.

It will be seen, in the general case, that linear functions are remarkable for the rigidity of their behavior in precisely this way. Similar considerations apply to linear sets.

The simplicity of linear functions and sets, of course, makes it possible to say a great deal more about them than about more general functions and sets. But what kinds of things do we want to say? For one thing, we want to be able to answer the questions about systems of linear equations posed above. Not only do we want general qualitative answers, although these are often helpful, but we also want more specific, quantitative answers (i.e., methods of solving the systems). However, this is not all that we shall want to say. After all, linear equations are by no means the only manifestations of linearity [cf. Examples (e), (f), (i), (j), (k)]. We shall, for example, want to say things about linear sets and functions that apply equally as well to $\mathscr{D}[a, b]$ and D [Examples (f) and (j)] as to $\mathbf{R}^k$ and A.

In order to give a unified presentation that applies to all our examples, therefore, we begin on an abstract, general level. In Chapter 2 we discuss the general notions of sets and functions. In Chapters 3 and 4 we present the general notions of linear set and linear function and investigate derivative** concepts. In later chapters, our presentation becomes more specific and concrete. For example, in Chapter 5 we present a thorough study of systems of linear equations.

We feel that in addition to its usefulness, as described above, the study of linearity provides a good vehicle for touching on some of the more important aspects of modern mathematics and its methods. Therefore, we shall place relatively heavy emphasis on mathematical rigor. Moreover, in some of the exercises, we shall depart somewhat from the development in the text to elaborate on ideas mentioned in passing in the text.

** The word "derivative" is used in its ordinary sense here, not in the sense of calculus.

CHAPTER 2

SETS AND FUNCTIONS

1 / SETS

1.1 Definitions and Notation

Definition 2.1

By the word "set" we mean nothing more nor less than what is ordinarily meant by the words "collection of objects" or by "collectivity." The words "family" or "collection" or "totality" will sometimes be used instead of the word "set." We shall usually denote sets by capital letters such as A, B, C, . . .

Definition 2.2

The objects comprising a particular set A are called elements of A or members of A and are usually denoted by lower-case letters, such as a, b, c, . . .

As shorthand for "a belongs to A" or "a is a member of A," we shall write "$a \in A$." For "a does not belong to A" we shall write $a \notin A$.

Implicit in the notion of a set is the fact that, given any object x and set A, either $x \in A$, or $x \notin A$. Or, in other words, the existence of a certain set is equivalent to the existence of a certain unambiguous membership list. This fact will have an important application in Section 1.2.

1.2† *Examples and Remarks*

It is clear from the above definitions that there are many sets. Here are some:

(a) $A =$ the set of all left-handed physicists
(b) $B =$ the set consisting of the number 1 and the symbol "ξ"
(c) $C =$ the set of all green umbrellas, the symbol "ξ," and the Rio Grande River
(d) $D =$ the set of all negative integers divisible by 47
(e) $E =$ the set whose elements are the sets A, B, C, D above
(f) $F =$ the set whose elements are the set E, the set A, the symbol "ξ," and the Rio Grande River

The remaining examples refer to sets that will occur over and over again in the text. Therefore, we shall assign to them standard symbols, *names*, as it were, and denote them by these symbols hereafter. These names are standard in much of mathematical literature.

(g) $\mathbf{N} =$ the set of natural numbers, 1, 2, 3, 4, . . . and so on
(h) $\mathbf{Q} =$ the set of rational numbers: that is, the set of all real numbers that can be expressed as the quotient of two integers
(i) $\mathbf{R} =$ the set of real numbers
(j) $\mathbf{Z} =$ the set of integers

Several things should be clear from these examples.

First, there is no limit on the "size" of a set, that is, on the number of elements in the set. We shall have more to say about this in Section 3 of this chapter.

Secondly, the same object may be both a set and an element of another set. For instance, in Example (a), above, A is the set of all left-handed physicists; in (e), the same set A is a member of the set E. There is no logical difficulty here. It is simply a question of context. If we are interested in left-handed physicists, we may consider their totality, A. In this context, we think of A as a *set*. If we are interested, on the other hand, in the collection S of all sets that we have thought of in the past seven minutes, then, in this context, we may think of A as a *member* of S.

Finally, the above examples point out that there is a close relationship between the notion of a *set* and that of a *defining property*. In all the examples, a certain property is described (e.g., being a negative integer and divisible by 47), and the set in question is defined as the collection of all objects satisfying the property. We shall exploit this relationship often throughout the book.

We caution the reader on two points however.

† A dagger following the number of a section or portion of a section, here and throughout the book, indicates a section or portion of a section that may be omitted in a one-semester course (see Preface).

First, the members of a set need not have very much in common. Examples (c) and (f), above, hint at this fact. The members, indeed, may have nothing more in common than that they are being considered as elements of a particular totality. Although, strictly speaking, this fact itself is a defining property of the totality in question (i.e., it is satisfied by those elements in the totality and only those), it should be obvious, that the members of a set can be completely heterogeneous.

Secondly, the reader must exercise some care in making use of the relationship between the notions of set and defining property. For every property need not determine a set. We give an example of such a property below.** The difficulty described by the footnote is known as Russell's Paradox (named after its inventor, Bertrand Russell).

The kinds of properties and sets discussed henceforth in this book, however, will not lead to such logical difficulties. Therefore, the reader may, for practical purposes, safely ignore the above word of caution.

1.3 More Notation

If we are considering a very small set, we may simply enumerate or list the objects of the set and place curly brackets around them to indicate that we are considering their totality. Thus, the set of letters a, b, c can be denoted by $\{a, b, c\}$. If n is some natural number greater than one, we may write, for the set of all natural numbers between 1 and n (including 1 and n), $\{1, 2, \ldots, n\}$. More often, however, it will be convenient to denote this particular set by $\mathbf{N}_n$.

If we want to discuss a very large set (perhaps even one with an infinite number of members), then such an enumeration procedure is, at best, impractical. In such cases, we may be forced, or may wish, to leave the identity of the members of the set anonymous. We may simply say, "consider the set A." Or if the set is a particular one that we have occasion to use frequently, then we may give it a boldface letter as name, as in Examples (g)–(j) in Section 1.2. Finally, if the members of the set can be characterized by some convenient property, then we might use the following notation: for example, consider the set A of Example (a) in Section 1.2; then, we may write, for A,

$$\{x \mid x \text{ is a left-handed physicist}\}$$

(to be read, "the set of all x such that x is a left-handed physicist").

** Let P be the property of non-self-membership. That is, an obejct x satisfies P if and only if $x \notin x$. Now suppose that P determines a set Y. That is, Y is the set of all x such that $x \notin x$. We ask, "Is $Y \in Y$?" If so, then Y satisfies P, since it is an object in the set described by P; but this means that $Y \notin Y$, a contradiction. On the other hand, if $Y \notin Y$, then Y satisfies P, so that, since P determines Y, $Y \in Y$, again a contradiction. Therefore, Y is an object satisfying neither $Y \in Y$ nor $Y \notin Y$. This means that Y fails to have one of the defining characteristics of sets (see the last paragraph of 1.1). That is, Y is not a set. This contradicts the assumption that P defines a set, and so it does not.

Finally, it will be convenient to introduce the notion of the set consisting of *no* objects whatsoever. We call this set the *empty set* and denote it by $\varnothing$. At times we shall be considering certain sets not defined directly but via other sets, and we shall not be in an immediate position to tell whether or not the set in question has any members. If it turns out *not* to have members, then we shall say that it equals $\varnothing$ or that it is *empty*. (The words "null" and "vacuous" are also commonly used instead of the word "empty.")

EXERCISES / 2.1

1. Express the sets B, C, D, E, F, above, in the "curly-bracket" notation.

2. List the elements of the following sets:

a. $\{1\}$ **b.** $\{\{1\}\}$ **c.** $\{\{\{1\}, 1\}, 1\}$ **d.** $\{\{\{1\}, 1\}, \{1\}, 1\}$ **e.** $\varnothing$ **f.** $\{\varnothing\}$

1.4 Equality and Inclusion

(a) We have defined a set to be a collection of objects, a membership list, as it were. However, when mathematicians use sets, they rarely have access to such lists. Instead, they are presented with certain descriptions of the membership. Now, it is clear that there are many ways of describing the membership of a given set. For example, the lone member of $\{1\}$ can be described as the unique real number x satisfying $x^3 = 1$, or as the solution to the equation $2x = 2$, and so on. It is typically the case that mathematicians are not certain *a priori* whether or not two descriptions define the same set. Indeed, much of mathematical methodology revolves around showing that two or more descriptions do actually refer to the same set.

In such situations, it is convenient to use the following convention. We are given several set-defining descriptions. We assign symbols to the sets thus presented so that each description corresponds to a distinct symbol. For example, using the descriptions in the preceding paragraph, we let $A = \{x \mid x \in \mathbf{R}$ and $x^3 = 1\}$ and $B = \{x \mid x \in \mathbf{R}$ and $2x = 2\}$. Or, if we like, the curly-bracket notation itself provides us with distinct symbols for the different descriptions of the set: namely, "$\{x \mid x \in \mathbf{R}$ and $x^3 = 1\}$" is one symbol and "$\{x \mid x \in \mathbf{R}$ and $2x = 2\}$" is another. Of course, as is obvious from the example, distinct symbols may be assigned to the same set. Until we prove that this is or is not the case, however, we shall remain uncommitted as to whether or not distinct symbols do refer to the same set. That is, *we shall act as if the various descriptions might actually determine distinct sets*. Our language will reflect this attitude in various ways. For example, when, indeed, we get around to showing that two descriptions determine the same set, we shall say, instead, something like: "Consider the *two sets A* and *B* determined by the two descriptions. We shall show that *A equals B*." In this sense, then, it is meaningful to talk about *two* sets being *equal.*

We now formalize the definition of set equality.

Definition 2.3

Two sets are equal, if and only if they consist of the same members.

In practice, to prove that two sets are equal, we must show that the two descriptions of the sets—in other words, the defining properties of the sets—determine the same membership.

From now on, when discussing sets, we shall assume the attitude described in the above discussion.

Definition 2.4

Let A and B be two sets and suppose that every member of A belongs to B. Then we say that A is included in B (or A is contained in B, or A is a subset of B), and we write $A \subset B$. Alternatively, we may say B contains A, and we may write $B \supset A$.

In practice, A and B are generally given via certain descriptions so that to show that $A \subset B$ we must show that every object satisfying the description of A's membership also satisfies the description of B's membership. If $A \subset B$ and $B \subset A$, it is easy to see that A and B consist of the same members, so that $A = B$. On the other hand, if $A = B$, then, clearly every member of A belongs to B, so that $A \subset B$, and every member of B belongs to A, so that $B \subset A$. Often a proof that two sets A and B are equal will be broken into two parts: In the first part we show that $A \subset B$; in the second, we show that $B \subset A$.

Consider the empty set $\varnothing$ and an arbitrary set X. Strictly speaking, every member of $\varnothing$ does belong to X, for to deny this would be to assert that $\varnothing$ had a member not belonging to X. And we know that $\varnothing$ has no members whatsoever, so that it cannot *have a member* not belonging to X. Therefore, $\varnothing \subset X$. *In other words, the empty set is a subset of every set.* This is the first of a series of somewhat unusual facts about $\varnothing$, unusual, not because they are illogical, but because we are not used to thinking of our otherwise very reasonable sounding definitions as applying to the null case. Our use of the null set will greatly simplify terminology and notation later, and so the reader is urged to rid himself of possible prejudice against this very handy idea.

It is important, at this point, for the reader to make sure that he understands the distinction between the membership relation, $\in$, and the inclusion relation, $\subset$. The following examples and exercises will point out the importance and some of the salient features of this distinction.

Consider the sets

$$A = \{1, \{1, 2, 3\}\}, \qquad B = \{1, 2, 3\}, \qquad C = \{1, 2, 3, \{1, 2, 3\}\}$$

The reader should convince himself that the following relations hold:

$A \subset C$ but $A \notin C$; $B \subset C$ and $B \in C$;
$B \not\subset A$ (B is *not* included in A) but $B \in A$;
$1 \in A$, $1 \in B$, $1 \in C$; $2 \notin A$, $2 \in B$, $2 \in C$;
$3 \notin A$, $3 \in B$, $3 \in C$

For another example of the distinction between the two relations, consider any three sets A, B, C, such that $A \subset B$ and $B \subset C$. Then $A \subset C$. (We pause for a moment to prove this fact: If $A \subset B$, then every element of A is in B, but, since $B \subset C$, all of these must belong to C; that is, every member of A is a member of C, or $A \subset C$.) We express this fact by saying that the *inclusion relation is transitive.*

Now, the membership relation is not transitive, as the following example shows:

Harvey Smith is a member of the United Auto Workers Union.
The United Auto Workers Union is a member of the C.I.O.-A.F.L.
But Harvey *is not* a member of the C.I.O.-A.F.L.

In a more famous example, the membership relations are implicit:

Sitting Bull is an Indian.
Indians are disappearing.
Sitting Bull, however, is not disappearing.

EXERCISES / 2.2

1. Consider the sets a–f listed in Exercise 2.1.2. Which of the following is true?

a. $a \subset b$ **b.** $b \subset c$ **c.** $c \in d$ **d.** $e \subset f$ **e.** $e \in f$

2. Rephrase the Sitting Bull example so as to make the membership relations explicit.

3. Let $A = \{x \mid x \in \mathbf{R} \text{ and } x^3 - 1 = 0\}$, $B = \{x \mid x \in \mathbf{R} \text{ and } x^2 - 1 = 0\}$, and $C = \{x \mid x \in \mathbf{R} \text{ and } x - 1 = 0\}$. Prove in detail that $A = C$ and $C \subset B$.

4. Given any set A, let $\mathscr{P}(A)$ be the collection of *all* subsets of A (including the null set).
a. List the elements of $\mathscr{P}(A)$, where $A = \{1, 2, 3\}$.
b. How many elements are there in $\mathscr{P}(A)$, where $A = \mathbf{N}_n$, where n is some given natural number (recall that $\mathbf{N}_n = \{1, \ldots, n\}$)?

1.5 Combinations of Sets

(a) *Unions and Intersections*

Let $\mathscr{S}$ be any nonempty collection of sets.

We may, under certain circumstances, wish to consider the totality of *all* the members of the sets of $\mathscr{S}$. We call this totality the *union set of* $\mathscr{S}$ or the *union of the sets of* $\mathscr{S}$ and denote it by $\cup\mathscr{S}$. Alternatively, if $\mathscr{S}$ consists of a finite number of sets $S_1, S_2, \ldots, S_n$, we may denote the union of these sets by $S_1 \cup S_2 \cup \cdots \cup S_n$. Notice that the order in which the symbols appear in this notation is irrelevant, according to the definition of union. We now restate the definition in more concise terms; the reader should make sure that he understands and agrees with this formulation.

Definition 2.5

$\cup\mathscr{S} = \{x \mid x \in S$ *for some* $S \in \mathscr{S}\}$. *That is,* $\cup\mathscr{S}$ *is the set of all* x *such that* x *belongs to some member of* $\mathscr{S}$.

Under other circumstances, we might be interested only in those members that all the sets of $\mathscr{S}$ have in common. The totality of such members is called the *intersection set of* $\mathscr{S}$ or the *intersection of the sets of* $\mathscr{S}$ and is denoted by $\cap\mathscr{S}$. If $\mathscr{S}$ consists only of $S_1, S_2, \ldots S_n$, we may denote the intersection of these sets by $S_1 \cap S_2 \cap \cdots \cap S_n$, or by $S_2 \cap S_1 \cap \cdots \cap S_n$, or any symbol obtained from these by permuting the S's. As our nonchalance implies, the order in which the symbols appear is, again, irrelevant. Reformulating the definition more concisely, we have:

Definition 2.6

$\cap\mathscr{S} = \{x \mid x \in S$ *for every* $S \in \mathscr{S}\}$. *That is,* $\cap\mathscr{S}$ *is the set of all* x *belonging to every member of* $\mathscr{S}$.

Notice that although we are assuming $\mathscr{S}$ to be nonempty, it is quite possible that one of its *members* is the empty set. Notice also that a given collection of sets $\mathscr{S}$ may have *no* members in common, so that $\cap\mathscr{S}$ may equal $\varnothing$.

Finally, a word about parentheses. We shall often be dealing with several sets, collections of sets, and so on, considering their unions or intersections. In these situations, it may be convenient to group some of these together by placing parentheses around them. This has the purpose of indicating that the object between the parentheses is to be considered as an entity in its own right and that symbols occurring outside the parentheses refer to this entity. In ordinary arithmetic, we do the same thing: "$5 \times (8 + (3 - 2))$" indicates that we are to multiply by 5 the *number* obtained from 8 by adding the *difference* between 3 and 2. In our case, for example, we may be given certain sets A, B, C, we may form the union of A and B, $A \cup B$, and then form the intersection of this with C: $(A \cup B) \cap C$.

EXERCISES / 2.3

1. Express $A \cup B$ and $A \cap B$ in curly-bracket notation, where A and B are as follows:

a. $A = \{1, \{2\}, 3\}$, $B = \{1, 2, 3\}$

b. $A = \{\varnothing\}$, $B = \varnothing$

c. $A = \{x \mid x \in \mathbf{R} \text{ and } x \geqq -2\}$
$B = \{x \mid x \in \mathbf{R} \text{ and } x < 2\}$

2. Let $\mathcal{S}$ and $\mathcal{T}$ be any two nonempty collections of sets.

a. Describe the set $(\cup\mathcal{S}) \cup (\cup\mathcal{T})$ and the set $\mathcal{S} \cup \mathcal{T}$.

b. Show that $(\cup\mathcal{S}) \cup (\cup\mathcal{T}) = \cup(\mathcal{S} \cup \mathcal{T})$.

c. Describe $(\cap\mathcal{S}) \cap (\cap\mathcal{T})$ and show that $(\cap\mathcal{S}) \cap (\cap\mathcal{T}) = \cap(\mathcal{S} \cup \mathcal{T})$.

d. Give reasons to indicate why the following pair of sets need not be equal: $(\cup\mathcal{S}) \cap (\cup\mathcal{T})$ and $\cup(\mathcal{S} \cap \mathcal{T})$. Do the same for the sets $(\cap\mathcal{S}) \cup (\cap\mathcal{T})$ and $\cap(\mathcal{S} \cup \mathcal{T})$.

3. a. Suppose that $\mathcal{S}$ consists of the single set A. Prove that $\cap\mathcal{S} = A = \cup\mathcal{S}$.

b. Prove that if $\mathcal{S}$ is a nonempty collection of sets and $\cap\mathcal{S} = \cup\mathcal{S}$, then $\mathcal{S}$ consists of a single set.

4. Let A, B, C be any three sets. Let $\mathcal{S} = \{A, B\}$, $\mathcal{T} = \{C\}$.

a. Express $(A \cup B) \cup C$ in terms of $\mathcal{S}$ and $\mathcal{T}$.

b. Use **2.b** to show that $(A \cup B) \cup C = A \cup B \cup C$.

c. Show, similarly, that $A \cup (B \cup C) = A \cup B \cup C$, and
$(A \cap B) \cap C = A \cap (B \cap C) = A \cap B \cap C$.

The equalities in **b.** and **c.** show that no matter how one groups three given sets (keeping the order unchanged—although that does not really matter in this situation) and applies the union operation to them one always gets the same result. A similar statement applies to the intersection operation. Moreover, these results can be generalized to the case of more than three sets. The equalities are known by the names: associative law of set union and associative law of set intersection.

5. Show that $A \cup B \cup C \cup D = (A \cup B) \cup (C \cup D) = [A \cup (B \cup C)] \cup D$, where A, B, C, D are any sets. Similar equalities hold for the other groupings of A, B, C, D. Prove the corresponding result for the intersection of A, B, C, D.

6. Let A and B be sets.
Prove: **a.** $A \cap B = A$, if and only if $A \subset B$.
b. $A \cup B = B$, if and only if $A \subset B$.

7. Let A, B, C be sets.
Prove: **a.** $A \cap (B \cup C) = (A \cap B) \cup (A \cap C)$.
b. $A \cup (B \cap C) = (A \cup B) \cap (A \cup C)$.

(b) *The Difference Between Two Sets*

Definition 2.7

Let A and B be any two sets. We consider all members of A that do not *belong to B. We call their totality the complement of B in A (or the difference between A and B in A) and denote it by* $A \setminus B$. *For example, the complement of* $\{1, 2, 3\}$ *in* $\{1\}$ *is* $\varnothing$, *since there are no members of* $\{1\}$ *that are not in* $\{1, 2, 3\}$. *For another example, the complement of* $\{x \mid x \in \mathbf{R} \text{ and } x \geqq 2\}$ *in* $\{x \mid x \in \mathbf{R} \text{ and } x \leqq 3\}$ *is* $\{x \mid x \in \mathbf{R} \text{ and } x < 2\}$.

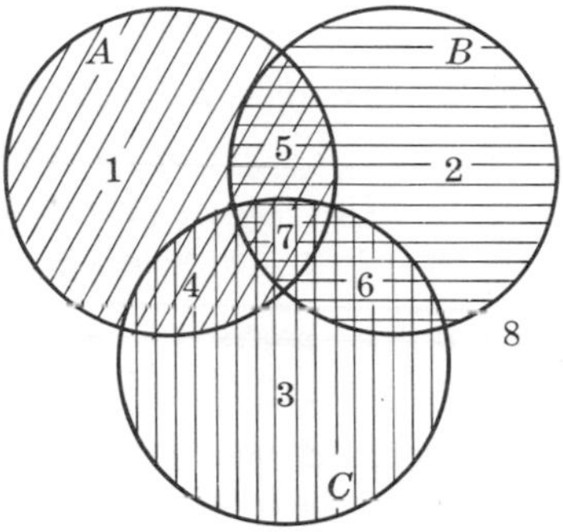

FIGURE 5

In Figure 5, three sets, A, B, and C, are given; they consist of points in the plane (i.e., on the sheet of paper) enclosed by circular boundaries. These boundaries determine eight regions in the plane, which we number as indicated. We denote the plane by $\mathbf{R}^2$.

To illustrate the concepts discussed above and in Example (a), we now express each region in terms of the sets A, B, C and $\mathbf{R}^2$, and we express the sets $A, B, C, \mathbf{R}^2$ and some of their combinations in terms of the regions 1–8.

TABLE 2.1

Region		Sets	
1	$(A \cup B \cup C) \setminus (B \cup C)$	A	Union of regions 1, 4, 5, 7
2	$(A \cup B \cup C) \setminus (A \cup C)$	B	Union of regions 2, 5, 6, 7
3	$(A \cup B \cup C) \setminus (A \cup B)$	C	Union of regions 3, 4, 6, 7
4	$(A \cap C) \setminus (A \cap B \cap C)$	$A \cup B$	Union of regions 1, 2, 4, 5, 6, 7
5	$(A \cap B) \setminus (A \cap B \cap C)$	$A \cup C$	Union of regions 1, 3, 4, 5, 6, 7
6	$(B \cap C) \setminus (A \cap B \cap C)$	$B \cup C$	Union of regions 2, 3, 4, 5, 6, 7
7	$(A \cap B \cap C)$	$A \cap B$	Union of regions 5, 7
8	$\mathbf{R}^2 \setminus (A \cup B \cup C)$		

EXERCISES / 2.4

1. Let A, B, C be as in the diagram above. Verify:

a. $(A \cup B) \cup C = A \cup (B \cup C)$

b. $A \cap (B \cup C) = (A \cap B) \cup (A \cap C)$

c. $A \setminus (B \cup C) = A \cup B \cup C \setminus B \cup C = (A \setminus B) \setminus C$

d. $(A \setminus B) \setminus C \neq A \setminus (B \setminus C)$.

2. For any sets X and Y, let

$$X \oplus Y = (X \setminus Y) \cup (Y \setminus X).$$

Prove that, for any sets, A, B, C the following hold:

a. $A \oplus B = B \oplus A$

b. $A \oplus \varnothing = A$

c. $A \oplus A = \varnothing$

d. $(A \oplus B) \oplus C = A \oplus (B \oplus C)$

e. $A \cap (B \oplus C) = (A \cap B) \oplus (A \cap C)$

f. If $A \oplus X = A$, then $\mathbf{X} = \varnothing$

g. The equation $A \oplus X = B$ has precisely one solution (where X is the "unknown"). What is it?

The set $A \oplus B$ is sometimes called the *symmetric difference* between the sets A and B. Notice that the sets A, B, C behave, with respect to the operations $\cap$ and $\oplus$, similarly to the way ordinary numbers behave with respect to $\times$ and $+$.

(c) *The (Cartesian) Product of Sets*

Definition 2.8

Suppose that we are given a finite number of sets—at least one set—in some fixed order: say, $A_1, A_2, \ldots, A_n$. *The subscripts* $1, 2, \ldots, n$ *are assigned to the sets to indicate the given order:* A_1 *comes first, then* A_2, *and so on. The product of this finite sequence of sets will be denoted by* $A_1 \times A_2 \times \cdots \times A_n$ *and is defined as follows:***

(1) *If at least one of the sets* $A_1, A_2, \ldots, A_n$, *is empty, then* $A_1 \times A_2 \times \cdots \times A_n$ *is defined to be the empty set* $\varnothing$.

(2) *If none of the sets* $A_1, A_2, \ldots, A_n$ *is empty, then* $A_1 \times A_2 \times \cdots \times A_n$ *is defined to be the set of all ordered n-tuples of the form* $(a_1, a_2, \ldots, a_n)$, *where* $a_1 \in A_1, \ldots, a_n \in A_n$.

Let us make the second part of this definition more precise. Choose an element of A_1; call it a_1. Choose an element a_2 of A_2, an element a_3 of A_3, and so on. The totality of these n selected elements is just the *set* $\{a_1, a_2, \ldots, a_n\}$. Notice that a set does not depend on the order in which its elements are listed: order of listing is not a feature of sets. Thus, if $n = 3$, the above set, $\{a_1, a_2, a_3\}$

** The subscripts are just a matter of notational convenience when we are dealing with a large number of sets. The crucial thing is the order in which the sets are written. Thus, when dealing with three sets, we may call them A, B, C, and their product (in that order) is $A \times B \times C$.

could also be written as $\{a_3, a_1, a_2\}$ or $\{a_2, a_1, a_3\}$, and so on. The ordered n-tuple of elements $(a_1, a_2, \ldots, a_n)$, therefore, is something more than a set. It is indeed, *a set together with a prescribed ordering of the elements of the set.* In order that two ordered n-tuples $(a_1, a_2, \ldots, a_n)$ and $(b_1, b_2, \ldots, b_n)$ be equal, it is no longer sufficient, as it was for sets, for them to consist of the same elements. *They must consist of the same elements, and these elements must occur in the same order. That is,* $(a_1, a_2, \ldots, a_n) = (b_1, b_2, \ldots, b_n)$ *if and only if* $a_1 = b_1, a_2 = b_2, \ldots, a_n = b_n$.

Thus, for example, although the set $\{1, 2, 3\}$ equals $\{3, 2, 1\}$, the ordered triple $(1, 2, 3)$ does not equal $(3, 2, 1)$.

An ordered n-tuple, then, is something slightly more complex than a set of n elements. We shall show in the exercises, however, that ordered n-tuples can be defined (in a certain sense) in terms of certain sets.

We emphasize by repeating: The product $A_1 \times A_2 \times \cdots \times A_n$ is the set of *all* ordered n-tuples, such that the first member of the n-tuple belongs to A_1, the second to A_2, and so on—provided, of course, that none of the sets $A_1, A_2, \cdots, A_n$ is empty. Otherwise, $A_1 \times A_2 \times \cdots \times A_n$ is the empty set.

For example, let $A_1 = \{a, b\}$ and $A_2 = \{1, 2, 3\}$. Then, $A_1 \times A_2 = \{(a, 1), (a, 2), (a, 3), (b, 1), (b, 2), (b, 3)\}$ and $A_2 \times A_1 = \{(1, a), (2, a), (3, a), (1, b), (2, b), (3, b)\}$. Notice the obvious fact that $A_1 \times A_2 \neq A_2 \times A_1$.

Nothing in the above definition of product prevents us from choosing A_i to be the same set A, for all $i = 1, 2, \ldots, n$. That is, we may form the n-fold product $A \times A \times \cdots \times A$. If $A = \{a, b\}$, then $A \times A = \{(a, a), (a, b), (b, a), (b, b)\}$. Often it is convenient to use the notation "A^n" to denote the n-fold product $A \times A \times \cdots \times A$. This is consistent with our earlier use of the symbols "$\mathbf{R}^2$," "$\mathbf{R}^3$," ..., "$\mathbf{R}^k$." For $\mathbf{R}^k$ was defined to be the set of all ordered k-tuples of real numbers, and this set is, of course, the k-fold product $\mathbf{R} \times \mathbf{R} \times \cdots \times \mathbf{R}$. Indeed, the fact that $\mathbf{R} \times \mathbf{R} = \mathbf{R}^2$, the Cartesian plane, led to the use of the term *Cartesian product* for what we have called more simply *product*.

To illustrate all of the concepts described in this section, let us look at the standard geometric representation of the Cartesian plane $\mathbf{R}^2$:

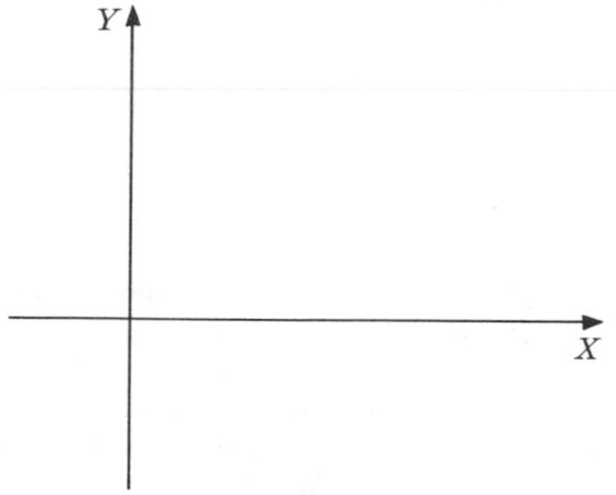

FIGURE 6

The X-axis consists of all ordered pairs of the form $(r, 0)$, where r ranges over $\mathbf{R}$. That is, the X-axis equals $\mathbf{R} \times \{0\}$. The Y-axis, by a similar argument, equals $\{0\} \times \mathbf{R}$. The intersection of the X-axis and Y-axis is just the set consisting of the ordered pair $(0, 0)$. That is $(\mathbf{R} \times \{0\}) \cap (\{0\} \times \mathbf{R}) = \{(0, 0)\}$. [Clearly, this is the only ordered pair of real numbers of the form $(r, 0)$ and $(0, s)$.] The union of the two axes is the cross-shaped set pictured above. $\mathbf{R} \times \{0\} \setminus \{0\} \times \mathbf{R}$ consists of all points on the X-axis that are not on the Y-axis: that is, all points on the X-axis except the origin.

EXERCISES / 2.5

1. Let A be the interval of real numbers x satisfying $1 \leqq x \leqq 3$; let B be the interval of real numbers y satisfying $-2 \leqq y \leqq 0$.

a. Show that $A \times B \subset \mathbf{R} \times \mathbf{R}$.

b. Representing $\mathbf{R} \times \mathbf{R}$ as the X-Y plane, sketch in the points representing the subset $A \times B$.

2. Let A, B, C, D be any nonempty sets. Prove that the following equalities hold.

a. $(A \cup B) \times C = (A \times C) \cup (B \times C)$

b. $(A \times B) \cap (C \times D) = (A \cap C) \times (B \cap D)$

c. Give an example of sets A, B, C, D such that

$$(A \times B) \cup (C \times D) \neq (A \cup B) \times (C \cup D)$$

d. If $A \cap B = \varnothing$, then $(A \times B) \cap (B \times A) = \varnothing$.

3. Let A, B, C be any nonempty sets. Given any elements $a \in A$, $b \in B$, and $c \in C$, let $\langle a, b, c\rangle$ be the *pair* $(a, (b, c))$ [i.e., the pair whose first member is a and whose second member is the pair (b, c)]. Prove that $\langle a, b, c\rangle = \langle a', b', c'\rangle$ if and only if $a = a'$, $b = b'$, and $c = c'$.

The entity $\langle a, b, c\rangle$, therefore, has the property that we described as central to the notion of the ordered triple (a, b, c).

4. Let A and B be any two nonempty sets. For any $a \in A$ and $b \in B$, let $\langle a, b\rangle$ be the set $\{\{a\}, \{a, b\}\}$. Prove that $\langle a, b\rangle = \langle a', b'\rangle$ if and only if $a = a'$ and $b = b'$. The entity $\langle a, b\rangle$, therefore, has the property that we described as central to the concept of the ordered pair (a, b).

The preceding two exercises suggest a way of defining the concept of ordered k-tuple differently from the definition in the text above. Namely, define an ordered pair of elements $a \in A$ and $b \in B$, in which a is considered first and b second, to be the object $\langle a, b\rangle$ defined above in Exercise 4. Define the ordered triple of elements $a \in A$, $b \in B$, $c \in C$, in that order, to be the pair $\langle a, \langle b, c\rangle\rangle$, analogously with Exercise 3. And continue in this way until the notion of ordered k-tuple is defined. Each such object has the central property that interests us: namely, two k-tuples so defined are equal, if and only if their components are equal in the same order. Thus, although this definition differs from the one given in the text, it shares with the latter the property described above. And since this property can be considered to be the defining property of the concept of ordered k-tuple, the two definitions determine the same concept. The definition in the text is somewhat more straightforward; the definition given here is of interest, since it shows that the concept of ordered pair (and, hence, of ordered k-tuple) can be expressed directly in terms of the notion of set: namely, $\langle a, b\rangle = \{\{a\}, \{a, b\}\}$, as in Exercise 4.

5. Use the definition of $\langle a, b\rangle$ given in Exercise 4. Show that $\bigcup\langle a, b\rangle = \{a, b\}$ and $\bigcap\langle a, b\rangle = \{a\}$.

1.6 Relations

(a) Mathematicians constantly deal with various relations between objects: geometers deal with the relations of congruence and similarity; algebraists deal with relations of numerical equality or inequality; set theorists deal with the relations of set membership and set inclusion. If for no other reason than this, therefore, it is desirable to have a a precise formulation of the general notion of *relation*.

We shall, in this text, confine our attention to the kind of relation described above: namely, to relations between two objects. These are known as *binary* relations.

For mathematical purposes, a binary relation can be considered to be *known*, if it is, in principle, possible to select from the set of all possible ordered pairs of objects relevant to the relation all those pairs (X, Y) such that *X is in that relation to Y*. One way of obtaining such knowledge is by means of a rule (a formula, a description, a testing procedure). Thus, for example, the reader is by now expected to know all about the inclusion relation between sets; his knowledge derives from the *description* given in Section 1.4: namely, $A \subset B$, if and only if every member of A is a member of B. But there are significant disadvantages in defining the notion of a relation in terms of the notion of a rule or description, the chief among these being that the notion of a rule is very hard to make precise and is immensely more complex than the notion of a relation. Thus, we look for other ways of obtaining the desired knowledge.

But one such way is right in front of us; namely, we would certainly have knowledge of the appropriate ordered pairs of objects if we had a list of them. Such a list gives us all we need, and so it can *stand for the concept of the relation*. We now formulate this precisely.

Definition 2.9

Let A and B be any two nonempty sets. A relation R from members of A to members of B is a subset of $A \times B$.

We say that a is R-related to b and write aRb whenever $(a, b) \in R$. If $(a, b) \notin R$, we may write $a\tilde{R}b$.

Notice that we are not assuming any symmetry properties of a relation. It may often be the case that aRb whereas $b\tilde{R}a$. Indeed, if A and B have no members in common, then neither do $A \times B$ and $B \times A$ (see Exercises 2.5,**2.d**). Thus, if $R \subset A \times B$, R can have no elements in common with $B \times A$, so that $(b, a) \notin R$.

Notice also that R *is a subset of* $A \times B$. It may be the empty set $\varnothing$ or the entire set $A \times B$ or any set in between. If $R = \varnothing$, we say that R is empty; if $R = A \times B$, we say that R is full. Clearly, empty and full relations are not very interesting.

Finally, some more terminology:

Let $\mathscr{D}_R = \{a \mid a \in A \text{ and } aRb \text{ for some } b \in B\}$.

Let $\mathscr{R}_R = \{b \mid b \in B \text{ and } aRb \text{ for some } a \in A\}$.

$\mathscr{D}_R$ is called the *domain of* R, and $\mathscr{R}_R$ is called the *range of* R. Briefly, $\mathscr{D}_R$ consists of all those a in A that appear as a first member of some ordered pair in R; $\mathscr{R}_R$ consists of all those $b \in B$ that appear as a second member of some ordered pair in R.

The reader should be able to prove that $R \subset \mathscr{D}_R \times \mathscr{R}_R$. This inclusion implies that every relation can be considered as a relation from its domain to its range. Is it always true that $R = \mathscr{D}_R \times \mathscr{R}_R$?

If $A = B$, then we say that R *is a relation on* A. The reader should be able to show that a relation from A to B is also a relation on $A \cup B$. This fact shows that every (binary) relation can be considered as a relation *on* such and such a set.

(b) *Examples of Relations*

(i) Let A be any nonempty set, and let the relation R on A consist of all ordered pairs $(a, b) \in A \times A$ such that $a = b$. Thus, aRb, if and only if $a = b$, so that R is simply the relation of *equality*.

(ii) Let $\mathscr{S}$ be any nonempty collection of sets, and suppose that $\bigcup\mathscr{S}$ is not empty. (Thus, the collection $\mathscr{S}$ may not consist of the empty set alone.) We define a relation R from $\bigcup\mathscr{S}$ to $\mathscr{S}$ as follows:

R consists of all ordered pairs $(x, S) \in (\bigcup\mathscr{S}) \times \mathscr{S}$ such that x is a member of S.

Thus, xRS if and only if $x \in S$, so that R is the usual membership relation.

(iii) Let A be any nonempty set, and let $\mathscr{P}(A)$ be the collection of all subsets of A (see Exercises 2.2.**4**). We define a relation R on $\mathscr{P}(A)$ as follows:

R consists of all ordered pairs $(S, T) \in \mathscr{P}(A) \times \mathscr{P}(A)$ such that S is a subset of T.

Thus, SRT, if and only if $S \subset T$, so that R is just the usual inclusion relation.

(iv) Let R consist of all ordered pairs $(x, y) \in R \times R$, such that x is less than y. Thus, xRy, if and only if $x < y$, so that R is just the "less than" relation.

(v) Let P be the set of all people on earth, and let R be the relation on P of "is the father of." That is, R consists of all ordered pairs $(p, q) \in P$ such that p is the father of q.

(vi) Let T be the set of all triangles on the Cartesian plane $\mathbf{R}^2$. Let R_1 be the relation on T of *congruence*. That is, R_1 consists of all ordered pairs $(\Delta_1, \Delta_2) \in T \times T$ such that Δ_1 is congruent to Δ_2. Let R_2 be the relation on T of *similarity*. Thus, R_2 consists of all ordered pairs $(\Delta_1, \Delta_2) \in T \times T$ such that Δ_1 is similar to Δ_2.

Notice that congruent triangles are similar, so that $R_1 \subset R_2$.

(vii) Let n be any natural number. We define the relation on $\mathbf{Z}$ (the integers) of congruence *modulo n*, $\equiv_n$, as follows: $\equiv_n$ consists of all ordered pairs $(x, y) \in \mathbf{Z} \times \mathbf{Z}$ such that x and y have the same remainder when divided by n; alternatively, $\equiv_n$ consists of all ordered pairs $(x, y) \in \mathbf{Z} \times \mathbf{Z}$ such that $x - y$ is divisible by n.

If $n = 1$, $\equiv_n = \mathbf{Z} \times \mathbf{Z}$ because *every* ordered pair $(x, y) \in \mathbf{Z} \times \mathbf{Z}$ has the property that $x - y$ is divisible by 1. Thus, $\equiv_1$ is full.

(viii) Let $A = \{1, 2, 3\}$, $B = \{x, y, z\}$, and let $R \subset A \times B$ be $\{(1, y), (2, y), (3, z)\}$.

We present this as an example of a relation that cannot be described by any significant rule. It is, simply, an arbitrarily selected subset of $A \times B$. Our intention here is to point out that the mathematical concept of a relation is nothing very profound. It is merely a representation of our intuitive idea of a relation within the framework of set theory; in this generality, it is little more than a convenient notational device. The concept attains some stature, however, when we use it to describe certain special cases, as we do in Definition **2.10** and in Section 2.

(c) *Some Properties of Relations*

Definition 2.10

Let R be a relation on a nonempty set A.

(1) *R is* reflexive, *if and only if for* every *$a \in A$ it is true that aRa, that is $(a, a) \in R$.*

(2) *R is* irreflexive, *if and only if for* every *$a \in A$, $a\tilde{R}a$, that is $(a, a) \notin R$.*

(3) *R is* symmetric, *if and only if for every ordered pair $(a, b) \in R$ it is true that $(b, a) \in R$, that is, if aRb, then bRa.*

(4) *R is* antisymmetric, *if and only if when aRb and bRa then $a = b$. In other words, to say that R is antisymmetric is to say that for distinct elements a, b in A,* at most one *of the relations aRb and bRa holds.*

(5) *R is* transitive, *if and only if the following is true: for any a, b, c in A, if aRb and bRc, then aRc; that is, if $(a, b) \in R$ and $(b, c) \in R$, then $(a, c) \in R$.*

In Table 2.2 the columns represent the various properties and the rows represent the relations described in Subsection 1.6(b). A check in the table signifies that the relation on that row has the property heading that column; a cross means that it does not. We do not verify the table here but leave that as an exercise for the reader.

TABLE 2.2 PROPERTIES

RELATIONS	Reflexivity	Irreflexivity	Symmetry	Antisymmetry	Transitivity
equality	√	×	√	√	√
membership	× *	√*	×	√	×
inclusion	√	×	×	√	√
less than	×	√	×	√	√
father of	×	√	×	√	×
congruence	√	×	√	×	√
similarity	√	×	√	×	√
$\equiv_n$	√	×	√	×	√

* We are assuming here that no set in the collection $\mathscr{S}$ and no member of $\bigcup\mathscr{S}$ is a member of itself.

EXERCISES / 2.6

1. Let R and S be two relations on the nonempty set A. We form new relations $\tilde{R}$, R^{-1}, and $R \circ S$ as follows:

$$\begin{aligned}\tilde{R} &= \{(a, b) \mid (a, b) \in A \times A \text{ and } (a, b) \notin R\} \\ &= (A \times A) \setminus R. \\ R^{-1} &= \{(a, b) \mid (b, a) \in R\} \\ R \circ S &= \{(a, b) \mid \text{for some } c \in A,\ (a, c) \in S \text{ and } (c, b) \in R\}.\end{aligned}$$

We call $\tilde{R}$ the relation on A complementary to R, R^{-1} the inverse of R, and $R \circ S$ the composition of R and S. In addition, we may, of course, form the relations $R \cup S$ and $R \cap S$.

a. Show that R is reflexive, if and only if $\tilde{R}$ is irreflexive.

b. Show that R is symmetric, if and only if $R \supset R^{-1}$ and that $R \supset R^{-1}$, if and only if $R = R^{-1}$.

c. Show that R is transitive, if and only if $R \circ R \subset R$.

d. Suppose that $R \circ R^{-1} \subset R$. Show that for every $a \in \mathscr{D}_R$, (a, a) belongs to R. Use this to conclude that $R^{-1} \subset R \circ R^{-1}$ and, hence, that R is symmetric. Then, use **(c)** to conclude that R is transitive.

e. Show that R is transitive, symmetric, and reflexive if and only if $\mathscr{D}_R = A$ and $R \circ R^{-1} = R$.

f. Prove that if R and S are symmetric, then so are $R \cup S$ and $R \cap S$.

2. Verify the entries in Table 2.2.

3. Consider the relations R_1 (congruence) and R_2 (similarity) of Example (b) (vi), above. Prove that $R_1 \circ R_2 = R_2 \circ R_1 = R_2$.

4. Let A be any nonempty, finite set, and let R be any irreflexive, transitive relation on A such that $A \subset \mathscr{D}_R \cup \mathscr{R}_R$. Prove that there is at least one element a in A such that $a\tilde{R}b$ for all $b \in A$. Prove that there is at least one element a' in A such that $b\tilde{R}a'$ for all b in A.

   In the special case in which R is the "less than" relation and A is any finite set of real numbers, the above results reduce to the statements that A has at least one smallest element and at least one greatest element.

5. Describe R^{-1} when R is
   a. the "less than" relation;
   b. the "the father of" relation;
   c. $\equiv_n$.

1.7† Equivalence Relations

Given two relations R and S on a nonempty set A, we say that R is *stronger* than S (or S is *weaker* than R) if $R \subset S$. Clearly, the empty relation on A is stronger than any other, and the full relation is weaker. These, of course, are uninteresting. It is often, however, interesting, useful, and, indeed, necessary in mathematics and various sciences to consider certain relations between objects that are closely parallel to the relation of *equality* (or sameness) yet *weaker* than it. These relations, which we now define, are called *equivalence relations.*

Definition 2.11

Let A be a nonempty set. Any reflexive, symmetric, and transitive relation on A is called an equivalence relation.

Let R be *any* equivalence relation on A. Select any elements from A, say a and a', and suppose that $a = a'$. Then, since R is reflexive, $(a, a') \in R$. That is, denoting the equality relation by "$=$", if $(a, a') \in =$, then $(a, a') \in R$, so that $= \subset R$. *This means that R is, indeed, weaker than* $=$.

Notice that $\mathscr{D}_R = \mathscr{R}_R = A$, since, given any $a \in A$, $(a, a) \in R$, so that a appears as a first member of a pair in R and as a second member. (This is the main reason that we require reflexivity. We want the domains and ranges of these relations to be the entire set. Indeed, if we have a relation S on A that is symmetric and transitive and satisfies $\mathscr{D}_S = A$, then we can show that it is reflexive and, hence, that $\mathscr{R}_S = A$. For, choose any $a \in A$. Since $\mathscr{D}_S = A$, it follows that $a \in \mathscr{D}_S$, so that a appears as a first member in some pair, say $(a, a') \in S$. Since S is symmetric, $(a', a) \in S$. Then, applying the transitivity property of S to the pairs (a, a') and (a', a), we conclude that $(a, a) \in S$, as desired.)

Notice, finally, that the full relation on A (namely, $A \times A$ itself) is an equivalence relation. The reader should be able to verify that this relation has the requisite properties. In theory, this equivalence relation is as good as any other. In practice, it is not very useful, and we mention it here merely for completeness.

Equivalence relations are useful because they provide the mathematician with a rigorous way of restricting his attention to certain properties of the objects of his study while ignoring other properties.

For example, suppose that for some reason a mathematician is interested only in the parity properties of integers: that is, he is interested only in whether a given integer is odd or even. He can express his interest rigorously, in the language of set theory, by means of the relation $\equiv_2$. If the reader will consult the above chart, he will see that $\equiv_2$ is a reflexive, symmetric, transitive relation on **Z**. To say that two integers have the same parity is to say that they are $\equiv_2$-related.

For another example, consider the notion of *congruence* in plane geometry. The geometer is primarily interested in the sizes and shapes of, say, triangles. He is not interested in their position on the plane. To express his interests rigorously, he defines a relation, *congruence*, that respects the first two of these properties and ignores the third: Two distinct geometric objects in the plane are congruent provided that they can be re-positioned in the plane so as to coincide. Again, the reader will note that congruence is reflexive, symmetric, and transitive.

So far, our examples do not really differ very much from examples of any other relations. However, as we shall show in general below, because the relations of congruence modulo two and congruence (of triangles) are equivalence relations, they can be used to *partition* (see the definition below) the objects of study into certain *mutually exclusive and collectively exhaustive* classes. For example, in the case of congruence (of triangles) the geometer may partition the set of all triangles in the plane into congruence classes: Each class can be described as the set of all triangles congruent to some fixed, given triangle. Thus, there is the class of *all* equilateral triangles with side of length 3 1/2. There is the class of *all* equilateral triangles with side of length 2,000. There is the class of *all* isoceles triangles with base of length 1 and base angles equal to 37°, etc.

The partitioning has a certain simplifying effect. For now the geometer need not confront the vast array of all triangles in the plane. He need deal only with one "representative" from each class of the partition. Any fact (involving only those properties in which he is interested: namely, size and shape) about this representative holds for all members of the class represented. The chief value of this partitioning procedure, then, is, as stated above, that it provides an explicit rigorous method for ignoring superfluous or extrinsic factors—it cuts down on the excess baggage, so to speak.

The process of systematically ignoring certain properties of objects is known as abstraction. Thus, let us think of triangles lying in the plane as being more or less concrete. If we ignore the property of position when considering these triangles, then we are actually passing to a more abstract level. Instead of such-and-such-a-triangle-lying-*there*, we abstract and consider the triangle-shape of which it is a particular manifestation.

This example, it is hoped, points to the abstracting role of equivalence relations. In any given context, we deal with certain objects, the identity of which we assume is known. (We may, heuristically, consider them to be concrete.) When we consider a certain equivalence relation between these objects, we are tacitly *ignoring* some of the properties that contribute to the individuality or identity of the objects (provided that the relation is strictly weaker than equality). Any two equivalent objects will be thought of as being the "same." Each class of the partition determined by the equivalence relation consists of all objects that are the "same." *This class itself then can be considered as an object, the result of abstracting the properties referred to.* The objects in the class can be considered as particular manifestations of the abstract object.

We now present some definitions and results to make the mathematical aspects of the preceding discussion complete.

Definition 2.12

Let A be a nonempty set. A partition of A is a nonempty collection $\mathscr{P}$ of nonempty subsets of A such that

(1) $\bigcup \mathscr{P} = A$, *and*

(2) *if S and T are members of $\mathscr{P}$, then $S \cap T = \varnothing$.*

Thus, a partition of A is a "division" of A into nonempty sets that are mutually disjoint (i.e., no two have an element in common).

Definition 2.13

Let A be a nonempty set, and let R be an equivalence relation on A. Choose any $a \in A$. The equivalence class (with respect to R) containing a is defined to be the set of all a' in A such that $(a, a') \in R$. We denote this equivalence class by $[a]_R$, or $[a]$ for short.

Notice that, since R is reflexive, $(a, a) \in R$, for every $a \in A$, so that $a \in [a]_R$, for every $a \in A$. This justifies the use of the phrase "equivalence class *containing a*."

Notice also that distinct symbols "$[a]_R$" and "$[a']_R$," where $a \neq a'$, may describe the same equivalence class. For example, if R is the full relation on A, then, for every $a \in A$, $[a]_R = A$. To see this, choose any $a \in A$ and notice that *every* $a' \in A$ satisfies $(a, a') \in R = A \times A$. Thus, in this case, distinct elements a and a' determine the same equivalence class, $[a]_R = A = [a']_R$.

The element a will be called a *representative* of the class $[a]_R$, where, now, "R" denotes again any equivalence relation.

Proposition 2.1

Let A be a nonempty set, and let R be any equivalence relation on A. Then, the set of all equivalence classes with respect to R is a partition of A.

Proof

Let $\mathscr{P}_R$ be the set of all equivalence classes with respect to R. (We shall use this notation from now on in the text.)

First, we show that $\bigcup\mathscr{P}_R = A$. Clearly, $\bigcup\mathscr{P}_R$ consists only of elements of A, so that $\bigcup\mathscr{P}_R \subset A$. Thus, it remains only to prove the reverse inclusion. Choose any $a \in A$. Then, $[a]_R \in \mathscr{P}_R$. Moreover, as we showed above, $a \in [a]_R$. Therefore $a \in \bigcup\mathscr{P}_R$. This means that every member of A belongs to $\bigcup\mathscr{P}_R$ and, hence, that $A \subset \bigcup\mathscr{P}_R$, as desired.

Next, we show that distinct equivalence classes are mutually disjoint. That is, we prove that if $[a]_R$ and $[a']_R$ are two equivalence classes, then either $[a]_R = [a']_R$ or $[a]_R \cap [a']_R = \varnothing$, the first equality holding, if and only if a and a' are R-related, the second otherwise.

Choose any elements a and a' in A, and suppose that $(a, a') \in R$. We shall show that $[a]_R = [a']_R$.

Choose any $a'' \in [a']_R$. Then, by definition, $(a', a'') \in R$. Applying the transitivity of R to the pairs (a, a') and (a', a''), we conclude that $(a, a'') \in R$ and, hence, that $a'' \in [a]_R$. Since a'' was *any* element of $[a']_R$, we conclude that $[a']_R \subset [a]_R$.

Since R is symmetric, $(a', a) \in R$. Now, repeat the argument of the preceding paragraph exchanging the roles of a and a'. The argument carries over precisely, *mutatis mutandis*, and yields the inclusion $[a]_R \subset [a']_R$.

The two inclusions combine to yield the desired equality, $[a]_R = [a']_R$.

On the other hand, if $(a, a') \notin R$, then we can show that $[a]_R \cap [a']_R = \varnothing$. For suppose, on the contrary, that there is an $a'' \in [a]_R \cap [a']_R$. Then, by definition, $a'' \in [a]_R$, so that $(a, a'') \in R$, *and* $a'' \in [a']_R$, so that $(a', a'') \in R$. Since R is symmetric, $(a'', a') \in R$, so that, applying the transitivity of R to this last pair and to (a, a'') we get $(a, a') \in R$, a contradiction. This means that if $(a, a') \notin R$, then $[a]_R \cap [a']_R = \varnothing$.

Thus, the union of all equivalence classes is the entire set A, and distinct equivalence classes have empty intersection. This means that $\mathscr{P}_R$ is a partition of A. Q.E.D.

This shows that every equivalence relation determines a partition, which we shall call the *partition belonging to the relation*. Conversely, we shall show that every partition determines an equivalence relation, which we shall call the *relation belonging to the partition*.

Indeed, given a partition $\mathscr{P}$, the partition belonging to the relation belonging to $\mathscr{P}$ is $\mathscr{P}$. Moreover, given a relation R, the relation belonging to the partition belonging to R is R. These facts, which we demonstrate below, show that the notions of equivalence relation and partition are completely equivalent. For, once one is given, the other is immediately and uniquely determined.

Definition 2.14

Let A be a nonempty set, and let $\mathscr{P}$ be a partition of A. We define a relation $R_{\mathscr{P}}$ on A as follows: $(a, a') \in R_{\mathscr{P}}$, *if and only if a and a' belong to the same member of the partition $\mathscr{P}$.*

Proposition 2.2

Using the notation of the above definition, $R_{\mathscr{P}}$ is an equivalence relation on A.
We leave the proof to the reader as an easy exercise.
We shall call $R_{\mathscr{P}}$ *the relation belonging to $\mathscr{P}$.*

Proposition 2.3

Let A be a nonempty set, let S be an equivalence relation on A, and let $\mathscr{Q}$ be a partition of A. Then,
(1) $R_{\mathscr{P}_S} = S$
(2) $\mathscr{P}_{R_{\mathscr{Q}}} = \mathscr{Q}$

Remark: 1. says: The relation belonging to the partition belonging to S is S.
2. says: The partition belonging to the relation belonging to $\mathscr{Q}$ is $\mathscr{Q}$.

Proof

(1) Recall that both $R_{\mathscr{P}_S}$ and S are subsets of $A \times A$.

Choose any pair $(a, a') \in R_{\mathscr{P}_S}$. By definition, a and a' belong to the same member of $\mathscr{P}_S$. That is, there is a set $B \in \mathscr{P}_S$ such that $a \in B$ and $a' \in B$. But, by definition of $\mathscr{P}_S$, $[a]_S \in \mathscr{P}_S$ and $[a']_S \in \mathscr{P}_S$, and $a \in [a]_S$ and $a' \in [a']_S$. This means that $[a]_S$ and B have the element a in common, and $[a']_S$ and B have the element a' in common. In Proposition 2.1, however, we showed that distinct members of a partition belonging to an equivalence relation are disjoint (i.e., have no members in common. Therefore, $[a]_S$, B, and $[a']_S$ are not distinct. That is, $[a]_S = B = [a']_S$. Therefore, $a' \in [a]_S$, or $(a, a') \in S$.

Therefore, $R_{\mathscr{P}_S} \subset S$.

On the other hand, if $(a, a') \in S$, then $a' \in [a]_S$, so that a and a' belong to the same member of $\mathscr{P}_S$. This means, by definition, that $(a, a') \in R_{\mathscr{P}_S}$.

Therefore, $S \subset R_{\mathscr{P}_S}$, and this inclusion combined with the first yields $S = R_{\mathscr{P}_S}$.

(2) Recall that $\mathscr{P}_{R_Q}$ and $\mathscr{Q}$ are both collections of subsets of A.

Choose any set $B \in \mathscr{P}_{R_{\mathscr{Q}}}$. By definition of *partition belonging to a relation*, B is of the form $[a]_{R_{\mathscr{Q}}}$, for some $a \in A$. Now, $[a]_{R_{\mathscr{Q}}}$ consists of *all* a', such that $(a, a') \in R_{\mathscr{Q}}$; that is, B consists of all a', such that a' is in the same set of the partition $\mathscr{Q}$ as a. But this means that B coincides with a certain set of the partition $\mathscr{Q}$: namely, the set in the partition that contains a. Therefore, $B \in \mathscr{Q}$. Thus, $\mathscr{P}_{R_{\mathscr{Q}}} \subset \mathscr{Q}$.

Choose any set $B \in \mathscr{Q}$, and let a be any member of B. Then, $B = [a]_{R_{\mathscr{Q}}}$. To see this, recall that $R_{\mathscr{Q}}$-related elements are precisely those that belong to the same member of the partition $\mathscr{Q}$. Thus, $[a]_{R_{\mathscr{Q}}}$ consists of all a' belonging to B—which is clearly B. But $\mathscr{P}_{R_{\mathscr{Q}}}$ is the set of *all* equivalence classes $[a]_{R_{\mathscr{Q}}}$. Therefore, $B \in \mathscr{P}_{R_{\mathscr{Q}}}$. Thus, $\mathscr{Q} \subset \mathscr{P}_{R_{\mathscr{Q}}}$, which, when combined with the previous inclusion yields the desired equality $\mathscr{Q} = \mathscr{P}_{R_{\mathscr{Q}}}$. Q.E.D.

In conclusion, we list some equivalence relations and describe the partitions belonging to them.

Description of relation	Description of partition
(a) Congruence (of *circles* lying in the plane)	(a) Each equivalence class consists of *all* circles in the plane of a given radius, since all such circles are congruent
(b) Similarity (of triangles lying in the plane)	(b) Each equivalence class consists of *all* triangles in the plane with three given angles, since all triangles with corresponding angles equal are similar
(c) Equality (of integers)	(c) Each equivalence class consists of one integer
(d) $\equiv_5$ (on the set of integers)	(d) Each equivalence class consists of *all* integers that have a certain given remainder after division by 5. There are precisely five such classes:

Remainder	Class
0	$\{0, \pm 5, \pm 10, \pm 15, \ldots\}$
1	$\{\ldots -9, -4, 1, 6, 11, \ldots\}$
2	$\{\ldots -8, -3, 2, 7, 12, \ldots\}$
3	$\{\ldots, -7, -2, 3, 8, 13, \ldots\}$
4	$\{\ldots, -6, -1, 4, 9, 14, \ldots\}$

EXERCISES / 2.7

1.* Consider the equivalence relation $\equiv_5$ on the set **Z** of integers. As indicated in the chart above, $\equiv_5$ determines five equivalence classes, which we denote by $\bar{0}$, $\bar{1}$, $\bar{2}$, $\bar{3}$, $\bar{4}$, respectively, according to the remainder to which they correspond.

a. Choose any representative of $\bar{1}$ and any representative of $\bar{2}$, and show that their sum is a representative of $\bar{3}$ and their product is a representative of $\bar{2}$.

b. Let S and T be any of the five equivalence classes above. (S may or may not equal T.) Show that there is an equivalence class U, one of the five above, *depending only on S and on T*, such that if a is any representative of S and if b is any representative of T, then $a + b$ is a representative of U.

In other words, choosing any a and a' in S and any b and b' in T, show that $a + b$ and $a' + b'$ are in the same equivalence class. This class, then, will depend, not on the particular choice of representatives of S and T, but only on S and T themselves.

To indicate the dependence of this U on S and T, we write $U = S \oplus T$.

c. Let S and T be as above. Show that there is an equivalence class V depending only on S and T, such that if a is any representative of S and b is any representative of T, then ab is a representative of V.

To indicate the dependence of this V on S and T, we write $V = S \otimes T$.

This exercise shows that, in some sense, the relation $\equiv_5$ respects the operations of addition and subtraction.

2.* Complete the "multiplication" and "addition" tables below:

$\otimes$	$\bar{0}$	$\bar{1}$	$\bar{2}$	$\bar{3}$	$\bar{4}$
$\bar{0}$					
$\bar{1}$		$\bar{1}$			
$\bar{2}$					
$\bar{3}$					$\bar{2}$
$\bar{4}$	$\bar{0}$				

$\oplus$	$\bar{0}$	$\bar{1}$	$\bar{2}$	$\bar{3}$	$\bar{4}$
$\bar{0}$					
$\bar{1}$		$\bar{2}$			
$\bar{2}$					
$\bar{3}$					$\bar{2}$
$\bar{4}$	$\bar{4}$				

3.* Use the tables in Exercise **2** to verify the following equalities:
a. $\bar{1} \oplus (\bar{2} \oplus \bar{3}) = (\bar{1} \oplus \bar{2}) \oplus \bar{3}$
b. $\bar{2} \otimes (\bar{3} \oplus \bar{1}) = (\bar{2} \otimes \bar{3}) \oplus (\bar{2} \otimes \bar{1})$
c. $\bar{4} \oplus \bar{2} \quad = \bar{2} \oplus \bar{4}$
d. $\bar{3} \oplus \bar{0} \quad = \bar{3} = \bar{0} \oplus \bar{3}$

4.* We use the notation and concepts introduced in Exercise **1** above. Let S, T, U be *any* of the $\equiv_5$-equivalence classes. Use the definitions of $\oplus$ and $\otimes$ to prove
a. $S \oplus (T \oplus U) = (S \oplus T) \oplus U$
b. $S \oplus T \quad = T \oplus S$
c. $S \oplus \bar{0} \quad = \bar{0} \oplus S = S$
d., e., f. The statements obtained from **a., b., c.** by replacing $\oplus$ by $\otimes$ and $\bar{0}$ by $\bar{1}$
g. $S \otimes (T \oplus U) = (S \otimes T) \oplus (S \otimes U)$

The above equalities are analogues of some (almost all) of the fundamental rules of the arithmetic of real numbers (or integers), If we replace S, T, U by numbers x, y, z, and if we replace $\oplus$ and $\otimes$ by $+$ and $\times$, we obtain equalities that are easily seen to hold.

The first and fourth equalities are known as *associative laws* (*for* $\oplus$ *and* $\otimes$), respectively (cf. Exercises 2.3.**4.**). The second and fifth equalities are known as *commutative laws* (*for* $\oplus$ *and* $\otimes$), respectively. The third and sixth equalities are known as *identity laws for* ($\oplus$ *and* $\otimes$), respectively. And, finally, the seventh equality is known as the *distributive law* (*of* $\otimes$ *over* $\oplus$). The equalities, it should be emphasized, are called *laws* because they are assumed to hold for all possible values of S, T, U; that is, S, T, and U are *any* three (not necessarily distinct) classes chosen from the set $\{\bar{0}, \bar{1}, \bar{2}, \bar{3}, \bar{4}\}$.

Such laws (together with one other which we mention later) are fundamental to arithmetic and to elementary algebra. Because the classes $\bar{0}$, $\bar{1}$, $\bar{2}$, $\bar{3}$, $\bar{4}$, together with $\oplus$ and $\otimes$, satisfy them, we are encouraged to say that these classes together with the operations form a special kind of arithmetic or algebraic system. We shall come back to such systems in later chapters.

It remains only to draw the reader's attention to the fact that we are now treating the *sets* or *classes* $\bar{0}$, $\bar{1}$, $\bar{2}$, $\bar{3}$, $\bar{4}$ very much as if they are *numbers*. However, they are more abstract than the usual "concrete" integers. They are precisely what the integers would appear to us to be, if we could no longer distinguish between two integers whose difference is a multiple of five.

And this "blindness" is not so far-fetched as it would appear at first glance. For is it not true that, for many purposes (sleeping, eating, working), we fail to distinguish between hours in the year that differ by a multiple of twenty-four (hours)?

2 / FUNCTIONS

2.1 Basic Definitions and Notation

According to a widely held point of view, the notion of a set is the basic notion in mathematics, and all other concepts, including those of relation and function, should be defined in terms of this notion. We accepted this point of view in defining the idea of a relation: It is defined to be a *set* of ordered pairs. It will be convenient to apply this viewpoint to the idea of a function. First, however, we present some intuitive background for this idea.

We often use or hear the expressions "functional relation between such and such objects," "this quantity is a function of that quantity," "y depends on x," or "y is a function of x." All of these statements refer to the following paradigm state of affairs: There are two nonempty sets of objects, say A and B, and there is a way (perhaps by explicit rule or description, perhaps by reference to observational data, or by reference to a table, etc.) of associating with each $a \in A$ precisely one member of B. *The identity of this element of B is completely determined by a, it depends on a, so to speak.* This "way" of associating, or better, this *association* is what we mean when we use the word "function."

Thus, for example, let A be the set of all people on earth at any one instant, and let B be the set of real numbers. Then, given any $a \in A$, we associate with him the real number $n(a)$ = the age of a in seconds at the instant in question. This is, certainly, a function. To put it another way, age (of a person) depends on the person in question. We present more detailed examples later.

Now, it is clear that functions are special kinds of relations (cf. the expression "functional relation"): every element in A is related (or made to correspond) to an element of B. What distinguishes functions from run-of-the-mill relations is that each $a \in A$ is (functionally) related to *precisely one* member of B. Most of the relations that we have discussed so far do not have this property. Indeed, if R is an equivalence relation on a nonempty set C, then each $c \in C$ is R-related to every member of $[c]_R$. Thus, unless R is the relation of equality (which means precisely that each $[c]_R$ consists of c alone), some $c \in C$

is R-related to *more than one* member of C. Thus, the only equivalence relation that is a function is the relation of equality.

We now present the definition of function and related notions.

Definition 2.15

Given two nonempty sets A and B, a function f from A to B, written $f: A \to B$ or $A \xrightarrow{f} B$, is a subset of $A \times B$ such that for every $a \in A$ precisely one pair (a, b) belongs to f. Given such a pair (a, b), we write $f(a) = b$ and say that b is the value of f at a (or b is the image of a under f, or b is the f-image of a) or that f takes a to b.

Thus, f is a (special kind of) relation from A to B, and, hence, the domain of f, $\mathscr{D}_f$, and the range of f, $\mathscr{R}_f$, are defined.** Notice that $\mathscr{D}_f = A$, for every $a \in A$ is the first member of a pair in f. We shall sometimes refer to B as the *co-domain* of f.

Let $f: A \to B$ and $g: C \to D$ be functions. We say that f equals g (written $f = g$) if they are equal as sets (of ordered pairs). (In other words, f and g are defined to be certain sets, and so we may apply the usual notion of set-equality to them.) We may formulate this relation of equality in slightly different terms, however. To say that the set f equals the set g is to say that they consist of the same ordered pairs. This means:

1. The set of first members of ordered pairs in f, $\mathscr{D}_f$, equals the set of first members of ordered pairs in g, $\mathscr{D}_g$. That is, $\mathscr{D}_f = \mathscr{D}_g$, or, in other words, $A = C$.

2. Every $a \in A (= C)$ corresponds to exactly one pair in f with first term a and, since $f = g$, to the same pair in g with first term a. Since the pairs are equal, their second members are equal, and so, for every $a \in A$, $f(a) = g(a)$.

Thus, we have the familiar statement that *two functions $f: A \to B$ and $g: C \to D$ are equal if and only if $A = C$ and $f(a) = g(a)$, for every $a \in A$. Notice that we do not require that $B = D$.*

2.2 Remarks

Before going further, we want to emphasize several important aspects of this definition.

First, the reader should make sure that he understands the distinction between the meaning of the symbol "f" and the meaning of the symbol "$f(a)$." The former denotes the entire association or function; the latter denotes the value of the function f at a.

The confusion between these symbols is at least partly due to imprecise terminology sometimes used in lower level courses. In such courses, one often encounters such statements as: "Consider the function $f(x) = x^2 + 2x + 3 \ldots$, or "Consider the function $\sin x \ldots$." According to the distinction that we

** In advanced mathematics the usual term for range is "image." See Definition 2.9 and the definitions following it in Subsection 1.6 (a).

make in the above paragraph, these statements should be rephrased approximately as follows: "Consider the function f whose value at the number x is given by $f(x) = x^2 + 2x + 3 \ldots$," or "Consider the sine function . . . ."

Secondly, our definition of a function as a set (of ordered pairs), although perfectly adequate from a mathematical or logical point of view, has a certain pedagogical or psychological disadvantage: It tends to obscure the fact that a function is a *mapping*. Let us make this more precise. Consider the process of map-making. Whatever the technique, the basic idea is to set up a correspondence or an association between points of the territory to be mapped and points on a sheet of paper. (The correspondence is very special, of course: It preserves some aspects of shape, and so forth. We ignore this, here, however.) We may say that the points of the boundary are *mapped onto the paper*. Given a point on the boundary in other words, there is uniquely determined a point corresponding to it on the paper. Thus, the process of map-making can be thought of as the process of constructing a function from points of land to points on paper. Now, the important thing is that every function can be visualized in roughly the same way. A function $f: A \to B$ can be thought of as a "map" of A in terms of elements of B. Figure 7 below illustrates the analogy. Now, the reader may ask why, if a function is a kind of mapping, do we define it to be a set of ordered pairs? How does this set of pairs fit into the picture? An answer to these questions may be obtained by reversing the above analogy. The set of ordered pairs corresponds, in terms of map-making, to a long list involving two columns. Each "point" of the boundary is entered into the first column, and, adjacent to it, the corresponding "point" on paper is entered into the second column. (Of course, we are speaking figuratively here, since, first of all, the list would have to be infinite, and second of all the *points* themselves couldn't be entered onto the list, but, rather, some abstract

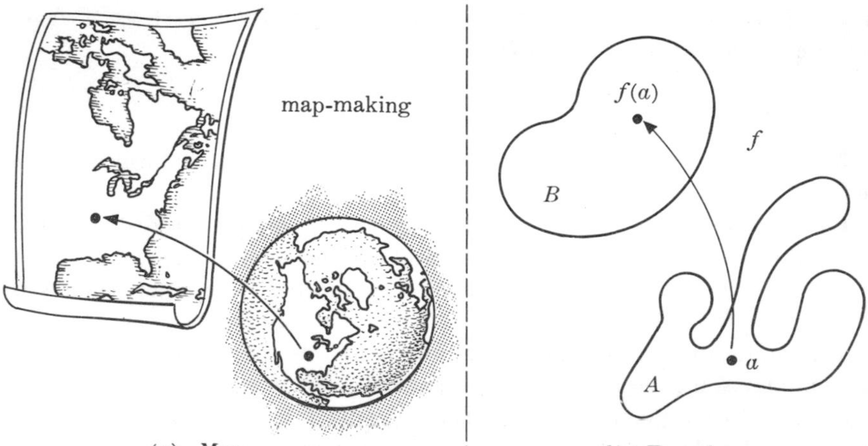

(a) Map (b) Function

FIGURE 7

representatives of these point—say, unambiguous verbal descriptions, or numerical descriptions via coordinate systems—must be entered in their stead.) Thus, the set of ordered pairs corresponds to a kind of data sheet. It is clear that knowledge of this list or sheet is equivalent to knowledge of the map. But, whereas the map-maker prefers the picture to the list, the mathematician prefers the list, since it fits handily into an existing framework of ideas: the theory of sets.

The reader is urged not to take this analogy literally, however. Everything that we shall deduce about functions will follow from the formal definition.

Thirdly, we draw the reader's attention to the requirement in the definition of function that every $a \in A$ be the first member of *precisely one* pair in the function, the second member of which we call *the* function value at a. This is just another form of the defining property of a "functional relation": namely, that to every $a \in A$ there corresponds via the function precisely one member of B.

We have already shown that no equivalence relation, except the relation of equality, satisfies this requirement. We give here one more example, of a numerical nature. Let $A = \{x \mid x \in \mathbf{R} \text{ and } 0 \leq x \leq 1\}$, $B = \{x \mid x \in \mathbf{R} \text{ and } -1 \leq x \leq 1\}$. Then, to every $x \in A$ make correspond those $y \in B$ satisfying $x - y^2 = 0$. For each $x \in A$ (except $x = 0$) there are exactly two $y \in B$ satisfying the equation (namely, $y = \sqrt{x}$, $y = -\sqrt{x}$). Thus, the correspondence is ambiguous, and it is not a function.

Finally, the preceding remark does *not* exclude the possibility that, in general, a function may have the same value at different elements in its domain. For example, consider the function $f: \mathbf{R} \to \mathbf{R}$ given by the equation $f(x) = x^2$ (f sends the real number x to its square). Clearly, $f(x) = x^2 = (-x)^2 = f(-x)$, so that f has the same value at a given real number as it has at the negative of that number.

Figure 8 indicates schematically the distinction between this case and the one described in the previous paragraph.

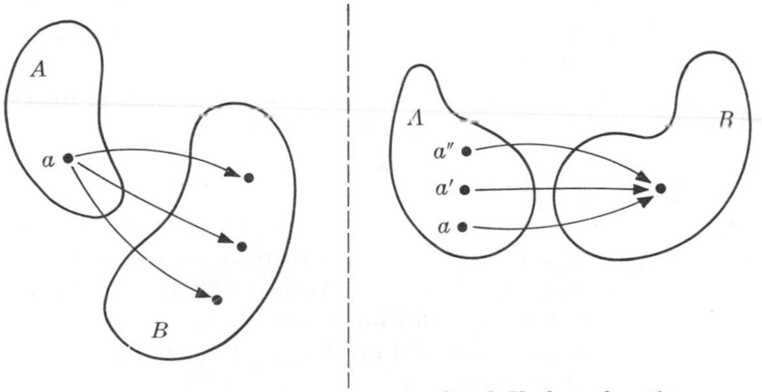

(*a*) Not O.K. for a function (*b*) O.K. for a function

FIGURE 8

EXERCISES / 2.8

1. Which of the following equations express y as a function of x? x as a function of y?

a. $2x + 3y = 8$
b. $2/x + 3/y = 8$
c. $2x^2 + 3y^2 = 8$
d. $2x + 3/y^2 = 8$
e. $x^3 + y = 1$
f. $x^3 + y^5 = 3$
g. $\sin x + \cos y = 0$
h. $e^x = y$

2. The following functions all have domain **R**. What are their ranges? The functions are given by the following equations:

a. $f_1 : f_1(x) = \sqrt{2 - [1/(1 + x^2)]}$
b. $f_2 : f_2(x) + 3x^2 = 0$
c. $f_3 : f_3(x) = \sin x$
d. $f_4 : f_4(x) - [1/(x^2 + 1)] = 1$

3. Let $A = \{1, 2, 3, 4, 5\}$, $B = \{2, 4, 6, 8, 10\}$.
Let the function f be (completely) given by the following table:

x	1	3	5
$f(x)$	2	4	6

What is the domain of f? The range of f?

2.3 Some Examples of Functions and Sets of Functions

(a) We mention, without elaborating, that the functions from **R** to **R** (or from subsets of **R** to **R**) commonly encountered in calculus are all functions in our sense of the word. These are usually expressed by an equation involving symbols x and y, where x stands for any value in the domain of the function and y stands for the function value in the range corresponding to x via the equation: $y = \sin x$, $y = \cos x$, $y = \tan x$, $y = e^x$, $y = \ell nx$, $g = 1/x$, $y = ax^2 + bx + c$, where a, b, c are given real numbers, etc.

(b) Given any two nonempty sets X and Y, let y be any fixed object in Y. The object y determines a function $\bar{y} : X \to Y$ by the equation $\bar{y}(x) = y$, for all $x \in X$. That is, $\bar{y}$ associates with every $x \in X$, the single object y. Notice that if X has more than one element, then $\bar{y}$ takes more than one member of X to y.

If X and Y are both equal to **R**, and we choose y to be $0 \in \mathbf{R}$, then the function $\bar{0}$ is just the constantly 0 function.

(c) Given any nonempty set Z, we define the function $I_Z : Z \to Z$ by the equation $I_Z(z) = z$, for all $z \in Z$. I_Z is called the identity function of Z.

If Z is equal to $\mathbf{R}$, then the identity function $I_{\mathbf{R}}:\mathbf{R} \to \mathbf{R}$ is given by the equation $I_{\mathbf{R}}(r) = r$, for all $r \in \mathbf{R}$.

Notice that all functions $f:\mathbf{R} \to \mathbf{R}$ are subsets of $\mathbf{R} \times \mathbf{R} = \mathbf{R}^2$ = the Cartesian plane. Indeed, the function f is a set of the form

$$\{(x, y) \mid (x, y) \in \mathbf{R}^2 \text{ and } y = f(x)\}$$

This set is precisely what we usually refer to as "the graph of f." Thus, according to our definition of function, a function is identified with (what we formerly called) its graph. Notice that the above described functions $\bar{0}$ and $I_{\mathbf{R}}$ are linear subsets of $\mathbf{R}^2$, in the sense of Chapter 1. Thus, again in the sense of Chapter 1, they are linear functions.

(d) Let A and B be nonempty sets. We define $\pi_1 : A \times B \to A$ and $\pi_2 : A \times B \to B$, by the equations $\pi_1(a, b) = a$ and $\pi_2(a, b) = b$. π_1 and π_2 are called the *first and second coordinate projections, respectively.*

If A and B are both equal to $\mathbf{R}$, then, $A \times B$ is just $\mathbf{R}^2$, a linear set, in the sense of Chapter 1. In this case, it is not hard to see that the functions $\pi_1 : \mathbf{R}^2 \to \mathbf{R}$ and $\pi_2 : \mathbf{R}^2 \to \mathbf{R}$ are linear.

(e) Let $a_1, \ldots, a_k$ be any given real numbers and consider the linear expression (cf. Chapter 1) in indeterminates $x_1, \ldots, x_k$,

$$a_1 x_1 + \cdots + a_k x_k$$

As indicated in Chapter 1, it determines a (linear) function $f:\mathbf{R}^k \to \mathbf{R}$ by the rule

$$f(x_1, \ldots, x_k) = a_1 x_1 + \cdots + a_k x_k$$

That is, to any ordered k-tuple of real numbers, $(x_1, \ldots, x_k)$, the function f assigns the value $a_1 x_1 + \cdots + a_k x_k$.

(f) Let $a_{11}, \ldots, a_{1k}, a_{21}, \ldots, a_{2k}, \ldots, a_{n1}, \ldots, a_{nk}$, be any kn real numbers. They determine n linear expressions

$$\begin{array}{c} a_{11}x_1 + \cdots + a_{1k}x_k \\ \vdots \\ a_{n1}x_1 + \cdots + a_{nk}x_k \end{array}$$

which determine a function $A:\mathbf{R}^k \to \mathbf{R}^n$ by the rule

$$A(x_1, \ldots, x_k) = (y_1, \ldots, y_n),$$

where y_i is given by

$$y_i = a_{i1}x_1 + \cdots + a_{ik}x_k,$$

for $i = 1, 2, \ldots, n$. As indicated in Chapter 1, this function is linear.

(g) Given any nonempty sets A and B, we may consider the set of *all* functions from A to B. We denote this set by the symbol "B^A."

Now, let $A = \{1, 2\}$. Then, $B^A = B^{\{1,2\}}$ is just the set of all possible functions $f: \{1, 2\} \to B$. Now, each such function f is determined by two function values namely, $f(1)$ and $f(2)$. Let us write $f(1) = b_1$ and $f(2) = b_2$. Then, f both determines and is determined by the pair (b_1, b_2). This establishes a certain correspondence between the functions f and the elements of $B \times B = B^2$, that we make it clear later. It suffices to say here that this correspondence shows that the sets $B^{\{1,2\}}$ and B^2 are closely related.

2.4 Some Properties of Functions

(a) *The "Onto" Property*

Definition 2.16

Let $f: A \to B$ be a function and let C be any subset of B. We say that f is onto C, if and only if for every $c \in C$ there is at least one $a \in A$ such that $f(a) = c$.

Consider the following examples:

(i) For any nonempty set A, the identity function $I_A: A \to A$ is onto A.

(ii) For any two nonempty sets A and B, the projections $\pi_1: A \times B \to A$ and $\pi_2: A \times B \to B$ are onto A and B, respectively.

(iii) Let $\mathbf{R}^+ = \{x \mid x \in \mathbf{R} \text{ and } x \geqq 0\}$. Then, the function $f: \mathbf{R} \to \mathbf{R}^+$ given by $f(x) = x^2$ is onto $\mathbf{R}^+$.

(iv) Let X be any nonempty set and let Y be any set consisting of more than one element. Choose any $y \in Y$. Then, the function $\bar{y}: X \to Y$ is onto $\{y\}$ but not onto Y.

(v) The function $f: \mathbf{R} \to \mathbf{R}$ given in (iii) is not onto $\mathbf{R}$.

Given a function f, together with a particularly specified codomain of f, then, if f is onto this codomain, and if there is no ambiguity about the co-domain referred to, we shall simply say "*f is onto*." The most straightforward way of specifying a particular codomain of f is by the notation we have been using (namely, $f: A \to B =$ codomain, $A \xrightarrow{f} B =$ codomain). Thus, henceforth, if we introduce a function $f: A \to B$ and later prove that *it is onto*, we shall mean that it is onto B.

Of the above examples of functions, (i), (ii), and (iii) are examples of onto functions, whereas (iv) and (v) are examples of non-onto functions. That this is true despite the fact that the function in (iii) *equals* the function in (iv), is a consequence of the convention established in the preceding paragraph: namely, the phrase "f is onto" refers not merely to f itself but to f together with a particular choice of codomain of f. The codomains chosen in (iii) and (iv) are different.

Notice that in example (i), *for every $a \in A$, there is exactly one $a' \in A$ (namely, $a' = a$) such that $I_A(a') = a$*. On the other hand, in example (iii), *for every nonzero $x \in \mathbf{R}^+$ there are exactly two elements y and y' (namely, $y = \sqrt{x}$ and $y = -\sqrt{x}$)*, such that $g(y) = x$ and $g(y') = x$. Finally, in example (ii), for each

$a \in A$, every ordered pair in $A \times B$ of the form (a, b) satisfies $\pi_1(a, b) = a$. Clearly, there are as many ordered pairs of the form (a, b) (where a is held fixed) as there are members of B. Since this number is arbitrary—it depends on B—*there is an arbitrary number, depending on B, of ordered pairs in $A \times B$ whose images under π_1 equal a.*

EXERCISES / 2.9

1. Verify that the functions in examples (i)–(iii), above, are onto and that the functions in examples (v) and (vi) are not.

2. Which of the following equations give functions $f: \mathbf{R} \to \mathbf{R}$ that are onto?

a. $f(x) = x^2 + 2$
b. $f(x) = x + 2$
c. $f(x) = x - [1/(x^2 + 1)]$
d. $f(x) = x \sin x$
e. $f(x) = 2$

3. Consider all the possible linear functions from **R** to **R** (see Exercises 1.2.5). Which of them are onto (**R**)?

4. Consider the linear function $A: \mathbf{R}^k \to \mathbf{R}^n$ defined, as in Chapter 1, by the system of linear expressions

$$\begin{matrix} a_{11}x_1 + \cdots + a_{1k}x_k \\ \vdots \\ a_{n1}x_1 + \cdots + a_{nk}x_k \end{matrix}$$

Suppose that A is onto. What does this imply about the solubility of the system of equations

$$\begin{matrix} a_{11}x_1 + \cdots + a_{1k}x_k = b_1 \\ \vdots \qquad\qquad\quad \vdots \\ a_{n1}x_1 + \cdots + a_{nk}x_k = b_n, \end{matrix}$$

where $(b_1, \cdots, b_n)$ is any n-tuple in $\mathbf{R}^n$?

(b) *1–1 Functions*

Definition 2.17

Let $f: A \to B$ be a function. We say that f is 1–1 (*"one to one"*) *if, for every $b \in B$, there is at most one $a \in A$ such that $f(a) = b$. There may, of course, be some $b \in B$ for which there is no such $a \in A$. That is, f need not be onto.*

The following are examples of 1–1 functions:

(i) For any nonempty set A, the identity function $I_A: A \to A$ is 1–1.

(ii) The function $d: \mathbf{N} \to \mathbf{N}$ given by $d(n) = 2n$, is 1–1.

The following are examples of functions that are not 1–1.

(iii) For any nonempty sets A and B, each consisting of more than one element, the projections $\pi_1: A \times B \to A$ and $\pi_2: A \times B \to B$ are not 1–1.

(iv) The function $\bar{0}: \mathbf{R} \to \mathbf{R}$ is not 1–1.

(v) The function $f: \mathbf{R} \to \mathbf{R}$ given by $f(x) = x^2$ is not 1–1.

Notice that in example (1), the function is 1–1 and onto, whereas in example (ii), the function is 1–1, but not onto. In example (iii), the functions are not 1–1, but they are onto. And in example (v), the function is neither 1–1 nor onto. Thus, it should be clear that, in general, *there is no relationship between the properties of being* 1–1 *and being onto*. That this general statement is *false* when applied to linear functions, as we shall see in Chapter 4, enhances their usefulness and enables us, in certain cases, to give particularly simple criteria for the solubility of systems of linear equations (cf. Exercises 2.10.**4**).

EXERCISES / 2.10

1. a. Verify that the functions in examples (i) and (ii), above, are 1–1, and that the functions in examples (iii)–(v) are not.

b. Verify that the function in example (ii) is not onto.

2. Which of the following equations determine 1–1 functions $f: \mathbf{R} \to \mathbf{R}$?

a. $f(x) = 2x - 3$

b. $f(x) = \sin^2 x + \cos^2 x$

c. $f(x) = e^x - e^{-x}$

d. $f(x) = 1 + x^3$

e. $f(x) = 2$

3. Consider all possible linear functions from $\mathbf{R}$ to $\mathbf{R}$ (see Exercises 1.2.**5**). Which of them are 1–1?

4. Consider the linear function $A: \mathbf{R}^k \to \mathbf{R}^n$, as described in Exercises 2.9.**4**. Suppose that it is 1–1. What does this imply about solutions to the system of equations described in that same exercise?

(c) *1–1 Correspondences*

Definition 2.18

Let $f: A \to B$ be a function. We say that f is a 1–1 *correspondence* (*from A to B*) *if f is both* 1–1 *and onto. This means that for every $b \in B$ there is exactly one $a \in A$ such that $f(a) = b$.***

The following are examples of 1–1 correspondences.

(i) For any nonempty set A, the identity function $I_A: A \to A$ is a 1–1 correspondence.

** The reader should not confuse this with the *reverse* requirement: for every $a \in A$ there is exactly one $b \in B$ such that $f(a) = b$. This is the defining property of a function.

(ii) If A is a nonempty set and B is a set consisting of exactly one member, then the projection $\pi_1 : A \times B \to A$ is a 1–1 correspondence.

(iii) Let $\mathbf{N}$ denote the set of natural numbers and let E denote the set of even natural numbers. Then, the function $d: \mathbf{N} \to E$, given by $d(n) = 2n$, is a 1–1 correspondence.

(iv) Let P denote the set of pages in the September 1963 San Francisco telephone book, and recall that $\mathbf{N}_{1176} = \{1, 2, 3, \ldots, 1174, 1175, 1176\}$. Let $F: P \to \mathbf{N}_{1176}$ be the function which assigns to each page its page number. Then F is a 1–1 correspondence.

(v) Given the nonempty set B, consider the sets B^2 and $B^{\{1,2\}}$ discussed in 2.3. We define a function $T: B^{\{1,2\}} \to B^2$ as follows: T associates with every $f \in B^{\{1,2\}}$ (remember that $B^{\{1,2\}}$ is a collection of functions) the ordered pair $(f(1), f(2))$; that is, T is given by $T(f) = (f(1), f(2))$. We pause to prove that T is a 1–1 correspondence.

To see that T is onto, choose any pair $(x, y) \in B^2$. Define a function $f: \{1, 2\} \to B$ by the equations $f(1) = x$ and $f(2) = y$. Since, by definition, $B^{\{1,2\}}$ consists of *all possible functions* from $\{1, 2\}$ to B, f belongs to $B^{\{1,2\}}$. Moreover, $T(f) = (f(1), f(2)) = (x, y)$. Since (x, y) was chosen arbitrarily, this means that every pair in B^2 is the T-image of some f in $B^{\{1,2\}}$. Thus, T is onto.

To see that T is 1–1, choose any $(x, y) \in B^2$. We must show that there is at most one $f \in B^{\{1,2\}}$ such that $T(f) = (x, y)$. Now suppose that $T(f) = (x, y)$ and $T(g) = (x, y)$, where f and g are not necessarily distinct. We shall show that $f = g$. We have the equalities $(f(1), f(2)) = T(f) = (x, y) = T(g) = (g(1), g(2))$, so that, by the definition of ordered pair $f(1) = g(1)$, and $f(2) = g(2)$. Moreover, $\mathscr{D}_f = \{1, 2\} = \mathscr{D}_g$. Therefore, by the definition of function equality, $f = g$. Hence, no more than one distinct function f is taken to (x, y) by T. Therefore, T is 1–1.

In Subsection 2.3, we said that B^2 and $B^{\{1,2\}}$ are closely related. The discussion above makes this statement more precise. In Chapter 4, we investigate the relationship more closely in the case that B is a linear set.

The above examples show that 1–1 correspondences between two sets reveal similarities between the sets that were not at first apparent. We discuss this in more detail in Section 3. We close the discussion here by introducing some terminology.

We say that *a set A is in* 1–1 *correspondence with a set B* (or that the members of A are in 1–1 correspondence with the members of B), if there exists a 1–1 correspondence $f: A \to B$.

Often, if A is a familiar set in 1–1 correspondence with a less familiar set B, we use the correspondence to identify members of B. Thus, we may talk about the member of B corresponding to $a \in A$. In such a case, A plays an "identifying" role, or, as we shall say, *A indexes B*. To be more precise, let $f: A \to B$ be a 1–1 correspondence. Then, we may say that A indexes B (by means of f). Often, we do not use the symbol f, or any ordinary function symbol, but denote the value of the correspondence at $a \in A$ by "b_a." It is clear that as a ranges over all of A, the values b_a range in a 1–1 manner over all of B. This notation is particularly useful when $A = \mathbf{N}_n$, for some natural number n. For let B be any set indexed by $\mathbf{N}_n(=\{1, 2, \ldots, n\})$. Then, the members of B can be written as $b_1, b_2, \ldots, b_n$, where b_i is the value at i of the correspondence $\mathbf{N}_n \to B$ referred to implicitly by our statement that $\mathbf{N}_n$ indexes B. This example of indexing, of course, is consistent with our earlier terminology.

Finally, it will be convenient at times to extend the notion of indexing to cases in which A is *not* in 1–1 correspondence with B, but in which there is a function $f: A \to B$ onto B. The same terminology and notation described above still apply, only now b_a may equal $b_{a'}$ even though $a \neq a'$.

EXERCISES / 2.11

1. Verify that the above examples (i)–(iv) are 1–1 correspondences.

2. Which of the following equations define 1–1 correspondences $f: \mathbf{R} \to \mathbf{R}$?

a. $f(x) = 3x - 5$

b. $f(x) = e^x$

c. $f(x) = \begin{cases} \log|x|, & x \neq 0 \\ 0, & x = 0 \end{cases}$

d. $f(x) = x^3 + 3$

e. $[f(x)]^5 = x + 1$

3. Consider all possible linear functions from $\mathbf{R}$ to $\mathbf{R}$ (see Exercises 1.2.5, 2.10.3, 2.11.3). Which of them are 1–1 correspondences?

4. Let A and B be any two nonempty sets. If $f: A \to B$ is any function, let $s_f: A \to A \times B$ be defined by the equation

$$s_f(a) = (a, f(a))$$

s_f is called the *section* (*or cross-section*) *of* $A \times B$ *corresponding to* f.

a. Show that s_f is 1–1, for every $f \in B^A$.

b. Show that if B consists of more than one element, then s_f is onto for *no* $f \in B^A$.

c. Define a function $S: B^A \to (A \times B)^A$ by the equation $S(f) = s_f$, for each $f \in B^A$. Show that S is 1–1.

5. Prove that $A \times B$ is in 1–1 correspondence with $B \times A$, for any two nonempty sets A and B.

6. Let A, B, C be any three nonempty sets. The set $(C^B)^A$ is defined to be the set of all functions from A to C^B. C^B, of course, is the set of all functions from B to C. Given any $h \in (C^B)^A$, define $t_h: B \times A \to C$ as follows:

$$t_h(b, a) = (h(a))(b),$$

for every $a \in A$, $b \in B$. (The reader should note that since $h \in (C^B)^A$, $h(a) \in C^B$, for every $a \in A$. That is, $h(a)$ is a function from B to C. Hence, it can be evaluated at b, yielding $(h(a))(b)$. Thus, the above equations makes sense: The value of t_h at any pair $(b, a) \in B \times A$ is defined to be the value of $h(a)$ at b.)

Now, let the function $T:(C^B)^A \to C^{B \times A}$ be defined as follows

$$T(h) = t_h$$

Prove: T is a 1–1 correspondence.

7. Let B be any nonempty set and n any natural number greater than 1. Show that there is a 1–1 correspondence between $B^{\{1,\ldots,n\}}$ and B^n.

2.5 New Functions from Old

(a) *The Restriction of a Function*

Let $f: A \to B$ be any function, and let C be a nonempty subset of A. Then, $C \times B$ is a nonempty subset of $A \times B$. (For, choose any pair $(c, b) \in C \times B$. Since $c \in C$ and $C \subset A$, we conclude that $c \in A$, so that $(c, b) \in A \times B$.)

Consider the set $f \cap (C \times B)$. (This expression makes sense, for both f and $C \times B$ are subsets of $A \times B$.) It is nonempty; indeed, it consists of all ordered pairs of the form $(c, f(c))$, where c ranges over the set C. Clearly, each $c \in C$ occurs precisely once as the first element of an ordered pair in $f \cap (C \times B)$: namely, it is the first member of $(c, f(c))$. Therefore, the set $f \cap (C \times B)$ is a nonempty subset of $C \times B$ (and, hence, a relation from C to B) that satisfies the crucial defining property of a function. That is, it is a function from C to B. *We call it the restriction of f to C and denote it by* "$f \mid C$." Thus, we have:

Definition 2.19

$f \mid C = f \cap (C \times B)$, *where f, C, and B are as above.*

Intuitively, the restriction of f to C, $f \mid C$, is the function from C to B whose value at every $c \in C$ coincides with the value of f at c, $f(c)$. That is, $f \mid C$ is defined by the equation

$$(f \mid C)(c) = f(c),$$

which holds for every $c \in C$.

Examples of restrictions of functions are easy to construct. Just take any function and any nonempty subset of its domain. To obtain the corresponding restriction to that subset, simply *restrict* your attention to the function values at elements in the subset.

EXERCISES / 2.12

1. Show that $\mathscr{D}_{f|C} = C$.

2. **a.** Show that if f is 1–1, then $f \mid C$ is 1–1, where C is any nonempty subset of the domain of f.
   b. Show that the corresponding statement about the "onto" property is false.

3. Show that if $f: A \to B$ is any function, then there exists a nonempty subset $C \subset A$, such that **a.** $f \mid C$ is 1–1, *and* **b.** $\mathscr{R}_f = \mathscr{R}_{f|C}$.

(b) *The Inverse of a Function*

Definition 2.20

Let $f: A \to B$ *be a* 1–1 *function. On an intuitive level, we define the inverse of* f *(or* f*-inverse), written* f^{-1}*, as follows: the domain of* f^{-1} *equals the range of* f*; and the range of* f^{-1} *equals the domain of* f*; given any* $b \in \mathscr{R}_f$*, there is at least one* $a \in A$ *such that* $f(a) = b$*—this follows from the fact that* $\mathscr{R}_f$ *is the set of all* f*-images; moreover, since* f *is* 1–1, *there is not more than* one *such* a*; thus, given* $b \in \mathscr{R}_f$*, there is determined precisely one* a *such that* $f(a) = b$*; we define* $f^{-1}(b)$ *to equal this* a*. Put more briefly, the defining property of* f^{-1} *is that* $f^{-1}(b) = a$ *if and only if* $f(a) = b$.

Schematically, we can illustrate the situation as follows in Figure 9.

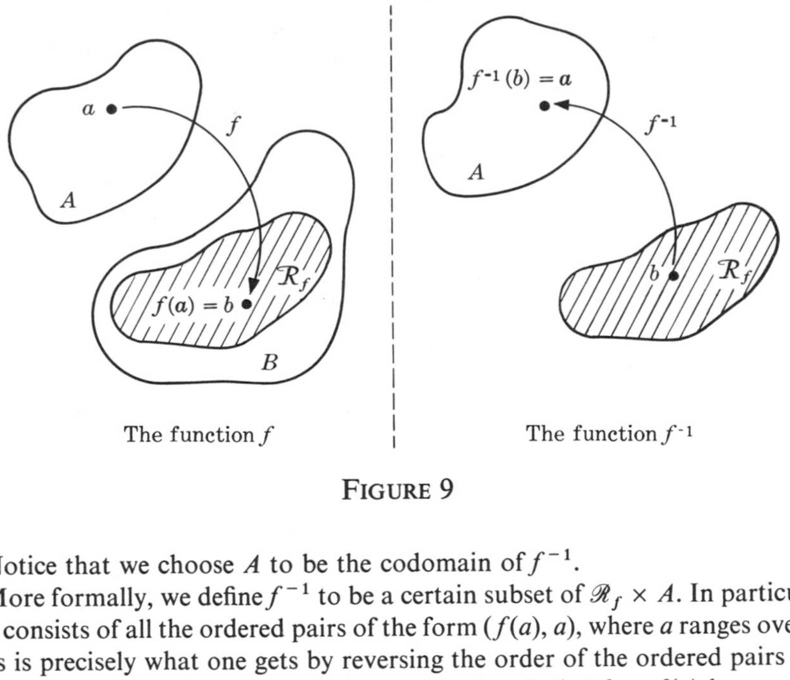

FIGURE 9

Notice that we choose A to be the codomain of f^{-1}.

More formally, we define f^{-1} to be a certain subset of $\mathscr{R}_f \times A$. In particular, f^{-1} consists of all the ordered pairs of the form $(f(a), a)$, where a ranges over A. This is precisely what one gets by reversing the order of the ordered pairs in f. Given any $b \in \mathscr{R}_f$, there is precisely one $a \in A$ such that $b = f(a)$ because f is 1–1. Thus, there is precisely one pair of the form $(f(a), a)$ of which b is a first member, and so, f^{-1} does, indeed, satisfy the central requirement for being a function.

The following are examples of inverses of functions:

(i) Let $I_A: A \to A$ be the usual identity function of the nonempty set A. It is 1–1. Since $\mathscr{R}_{I_A} = A$, $I_A{}^{-1}$ takes A to A. Now, I_A is given by the equation $I_A(a) = a$, for all $a \in A$. Hence, $I_A{}^{-1}$ is also given by $I_A{}^{-1}(a) = a$, for all $a \in A$. Therefore, $I_A = I_A{}^{-1}$.

Alternatively, the set $I_A \subset A \times A$ consists of all pairs of the form $(a, I_A(a)) = (a, a)$, as a ranges over A. Reversing the order of such pairs leaves them unchanged. Hence, again $I_A = I_A^{-1}$.

(ii) Let $d: \mathbf{N} \to E$ be given, as in Subsection 2.4(c) (iii) by the equation $d(n) = 2n$. Since d is a 1–1 correspondence from $\mathbf{N}$ to E, it is onto E; that is, $\mathcal{R}_d = E$. Therefore, d^{-1} takes E to $\mathbf{N}$. It is given by the equation $d^{-1}(m) = \frac{1}{2}m$, where m ranges over E.

(iii) Let $\mathbf{R}^+$ denote, as in 2.4(a) (iii) the set of nonnegative real numbers, and let $s: \mathbf{R}^+ \to \mathbf{R}^+$ be given by $s(x) = x^2$. We leave to the reader the task of showing that s is 1–1 (and onto). The inverse of s, $s^{-1}: \mathbf{R}^+ \to \mathbf{R}^+$, is given by the equation $s^{-1}(x) = \sqrt{x}$.

Notice that if $f: A \to B$ is not 1–1, we cannot define its inverse uniquely. For in this case there are some $b \in B$ for which *more than one* $a \in A$ satisfies $f(a) = b$. Hence, there is no unique way to define $f^{-1}(b)$. Therefore, we do not speak of *the inverse* of f, and we do not use the symbol "f^{-1}," unless f is 1–1.

Proposition 2.4

If $f: A \to B$ is 1–1, then f^{-1} is a 1–1 correspondence between $\mathcal{R}_f$ and A.

Proof

(1) f^{-1} is 1–1.

Choose any $a \in A$. We must show that *at most* one $b \in \mathcal{R}_f$ satisfies $f^{-1}(b) = a$. But we know that the equation $f^{-1}(b) = a$ is equivalent to the equation $f(a) = b$. Thus, it suffices to show that at most one $b \in \mathcal{R}_f$ satisfies $f(a) = b$. But, according to the definition of function, *precisely* one $b \in \mathcal{R}_f$ satisfies $f(a) = b$, and, thus, certainly *no more* than one satisfies $f(a) = b$. Therefore, f^{-1} is 1–1.

(2) f^{-1} is onto.

Choose any $a \in A$. We must show that *at least* one $b \in \mathcal{R}_f$ satisfies $f^{-1}(b) = a$. Let $b = f(a)$. This equation is equivalent to $f^{-1}(b) = a$, so that at least one b [namely, $b = f(a)$] is taken onto a by f^{-1}. Therefore f^{-1} is onto. Q.E.D.

Corollary to Proposition 2.4

If f is a 1–1 correspondence from A to B, then f^{-1} is a 1–1 correspondence from B to A.

Proof

According to the preceding proposition, $f^{-1}: \mathcal{R}_f \to A$ is a 1–1 correspondence. In this case, since f is a 1–1 correspondence, it is onto, so that $\mathcal{R}_f = B$ (that is, every $b \in B$ is an f-image of some $a \in A$). Therefore, $f^{-1}: B \to A$ is a 1–1 correspondence. Q.E.D.

EXERCISES / 2.13

1. What is the inverse of the function of $f:\mathbf{R}\to\mathbf{R}$ given by $f(x)=e^x$?

2. a. What is the inverse of the function $g:\mathbf{R}\to\mathbf{R}$ given by $g(x)=ax+b$, where a and b are any fixed real numbers satisfying $ab\neq 0$?
   b. Sketch the graphs of g and g^{-1} in case $a=2$ and $b=1$.

3. Show that if $f:A\to B$ and $g:C\to D$ are 1–1 correspondences, then $f=g$ if and only if $f^{-1}=g^{-1}$.

4. Let $f:A\to B$ be any 1–1 function. Show that $(f^{-1})^{-1}=f$. [The symbol "$(f^{-1})^{-1}$" of course, denotes the inverse of the inverse of f.]

5.* Let $\mathscr{F}$ be any nonempty family of sets. We define a relation *on* $\mathscr{F}$, which we denote by "$\tilde{\#}$," as follows: given $A\in\mathscr{F}$ and $B\in\mathscr{F}$, we shall say that $A\,\tilde{\#}\,B$, if and only if *A is in* 1–1 *correspondence with B*. (Recall that A is in 1–1 correspondence with B, by definition, if and only if there is a 1–1 correspondence $f:A\to B$.)
   a. Prove that $\tilde{\#}$ is reflexive.
   b. Prove that $\tilde{\#}$ is symmetric. (*Hint:* cf. Corollary to Proposition 2.4.)

(c) *The Composition of Two Functions*

Definition 2.21

Let $f:A\to B$ and $g:B\to C$ be any two functions. We define their composition $g\circ f$ to be a function from A to C satisfying the following equation, for every $a\in A$:

$$(g\circ f)(a)=g(f(a))$$

In other words, $g\circ f$ takes a to the member of C to which g takes $f(a)$. Schematically, we can picture the situation as in Figure 10.

The set of ordered pairs $g\circ f$ can be described in the following way: $g\circ f$ *consists of all pairs* (a, c) *for which there is an element* $b\in B$ *such that* $(a, b)\in f$ *and* $(b, c)\in g$. *To see this, notice* that by the definition above (together with that of *function*) $g\circ f$ consists of all pairs of the form $(a, g(f(a)))$. Given such a pair, let $b=f(a)$. Then, $(a, b)=(a, f(a))\in f$ and $(b, g(f(a)))=(b, g(b))\in g$, by definition of function. Thus, $(a, g(f(a)))$ satisfies the description. Conversely, given a pair (a, c) for which there is a b such that $(a, b)\in f$ and $(b, c)\in g$, notice that $b=f(a)$ and $c=g(b)$, by definition of function. Therefore, $c=g(b)=g(f(a))$, so that $(a, c)=(a, g(f(a)))\in g\circ f$.

Thus, we have shown that every pair in $g\circ f$ satisfies the description given,

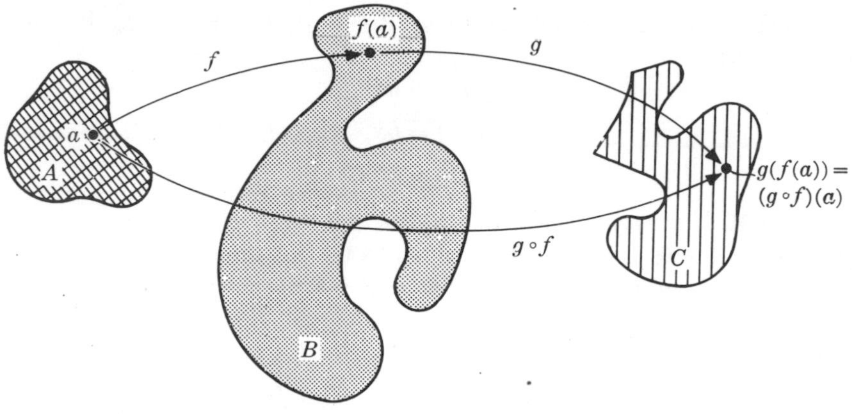

FIGURE 10

and every pair satisfying the description is in $g \circ f$. This means, that the description given at the beginning of the previous paragraph actually does describe $g \circ f$.

The following are examples of the composition of two functions.

(i) Let $f: A \to B$ be any function and $I_B: B \to B$ be the identity function. Then, it is not hard to see that $(I_B \circ f)(a) = I_B(f(a)) = f(a)$, for every $a \in A$, so that $I_B \circ f = f$. Similarly, $f \circ I_A$ is defined and equals f. In some sense, then, the identity function behaves, with respect to composition, in much the same way as does the number 1 with respect to multiplication.

If $A = B$, and if the function $f: A \to B$ is the identity function, I_B, then the above equation $I_B \circ f$ becomes $I_B \circ I_B = I_B$. This is analogous to the numerical equation $1 \cdot 1 = 1$.

(ii) Let $f: A \to B$ be a 1–1 function. Then, it has an inverse $f^{-1}: \mathscr{R}_f \to A$. Consider $f \circ f^{-1}$. We evaluate it at an arbitrary $b \in \mathscr{R}_f$. Recall that, by definition of inverse, the equation $f^{-1}(b) = a$ is equivalent to the equation $f(a) = b$. Now, choose any $b \in \mathscr{R}_f$ and let $a = f^{-1}(b)$. Then,

$$f \circ f^{-1}(b) = f(f^{-1}(b)) = f(a) = b = I_{\mathscr{R}_f}(b)$$

Thus, $f \circ f^{-1} = I_{\mathscr{R}_f}$. This is analogous to the numerical equation $x \cdot (1/x) = 1$, meaningful and valid for $x \neq 0$.

Notice that f may be considered as a function from A to $\mathscr{R}_f$. Thus, we may consider $f^{-1} \circ f$. As above, we can show that $f^{-1} \circ f = I_A$.

(iii) Let a and b be any fixed real numbers. Define functions $f_a: \mathbf{R} \to \mathbf{R}$, $f_b: \mathbf{R} \to \mathbf{R}$, $f_{a+b}: \mathbf{R} \to \mathbf{R}$ by the equations

$$f_a(x) = x + a$$
$$f_b(x) = x + b$$
$$f_{a+b}(x) = x + a + b$$

for all $x \in \mathbf{R}$. It is easy to show that $f_a \circ f_b = f_b \circ f_a = f_{a+b}$.

(iv) Let a and b be as in (iii). Define $g_a: \mathbf{R} \to \mathbf{R}$, $g_b: \mathbf{R} \to \mathbf{R}$, and $g_{ab}: \mathbf{R} \to \mathbf{R}$ by the equations

$$g_a(x) = ax$$
$$g_b(x) = bx$$
$$g_{ab}(x) = abx,$$

for all $x \in \mathbf{R}$. It is easy to show that $g_a \circ g_b = g_b \circ g_a = g_{ab}$.

(v) Let $k: \mathbf{R} \to \mathbf{R}$ and $\ell: \mathbf{R} \to \mathbf{R}$ be given by the equations $k(x) = x^2 + 2$ and $\ell(x) = x + 1$. Then, $k \circ \ell: \mathbf{R} \to \mathbf{R}$ and $\ell \circ k: \mathbf{R} \to \mathbf{R}$ are given by the equations:

$$k \circ \ell(x) = k(\ell(x))$$
$$= k(x + 1) = (x + 1)^2 + 2,$$
$$\ell \circ k(x) = \ell(k(x)) = \ell(x^2 + 2) = x^2 + 2 + 1 = x^2 + 3$$

It should be clear that $k \circ \ell \neq \ell \circ k$.

According to the definition, the composition $g \circ f$ of two functions f and g is defined only when the codomain of f equals the domain of g. Now, as example (ii) shows, this requirement is not absolutely essential. Indeed, all that is needed is that $\mathscr{R}_f \subset \mathscr{D}_g$. Hence, given two functions $f: A \to B$ and $g: C \to D$, such that $\mathscr{R}_f \subset C(=\mathscr{D}_g)$, we can define the composition of f with g, $g \circ f: A \to D$, as before, by the equation $(g \circ f)(a) = g(f(a))$, for all $a \in A$.

Notice that although $g \circ f$ may be defined, $f \circ g$ need not be. Indeed, this happens when $\mathscr{R}_f \subset C$ but $\mathscr{R}_g \not\subset A$. Moreover, even when both are defined, example (v) above shows that they need not be equal.

Proposition 2.5

If $f: A \to B$ and $g: B \to C$ are onto functions, then so is $g \circ f$.

Proof

Choose any $c \in C$. Since g is onto, there is a $b \in B$ such that $g(b) = c$. Moreover, since f is onto, there is an $a \in A$ such that $f(a) = b$. Thus, $(g \circ f)(a) = g(f(a)) = g(b) = c$, which means that $g \circ f$ is onto. Q.E.D.

Proposition 2.6

If $f: A \to B$ and $g: B \to C$ are 1–1 functions, then so is $g \circ f: A \to C$.

Proof

It suffices to show that any two distinct elements $a \in A$ and $a' \in A$ are taken by $g \circ f$ to distinct elements of C. For then, no $c \in C$ is the $g \circ f$-image of more than one $a \in A$.

Choose any two distinct elements a and a' in A. Since f is 1–1, $f(a) \neq f(a')$. Similarly, since g is 1–1, $g(f(a)) \neq g(f(a'))$. Therefore, $(g \circ f)(a) = g(f(a)) \neq g(f(a')) = (g \circ f)(a')$. Q.E.D.

Corollary to Proposition 2.6

If $f: A \to B$ *and* $g: B \to C$ *are* 1–1 *correspondences, then so is* $g \circ f: A \to C$.

Proof

Since both f and g are 1–1, so is $g \circ f$, and since both f and g are onto, so is $g \circ f$. Q.E.D.

Now suppose that $f: A \to B$ is a 1–1 correspondence. Then, according to the Corollary to Proposition 2.4, $f^{-1}: B \to A$ is also a 1–1 correspondence. According to Example (ii) above, $f^{-1} \circ f = I_A$ and $f \circ f^{-1} = I_B$. We now prove a proposition and corollary that are, in some sense, converse to this situation.

Proposition 2.7

Let $f: A \to B$ *and* $g: B \to A$ *be functions satisfying* $f \circ g = I_B$. *Then,* f *is onto* B *and* g *is* 1–1.

Proof

(1) f is onto.

Choose any $b \in B$, and let $a = g(b)$. Then, $b = I_B(b) = (f \circ g)(b) = f(g(b)) = f(a)$. That is, any $b \in B$ is the f-image of some $a \in A$. Thus, f is onto.

(2) g is 1–1.

As explained in the proof of Proposition 2.6, it suffices to show that g takes distinct elements of B to distinct elements of A. Now, choose any $b \in B$ and $b' \in B$, such that $b \neq b'$. Then, $f(g(b)) = (f \circ g)(b) = I_B(b) = b \neq b' = I_B(b') = (f \circ g)(b') = f(g(b'))$. That is, $f(g(b)) \neq f(g(b'))$. Therefore, $g(b) \neq g(b')$, since if $g(b) = g(b')$, then f would be taking this single element of A to the distinct elements of B, $f(g(b))$ and $f(g(b'))$, an impossible eventuality in view of the fact that f is a function. Q.E.D.

Corollary to Proposition 2.7

Let $f: A \to B$ *be a function, and let* $g: B \to A$ *and* $h: B \to A$ *be functions satisfying* $f \circ g = I_B$ *and* $h \circ f = I_A$. *Then,*

(1) f, g, *and* h *are* 1–1 *correspondences.*

(2) $g = h = f^{-1}$.

Proof

(1) If we apply the preceding proposition to f and g, we obtain the result that f is onto and g is 1–1. If we apply the proposition to h and f, we obtain the result that h is onto and f is 1–1.

Thus, f is onto and 1–1, and so it is a 1–1 correspondence, as desired.

Consequently, by the Corollary to Proposition 2.4, $f^{-1}: B \to A$ is a 1–1 correspondence. Therefore, to prove that g and h are 1–1 correspondences, it suffices to prove that they equal f^{-1}. This also proves statement (2) above, so that that is all that remains to be done.

(2) To prove that $g = f^{-1}$, we choose any $b \in B$. Then $b = I_B(b) = (f \circ g)(b) = f(g(b))$. Applying f^{-1} to both sides of this equation, we get,

$$f^{-1}(b) = f^{-1}(f(g(b))) = g(b),$$

since $f^{-1}(f(a)) = a$, for all $a \in A$ [see example (ii), above]. That is, for every $b \in B$, $f^{-1}(b) = g(b)$. This, together with the obvious equality

$$\mathscr{D}_{f^{-1}} = B = \mathscr{D}_g$$

means that $g = f^{-1}$.

To show that $h = f^{-1}$, we choose any $b \in B$, and let $a = f^{-1}(b)$. Then, by definition of inverse, $f(a) = b$. Therefore,

$$h(b) = h(f(a)) = (h \circ f)(a) = I_A(a) = a = f^{-1}(b)$$

That is, for every $b \in B$, $h(b) = f^{-1}(b)$. This, together with the obvious equality

$$\mathscr{D}_{f^{-1}} = B = \mathscr{D}_h$$

means that $h = f^{-1}$. Q.E.D.

Remark: Let $f: A \to B$ be any function. We shall call any function $g: B \to A$ satisfying $f \circ g = I_B$ *a right inverse of f*. That a given f may have more than one right inverse will be demonstrated (by the reader) in a subsequent exercise. Hence, the phraseology "*a* right inverse . . . ." Proposition 2.7 says that if f has a right inverse, then f is onto, and the right inverse is 1–1.

We call any function $h: B \to A$ satisfying $h \circ f = I_A$ *a left inverse of f*. A given f may have more than one left inverse. Clearly, if h is a left inverse of f, then f is a right inverse of h. Hence, Proposition 2.7 implies that if f has a left inverse, then it is onto and f is 1–1.

Finally, the corollary says that if f has a right inverse *and* if f has a left inverse, then f is a 1–1 correspondence and both the given right inverse of f and the given left inverse of f are equal to *the* inverse of f.

As a special case of this corollary then, we may conclude that a function g is the inverse of a function f *if* $g \circ f = I_A$ and $f \circ g = I_B$ (where $f: A \to B$ and $g: B \to A$).

This is the converse of the situation initially described: namely, *if* g is the inverse of f, *then* $g \circ f = I_A$ and $f \circ g = I_B$.

We conclude this section with a brief discussion about the composition of more than two functions.

Suppose that we have three functions

$$f: A \to B,\ g: B \to C,\ h: C \to D$$

Then, we may form compositions

$$g \circ f: A \to C,\ h \circ g: B \to D,$$

and, then, form compositions of these with h and f, respectively:

$$h \circ (g \circ f): A \to D, \ (h \circ g) \circ f: A \to D.$$

Schematically, we can picture the situation as in Figure 11.

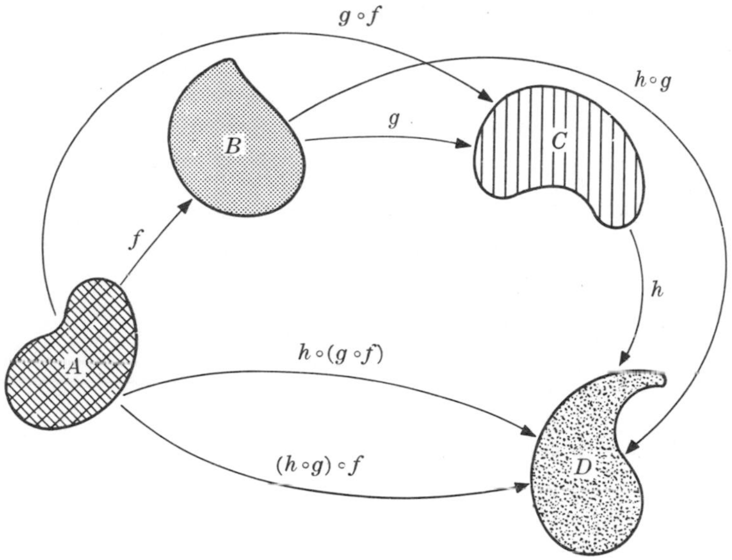

FIGURE 11

Proposition 2.8

Using the above notation,

$$h \circ (g \circ f) = (h \circ g) \circ f$$

Proof

Choose any $a \in A$. Then,

$$h \circ (g \circ f)(a) = h(g \circ f(a)) = h(g(f(a))),$$

and

$$(h \circ g) \circ f(a) = (h \circ g)(f(a)) = h(g(f(a))),$$

so that

$$(h \circ g) \circ f(a) = h \circ (g \circ f)(a) \quad \text{Q.E.D.}$$

Remark: This result is known as the associative law for function composition. It can be generalized to the case of more than three functions.

If, above, $A = B = C = D$, and $f = g = h$ is a function from A to A, then we may form $(f \circ f) \circ f$ and $f \circ (f \circ f)$, and these two are equal. Henceforth, then, we may write $(f \circ f) \circ f$ [or $f \circ (f \circ f)$] as $f \circ f \circ f$ without worrying about parentheses, since no matter which way we insert them (meaningfully, of course), the result is the same.

In a similar way, we may write $f \circ f \circ f \circ f$ and $f \circ f \circ f \circ f \circ f$, etc., since (although we do not prove this in full generality) the insertion of parentheses in any meaningful way always results in the same function.

It will be convenient to write

$$\underbrace{f \circ f \circ \cdots \circ f}_{n \text{ times}}$$

as f^n, where $n \in \mathbf{N}$. Thus, $f = f^1$, $f^2 = f \circ f$, and $f^3 = f \circ f \circ f$, etc. [When evaluating, say f^3, it will be convenient to use parentheses again: thus, $f^3(x) = f(f(f(x)))$.] It will also be convenient, as in the case of numerical powers, to write $f^0 = I_A$.

EXERCISES / 2.14

1. a. Let $f:\mathbf{R} \to \mathbf{R}^+$ and $g:\mathbf{R}^+ \to \mathbf{R}$ be given by: $f(x) = x^2$ and $g(x) = \sqrt{x}$, respectively. Show that $f \circ g = I_{\mathbf{R}^+}$ but that $g \circ f \neq I_{\mathbf{R}}$.
   b. Let $h:\mathbf{R}^+ \to \mathbf{R}$ be given by: $h(x) = -\sqrt{x}$. Clearly, $h \neq g$. Show that $f \circ h = I_{\mathbf{R}^+}$ but that $h \circ f \neq I_{\mathbf{R}}$.

This exercise gives an example of a function f that has a right inverse (namely, g or h), but no left inverse. For if f had a left inverse, then Corollary to Proposition 2.7 would imply that $g = f^{-1}$, and so, that $g \circ f = f^{-1} \circ f = I_{\mathbf{R}}$, which is false (and f^{-1} is not even defined). Moreover, it gives an example of a function with more than one right inverse.

2. What are the function values $(f \circ g)(x)$ and $(g \circ f)(x)$ when $f:\mathbf{R} \to \mathbf{R}$ and $g:\mathbf{R} \to \mathbf{R}$ are given by the following equations?
   a. $f(x) = x + 2$, $g(x) = x - 2$
   b. $f(x) = e^x$, $g(x) = \ell n x$
   c. $f(x) = x^2 + 2x + 6$, $g(x) = \sin x$
   d. $f(x) = x^2 + 2$, $g(x) = \sqrt{x + 2}$

3.* Recall that in Exercises 2.13.5, we considered a nonempty collection of sets $\mathscr{F}$ and the relation $\#$ on $\mathscr{F}$, where $\#$ is the relation "to be in 1–1 correspondence with." In that exercise the reader was asked to show that $\#$ is reflexive and symmetric.

   Prove that $\#$ is transitive. (*Hint:* Use Corollary to Proposition 2.6.)

   This result shows that $\#$ is an equivalence relation on $\mathscr{F}$.**It will be useful in Section 3.

** See Definitions 2.10 and 2.11.

4. a. Let X, Y, Z be any nonempty sets. Recall that X^Y and X^Z are, respectively, the set of all functions from Y to X and the set of all functions from Z to X. Suppose that $f: Y \to Z$ is a 1–1 correspondence. Define a function $F: X^Z \to X^Y$ as follows: for any function $g: Z \to X$, let $F(g)$ be the function $g \circ f: Y \to X$. Prove that F is a 1–1 correspondence between X^Z and X^Y.

   b. In Exercises 2.3.5, we proved that, for any nonempty sets A, B, C, $(C^B)^A \overline{\#} C^{B \times A}$, where $\overline{\#}$ is as in Exercise 3 above.

   In Exercises 2.3.5, we proved that there is a 1–1 correspondence between $A \times B$ and $B \times A$. Part a above, now, implies that

$$C^{B \times A} \overline{\#} C^{A \times B}$$

   Use these facts together with the conclusion of Exercise 3 above to prove that

$$(C^B)^A \overline{\#} (C^A)^B$$

5. Let A and B be any two nonempty sets such that B has more than one element, and let b_1 be some element in B. Recall that $p_1: A \times B \to A$ is the first coordinate projection given by $p_1(a, b) = a$, for all $(a, b) \in A \times B$. It is onto but not 1–1.

   Let $j_1: A \to A \times B$ be given by $j_1(a) = (a, b_1)$, for every $a \in A$.

   Show that $p_1 \circ j_1 = I_A$ (and, hence, that j_1 is 1–1), but that $j_1 \circ p_1 \neq I_{A \times B}$.

   Thus, p_1 has a right inverse, but it has no left inverse (since it is not a 1–1 correspondence).

   If b_2 is any other element of B, let $j_2: A \to A \times B$ be given by $j_2(a) = (a, b_2)$, for all $a \in A$.

   Show that $p_1 \circ j_2 = I_A$, but that $I_{A \times B} \neq j_2 \circ p_1 \neq j_1 \circ p_1$.

6. Let A be any nonempty set, let Rel A be the set of all equivalence relations on A, and let Par A be the set of all partitions of A.

   We define functions $\mathscr{P}$: Rel $A \to$ Par A and $\mathscr{R}$: Par $A \to$ Rel A as follows:

   For any $R \in$ Rel, we let $\mathscr{P}(R) = \mathscr{P}_R$, the partition determined by R, as in Subsection 1.6. For any $P \in$ Par A, we let $\mathscr{R}(P) = R_P$, the equivalence relation determined by P, as in 1.6.

   Prove that $\mathscr{R}$ and $\mathscr{P}$ are 1–1 correspondences and that $\mathscr{R} = \mathscr{P}^{-1}$.

   (*Hint:* Apply Corollary to Proposition 2.7 to what you obtain by using Proposition 2.3.)

(d)† *The Union of Two Functions*

Definition 2.22

Let $f: A \to B$ and $g: C \to D$ be any functions. Under certain circumstances, they determine a function from $A \cup C$ to $B \cup D$ called the union of f and g, written $f \cup g$. The circumstances are these (and only these):

$f \cup g: A \cup C \to B \cup D$ is defined, if and only if either (1) $A \cap C = \varnothing$, *or* (2) $A \cap C \neq \varnothing$ *but* $f \mid A \cap C = g \mid A \cap C$.

If either of these conditions is satisfied, then we define $f \cup g$ as follows:

$$(f \cup g)(x) = \begin{cases} f(x) & \text{if } x \in A \\ g(x) & \text{if } x \in C \end{cases}$$

Notice that the conditions listed above are precisely those needed to insure against ambiguity in the definition. Such ambiguity can occur only if x is both in A and in C, that is, in $A \cap C$. Thus, if $A \cap C \neq \varnothing$, then, for $x \in A \cap C$, in view of condition (2),

$$f(x) = (f \mid A \cap C)(x) = (g \mid A \cap C)(x) = g(x),$$

so that there is no ambiguity in this case either.

Since f and g are simply sets (of ordered pairs), we can, under *any* circumstances, form their union. The result will also be a set of ordered pairs, that is, a relation. This relation, however, need not be a function. For, in the absence of conditions on f and g, there may exist a pair $(x, b) \in f$ and a pair $(x, d) \in g$, where $b \neq d$ and $x \in A \cap C$. Then, both $(x, b) \in f \cup g$ and $(x, d) \in f \cup g$, so that x is the first element of more than one ordered pair in $f \cup g$.

The conditions listed above are precisely those needed to insure that this will not happen.

We illustrate the situation schematically in Figure 12.

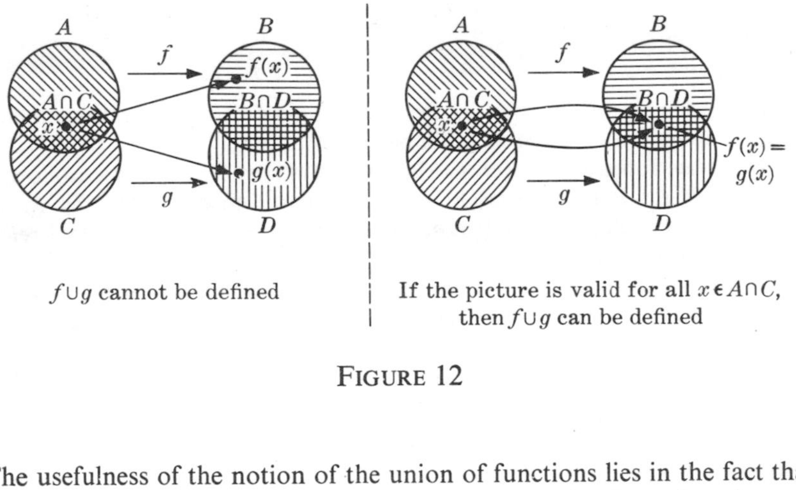

FIGURE 12

The usefulness of the notion of the union of functions lies in the fact that it can be used to create functions with "large" domains from functions with small domains.

As a simple example, consider the set $\mathbf{R} \setminus \{0\}$ and the function $f: \mathbf{R} \setminus \{0\} \to \mathbf{R}^+$ given by $f(x) = e^{-(1/x^2)}$. This is an infinitely differentiable function. Let $g: \{0\} \to \mathbf{R}^+$ be given by the equation $g(0) = 0$. Since $(\mathbf{R} \setminus \{0\}) \cap \{0\} = \varnothing$, we may form $f \cup g$. This is a function from $(\mathbf{R} \setminus \{0\}) \cup \{0\} = \mathbf{R}$ to $\mathbf{R}^+$. (Indeed, this is a very interesting function, for, as is well known, it is infinitely differentiable on $\mathbf{R}$ but it does not equal its Taylor series expanded around 0.)

Notice that any nonempty set A can be regarded as the union of one-member sets (i.e., sets consisting of only one member): namely, let $\mathscr{A}$ be the collection of *all* sets of the form $\{a\}$, where $a \in A$; then $A = \bigcup\mathscr{A}$.

Similarly, every function $f: A \to B$ can be regarded as the union of "one-member functions" (i.e., functions consisting of only one ordered pair): namely, let $\mathscr{F}$ be the family of *all* functions of the form $f|\{a\}$, where $a \in A$; then, $\bigcup\mathscr{F} = f$.

(e) *The Product and Pairing of Two Functions*

Definition 2.23

Let $f: A \to B$ and $g: C \to D$ be any functions. We define the product $(f \times g): A \times C \to B \times D$ as follows: $f \times g$ is the subset of $(A \times C) \times (B \times D)$ consisting of all ordered pairs (of ordered pairs) of the form $((a, c), (f(a), g(c)))$, where (a, c) ranges over $A \times C$, that is, a ranges over A and c ranges over C.

Equivalently, $f \times g: A \times C \to B \times D$ is given as follows: for every $(a, c) \in A \times C$,

$$(f \times g)(a, c) = (f(a), g(c)) \in B \times D$$

The following are examples of products of functions:

(i) Let A, B, C, D be any nonempty sets, and choose elements $b \in B$ and $d \in D$. Recall that if X and Y are nonempty sets, and if $y_0 \in Y$, then $\bar{y}_0: X \to Y$ is the function sending every $x \in X$ to the element $y_0 \in Y$.

Thus, $\bar{b}: A \to B$ and $\bar{d}: C \to D$ are defined to be the functions sending, respectively, every $a \in A$ to b and every $c \in C$ to d.

It is easy to see that $\bar{b} \times \bar{d}: A \times C \to B \times D$ sends every pair $(a, c) \in A \times C$ to (b, d). But, this is just the function $\overline{(b, d)}: A \times C \to B \times D$.

Therefore, $\bar{b} \times \bar{d} = \overline{(b, d)}$.

(ii) Let A and B be any nonempty sets, and let $I_A: A \to A$ and $I_B: B \to B$ be the identity functions. Then, $I_A \times I_B: A \times B \to A \times B$ satisfies: For every pair $(a, b) \in A \times B$,

$$(I_A \times I_B)(a, b) = (I_A(a), I_B(b)) = (a, b)$$

But, this is just the identity function of $A \times B$. Thus,

$$I_A \times I_B = I_{A \times B}$$

(iii) Let $f: \mathbf{R} \to \mathbf{R}$ and $g: \mathbf{R} \to \mathbf{R}$ be given by $f(x) = 2x + 1$ and $g(x) = -x + 2$. Then, $f \times g: \mathbf{R}^2 \to \mathbf{R}^2$ is given by

$$(f \times g)(x, y) = (f(x), g(y)) = (2x + 1, -y + 2),$$

for every $(x, y) \in \mathbf{R}^2$.

A slight variation of the definition of product yields what we shall call the *pairing of two functions*.

Suppose that $f: A \to B$ and $g: A \to C$ are functions. We define *the pairing of f and g, written (f, g), to be a function from A to $B \times C$ consisting of all the ordered pairs in $A \times (B \times C)$ of the form $(a, (f(a), g(a)))$, where a ranges over A.*

Equivalently, $(f, g): A \to B \times C$ is given as follows: for every $a \in A$,

$$(f, g)(a) = (f(a), g(a))$$

That the notions of product and pairing of functions are closely related is intuitively clear. We can make this relationship mathematically precise in the following way. Let $f: A \to B$ and $g: A \to C$ be any two functions. Let $\Delta_A: A \to A \times A$ be the function defined by $\Delta(a) = (a, a)$, for all $a \in A$. (The function Δ_A is called the *diagonal function of A*. This is because when $A = \mathbf{R}$, $A \times A = \mathbf{R}^2$, the Cartesian plane, and the range of $\Delta_\mathbf{R}$—that is, all pairs in $\mathbf{R}^2$ of the form (x, x)—is just the line through the origin given by $y = x$: The "diagonal" of the Cartesian plane.)

The reader should have no difficulty in verifying the following relation

$$(f, g) = (f \times g) \circ \Delta_A$$

Please note that the *product* $f \times g$ is defined for *any* two functions f and g, whereas the *pairing* (f, g) is defined only if $\mathscr{D}_f = \mathscr{D}_g$.

The following are examples of pairings of functions:

(iv) Let A be any nonempty set, and consider $I_A: A \to A$, the identity function. According to the above relation,

$$(I_A, I_A) = (I_A \times I_A) \circ \Delta_A$$

But, we showed before that $I_A \times I_B = I_{A \times B}$. Therefore,

$$(I_A, I_A) = I_{A \times A} \circ \Delta_A = \Delta_A$$

The equality on the right follows from a fact that we have already demonstrated: namely, that composition with the identity function leaves a function unchanged [cf. Subsection 2.5(c), Example (i)].

Thus, the diagonal function of a set is the pairing of the identity function of the set with itself.

(v) Let A and B be any nonempty sets, and recall that $\pi_1: A \times B \to A$ and $\pi_2: A \times B \to B$ are the first and second coordinate projections, respectively. Then,

$$(\pi_1, \pi_2): A \times B \to A \times B$$

satisfies $(\pi_1, \pi_2)(a, b) = (\pi_1(a, b), \pi_2(a, b)) = (a, b)$, for every $(a, b) \in A \times B$. That is,

$$(\pi_1, \pi_2) = I_{A \times B}$$

(vi) Let $f: \mathbf{R} \to \mathbf{R}$ and $g: \mathbf{R} \to \mathbf{R}$ be given as in (iii) above. Then (f, g) is given by the equation

$$(f, g)(x) = (2x + 1, -x + 2),$$

for all $x \in \mathbf{R}$.

EXERCISES / 2.15

1. Verify the relation

$$(f, g) = (f \times g) \circ \Delta_A$$

given in the text above.

2. Given any natural number $n > 1$ and any n functions

$$f_1: A_1 \to B_1, f_2: A_2 \to B_2, \ldots, f_n: A_n \to B_n,$$

give a definition of the n-fold product

$$f_1 \times f_2 \times \cdots \times f_n: A_1 \times A_2 \times \cdots \times A_n \to B_1 \times \cdots \times B_n$$

which, when $n = 2$, reduces to the definition of product given in the text. Can you give more than one such definition? Discuss.

Given any set A consider the n-fold product $A \times \cdots \times A = A^n$ and define the map

$$\Delta_{A^n}: A \to A^n$$

by the equation $\Delta_{A^n}(a) = (a, a, \ldots, a, a) \in A^n$.

Whatever your definition of n-fold product, give a definition of n-fold pairing such that for any n functions $f_1: A \to B_1, f_2: A \to B_2, \ldots, f_n: A \to B_n$, we have

$$(f_1, \ldots, f_n) = (f_1 \times \cdots \times f_n) \circ \Delta_{A^n}$$

3. Let $f: A \to B$ and $g: A \to C$ be any functions, and let

$$\pi_1: B \times C \to B \text{ and } \pi_2: B \times C \to C$$

be the first and second coordinate projections. Show that

$$\pi_1 \circ (f, g) = f$$

$$\pi_2 \circ (f, g) = g$$

(f)† *The Equivalence Relation Determined by a Function***

Definition 2.24

Let $f: A \to B$ be any function. We define a relation R_f on A, called the relation determined by f, as follows: $(a, a') \in R_f$ if and only if $f(a) = f(a')$. That is, elements of A are R_f-related if and only if their f-images are equal.

Proposition 2.9

Let $f: A \to B$ be any function. The relation R_f is an equivalence relation on A.

** See Subsection 1.7.

Proof

(1) R_f is reflexive.

For any $a \in A$, $(a, a) \in R_f$ since $f(a) = f(a)$.

(2) R_f is symmetric.

If $(a, a') \in R_f$, then $f(a) = f(a')$. Since $=$ is symmetric, $f(a') = f(a)$. Hence, $(a', a) \in R_f$.

(3) R_f is transitive.

Suppose that $(a, a') \in R_f$ and $(a', a'') \in R_f$. Then, $f(a) = f(a')$ and $f(a') = f(a'')$. Since $=$ is transitive, $f(a) = f(a'')$, and, therefore, $(a, a'') \in R_f$. Q.E.D.

Consider the partition of A determined by R_f. We shall denote this partition by A/f. Recall that each set in the partition consists of all those $a \in A$ that are sent by f to some given $b \in B$. Although f^{-1} need not be defined (i.e., f need not be 1–1), we may borrow the symbol "f^{-1}" to denote by $f^{-1}(b)$ that member of the partition consisting of those elements of A sent to b by f. Of course, this only makes sense if $b \in \mathscr{R}_f$. If $b \notin \mathscr{R}_f$, then we let $f^{-1}(b)$ be the empty set.

An example of a set A and a function $f: A \to B$ for which R_f and A/f are particularly meaningful is provided by a map and the altitude function.

Let A denote the set of points on the map of some (preferably rugged) terrain. Let $f: A \to \mathbf{R}^+$ be the function that associates with every $a \in A$ the height above sea-level of the point of terrain that a represents on the map.

Given any $r \in \mathbf{R}^+$, $f^{-1}(r)$ is the set of all $a \in A$ representing points of terrain of height r feet above sea-level. That is, $f^{-1}(r)$ *is a certain contour line on the map.*

Thus, the partition A/f is the set of all contour lines on the map A.

Now, back to the general situation, in which $f: A \to B$ is any function. We may define a function

$$\bar{f}: A/f \to B$$

in the following way. Choose any member of the partition; that is, choose any R_f-equivalence class. It is of the form $f^{-1}(b)$, for some $b \in B$; that is, it consists of all $a \in A$ sent to that b by f. We define the $\bar{f}$-image of this equivalence class to be b. In other words, choosing any $a \in A$ and letting $[a]$ be the equivalence class determined by a, then we have

$$\bar{f}[a] = f(a)$$

We call $\bar{f}$ *the function on* A/f *induced by* f.

Proposition 2.10

The function $\bar{f}: A/f \to B$ *is* 1–1.

Proof

By the above equation, the set of all $\bar{f}$-images equals the set of all f-images. That is, $\mathscr{R}_{\bar{f}} = \mathscr{R}_f$. We must show that to each $b \in \mathscr{R}_{\bar{f}}$, there corresponds exactly one $[a] \in A/f$ such that $\bar{f}[a] = b$.

Choose any $b \in R_{\bar{f}} = R_f$, and choose any $a \in A$ such that $f(a) = b$. Then, $\bar{f}[a] = f(a) = b$. Moreover, if $\bar{f}[a'] = b$, then, by definition, $f(a') = b$, so that $(a, a') \in R_f$ and $[a] = [a']$. Q.E.D.

EXERCISES / 2.16

1. Show that the equation

$$\bar{f}[a] = f(a)$$

given in the text is unambiguous. That is, show that if a' is another representative of $[a]$ (so that $[a'] = [a]$), then $\bar{f}[a'] = \bar{f}[a]$.

2. Let $f: A \to B$ be any function, and let S be an equivalence relation on B. Define an equivalence relation on A, $R_{f,S}$ as follows:

$$(a, a') \in R_{f,S}, \text{ if and only if } (f(a), f(a')) \in S$$

Prove that $R_{f,S}$ is an equivalence relation on A. Show that $R_{f,=} = R_f$.

3. Consider any equivalence relation R on a nonempty set A. It determines a partition $\mathscr{P}_R$: namely, the set of equivalence classes $[a]$, where a ranges over A. Let $\pi_R: A \to \mathscr{P}_R$ be the function given by $\pi_R(a) = [a]$. It is called the *projection determined by* R. Notice that π_R is onto.

   Now, let $f: A \to B$ be any function.

   a. Prove that $\bar{f} \circ \pi_{R_f} = f$.

   This shows that every function is the composition of a 1–1 function and an onto function.

   b. Prove that π_R is 1–1, if and only if R is the relation of equality on A.

   c. Use **a.** and **b.** to prove that f is 1–1 if and only if R_f is the relation of equality on A.

4. **a.** Let R be any equivalence relation on a set A, and let $\pi_R: A \to \mathscr{P}_R$ be the projection determined by R, as defined in **3** above. Consider the equivalence relation determined by π_R: Namely, R_{π_R}.

   Prove that $R_{\pi_R} = R$.

   This exercise shows that every equivalence relation can be thought of as the equivalence relation determined by some function.

3† / COUNTING

In its most rudimentary form, the process of counting consists of forming a 1–1 correspondence between a familiar set and an unfamiliar set: We have also called the process "indexing." For example, the set of fingers on both hands is a most familiar set; for many of us, the earliest form of counting consists of associating fingers in a 1–1 way with the objects to be counted. Later, we become familiar with the natural numbers 1, 2, 3, . . . , and so on; that is we become familiar with the sets $\mathbf{N}_n$ and $\mathbf{N}$. Counting then becomes a procedure whereby we associate natural numbers with objects.

Now, the notion of 1–1 correspondence is a very general one, not one that is restricted to the realm of fingers or natural numbers. Thus, there is an easy way to generalize the above described notion of counting.

Definition 2.25

Let A and B be two sets. We shall say that A and B are equinumerous, or that they have the same number of members, or that they have the same cardinality if there is a 1–1 correspondence $f: A \to B$ or if $A = \varnothing = B$. To indicate that A and B are equinumerous, we shall write $A \approx B$. (This conforms to the terminology introduced in the exercises.)

Definition 2.26

We shall say that a set A is finite if either $A = \varnothing$ or there is a natural number n such that $A \approx \mathbf{N}_n$. In the second case we say that A has n members. If A is not finite, we shall say that it is infinite.

Definition 2.27

If A is a set satisfying $A \approx \mathbf{N}$, then we say that A is countable.

Definition 2.28

Let A and B be sets. We say that A has fewer members than B, or A has cardinality less than that of B, written $A \leqq B$, if there is a subset C of B such that $A \approx C$. We say that A has strictly fewer members than B, or A has cardinality strictly less than B, written $A < B$, if it is true that $A \leqq B$ but false that $A \approx B$.

The reader should be warned that in the case of infinite sets, it is not at all clear that the notions of "$\leqq$" or "$<$" operate in the usual way. Indeed, part of our efforts in this section will be devoted to proving that they do operate in the usual way.

We shall assume known the usual notions of counting and comparing *natural numbers* (e.g., $1 < 2$, $n < n + 1$, either $n \leqq m$ or $n > m$, etc.).

Proposition 2.11

$\mathbf{N}$ *is infinite.*

Proof

Clearly, $\mathbf{N} \neq \varnothing$. Therefore, if $\mathbf{N}$ is finite, there is a natural number n such that $\mathbf{N} \approx \mathbf{N}_n$. Hence, since $\approx$ is symmetric, $\mathbf{N}_n \approx \mathbf{N}$, which means that there is a 1–1 correspondence $f: \mathbf{N}_n \to \mathbf{N}$. Compare the numbers $f(1), f(2), \ldots, f(n)$.

There is one, say $f(k)$, that is bigger than all the others. Thus, any $n' \in \mathbf{N}$ such that $n' > f(k)$ cannot lie in R_f. But, this contradicts the fact that f is onto. Thus, no such f can exist, and it is false that $\mathbf{N}_n \cong \mathbf{N}$ or $\mathbf{N} \cong \mathbf{N}_n$. Q.E.D.

Corollary to Proposition 2.11

Every countable set is infinite.

Proof

If A is countable, then $A \cong \mathbf{N}$. Thus, it is not possible for A to equal $\varnothing$ or for there to exist a natural number n such that $A \cong \mathbf{N}_n$. For if $A = \varnothing$, then it would follow that $\mathbf{N} = \varnothing$, which is impossible. If $A \cong \mathbf{N}_n$, then $\mathbf{N} \cong \mathbf{N}_n$, which is impossible, by the previous proposition. Q.E.D.

Proposition 2.12

Every infinite set has a countable subset. That is, if A is infinite, then $\mathbf{N} \leqq A$.

Proof

Let A be infinite; by definition, $A \neq \varnothing$. Therefore, there is at least one element in A. Let us call it a_1. Now if $A \setminus \{a_1\} = \varnothing$, then it is easy to show that $A = \{a_1\}$, so that $A \cong \mathbf{N}_1$. Since this is impossible, $A \setminus \{a_1\} \neq \varnothing$. Therefore, it has a member, say a_2. Now consider $(A \setminus \{a_1\}) \setminus \{a_2\} = A \setminus \{a_1, a_2\}$. If it were empty, then $A = \{a_1, a_2\} \cong \mathbf{N}_2$, which is impossible. Thus, it has a member, say a_3. Clearly, this process can be continued indefinitely, so that we end up with a collection of members of A indexed by $\mathbf{N}$. This collection is the desired countable subset of A. Q.E.D.

Proposition 2.13

There are infinite sets that are not countable. In particular, the set $\mathbf{R}$ is not countable. Thus, $\mathbf{N} < \mathbf{R}$.

Proof

(The author of this result and its proof is Georg Cantor. Indeed, he is the originator of much of the theory of sets.)

First for convenience, we alter the problem somewhat. Let $(-1, 1)$ denote the interval of real numbers between -1 and 1 (not including ± 1). We define a function $f: (-1, 1) \to \mathbf{R}$ as follows:

$$f(x) = \begin{cases} \dfrac{x}{1-x}, & \text{if } \; 0 < x < 1 \\ 0 & \text{if } \; x = 0 \\ \dfrac{x}{1+x}, & \text{if } \; -1 < x < 0 \end{cases}$$

If $0 < x < 1, f'(x) = 1/(1 - x)^2$, and if $-1 < x < 0, f'(x) = 1/(1 + x)^2$, so that f is a strictly increasing function of x. This implies that f is 1–1. Moreover, let y be any real number. Then

$$f(y/1 + y) = y \qquad \text{if } y \geqq 0$$

$$f(y/1 - y) = y \qquad \text{if } y < 0$$

Thus, f is onto.

In other words, f is a 1–1 correspondence, so that $(-1, 1) \not\approx \mathbf{R}$.

Let $(0, 1)$ denote the interval of real numbers between 0 and 1 (not including 0, 1). We define a function $g:(0, 1) \to (-1, 1)$ and a function $h:(-1, 1) \to (0, 1)$ as follows:

$$g(x) = 2x - 1, \; 0 < x < 1$$

$$h(x) = \tfrac{1}{2}x + \tfrac{1}{2}, \; -1 < x < 1$$

Then, if $\quad 0 < x < 1, (h \circ g)(x) = h(g(x)) = h(2x - 1)$

$$= \tfrac{1}{2}(2x - 1) + 1/2 = x,$$

and, if $\quad -1 < x < 1, (g \circ h)(x) = g(h(x)) = g(\tfrac{1}{2}x + \tfrac{1}{2})$

$$= 2(\tfrac{1}{2}x + \tfrac{1}{2}) - 1 = x.$$

That is, $g \circ h = I_{(-1,1)}$ and $h \circ g = I_{(0,1)}$, so that g and h are 1–1 correspondences.

Therefore, $(0, 1) \not\approx (-1, 1)$. Since $(-1, 1) \not\approx \mathbf{R}$, we have, using the transitivity of $\not\approx$,

$$(0, 1) \not\approx \mathbf{R}$$

We shall show that $(0, 1)$ is not countable. This implies that $\mathbf{R}$ is not countable (for if $\mathbf{R} \not\approx \mathbf{N}$, then $(0, 1) \not\approx \mathbf{N}$, by the transitivity of $\not\approx$, and this, it will have been proved, is impossible.)

We start by supposing that $(0, 1)$ is countable. That is, we assume that there is a 1–1 correspondence $f: \mathbf{N} \to (0, 1)$.

Now, we may represent each member of $(0, 1)$ by its infinite decimal expansion. Indeed, if we outlaw infinite successions of 9's, each number in $(0, 1)$ has a *unique* decimal expansion (e.g., 0.3428199999 . . . is replaced by 0·342820000 . . . , etc.).

Let us represent the decimal expansion of $f(n)$ by $\cdot a_1^{(n)} a_2^{(n)} a_3^{(n)} \ldots$, where each $a_i^{(n)}, i = 1, 2, 3, \ldots$, is a digit between 0 and 9. Now, consider the numbers $a_n^{(n)}$, digits between 0 and 9; that is, we consider, for each n, the nth digit in the decimal expansion of $f(n)$.

We define a new sequence of digits between 0 and 9, $b_1, b_2, b_3, \ldots, b_n, \ldots$ as follows:

$$b_n = \begin{cases} 1 & \text{if } a_n^{(n)} \neq 1 \\ 2 & \text{if } a_n^{(n)} = 1 \end{cases}$$

Thus, for each n, $b_n \neq a_n^{(n)}$.

Now, consider the number given by the decimal expansion $.b_1b_2b_3 \ldots$. Clearly, it lies between 0 and 1, that is, in (0, 1). Therefore, there must be exactly one natural number k such that

$$f(k) = .\, b_1b_2b_3, \ldots$$

But, the kth digit of $f(k)$ is $a_k^{(k)}$, whereas the kth digit of $.b_1b_2b_3 \ldots$ is b_k, and we have constructed the b's so that $b_n \neq a_n^{(n)}$ for *every* n. In particular, $b_k \neq a_k^{(k)}$, contradicting the above equation.

Thus, our supposition that (0, 1) is countable leads to a contradiction, so that we conclude that it is not countable. Q.E.D.

Next, we show that $\leqq$ behaves for infinite sets in the same way that it behaves for numbers. The crucial properties of $\leqq$, with respect to numbers, are the following: (1) For any a, $a \leqq a$ (Reflexivity); (2) For any a, b, c, if $a \leqq b$ and $b \leqq c$, then $a \leqq c$ (Transitivity); (3) For any a, b, if $a \leqq b$ and $b \leqq a$, then $a = b$ (Anti-symmetry); (4) For any a, b, either $a \leqq b$ or $b \leqq a$.

Proposition 2.14

Let A, B, C be any sets. Then, (1) $A \leqq A$; (2) *if $A \leqq B$ and $B \leqq C$, then $A \leqq C$.*

Proof

(1) It is always true that $A \mathrel{\#} A$; for if $A = \varnothing$, it is trivially true, and if $A \neq \varnothing$, the identity map $I_A : A \to A$ is a 1–1 correspondence. Thus, there is a subset of A, namely A itself, such that A and this subset are equinumerous.

(2) If $A = \varnothing$, the result is trivial. Thus, assume that $A \neq \varnothing$. Let B' be a subset of B, and let $f: A \to B'$ be a 1–1 correspondence. Let C' be a subset of C, and let $g: B \to C'$ be a 1–1 correspondence. Then, $g \circ f: A \to C$ is a 1–1 function (because g and f are 1–1), and $\mathscr{R}_{g \circ f}$ is (of course) a subset of C. (Indeed, it is precisely $\mathscr{R}_{g|B'}$, but this is not important.) Thus $g \circ f$ is a 1–1 function from A onto $\mathscr{R}_{g \circ f}$; that is, it is a 1–1 correspondence between A and $\mathscr{R}_{g \circ f}$. This means that $A \leqq C$. Q.E.D.

Proposition 2.15

Let A and B be any two sets satisfying $A \leqq B$ and $B \leqq A$. Then, $A \mathrel{\#} B$.

Remark: This intuitively "obvious" result is by no means trivial. It is known as the Schröder-Bernstein Theorem. We present below a proof based on the method of Birkhoff and MacLane.

Proof

Since $A \leqq B$, there is a subset $B' \subset B$ and a 1–1 correspondence $f: A \to B'$. Since $B \leqq A$, there is a subset $A' \subset A$ and a 1–1 correspondence $g: B \to A'$.

To show that $A \ncong B$, we must show that there is a 1–1 correspondence between A and B. If $B' = B$, we could take f to be this correspondence; if $A' = A$, we could take g^{-1}. Therefore, since these cases have been disposed of, let us assume that $B' \neq B$ and $A' \neq A$.

Given any $a \in A$, we say that an element $b \in B$ is an *immediate ancestor of a* if $g(b) = a$. Similarly, given any $b \in B$, we say that an element of $a \in A$ is an immediate ancestor of b if $f(a) = b$. Note that each a or b has *at most* one immediate ancestor.

Now, choose any $a \in A$. We shall say that an element $b \in B$ is an *ancestor* of a, if there exist a finite number of elements of A, $a_1, a_2, \ldots, a_n$, and a finite number of elements of B, $b_1, \ldots, b_n$, such that $b = b_1$, b_i is an immediate ancestor of a_i, a_i is an immediate ancestor of b_{i+1}, and $a_n = a$. We may illustrate this as follows (an arrow from one element to another signifies that the former is an immediate ancestor of the latter):

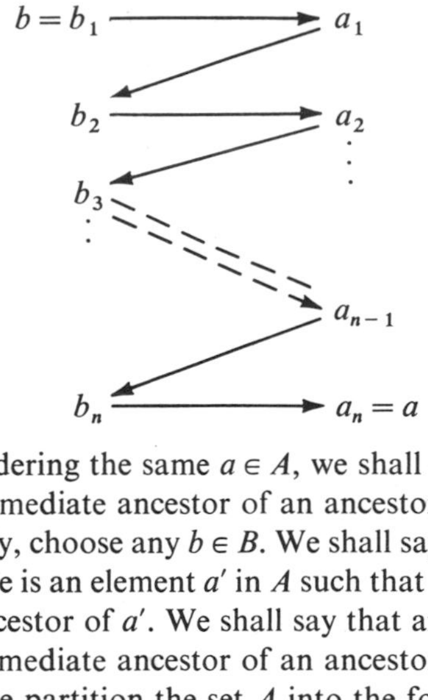

Still considering the same $a \in A$, we shall say that $a' \in A$ is an ancestor of a, if it is an immediate ancestor of an ancestor of a.

Similarly, choose any $b \in B$. We shall say that an element $a \in A$ is an ancestor of b if there is an element a' in A such that a' is an immediate ancestor of b and a is an ancestor of a'. We shall say that an element $b' \in B$ is an ancestor of b, if it is an immediate ancestor of an ancestor of b.

Now, we partition the set A into the following three subsets:

$$A_1 = \{a \mid a \in A, \text{ and } a \text{ has an even number of ancestors}\},$$
$$A_2 = \{a \mid a \in A, \text{ and } a \text{ has an odd number of ancestors}\},$$
$$A_3 = \{a \mid a \in A, \text{ and } a \text{ has infinitely many ancestors}\}.$$

Notice that 0 is an even number so that those elements of A with no ancestors belong to A'. Notice also, that an element of A has at least one ancestor, if and only if it belongs $\mathcal{R}_g = A'$. Partition B analogously into B_1, B_2, B_3.

Now, if a has an odd number of ancestors, it must have at least one. Therefore $A_2 \subset A' = \mathcal{R}_g$. Recall that $\mathcal{R}_g$ is the domain of g^{-1}. Thus, we may consider the functions $g^{-1} \mid A_2$ and $f \mid A_1 \cup A_3$. Both are 1–1. Since no member of a has both an odd number of ancestors and an even or infinite number,

$A_2 \cap (A_1 \cup A_3) = \varnothing$. Therefore, $g^{-1} \cup f: A_2 \cup (A_1 \cup A_3) \to B$ is defined. Since $A_2 \cup (A_1 \cup A_3) = A$, $g^{-1} \cup f$ is a function from A to B. We shall show that it is 1–1 and onto.

To see that $g^{-1} \cup f$ is onto, choose any $b \in B$. If b has an even number of ancestors, say $a_1, b_1, a_2, b_2, \ldots, a_n, b_n$ then $g(b)$ has an odd number: namely, $a_1, b_1, a_2, b_2, \ldots, a_n, b_n$, and b. Therefore, g takes any b in B_1 to $g(b)$ in A_2. But then, $(g^{-1} \cup f)(g(b)) = g^{-1}(g(b)) = b$, so that b belongs to the range of $g^{-1} \cup f$ in this case. If b has an infinite number of ancestors, then its immediate ancestor a must have an infinite number of ancestors, that is, it must belong to A_3. Thus, $a \in A_3$, and so, $(g^{-1} \cup f)(a) = f(a) = b$. In this case too, therefore, b is in the range of $g^{-1} \cup f$. Finally, a similar argument shows that if b has an odd number of ancestors, its immediate ancestor a has an even number, so that $a \in A_1$, and $(g^{-1} \cup f)(a) = f(a) = b$. Thus, f is onto.

To see that $g^{-1} \cup f$ is 1–1, choose any distinct a, a', in A. If both lie in A_2, then $(g^{-1} \cup f)(a) = g^{-1}(a) \neq g^{-1}(a') = (g^{-1} \cup f)(a')$, because g^{-1} is 1–1. If both lie in $A_1 \cup A_3$, $(g^{-1} \cup f)(a) = f(a) \neq f(a') = (g^{-1} \cup f)(a')$ because f is 1–1. Suppose, finally, that one of them, say a, lies in A_2 and the other in $A_1 \cup A_3$. Then, $(g^{-1} \cup f)(a) = g^{-1}(a)$ and $(g^{-1} \cup f)(a') = f(a')$. Now, it is not hard to show that g^{-1} takes members of A_2 into B_1 whereas f takes members of $A_1 \cup A_3$ into $B_2 \cup B_3$. Since B_1 has no element in common with $B_2 \cup B_3$, $g^{-1}(a)$, which is in B_1 cannot equal $f(a')$, which is in $B_1 \cup B_2$. Therefore, in all cases, $g^{-1} \cup f$ takes distinct elements of A into distinct elements of B, so that $g^{-1} \cup f$ is 1–1. Q.E.D.

We do not prove the following result.

Proposition 2.16

Given any two sets A and B, either $A \leqq B$ or $B \leqq A$.

Proposition 2.17

Given any set A, let $\mathscr{P}(A)$ be the set of all subsets of A. Then $A < \mathscr{P}(A)$.

Proof

Let $f: A \to \mathscr{P}(A)$ be the function satisfying $f(a) = \{a\}$. It is easy to show that f is a 1–1 correspondence between A and the subset of $\mathscr{P}(A)$ consisting of all sets of the form $\{a\}$, where a ranges over A. Therefore $A \leqq \mathscr{P}(A)$.

Next we show that it is impossible for $A \not\approx \mathscr{P}(A)$. For suppose that there is a 1–1 correspondence $f: A \to \mathscr{P}(A)$. Then, since the empty set $\varnothing$ is a subset of A, $\varnothing$ belongs to $\mathscr{P}(A)$, and there must be an $a \in A$ such that $f(a) = \varnothing$. Since $\varnothing$ contains no elements, $a \notin \varnothing$, or $a \notin f(a)$.

Now, consider the subset of A consisting of all a such that $a \notin f(a)$. Call it X. We have just shown that X contains at least one member: namely, that a satisfying $f(a) = \varnothing$. Therefore, $X \neq \varnothing$. Since X is a subset of A, X belongs to $\mathscr{P}(A)$, and so, there is an $a' \in A$ such that $f(a') = X$.

Does $a' \in f(a') = X$? If so, then, by definition of X, $a' \notin f(a')$, a contradiction. Thus, $a' \notin f(a')$. But again by definition of X, this means that $a' \in X = f(a')$, another contradiction.

Thus, there can be no 1–1 correspondence between A and $\mathscr{P}(A)$. Q.E.D.

The above proposition is significant because it shows that there are "at least" a countable number of cardinalities.

For, start with the set **N**. It is countable. Then, form $\mathscr{P}(\mathbf{N})$, it is uncountable; indeed, $\mathbf{N} < \mathscr{P}(\mathbf{N})$. Then, form $\mathscr{P}(\mathscr{P}(\mathbf{N}))$, $\mathscr{P}(\mathscr{P}(\mathscr{P}(\mathbf{N})))$, and so on. We get a sequence of sets, each strictly more numerous than the preceding:

$$\mathbf{N} < \mathscr{P}(\mathbf{N}) < \mathscr{P}(\mathscr{P}(\mathbf{N})) < \mathscr{P}(\mathscr{P}(\mathscr{P}(\mathbf{N}))) < \cdots$$

EXERCISES / 2.17

1. Given any nonempty set A, define a function $K: \mathscr{P}(A) \to \{0, 1\}^A$ as follows:

For every subset A' of A, $K(A')$ is the following function from A to $\{0, 1\}$:

$$(K(A'))(a) = \begin{cases} 0, & \text{if} \quad a \notin A' \\ 1, & \text{if} \quad a \in A' \end{cases}$$

$K(A')$ is called the *characteristic function of A'*.

a. Prove that K is a 1–1 correspondence between $\mathscr{P}(A)$ and $\{0, 1\}^A$.

b. If $A = \mathbf{N}_n$, how many functions are there in $\{0, 1\}^A$?

2. Establish a 1–1 correspondence between **R** and $\mathbf{R}^2$; between **R** and $\mathbf{R}^n$.

3. Establish a 1–1 correspondence between the closed interval $[a, b]$, $a < b$, and the closed interval $[c, d]$, $c < d$.

4. Establish a 1–1 correspondence between the closed interval $[0, 1]$ and the open interval $(0, 1)$.

5. Establish a 1–1 correspondence between **N** and **Z** (the set of all integers).

6. a. Given any natural number n, let k_n be the largest natural number k satisfying

$$(1/2)k(k-1) < n$$

Define a function $f: \mathbf{N} \to \mathbf{N} \times \mathbf{N}$ as follows:

$$f(n) = (1 + (1/2)k_n, (k_n + 1) - n, n - (1/2)k_n(k_n - 1))$$

Prove that f is a 1–1 correspondence between **N** and $\mathbf{N} \times \mathbf{N}$.

Therefore, $\mathbf{N} \times \mathbf{N}$ is countable.

b. Let $g: \mathbf{N} \to \mathbf{Z}$ be the 1–1 correspondence established in **5** above. Prove that $g \times g: \mathbf{N} \times \mathbf{N} \to \mathbf{Z} \times \mathbf{Z}$ is a 1–1 correspondence. Thus, $\mathbf{Z} \times \mathbf{Z}$ is countable.

Is $(g \times g) \circ f \circ g^{-1}$ a 1–1 correspondence? If not, why not? If so, between which sets.

7. A rational number is a quotient of integers. Each rational number can be written uniquely in the form p/q or $-p/q$, or 0, where p and q are natural numbers whose only common factor is 1. The set of all rational numbers is called **Q**.

Define a function $f: \mathbf{Q} \to \mathbf{Z} \times \mathbf{Z}$ as follows:

$$f(p/q) = (p, q), f(-p/q) = (-p, q),$$

where p and q are natural numbers, as above, and $f(0) = (0, 0)$.

Prove that f is 1–1. Thus, $\mathbf{Q} \leqq \mathbf{Z} \times \mathbf{Z}$. Since $\mathbf{Z} \times \mathbf{Z} \approx \mathbf{N}$, $\mathbf{Q} \leqq \mathbf{N}$. But, according to Proposition 2.12, (since **Q** is, clearly, infinite), $\mathbf{N} \leqq \mathbf{Q}$. Therefore, by the Schröder-Bernstein Theorem, $\mathbf{Q} \approx \mathbf{N}$, or **Q** is countable.

4 / INDUCTION

The set **N** has a very useful property. To describe it we introduce the following terminology.

Definition 2.29

A subset S of **N** *is said to be* inductive *if and only if it satisfies both of the following conditions*: (1) $1 \in S$; (2) *if* $n \in S$, *then* $n + 1 \in S$.

For example, the set **N** itself is inductive, for clearly $1 \in \mathbf{N}$ and, for any $n \in \mathbf{N}$, of course $n + 1 \in \mathbf{N}$.

The interesting fact about **N** is that it itself is the *only* example of an inductive set, as we now prove.

Proposition 2.18

If a subset S of **N** *is inductive, then* $S = \mathbf{N}$.

Remark: We are listing this statement as a proposition, because we are going to appeal to an "intuitively obvious" fact about **N** to *prove* the statement. In most careful, detailed presentations of natural numbers, however, it is made clear that this fact has no more fundamental or primitive a status mathematically than does the above statement. Indeed, it is often the above statement that is used as an axiom and the "obvious" fact that is a proposition deduced from it: this axiom is called the *Axiom of Induction*.

Nevertheless, it is our point of view here that **N** *is known* and that the following fact about **N** is easier to grasp than what we have stated above as a proposition.

Fact about **N**: *Every nonempty subset of* **N** *has a smallest member.*

Proof of Proposition 2.18

Suppose that S is an inductive subset of **N**. We shall show that $\mathbf{N} \setminus S$ is empty, so that, then, $S = \mathbf{N}$, as desired.

If $\mathbf{N} \setminus S$ is nonempty, we appeal to the above *Fact about* **N** to obtain a smallest member n_0 of $\mathbf{N} \setminus S$. Since S is inductive, $1 \in S$, so that $1 \notin \mathbf{N} \setminus S$. Therefore,

$n_0 > 1$, so that $n_0 - 1$ is a natural number. Moreover, $n_0 - 1$ is smaller than n_0. Since n_0 is the smallest member of $\mathbf{N} \setminus S$, it follows that $n_0 - 1 \notin N \setminus S$, or, equivalently, that $n_0 - 1 \in S$. But S is inductive. Therefore, $n_0 = (n_0 - 1) + 1 \in S$, contradicting the fact that $n_0 \in \mathbf{N} \setminus S$.

Thus, our assumption that $\mathbf{N} \setminus S$ is nonempty has led to a contradiction, and so $\mathbf{N} \setminus S$ must be empty. Q.E.D.

Our interest in Proposition 2.18 lies chiefly in its application to the following kind of situation:

We are given a sequence of propositions P_n, where n ranges over $\mathbf{N}$, and we wish to prove that *all of them are true*. To put it another way, we consider the *truth set S of the sequence*, that is, the set of all $n \in \mathbf{N}$ for which P_n is true, and we wish to prove that $S = \mathbf{N}$. Proposition 2.18 says that to prove $S = \mathbf{N}$ it suffices to show that S is an inductive set. The advantage of this technique is that it is often easier to show that S is inductive than to show directly that $S = \mathbf{N}$.

We now give some examples of sequences of propositions P_n.

(a) $1 + 2 + \cdots + n = (1/2)n(n+1)$.

(b) $1^2 + 2^2 + \cdots + n^2 = 1/6n(n + 1)(2n + 1)$.

(c) $2^n > n$.

Notice that, say in (a), for each value of n, the equation in (a) is a different proposition. Thus, for $n = 2$, the equation states that $1 + 2 = (1/2)2(3)$; or, for $n = 5$, the equation states that $1 + 2 + 3 + 4 + 5 = 1/2 \cdot 5 \cdot 6$. Of course, all these different propositions are closely related: Witness the fact that they can all be put in the general form of the equation in (a). Similar comments apply to (b) and (c). Proving the validity of the general relation in (a), (b), or in (c) actually involves proving a countable number of propositions. Were the propositions in each sequence not closely related, of course, we would not have a chance in proving them all true.

Sometimes a given statement to be proved does not immediately reveal a dependence on natural numbers. By rephrasing the statement, however, the dependence may be revealed and the given statement thereby broken up into a sequence of statements, as above. Much of the skill in using this method of proof resides in such rephrasing. We present a simple example of this now.

(d) The product of any three consecutive natural numbers is divisible by 6.

We rephrase this as follows:

$$n(n + 1)(n + 2) \text{ is divisible by 6, for all } n \in \mathbf{N}$$

Let P_n be the statement "$n(n + 1)(n + 2)$ is divisible by 6." Then, the validity of *all* the P_n is equivalent to the validity of the original proposition. Thus, we have broken the original proposition into a countable number of propositions.

We now illustrate the *inductive method of proof* by proving (a), (c), and (d).

Proof of (a)

Let S be the truth set for the sequence of propositions in (a).

Since $1 = 1/2 \cdot 1(1 + 1)$, P_1 is true, so that $1 \in S$.

Suppose that $n \in S$; that is, suppose that P_n is true. Then, $1 + 2 + \cdots + n = (1/2)n(n + 1)$. Adding $n + 1$ to both sides of this equation, we obtain, $1 + 2 + \cdots + n + (n + 1) = (1/2)n(n + 1) + (n + 1) = (1/2)(n + 1)(n + 2)$. But, the equality $1 + 2 + \cdots + n + (n + 1) = (1/2)(n + 1)(n + 2)$ is precisely the statement P_{n+1}. Therefore, if $n \in S$, then P_{n+1} is true, and, hence, $(n + 1) \in S$.

Thus, S is inductive, so that $S = \mathbf{N}$, as desired. In other words, the proposition P_n of (a) holds for every $n \in \mathbf{N}$.

Proof of (c)

Let S be the truth set for the sequence of propositions P_n of (c).

Since $2^1 = 2 > 1$, P_1 is true, so that $1 \in S$.

Suppose that $n \in S$; that is, suppose that P_n is true. Then, $2^n > n$. Multiplying both sides of the inequality by 2, we get $2^{n+1} > 2n$. Now, if $n \geqq 1$, then $2n = n + n \geqq n + 1$. Thus, $2^{n+1} > n + 1$. But, this is precisely the statement P_{n+1}. Therefore, if $n \in S$, then P_{n+1} is true, and, hence, $n + 1 \in S$.

Thus, S is inductive, so that $S = \mathbf{N}$, as desired. Q.E.D.

Proof of (d)

Let S be the truth set for the sequence of propositions P_n obtained by rephrasing the proposition in (d).

The statement P_1 is "$1 \cdot (1 + 1)(1 + 2)$ is divisible by 6." Since $1 \cdot (1 + 1)(1 + 2) = 6$, P_1 is, clearly, true, so that $1 \in S$.

Suppose that $n \in S$. That is, suppose that P_n is true: $n(n + 1)(n + 2)$ is divisible by 6. Consider $(n + 1)(n + 2)(n + 3)$, and compare it to $n(n + 1)(n + 2)$: $(n + 1)(n + 2)(n + 3) = n(n + 1)(n + 2) + 3(n + 1)(n + 2)$. Now, of the two consecutive numbers $(n + 1)$ and $(n + 2)$, one must be even. Therefore, $(n + 1)(n + 2)$ is even (i.e., divisible by 2), and so $3(n + 1)(n + 2)$ is divisible by 6. Since $n(n + 1)(n + 2)$ is also divisible by 6, so is the sum $n(n + 1)(n + 2) + 3(n + 1)(n + 2)$. But this sum is just $(n + 1)(n + 2)(n + 3)$, and so, this quantity is divisible by 6. This assertion is precisely P_{n+1}. Therefore, if $n \in S$, then P_{n+1} is true, and, hence, $n + 1 \in S$.

Thus, S is inductive, so that $S = \mathbf{N}$.

This means that *all* of the propositions P_n of (d) are true and, therefore, that the initial proposition of (d) is true.

In addition to supplying us with a new method of proof, *the inductive method*, Proposition 2.18, provides us with an *inductive method of definition*. Consider the following situation.

We are trying to define a certain function with domain $\mathbf{N}$. Clearly, this can be accomplished by specifying the value of the function at every $n \in \mathbf{N}$. Now, suppose that we are able to define the value of the function of 1. Moreover, suppose that, for any $n \in \mathbf{N}$, *if* we can specify the value of the function at n, *then* we can also specify the value of the function at $n + 1$.

Under the circumstances described in the above paragraph, the function is indeed determined at every $n \in \mathbf{N}$. For, let S be the set of all $n \in \mathbf{N}$ at which the value of the function is determined. Then, by the above description, $1 \in S$; moreover, if $n \in S$, then $n + 1 \in S$. Thus, S is inductive, and so, $S = \mathbf{N}$.

In subsequent chapters, we shall have occasion to use this method of definition.

EXERCISES / 2.18

1. Prove, by the inductive method, that the following relations hold for every $n \in \mathbf{N}$:

a. $1^2 + 2^2 + \cdots + n^2 = (1/6)n(n+1)(2n+1)$

b. $1^3 + 2^3 + \cdots + n^3 = (1/4)n^2(n^2 + 2n + 1)$

c. $2^n < 3^n$

2. For any $n \in \mathbf{N}$, let $n! = n(n-1)(n-2) \cdots 3 \cdot 2 \cdot 1$, and for any natural numbers n and k such that $k < n$, let

$$\binom{n}{k} = \frac{n!}{k!(n-k)!}$$

Prove, by the inductive method, that if x and y are any given real numbers, then, for every $n \in \mathbf{N}$,

$$(x+y)^n = x^n + \binom{n}{1}x^{n-1}y + \binom{n}{2}x^{n-2}y^2 + \cdots + \binom{n}{k}x^{n-k}y^k + \cdots + \binom{n}{n-2}x^2y^{n-2} + \binom{n}{n-1}xy^{n-1} + y^n$$

3. Assume Proposition 2.18 as an axiom and derive from it the *Fact about* $\mathbf{N}$.

4. Let $n_\circ$ be any fixed natural number, and let $\mathbf{N}(n_\circ)$ be the set of all natural numbers greater than or equal to $n_\circ$.

Let $P_{n_\circ}$ be the following proposition: *If S is a subset of* $\mathbf{N}(n_\circ)$ *satisfying*: (1) $n_\circ \in S$, *and* (2) *if $n \in S$, then $n + 1 \in S$; then $S = $* $\mathbf{N}(n_\circ)$.

a. Use the *Fact about* $\mathbf{N}$ (and not Proposition 2.18) to prove that $P_{n_\circ}$ is true.

b. Prove that $P_{n_\circ}$ is true for every $n_\circ \in \mathbf{N}$, using the inductive method of proof. (Notice that P_1 is precisely Proposition 2.18.)

5. Recall that $\mathbf{N}_{n_\circ}$ is the set of all $n \in \mathbf{N}$ such that $n \leqq n_\circ$.

Let $P_{n_\circ}$ be the following proposition: *If S is a subset of* $\mathbf{N}_{n_\circ}$ *satisfying*: (1) $1 \in S$, and (2) if $n \in S$ *and* $n < n_\circ$ *then* $n + 1 \in S$; *then* $S = \mathbf{N}_{n_\circ}$.

Prove that $P_{n_\circ}$ is true. (*Hint:* Let $T = S \cup \mathbf{N}(n_\circ + 1)$—see Exercise 4, above—and prove that T is inductive.)

6. Let $f: \mathbf{N} \to \mathbf{N}$ be a function with the following properties: (1) $f(1) = 1$; (2) for any n for which $f(n)$ is defined, $f(n+1)$ is defined and $f(n+1) = (n+1)f(n)$. Prove, by the inductive method, that $f(n) = n!$

7. Let $f: \mathbf{N} \to \mathbf{N}$ be a function with the following properties: (1) $f(1) = 1$; (2) for any n for which $f(n)$ is defined, $f(n+1)$ is defined and $f(n+1) = f(n) + (n+1)$. Prove, by the inductive method that $f(n) = (1/2)n(n+1)$.

8. Prove that $1 + 2 + \cdots + n = (1/2)n(n+1)$ directly, not using the inductive method.

CHAPTER 3

VECTOR SPACES

In Chapter 1, we introduced informally the notion of a linear set, as well as some examples illustrating the prevalence and usefulness of this idea. In this chapter, we begin by presenting a precise, formal definition of this concept. The resulting object will be known as a *vector space*. We then deduce a wide variety of consequences from this definition, the first ones being quite rudimentary, the later ones, using the important subsidiary notions of *linear independence* and *dimension*, being quite sophisticated. These consequences enable us to go a long way in answering questions about systems of linear equations. The importance of this theoretical framework, however, resides not only in its direct applicability to the solution of such problems, but also in the fact that it is the setting in which these problems assume their fullest meaning.

1 / DEFINITIONS AND EXAMPLES

1.1 Definitions

The informal notion of a linear set introduced in Chapter 1 is composed of two parts. First, there is a *set* of objects. Secondly, there are *two operations* defined on this set, which we have called "addition" and "real multiplication" because they resemble the ordinary operations of addition and multiplication of real numbers.

The first component presents no problem: We have discussed the notion of a set at length in the previous chapter. The second component raises two serious questions, however: (1) What is an "operation"? (2) What, precisely, do we require of an operation for it to qualify as *resembling* the operation of ordinary addition of real numbers or the operation of ordinary multiplication of real numbers?

To answer the first question, we first draw the reader's attention to the fact that the two operations repeatedly illustrated in Chapter 1 differ from each other in the following respect: The operation of "addition" involves two elements of the same kind, both from the linear set—that is, we consider the "sum" of *two members of the set*—whereas the operation of "real multiplication" involves two possibly different kinds of elements, a real number and a member of the linear set—that is, we consider a *real* "multiple" of *a member of the linear set*. Thus, we must consider two different kinds of operations.

The two kinds of operations, however, have the following in common: We are given two elements (either of the same kind, or of different kinds) and associate with them a third element (their "sum" or "product"). Moreover, this third element is in the same set as at least one of the two given elements (the "sum" of two members of a linear set is a member of the linear set, any real "multiple" of a member of the linear set is a member of the linear set). These observations motivate the following definition.

Definition 3.1

Let A and B be nonempty sets. A binary operation of A on B is, simply, a function $f: A \times B \to B$.

A *binary operation of A on A* (that is, a function from $A \times A$ to A) *is called, more briefly, a binary operation on A.*

The most familiar examples of binary operations of a set on itself are the operations of ordinary addition and muitiplication of real numbers.

More precisely, let $\Sigma : \mathbf{R} \times \mathbf{R} \to \mathbf{R}$ be defined by $\Sigma(x, y) = x + y$, for all pairs $(x, y) \in \mathbf{R} \times \mathbf{R}$. Σ is the ordinary *sum* operation. The ordinary *product* operation is a function $\Pi : \mathbf{R} \times \mathbf{R} \to \mathbf{R}$ given by $\Pi(x, y) = xy$, for all pairs $(x, y) \in \mathbf{R}$.

A simple example of an operation of one set on another is the operation of $\mathbf{R}$ on $\mathbf{R}^2$ given by real multiplication of ordered pairs. More precisely, this operation is a function $\mu : \mathbf{R} \times \mathbf{R}^2 \to \mathbf{R}^2$ given by $\mu(r, (x, y)) = (rx, ry)$, for all pairs $(r, (x, y)) \in \mathbf{R} \times \mathbf{R}^2$.

Of course, these particular operations are very special. In general, an operation of $\mathbf{R}$ on itself or of $\mathbf{R}$ on $\mathbf{R}^2$ is merely an arbitrary function from $\mathbf{R} \times \mathbf{R}$ to $\mathbf{R}$, or from $\mathbf{R} \times \mathbf{R}^2$ to $\mathbf{R}^2$, respectively. It is not hard to show that there are an uncountable number of such functions. The particular operations just mentioned, however, are very special because they satisfy certain very restrictive properties, properties that are shared by relatively "few" of these uncountably many operations. We now list the most important of these properties: it is these that we shall require of operations to qualify as resembling real addition or real multiplication.

(a) *Properties of Real Addition*

(i) *For any real numbers r, s, t,*

$$r + (s + t) = (r + s) + t$$

Using the function Σ introduced above, we may write this property as follows: For any real numbers r, s, t,

$$\Sigma(r, \Sigma(s, t)) = \Sigma(\Sigma(r, s), t)$$

This property is known as the *associative law of real addition*. To put it another way: Σ is associative.

The significance of this rule stems from the fact that addition (as conceived here) is a *binary* operation. Thus, to add more than two numbers, we must do so step-by-step, two at a time. If we are given three numbers—in a certain order that we do not alter—then there are exactly two ways to perform such step-by-step addition: Namely, the ways indicated on either side of the equation above. That both methods yield the same result—thus states the associative law—allows us to define unambiguously what we mean by the sum of three numbers: Namely, *the* sum of r, s, t is the quantity given by either side of the above equation.

That the associative law has tremendous importance is almost trivially obvious in the case of real numbers: Without it most "numerical calculations" are meaningless. In a less trivial sense, the importance of the associative law will become clear to the reader when he sees how it features in the proofs of many of the most rudimentary abstract results.

(ii) *There is a real number*, 0, *such that for all real numbers r,*

$$0 + r = r$$

Using Σ, we may express the property as: For every real number r, $\Sigma(0, r) = r$.

The number 0 is called an *identity for* Σ, and the rule is known as the *additive identity rule*.

(iii) *For any real number r, there is a real number* $-r$, *such that*

$$r + (-r) = 0$$

Alternatively, we say that for every real number r, there is a real number $-r$, such that $\Sigma(r, -r) = 0$.

The number $-r$ is usually called the negative of r. We may also call $-r$ a Σ-inverse of r. This rule is known as the *inverse rule for* Σ.

(iv) *For any real numbers r and s*

$$r + s = s + r$$

That is, for any real numbers r and s, $\Sigma(r, s) = \Sigma(s, r)$.

This property is known as the *commutative law of real addition.* Or, equivalently, we say that Σ is commutative.

(b) *Properties of Real Multiplication*
(i) *For any real numbers, r, s, t*

$$r(st) = (rs)t$$

That is, for any real numbers r, s, t, $\Pi(r, \Pi(s, t)) = \Pi(\Pi(r, s), t)$.

This is the *associative law for real multiplication* (i.e., Π is associative). The comments of (a) (i) apply here as well.

(ii) *There is a real number* 1, *such that for all real numbers r,*

$$1 \cdot r = r$$

Equivalently: For every real number r, $\Pi(1, r) = r$.

The number 1 is called an identity for Π, and the rule is known as the *identity rule for* Π, or the *multiplicative identity rule.*

(iii) *For every real number* $r \neq 0$, *there is a real number* $1/r$ *satisfying*

$$r \cdot 1/r = 1$$

Equivalently: for every real number $r \neq 0$, there is a number $1/r$ satisfying $\Pi(r, 1/r) = 1$.

The number $1/r$ is usually called the reciprocal of r. We may also call it a Π-inverse of r. The property of Π described here is known as the *inverse rule or law for* Π.

Notice that the inverse laws for Σ and Π differ in one important respect. Whereas, according to the inverse rule for Σ, every real number has a Σ-inverse, the inverse rule for Π does not state that every real number has a Π-inverse. It states, instead, that every real number *except possibly zero*, has a Π-inverse. The rule does not definitely exclude the possibility that zero may have a Π-inverse; it merely fails to take a definite stand on this issue.** Notice that the inverse rule for Σ has no such qualms about 1; the number 1 definitely has a Σ-inverse: namely, -1, of course.

(iv) *For any real numbers r and s*

$$rs = sr$$

That is, for any real numbers r, s, $\Pi(r, s) = \Pi(s, r)$.

This property is known as the *commutative law of real multiplication.* Or, alternatively, we say that Π is commutative.

(c) *A Joint Property of* Σ *and* Π
For any real numbers, r, s, t,

$$r(s + t) = rs + rt$$

** It can easily be proved, however, that 0 definitely has no Π-inverse.

That is, for any real numbers r, s, and t

$$\Pi(r, \Sigma(s, t)) = \Sigma(\Pi(r, s), \Pi(r, t)) \tag{1}$$

This property is known as the *distributivity of multiplication over addition*, or the *distributive law for real multiplication over real addition*. Equivalently we may say that Π distributes over Σ.

Actually, if we use the fact that Π is commutative, we get another formulation of this same law: namely, for all real numbers r, s, t,

$$(r + s)t = rt + st,$$

or

$$\Pi(\Sigma(r, s), t) = \Sigma(\Pi(r, t), \Pi(s, t)) \tag{2}$$

We leave to the reader the task of showing that these two formulations are equivalent. (Assume only that Π is commutative.)

In certain cases, however, both formulations may hold, although we are dealing with an operation that is not commutative. In those cases, we may not be able to derive one formulation from the other, so that—to assert that they both hold—we must state them both separately. To distinguish between the formulations, we say that, in case (1), Π distributes over Σ on the left, and in case (2), Π distributes over Σ on the right.

(d) *A Property of Real Multiplication of Ordered Pairs*

For any real numbers r and s and any ordered pair of real numbers (x, y)

$$(rs)(x, y) = r(s(x, y)),$$

or

$$\mu(\Pi(r, s), (x, y)) = \mu(r, \mu(s, (x, y)))$$

To see that this property actually holds, notice that, by definition, $(rs)(x, y) = (rsx, rsy)$ and that, by definition, $r(s(x, y)) = r(sx, sy) = (rsx, rsy)$.

This property is a kind of *associative law for real multiplication of ordered pairs of real numbers*. Essentially, the same comments that applied in (a) (i) apply here. That is, given any real numbers r and s and any order pair (x, y), there are exactly two ways to multiply (x, y) by r and s—provided that we keep the terms in a fixed order: Either, first multiply (x, y) by s and, then, the result by r, or multiply (x, y) by the result of multiplying s by r. Both methods, according to this rule, yield the same result.

We shall describe this property by saying that μ *is associative with respect to* Π.

We now generalize these specific observations about Σ, Π, and μ.

Definition 3.2

Let A and B be any nonempty sets, let σ be an operation on A, let τ be an operation of A on B, and let ν be an operation on B.

(1) *We say that* σ is associative, *if and only if for all elements* x, y, z *in* A

$$\sigma(x, \sigma(y, z)) = \sigma(\sigma(x, y), z)$$

(2) We say that τ is associative with respect to σ *if and only if, for all* x, y in A *and all* $u \in B$,

$$\tau(x, \tau(y, u)) = \tau(\sigma(x, y), u)$$

(3) *We say that a fixed element* $a \in A$ *is a* σ-identity *if and only if for all* $a' \in A$,

$$\sigma(a', a) = \sigma(a, a') = a'$$

(4) *We say that a fixed element* $a \in A$ *is a* τ-identity *if and only if for all* $b \in B$,

$$\tau(a, b) = b$$

(5) *Given an element* $a \in A$, *we say that an element* $a' \in A$ *is a* σ-inverse *of* a, *if and only if*

$$\sigma(a, a') \textit{ is a } \sigma\textit{-identity of } A$$

and $$\sigma(a', a) \textit{ is a } \sigma\textit{-identity of } A^{**}$$

(6) *We say that* σ is commutative *if and only if for all pairs* (x, y) *in* $A \times A$

$$\sigma(x, y) = \sigma(y, x)$$

(7) *We say that* τ distributes over ν on the left *if and only if for all pairs* $(u, v) \in B \times B$ *and for all* $x \in A$,

$$\tau(x, \nu(u, v)) = \nu(\tau(x, u), \tau(x, v))$$

[*cf. property* (c) *above*].

If $A = B$, so that τ is an operation on B, we can define what it means for τ to distribute over ν on the right: for all x, y, z in B,

$$\tau(\nu(x, y), z) = \nu(\tau(x, z), \tau(y, z))$$

Until now, we have used the usual function notation for an operation. That is, an operation σ takes a pair (x, y) to $\sigma(x, y)$. It will be convenient, henceforth, to change this notation to conform more closely to our notation in the case of ordinary addition and multiplication. Thus, instead of $\sigma(x, y)$, we shall write $x\sigma y$. The reader should rewrite the above definitions using this notation.

We may now summarize the basic properties of real addition and multiplication. Briefly, Σ and Π are associative, commutative operations on **R**, Π distributing over Σ on the left and right, such that: 1. **R** has a Σ-identity

** If σ is commutative, then $\sigma(a, a') = \sigma(a', a)$ so that the two requirements are redundant. If σ is not commutative, however, they are by no means redundant (cf. Exercises 3.1. **12**, and Proposition 2.7). If a' satisfies the first condition, we say that it is a *right* σ*-inverse of* a. *If* a' *satisfies the second condition, we say that it is a left* σ*-inverse of* a.

(namely, 0); 2. **R** has a Π-identity (namely, 1) not equal to the Σ-identity; 3. every member of **R** has a Σ-inverse; 4. every nonzero member of **R** has a Π-inverse.

Definition 3.3

Let A be a nonempty set, and let σ and τ be associative, commutative operations on A, τ distributing over σ on the left and right, such that: (1) *A has at least one σ-identity, say a_0;* (2) *A has at least one τ-identity, say a_1, such that $a_0 \neq a_1$;* (3) *every member of A has a σ-inverse (that is, at least one σ-inverse);* (4) *every member of A, except possibly a_0, has a τ-inverse (that is, at least one τ-inverse).*

Then, we say that A, together with the operations σ and τ, is a field. We shall find it convenient, notationally, to say that A, σ, τ is a field.

In particular, **R**, together with Σ and Π, is a field. However, it is by no means the only example of a field. Two other important examples are:

1. The set of complex numbers **C**, together with the operations of ordinary addition and multiplication of complex numbers.
2. The set of rational numbers, **Q**, together with the operations of ordinary addition and multiplication.

It should be clear that, although there may be many different kinds of examples of fields, they all have a great deal in common, because of the properties necessarily shared by their operations. Indeed, they all have so much in common that, in the historical development of the subject, the abstract symbols for the field operations were never (or hardly ever) used: Instead of the abstract "σ" and "τ," the usual symbols "+" and "·" were used, respectively. We shall adopt this convention, taking care, however, to emphasize that, *unless we are explicitly dealing with real, complex, or rational numbers, the symbols "+" and "·" will denote the field operations of the particular field that we happen to be dealing with and not necessarily the operations of ordinary addition and multiplication.* Thus, for example, instead of $x\sigma y$ we shall write $x + y$, and instead of $x\tau y$, we shall write $x \cdot y$.

We may now refer to a certain field with set F as the field, F, +, ·.**

In most of the rest of this book we shall be dealing with an arbitrary but fixed field F, +, ·. We shall never, without explicit announcement, use any fact about F that cannot be directly deduced from the basic definition of F. Since **R** satisfies this definition, all of the unannounced facts that we use about F will hold for **R**. Thus, the reader may, if he has difficulty with the notion of an abstract field, pretend that we are dealing with **R**.

However, some caution is needed. **R** is not just any old field; it is very special. (For example, there is an ordering of the elements of **R**—e.g. $-1 <$

** Note that the operations of a field are intrinsic to the definition of a field. Change the operations and you change the field, even though you leave the set unchanged!

$0 < 1 < 1\,1/2 \ldots$, etc., that is, in a certain sense, compatible with the operations of addition and multiplication. The same is not true of the field of complex numbers.) Thus, while pretending that our abstract field F is $\mathbf{R}$, the reader should make sure that he uses no facts about $\mathbf{R}$ that cannot be deduced from the basic properties of addition or multiplication, as listed in Examples (a), (b), (c), above, or as stated above in Definition 3.2.

We now pause, with some exercises on operations and fields, before presenting the definition of a vector space.

EXERCISES / 3.1

1. Define a binary operation σ on $\mathbf{R}$ as follows: For every pair $(r, s) \in \mathbf{R} \times \mathbf{R}$ let $\sigma(r, s) = r - s$. Show, by example, that the following statements are true:

a. $\sigma(r, \sigma(s, t)) \neq \sigma(\sigma(r, s), t)$, for some r, s, t in $\mathbf{R}$.

b. $\sigma(r, s) \neq \sigma(s, r)$, for some pairs $(r, s) \in \mathbf{R} \times \mathbf{R}$.

2. Let $A = \mathbf{R}$ and $B = \mathbf{R} \setminus \{0\}$. Define an operation & of A on B as follows: for any pair $(x, y) \in \mathbf{R} \times (\mathbf{R} \setminus \{0\})$, let $\&(x, y) = x \cdot 1/y$. Show, by example, that the following statements are true:

a. $\&(x, \&(y, z)) \neq \&(\&(x, y), z)$, for some $x \in \mathbf{R}$ and y and z in $\mathbf{R} \setminus \{0\}$.

b. $\&(y, z) \neq \&(z, y)$, for some y and z in $\mathbf{R} \setminus \{0\}$.

3.* Recall that $\mathbf{R}^+ = \{x \mid x \in \mathbf{R} \text{ and } x \geqq 0\}$. Define operations $\oplus$ and $\otimes$ on $\mathbf{R}^+$ as follows for any pair $(x, y) \in \mathbf{R}^+ \times \mathbf{R}^+$,

$$x \oplus y = x \cdot y \text{ (where " $\cdot$ " is ordinary multiplication)}$$

and

$$x \otimes y = \begin{cases} y^x, & y \neq 0 \\ 0, & y = 0 \end{cases}$$

Prove or disprove each of the following statements:

a. $x \oplus y = y \oplus x$, for all $(x, y) \in \mathbf{R}^+ \times \mathbf{R}^+$.

b. $x \otimes y = y \otimes x$, for all $(x, y) \in \mathbf{R}^+ \times \mathbf{R}^+$.

c. $x \oplus (y \oplus z) = (x \oplus y) \oplus z$, for all x, y, z in $\mathbf{R}^+$.

d. $x \otimes (y \otimes z) = (x \otimes y) \otimes z$, for all x, y, z in $\mathbf{R}^+$.

e. $x \otimes (y \otimes z) = (x \oplus y) \otimes z$, for all x, y, z in $\mathbf{R}^+$.

f. $x \otimes (y \oplus z) = (x \otimes y) \oplus (x \otimes z)$, for all x, y, z in $\mathbf{R}^+$.

g. $(x \oplus y) \otimes z = (x \otimes z) \oplus (y \otimes z)$, for all x, y, z in $\mathbf{R}^+$.

4.* Define $\oplus$ on all of $\mathbf{R}$, as above: that is, for any pair $(x, y) \in \mathbf{R} \times \mathbf{R}$,

$$x \oplus y = x \cdot y$$

Let $\otimes$ be the operation of $\mathbf{R}$ on $\mathbf{R}^+ \setminus \{0\}$ given by $r \otimes s = s^r$, for every pair $(r, s) \in \mathbf{R} \times (\mathbf{R}^+ \setminus \{0\})$. Prove the following statements:

a. $r \otimes (r' \otimes s) = (r \cdot r') \otimes s$, for all $r, r' \in \mathbf{R}$ and all $s \in \mathbf{R}^+ \setminus \{0\}$ (this statement is precisely: $\otimes$ is associative with respect to $\cdot$, ordinary multiplication of real numbers.)

b. $1 \otimes s = s$, for all $s \in \mathbf{R}^+ \setminus \{0\}$. (1 is a $\otimes$-identity.)

c. $r \otimes (s \oplus s') = (r \otimes s) \oplus (r \otimes s')$, for all s, s' in $\mathbf{R}^+ \setminus \{0\}$, and all $r \in \mathbf{R}$. ($\otimes$ distributes over $\oplus$ on the left.)

d. $1 \oplus s = s$, for all $s \in \mathbf{R}^+ \setminus \{0\}$. (1 is a $\oplus$-identity.)

e. $0 \otimes s = 1$, for all $s \in \mathbf{R}^+ \setminus \{0\}$.

5.* Let $F, +, \cdot$ be any given field.

a. Suppose that e_1 and e_2 are both $+$-identities in F. Prove that $e_1 = e_2$. (*Hint:* Evaluate $e_1 + e_2$).

b. Suppose that f_1 and f_2 are both $\cdot$-identities in F. Prove that $f_1 = f_2$. (*Hint:* Evaluate $f_1 \cdot f_2$).

Thus, in a field, there is precisely one $+$-identity and one $\cdot$-identity. From now on, we call the $+$-identity 0 and the $\cdot$-identity 1. Again, we emphasize that these symbols are chosen only because the objects that they represent *bear a close resemblance* to the ordinary real numbers 0 and 1; unless the contrary is stated or is implied by the context, however, these symbols do *not* denote the numbers 0 and 1, but only the $+$-identity and $\cdot$-identity in the particular field that we are considering.

c. Let x be a given member of F, and let y and y' be $+$-inverses of F. Prove that $y = y'$. (*Hint:* Use the associativity of $+$ with respect to the sum of y, x, and y'.) Thus, x has a single $+$-inverse. We shall, henceforth, call the $+$-inverse of an element x of a field $-x$, *the negative of* x. This notation and terminology is again to be viewed in the spirit described above: The word "negative" is not to be taken as literally referring to negative numbers.

d. Let x be a nonzero member of F,and let y and y' be $\cdot$-inverse of F. Prove that $y = y'$.

Thus, x has a single $\cdot$-inverse, which, henceforth we denote by x^{-1} and refer to as *x-inverse*.

e. Prove that $(-1) \cdot x = -x$. [*Hint:* Compute $x + (-1)x$ and use **c.**]

f. Prove that $0 \cdot x = 0$, for all $x \in F$. (*Hint:* What is $0 \cdot x + 0 \cdot x$?)

g. Use **f.** to show that 0 cannot have a $\cdot$-inverse.

h. Let e and f be any given members of F. Prove that the equation $x + e = f$ has a unique solution in F. (That is, prove that there is one and only one member, say d, of F satisfying $d + e = f$.)

i. Let e and f be any given members of F, where $e \neq 0$. Prove that the equation $x \cdot e = f$ has a unique solution in F.

j. For any $x \in F$, prove that $-(-x) = x$. For any $x \in F$, $x \neq 0$, prove that $(x^{-1})^{-1} = x$.

6. Let F be any set consisting of at least two members. Let $+$ and $\cdot$ be associative, commutative operations on F, $\cdot$ distributing over $+$ both on the left and on the right. Moreover, suppose that there is an element of F, which we shall denote by "0", such that **5.i** above is true. Finally, suppose that, in addition, **5.h** is true. Prove that $F, +, \cdot$ is a field.

7. Let "$+$" denote the "addition" of ordered pairs of real numbers, as defined in Chapter 1, and let "$\cdot$" denote real multiplication of ordered pairs of real numbers.

a. Prove that $\boldsymbol{+}$ is associative and commutative, that $\cdot$ is associative with respect to ordinary multiplication of real numbers, and that $\cdot$ distributes over $\boldsymbol{+}$ on the left.

b. Prove that for any ordered pair $(r, s) \in \mathbf{R}^2$, and for any real numbers x, y

$$(x+y)\cdot(r, s) = x\cdot(r, s) \boldsymbol{+} y\cdot(r, s)$$

(This is a kind of distributive law: were the operations $\boldsymbol{+}$ and $+$ the same, we would say that $\cdot$ distributes over $\boldsymbol{+}$ on the right.)

c. Prove that there is precisely one $\boldsymbol{+}$-identity in $\mathbf{R}^2$. What is it?

d. Prove that there is precisely one $\cdot$-identity in $\mathbf{R}$. What is it?

e. Let (r, s) be any given ordered pair. Show that (r, s) has precisely one $\boldsymbol{+}$-inverse. What is it?

f. Let (a, b) and (c, d) be fixed members of $\mathbf{R}^2$. Prove that the equation $(x, y) \boldsymbol{+} (a, b) = (c, d)$ has precisely one solution. What is it?

g. Let (a, b) be a fixed member of $\mathbf{R}^2$ and let r be a fixed, nonzero real number. Prove that the equation $r\cdot(x, y) = (a, b)$ has a unique solution. What is it?

8. Verify that $\mathbf{C}, +, \cdot$ and $\mathbf{Q}, +, \cdot$ are fields.

9.* Let F be the set $\{0, 1\}$. Define binary operations $+$ and $\cdot$ on F by means of the following "addition" and "multiplication" tables.

$+$	0	1
0	0	1
1	1	0

$\cdot$	0	1
0	0	0
1	0	1

Verify that $F, +, \cdot$ is a field. This field is often denoted by "$\mathbf{Z}_2$."

10. Let p be any odd, prime, natural number (i.e., the only natural numbers dividing p are p and 1). Let $\mathbf{Z}$ be the set of integers, and let $+$ and $\cdot$ be the operations of ordinary addition and multiplication of integers. Let $\equiv_p$ be the equivalence relation of congruence mod p, as defined in 2.1.7, and let $\mathbf{Z}_p$ denote the set of $\equiv_p$ equivalence classes. Given any $n \in \mathbf{Z}$, let $[n]$ be the $\equiv_p$ equivalence class in which it is contained.

a. Show that if $[n] = [n']$ and $[m] = [m']$, then $[n+m] = [n'+m']$ and $[nm] = [n'm']$.

Define operations $\oplus$ and $\otimes$ on $\mathbf{Z}_p$ as follows:

$$[n] \oplus [m] = [n+m], \qquad [n] \otimes [m] = [nm]$$

Part **a.** shows that if we had chosen different representatives n' of $[n]$ and m' of $[m]$, then the resulting classes $[n'+m']$ and $[n'm']$ would still be the same, so that $[n] \oplus [m]$ and $[n] \otimes [m]$ are unambiguously defined.

b. Show that $\mathbf{Z}_p, \oplus, \otimes$ is a field.

c. Show that $\mathbf{Z}_p$ contains precisely p members.

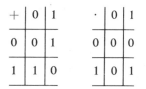

11. **a.** Let $m: A \times A \to A$ be any associative operation. Let a_1, a_2, a_3, a_4 be any members of A. Prove that

$$(a_1 m a_2)m(a_3 m a_4) = ((a_1 m a_2)m a_3)m a_4 = a_1 m(a_2 m(a_3 m a_4)) =$$
$$a_1 m((a_2 m a_3)m a_4) = (a_1 m(a_2 m a_3))m a_4 .$$

These are all the possible ways to apply m to four elements of A, without changing their order. The associativity of m implies that all these methods have the same result. Thus, we may write $a_1 m a_2 m a_3 m a_4$ without any fear of ambiguity.

b. Let A and m be as above. Let P_n, $n \geqq 3$ be the proposition: Select any n members of A in some fixed order and consider all possible ways of applying m to them, keeping the order fixed; the resulting member of A is always the same. Prove this by the inductive method.

This result is known as the *generalized associative law*. That it holds allows us, for any $n \in \mathbf{N}$ and any $a_1, \ldots, a_n$ in A, to write, with unambiguous meaning, the member of A as $a_1 m a_2 m \cdots a_{n-1} m a_n$. If $a_1 = a_2 = \cdots = a_n$ we may write $a_1 m a_2 \cdots m a_n = a_1 m a_1 \cdots m a_1 = a_1{}^n$, whenever it is understood that the operation in question is m.

c. Let $k: A \times A \to A$ be any associative and commutative operation. Let $n \in \mathbf{N}$ be any natural number, and let $a_1, a_2, \ldots, a_n$ be any elements of A. Prove that no matter how we apply k to the elements $a_1, a_2, \ldots, a_n$—including possibly changing their order—the resulting member of A will be the same. Or, in other words, suppose that the elements are rearranged in some way: $a_{i_1}, a_{i_2}, \ldots, a_{i_n}$, where $i_1, i_2, \ldots, i_n$ is some rearrangement of the ordered sequence of natural numbers $1, 2, \ldots, n$. Show that $a_{i_1} k a_{i_2} k \cdots k a_{i_n} = a_1 k a_2 \cdots k a_n$.**

This result is known as the *generalized commutative law*.

The results of **b.** and **c.** are that any associative, commutative operation satisfies the generalized associative and commutative laws. The generalized associative law allows us to operate on arbitrarily long strings of elements without worrying about parentheses. Or, in calculations, it allows us to move parentheses around with almost complete abandon—a very useful license, as the reader who has succeeded in proving Exercise **5.c** will agree. The generalized commutative law, in addition, permits us to forget about the order of the elements. Or, in calculations, it permits us to change the order, sometimes with very happy results. (For example, we are able to prove, in a field $F, +, \cdot$, that a sum $x + y + (-x) + (-y) = 0$ only by applying the commutative and associative laws several times.) Without such generalized laws, the operations of $F, +, \cdot$, although they resemble ordinary addition and multiplication when it is only a question of two or three elements at a time, would look quite different from the ordinary operations when more than three elements are involved. Fortunately, this state of affairs is not possible.

** Notice that, by the generalized associative law, we may write these terms without parentheses to indicate how to pair off the a_i: the result will be the same in every case.

12. Let A be any nonempty set, and consider A^A, the set of all functions from A to A. We define an operation $\circ$ on A^A to be ordinary composition of functions: that is, $\circ$ takes (f, g) to $f \circ g$. Is the operation $\circ$ associative? Commutative? Does A^A have a $\circ$-identity? More than one? Does every $f \in A^A$ have a $\circ$-inverse? A right (left) $\circ$-inverse? Which f have $\circ$-inverses? Right $\circ$-inverses? Left $\circ$-inverses? Substantiate your answers. (See Proposition 2.7.)

Definition 3.4

Let $F, +, \cdot$ *be a given field. A vector space over* $F, +, \cdot$ *consists of* (1) *a nonempty set* V, (2) *an associative, commutative operation on* V, *which we denote by* $+$, *and* (3) *an operation of* F *on* V, *which we denote by* $\cdot$. *These operations must satisfy certain additional conditions listed below.*

Elements of V are called *vectors* and will be denoted by bold-face letters $\mathbf{v}, \mathbf{w}, \mathbf{x}, \ldots$. The *sum* of two vectors $\mathbf{v}$ and $\mathbf{w}$ is $\mathbf{v} + \mathbf{w}$. Members of F are called *scalars* and will be denoted by ordinary letters $a, b, c, d, \ldots$. A *scalar multiple* a of a vector $\mathbf{v}$ is $a \cdot \mathbf{v}$.

The operations $+$ and $\cdot$ are an intrinsic part of the definition; if they change, then the vector space changes, even though the set V remains the same. Sometimes, if we want to emphasize this point, we refer to the vector space as $V, +, \cdot$. Whenever we deliberately ignore the vector-spacc structure and consider only the set V, we shall refer to V as the *underlying set* of the vector space. Usually, when referring to the vector space, we speak only of "V."

Additional Conditions on $+$ *and* $\cdot$

(a) V has a $+$-identity. (b) Every $\mathbf{v} \in V$ has a $+$-inverse. (c) The field element $1 \in F$ is a $\cdot$-identity. (d) $\cdot$ is associative with respect to the field multiplication $\cdots$ that is, for all $a, b \in F$ and $\mathbf{v} \in V$, $(a \cdot b) \cdot \mathbf{v} = a \cdot (b \cdot \mathbf{v})$. (e) $\cdot$ distributes over $+$ on the left $\cdots$ that is, for all $a \in F$, and $u, v \in V$, $a \cdot (\mathbf{u} + \mathbf{v}) = (a \cdot \mathbf{u}) + (a \cdot \mathbf{v})$. (f) For all $a, b \in F$ and all $\mathbf{v} \in V$, $(a + b) \cdot \mathbf{v} = (a \cdot \mathbf{v}) + (b \cdot \mathbf{v})$.

We shall say that two vector spaces $V, +, \cdot$ and $V', +', \cdot'$ are *equal*, if and only if $V = V'$, $+ = +'$ (these are both functions, so that the equation makes sense), and $\cdot = \cdot'$. This, of course, amounts to saying that two vector spaces are equal, if and only if their underlying sets are equal and their operations are identical.

Given that the symbols "$+$" and "$\cdot$" can be modified in only a very limited number of ways and still be recognizable, we shall, when considering more than one vector space use these same symbols to denote the operations of the different spaces. The underlying sets will, of course, have different symbols. This notational convention, however, should not be construed to imply anything special about the different pairs of vector-space operations so denoted. If they are, indeed, equal, and if we are interested in this fact, we shall say so explicitly.

Notice that Condition (f) above is a kind of right distributive law; indeed, if $+$ and $\boldsymbol{+}$ were the same, we could express (f) by saying that $\cdot$ distributes over $+$ on the right. Notice also that, in Condition (d) if $\boldsymbol{\cdot}$ and $\cdot$ were the same, and if $F = V$, we could express the equation $(a \cdot b)\boldsymbol{\cdot}\mathbf{v} = a\boldsymbol{\cdot}(b\boldsymbol{\cdot}\mathbf{v})$ by saying that $\boldsymbol{\cdot}$ is associative.

1.2 Some Examples of Vector Spaces

(a) The reader should turn back to Chapter 1 and consider Examples (a)–(f): $\mathbf{R}$, ℓ, $\mathbf{R}^2$, $\mathbf{R}^A$, $\mathscr{C}[a, b]$, $\mathscr{D}[a, b]$, together with the operations defined there. These are all vector spaces over the field $\mathbf{R}$.

We leave a verification of this assertion to the reader.

(b) Let F, $+$, $\cdot$ be any field. The operation $+$ is an operation on F; it is associative and commutative. The operation $\cdot$ is an operation of F on F.

Moreover: (i) F has a $+$-identity. (ii) Every member of F has a $+$-inverse. (iii) The field element $1 \in F$ is a $\cdot$-identity. (iv) $\cdot$ is associative. (v) $\cdot$ distributes over $+$ on the left. (vi) $\cdot$ distributes over $+$ on the right.

All of these assertions follow immediately from the definition of a field. The reader, upon comparing this list with the list of additional conditions in Definition 3.4, will see that F, $+$, $\cdot$ *is a vector space over itself.*

(c) Consider Exercises 3.1.**4**. There we defined an operation $\oplus$ on $\mathbf{R}^+ \setminus \{0\}$ and on operation $\otimes$ of $\mathbf{R}$ on $\mathbf{R}^+ \setminus \{0\}$. In the preceding exercise, parts **a.** and **c.**, the reader was asked to prove or disprove the assertions that $\oplus$ was commutative and associative. He should have *proved* them, because they are true. In **4.** he was asked to prove that $\otimes$ is associative with respect to real multiplication, that 1 is a $\otimes$-identity, that $\otimes$ distributes over $\oplus$ on the left, and that $\mathbf{R}^+ \setminus \{0\}$ has a $\oplus$-identity. Thus, $\oplus$ and $\otimes$ have already been shown to satisfy most of the conditions of Definition 3.4.

It remains to verify that every $r \in \mathbf{R}^+ \setminus \{0\}$ has a $\oplus$-inverse and that, for any x and y in $\mathbf{R}$, and any $r \in \mathbf{R}^+ \setminus \{0\}$, $(x + y) \otimes r = (x \otimes r) \oplus (y \otimes r)$.

Now, given any $r \in \mathbf{R}^+ \setminus \{0\}$, since $r \neq 0$, we may form its reciprocal $1/r$. Then, $r \oplus 1/r = r \cdot 1/r = 1$. Recall that 1 is a $\oplus$-identity. Therefore, $1/r$ is a $\oplus$-inverse of r.

To verify the second assertion, let x, y, and r be as stated above. Then $(x + y) \otimes r = r^{x+y} = (r^x)(r^y) = (x \otimes r) \oplus (y \otimes r)$, as desired.

Therefore, $\mathbf{R}^+ \setminus \{0\}$, $\oplus$, $\otimes$ is a vector space over $\mathbf{R}$, $+$, $\cdot$.

(d) Let $\mathscr{P}$ denote the set of all polynomials in one variable, x, with real coefficients. (Actually, we could consider the coefficients to lie in any field F, $+$, $\cdot$; we do so in a later chapter). Define the *sum* of two such polynomials as the polynomial whose ith coefficient (i.e., coefficient of x^i) is the sum of the ith coefficients of the original two. Given a real number r and a polynomial $P(x)$, define the product $r \cdot P(x)$ to be the polynomial whose ith coefficient equals r times the ith coefficient of $P(x)$.

We leave to the reader the task of verifying that $\mathscr{P}$, together with these operations, is a vector space over $\mathbf{R}$.

(e) Let $\mathcal{S}$ be the set of all "infinite polynomials" in one variable, x with real coefficients. For those readers who are familiar with infinite series, you will recognize $\mathcal{S}$ to be the set of all possible *formal power series*, in the variable x, with real coefficients. (We are *not* interested in their convergence or divergence.) For those readers not familiar with infinite series, a typical member of $\mathcal{S}$ is merely an expression $a_0 + a_1x + a_2x^2 + a_3x^3 + \cdots$, which we write more conveniently as

$$\sum_{n=0}^{\infty} a_n x^n$$

The variable x is not to be regarded as a real number but rather as an indeterminate, abstract entity, a kind of place-holder.

We define operations $+$ and $\cdot$ as follows:

$$\left(\sum_{n=0}^{\infty} a_n x^n\right) + \left(\sum_{n=0}^{\infty} b_n x^n\right) = \sum_{n=0}^{\infty} (a_n + b_n)x^n$$

$$r \cdot \left(\sum_{n=0}^{\infty} a_n x^n\right) = \sum_{n=0}^{\infty} (r \cdot a_n)x^n.$$

Notice that, since x is not a number, it does not make sense to write $0x = 0$, or $0x^2 = 0$, and so on. Thus, suppose that all $a_n = 0$, $n = 0, 1, 2, 3, \ldots$. Then, it is meaningless to write

$$\sum_{n=0}^{\infty} a_n x^n = 0.$$

However, this series *plays the role of* 0. That is, it is a $+$-identity in $\mathcal{S}$.

Show that $\mathcal{S}$, $+$, $\cdot$ is a vector space over **R**.

(f) The set **C** of all complex numbers, together with the usual operations of addition and multiplication of complex numbers, is, as has already been asserted, a field. Thus, according to Example (b), above, **C** *is a vector space over itself.*

Now, every real number is also a complex number (i.e., every real number $r = r + 0 \cdot i$), or, $\mathbf{R} \subset \mathbf{C}$. Thus, ordinary multiplication of complex numbers includes multiplication of complex numbers by real numbers.

Let us then consider the set **C** together with the following operations: The usual operation on **C** of addition, and the operation of **R** on **C**, consisting of real multiplication of complex numbers.

The reader should verify *that* **C**, *together with these new operations, is a vector space over* **R**! *It is by no means to be considered the same as the example above.* These are two distinct vector spaces having the same underlying set, but they are *over different fields.* We shall be able later to describe more precisely how these two examples differ.** One clue as to how they differ can be obtained from the following observation:

** Aside from the obvious difference of their being over different fields.

If we regard **C** as a vector space over itself, then it is easy to see that *every* vector in **C** can be obtained from $1 \in \mathbf{C}$ by multiplication with some member of $F(=\mathbf{C})$. However, if we regard **C** as a vector space over **R**, then it is easy to see that there are vectors in **C** not obtainable from 1 by multiplying by some member of $F(=\mathbf{R}$, in this case).

(g) An example similar to the one above is afforded by the case of the field of rational numbers **Q**. Clearly, $\mathbf{Q} \subset \mathbf{R}$ so that there is a well-defined notion of multiplying a real number by a rational number. This operation, together with ordinary addition of real numbers, makes **R** into a vector space over **Q**.

Again, this example is not to be confused with the standard example of **R** as a vector space over itself.

In general, when we talk about a field F, we shall consider it either as a field or as *a vector space over itself*. Thus, **Q**, **R**, **C** are all to be considered in this way—*unless otherwise specified*! Indeed, we shall have occasion to return to the above examples.

EXERCISES / 3.2

1. Let $F: \mathbf{R} \to \mathbf{R}^+ - \{0\}$ be defined as follows: For any $x \in \mathbf{R}$, $f(x) = e^x$.
  a. Show that f is 1–1 and onto.
  b. Prove that, for all r, x and y in $\mathbf{R}$ $f(x+y) = f(x) \oplus f(y)$, and $f(rx) = r \otimes f(x)$, where $\oplus$ and $\otimes$ are the operations defined in Exercises 3.1.4.

2. Let n be any natural number, and let $\mathscr{P}^n$ be the set of all polynomials in one variable x, with real coefficients, such that their degree is $\leqq n$. Define the sum of two such polynomials and real multiples of such polynomials in the usual way: That is, in the way described in Example (d) above; denote the sum operation by "$+$" and the real multiplication operation by "$\cdot$".
  Prove that $\mathscr{P}^n, +, \cdot$ is a vector space over **R**.

3.* Let $V, +, \cdot$ be a vector space over a field $F, +, \cdot$.
  a. Suppose that $\mathbf{v}_1$ and $\mathbf{v}_2$ are $+$-identities for V. Prove that $\mathbf{v}_1 = \mathbf{v}_2$.
  This exercise shows that a vector space has precisely one $+$-identity; we shall, henceforth, always denote this element by $\mathbf{0}$, because it *resembles* the number 0.
  Given two vector spaces $V, +, \cdot$ and $W, +, \cdot$, they both have $+$-identities, which we call "$\mathbf{0}$". But, just as the $+$ operation on V is not necessarily the same as the $+$ operation on W, the $\mathbf{0}$ in V is to be considered, in general, distinct from the $\mathbf{0}$ in W.
  b. Suppose that $\mathbf{v}$ is a given vector of V and that $\mathbf{v}_1$ and $\mathbf{v}_2$ are $+$-inverses of $\mathbf{v}$. Prove that $\mathbf{v}_1 = \mathbf{v}_2$.
  Thus, every $\mathbf{v} \in V$ has a *unique* $+$-inverse. We denote the $+$-inverse of $\mathbf{v}$ by $-\mathbf{v}$. We abbreviate the sum $\mathbf{u} + (-\mathbf{v})$ to $\mathbf{u} - \mathbf{v}$ and refer to this vector as the difference between $\mathbf{u}$ and $\mathbf{v}$. All of this convenient notation and terminology is motivated by

the *analogy* with real numbers. [For example, instead of $2+(-3)$, we write $2-3$, and so on.]

By the way, these same conventions apply to the field F. Thus, "$a+(-b)$" becomes $a-b$, and "$a \cdot b^{-1}$" becomes "a/b."

c. Prove that, for every $\mathbf{v} \in V$, $-(-\mathbf{v})=\mathbf{v}$.

d. Let $\mathbf{u}$ and $\mathbf{v}$ be any given vectors in V. Consider the equation $\mathbf{u}+\mathbf{x}=\mathbf{v}$.

i. Prove that, if $\mathbf{x}_1$ and $\mathbf{x}_2$ are solutions to this equation, then $\mathbf{x}_1=\mathbf{x}_2$. State all your steps and reasons carefully.

ii. Prove that $\mathbf{v}-\mathbf{u}$ is a solution to the equation.

Thus, the above equation has precisely one solution: Namely $\mathbf{v}-\mathbf{u}$.

e. Let $\mathbf{w}$ be any vector in V. Prove that $0 \cdot \mathbf{w}+0 \cdot \mathbf{w}=0 \cdot \mathbf{w}$. [*Hint:* Use Condition (f) of Definition 3.4, together with the fact that 0 is the +-identity for F.]

Notice, however, that since $\mathbf{0}$ is the +-identity for V, $0 \cdot \mathbf{w}+\mathbf{0}=0 \cdot \mathbf{w}$.

Now, in Exercise **d**, above, let $\mathbf{u}=0 \cdot \mathbf{w}$ and let $\mathbf{v}=0 \cdot \mathbf{w}$. Then, according to the result of **d**, the equation $0 \cdot \mathbf{w}+\mathbf{x}=0 \cdot \mathbf{w}$ has *precisely one* solution.

But the reader has just shown that $0 \cdot \mathbf{w}$ is a solution to this equation, and, of course, $\mathbf{0}$ is also a solution.

The inescapable conclusion, then, is that, for every $\mathbf{w} \in V$, $0 \cdot \mathbf{w}=\mathbf{0}$.

f. Prove that $(-1) \cdot \mathbf{v}=-\mathbf{v}$, for every $\mathbf{v} \in V$, where -1 is the +-inverse of the ·-identity, of F. [*Hint:* Use Conditions (c) and (f) of Definition 3.4, together with Exercise **e** above, to evaluate $\mathbf{v}+(-1) \cdot \mathbf{v}$. Then, apply Exercise **b**, above.]

g. Let $\mathbf{v}$ be any vector in V, and let a be any nonzero member of F. Consider the equation $a\mathbf{x}=\mathbf{v}$.

i. Suppose that $\mathbf{x}_1$ and $\mathbf{x}_2$ are solutions to this equation. Prove that $\mathbf{x}_1=\mathbf{x}_2$.

ii. Show that $a^{-1} \cdot \mathbf{v}$ is a solution to the equation.

Thus, the above equation has precisely one solution, namely, $a^{-1} \cdot \mathbf{v}$.

h. Use the result of Exercise **e**, above, to prove that $a \cdot \mathbf{0}=\mathbf{0}$, for any $a \in F$.

i. Let a be any nonzero member of F, and let $\mathbf{v}$ be any nonzero member of V. Prove that $a \cdot \mathbf{v} \neq \mathbf{0}$.

The above Exercises **a–i** are useful because they show that many of the standard rules that we apply in ordinary numerical or algebraic calculations also apply to the case of abstract vector spaces. That is, the vector-space operations do, indeed, *resemble* the operations of ordinary addition and multiplication. Moreover, consider the vector space over $\mathbf{R}$, $\mathbf{R}^2$. Recall that the members of $\mathbf{R}^2$ can be represented geometrically as points in the Cartesian plane. Alternatively, we can regard members of $\mathbf{R}^2$ as line segments or "arrows" issuing forth from the origin and ending at the point in question:

Now, it is intuitively clear that multiplication of such a vector by a negative number simply reverses the direction of the arrow (and, possibly the magnitude) of the vector. (Multiplication of a vector by -1 certainly results in the negative of the vector, that is, in its +-inverse.) Multiplication by 0, of course, shrinks the arrow to the origin. (Multiplication of a nonzero vector by a nonzero real number results, of course, in a nonzero vector.)

Exercises **f**, **e**, **c**, then, show that these "concrete facts" are special cases of very general facts that apply to every vector space.

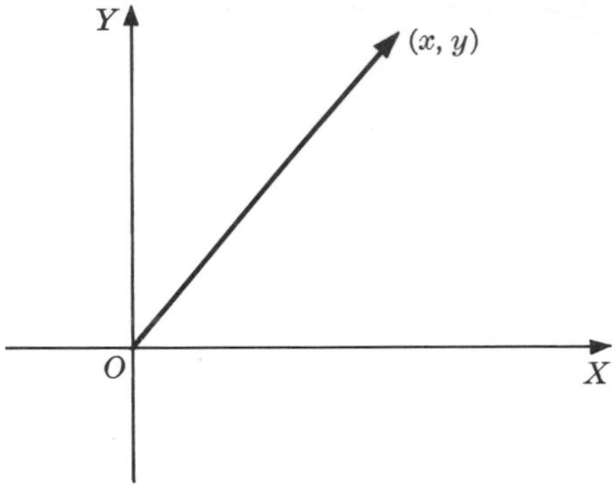

FIGURE 13

Thus, the definition of vector space presented here seems to have met its preliminary objective. It is abstract and general enough to cover all the cases that interest us. Yet it is sufficiently restrictive to insure that *every* abstract vector space bears a reasonable resemblance to the concrete examples listed in Chapter 1.**

Our work later in this chapter and in Chapter 4 will show even more clearly just how close this resemblance is.

2 / PRODUCTS AND POWERS OF VECTOR SPACES

The following constructions will have useful applications throughout this book.

Construction 1

Product of Vector Spaces

Let n be any natural number greater than 1, *and let* $V_1, V_2, \ldots, V_n$ *be n (not necessarily distinct) vector spaces over a given field* $F, +, \cdot$. *Form the product of the underlying sets* $V_1, V_2, \ldots, V_n$. *We get* $V_1 \times V_2 \cdots \times V_n$. *We shall define a binary operation* $+$ *on this product, and an operation* $\cdot$ *of F on the product. (We remind the reader that although we use the symbol "+" repeatedly, it stands for possibly distinct operations on possibly distinct sets. A similar comment applies to "·".) The set* $V_1 \times V_2 \times \cdots \times V_n$, *together with the operations* $+$ *and* $\cdot$, *will be a vector space over* $F, +, \cdot$. We call it the product of the vector spaces $V_1, +, \cdot, V_2, +, \cdot, \ldots, V_n, +, \cdot$.‡

** This second condition is even more important than the first. It is no trick at all to generalize the various cases that interest us: every one of them (cf. Chapter 1) is, for example, a *set with some operations*. Such an abstract object, however, is much too general: it is almost useless.

‡ This is sometimes called the exterior direct sum of $V_1, V_2, \ldots, V_n$.

Definition of +

For any ordered n-tuples $(\mathbf{v}_1, \mathbf{v}_2, \ldots, \mathbf{v}_n)$ *and* $(\mathbf{w}_1, \mathbf{w}_2, \ldots, \mathbf{w}_n)$ *in* $V_1 \times V_2 \times \cdots \times V_n$ *let*

$$(\mathbf{v}_1, \mathbf{v}_2, \ldots, \mathbf{v}_n) + (\mathbf{w}_1, \mathbf{w}_2, \ldots, \mathbf{w}_n) = (\mathbf{v}_1 + \mathbf{w}_1, \mathbf{v}_2 + \mathbf{w}_2, \ldots, \mathbf{v}_n + \mathbf{w}_n)$$

(The "+" on the left is being defined by the equation. The "+"'s on the right are given.)

Definition of ·

For any $a \in F$ *and any* $(\mathbf{v}_1, \mathbf{v}_2, \ldots, \mathbf{v}_n) \in V_1 \times V_2 \times \cdots \times V_n$, *let*

$$a \cdot (\mathbf{v}_1, \mathbf{v}_2, \ldots, \mathbf{v}_n) = (a \cdot \mathbf{v}_1, a \cdot \mathbf{v}_2, \ldots, a \cdot \mathbf{v}_n)$$

(The "·" on the left is being defined by the equation. The "·"'s on the right are given.)

We shall leave to the reader a thoroughgoing proof that the result is a vector space over F. That is, he must verify that the operations + and · defined above satisfy *all* the conditions of Definitions 3.4. We shall supply only one sample verification and some remarks.

Verification That + is Commutative

Choose any n-tuples $(\mathbf{v}_1, \mathbf{v}_2, \ldots, \mathbf{v}_n)$ *and* $(\mathbf{w}_1, \mathbf{w}_2, \ldots, \mathbf{w}_n)$ *in* $V_1 \times V_2 \times \cdots \times V_n$. *Then,*

$$\begin{aligned}(\mathbf{v}_1, \mathbf{v}_2, \ldots, \mathbf{v}_n) + (\mathbf{w}_1, \mathbf{w}_2, \ldots, \mathbf{w}_n) &= (\mathbf{v}_1 + \mathbf{w}_1, \mathbf{v}_2 + \mathbf{w}_2, \ldots, \mathbf{v}_n + \mathbf{w}_n)\\ &= (\mathbf{w}_1 + \mathbf{v}_1, \mathbf{w}_2 + \mathbf{v}_2, \ldots, \mathbf{w}_n + \mathbf{v}_n)\\ &= (\mathbf{w}_1, \mathbf{w}_2, \ldots, \mathbf{w}_n) + (\mathbf{v}_1, \mathbf{v}_2, \ldots, \mathbf{v}_n).\end{aligned}$$

The reader should be able to supply precise reasons justifying each of the equalities written above. Particularly, he should be able to justify the passage from the first equality to the second.

Remarks: 1. The reader will easily verify that the n-tuple $(\mathbf{0}, \mathbf{0}, \ldots, \mathbf{0})$ is a +-identity in $V_1 \times V_2 \times \cdots \times V_n$, where the ith "$\mathbf{0}$" in the n-tuple is the +-identity of V_i, $i = 1, 2, \ldots, n$. Thus, since $V_1 \times V_2 \times \ldots \times V_n$, +, · will turn out to be a vector space, we may anticipate and call $(\mathbf{0}, \mathbf{0}, \ldots, \mathbf{0})$ *the* +-identity of $V_1 \times V_2 \times \cdots \times V_n$ (in view of Exercises 3.2.3.**a**). We shall dispense with the usual "$\mathbf{0}$" symbol here and refer to this +-identity always as "$(\mathbf{0}, \mathbf{0}, \ldots, \mathbf{0})$."

2. The reader will verify that for any $(\mathbf{v}_1, \mathbf{v}_2, \ldots, \mathbf{v}_n) \in V_1 \times V_2 \times \cdots \times V_n$, $(-\mathbf{v}_1, -\mathbf{v}_2, \ldots, -\mathbf{v}_n)$ is a +-inverse. That is, anticipating that $V_1 \times V_2 \times \cdots \times V_n$ is a vector space, so that $(\mathbf{v}_1, \mathbf{v}_2, \ldots, \mathbf{v}_n)$ has only one +-inverse, denoted by $-(\mathbf{v}_1, \mathbf{v}_2, \ldots, \mathbf{v}_n)$, we have $-(\mathbf{v}_1, \mathbf{v}_2, \ldots, \mathbf{v}_n) = (-\mathbf{v}_1, -\mathbf{v}_2, \ldots, -\mathbf{v}_n)$. Here, of course, $-\mathbf{v}_i$ is the +-inverse of $\mathbf{v}_i$ in V_i.

Example 1

In the above construction, suppose that we let each $V_i = F$. This is legitimate since, as we have shown, F is a vector space over itself. Then, the set $V_1 \times V_2 \times \cdots \times V_n$ is what we have called F^n, the set of ordered n-tuples of members of F. The set F^n, together with the operations $+$ and $\cdot$ defined above, is, thus, a vector space over F.

In case $F = \mathbf{R}$, we have the familiar set $\mathbf{R}^n$, together with the operations of adding and real multiplying n-tuples of real numbers as defined in Chapter 1. This set, then, together with the stated operations, is, indeed, a vector space over $\mathbf{R}$.

It will be desirable to give the symbol "F^n" a meaning when $n = 1$ and $n = 0$. "F^1" should denote the one-fold $\cdot$ product of F with itself. If this means anything, it certainly means F. Thus, we let $F^1 = F$. Moreover, without explanation yet we let $F^0 = \{0\}$, where 0 is the zero element of F (and the superscript "0" stands for the natural number zero).

The reader should understand this example thoroughly. For it is not so special as it might seem. Indeed, we show in Chapter 4, that every one of a large class of vector spaces over F is an exact duplicate (whatever that means—wait and see) of some F^n, $n = 0, 1, 2, \ldots$.

Construction 2

Powers of a Vector Space

Let $V, +, \cdot$ be any vector space over $F, +, \cdot$, and let S be any nonempty set. Consider the set V^S of all functions from S to V. *For various reasons it is suggestive to call V^S the Sth power of V. We shall define a binary operation $+$ on V^S and an operation $\cdot$ of F on V^S, so that $V^S, +, \cdot$ is a vector space over F. We define the operations below and then give a sample verification that $+$ satisfies one of the conditions of Definition* 3.4. *We also make remarks similar to those in the previous construction. We expect the reader to complete the verification that $V^S, +, \cdot$ is a vector space over F.*

Definition of +

Let f and g be any members of V^S. That is, they are functions from S to V. Their sum $f + g$ is defined to be the function from S to V satisfying

$$(f + g)(s) = f(s) + g(s),$$

for every $s \in S$. (The "$+$" on the left is being defined by the equation, the "$+$" on the right is the given operation on V.)

Definition of ·

Let f be any member of V^S, and let a be any member of F. Then $a \cdot f$ is defined by the equation

$$(a \cdot f)(s) = a \cdot [f(s)]$$

which is required to hold for every $s \in S$. (The "$\cdot$" on the left is being defined by the equation. The "$\cdot$" on the right is the given operation of F on V.)

Verification that + is associative

Choose any $f, g, h \in V^S$, *and compare the values of* $f + (g + h)$ *and* $(f + g) + h$ *at any* $s \in S$.

$$[f + (g + h)](s) = f(s) + (g + h)(s)$$

$$= f(s) + [g(s) + h(s)], \qquad \text{by definition of } + \textit{ on } V^S,$$

and

$$[(f + g) + h](s) = (f + g)(s) + h(s)$$

$$= [f(s) + g(s)] + h(s), \qquad \textit{by definition of } + \textit{ on } V^S$$

Then, use the fact that + *on* V *is associative to conclude that* $[f(s) + g(s)] + h(s) = f(s) + [g(s) + h(s)]$. Therefore, for every $s \in S$,

$$[f + (g + h)](s) = [(f + g) + h](s),$$

so that the function $f + (g + h)$ *equals the function* $(f + g) + h$.

Remarks: 1. The constantly **0** function (that is, the function that sends every $s \in S$ to $\mathbf{0} \in V$), the reader will easily verify, is a +-identity in V^S. Conforming to earlier notation, it will be denoted by "$\overline{\mathbf{0}}$."

2. Let $f \in V^S$ be any function. Then, the function that sends each $s \in S$ to $-f(s) \in V$, is, as the reader can verify, a +-inverse of f. Thus, since V^S will be a vector space, this function is *the* +-inverse of f and will be denoted by "$-f$." Thus, we have $(-f)(s) = -f(s)$, for all $s \in S$ (the "$-$" on the left being newly defined, the "$-$" on the right being given with V).

Example 2

In the above construction, suppose that we let $V = F$. Then, the set F^S is just the set of all possible functions from S to F. This set, together with the operations + and · defined above, is a vector space over F. When $S = \{1, 2 \cdots n\}$, it was shown (Exercise 2.12.7) that the set F^S is in 1-1 correspondence with F^n. Indeed, it can be shown—and we will show in Chapter 4—that the correspondence respects the two pairs of vector space operations. This means, as we shall see, that $F^{\{1, \ldots, n\}}$ and F^n are duplicates of one another as abstract vector spaces.

In case $F = \mathbf{R}$, we have the set $\mathbf{R}^S$, described in Chapter 1, together with the vector-space operations defined there. Thus, $\mathbf{R}^S$ is, indeed, a vector space over $\mathbf{R}$.

It will be convenient to give the symbol "V^S" a meaning in case $S = \varnothing$. For reasons that become clear later, we let $V^\varnothing = \{\mathbf{0}\}$, where $\mathbf{0} \in V$ is the +-identity.

The reader should understand this example thoroughly. It is even more general than the previous example (which, we remarked, is quite general). Indeed, we show in Chapter 4 that *every vector space over F is an exact duplicate of* F^S *or of some "subspace" of* F^S *(see Section* 3), for an appropriate choice of the set S. Thus, the most general, abstract vector space over F is, for almost all purposes, already contained in this example.

When $F = \mathbf{R}$, this leads to the not-so-obvious conclusion that every vector space over $\mathbf{R}$ can be regarded as the vector space of some real-valued functions on some appropriate domain.

EXERCISES / 3.3

1. Verify that $V_1 \times V_2 \times \cdots \times V_n, \boldsymbol{+}, \boldsymbol{\cdot}$ is a vector space over $F, +, \cdot$.

2. Verify that $V^S, \boldsymbol{+}, \boldsymbol{\cdot}$ is a vector space over $F, +, \cdot$, when $S \neq \varnothing$.

3. Let $F, +, \cdot$ be any field, and let X be any set consisting of precisely one element x. That is, $X = \{x\}$. Define functions $\sigma: X \times X \to X$ and $\tau: F \times X \to X$ to be the second coordinate projections. That is, $\sigma(x, x) = x$, and $\tau(a, x) = x$, for every $a \in F$.
   Prove that X, σ, τ is a vector space over F.

4. Let $V, \boldsymbol{+}, \boldsymbol{\cdot}$ be any vector space over any field $F, +, \cdot$. Consider the set $\{\mathbf{0}\} \subset V$. The set $\{\mathbf{0}\} \times \{\mathbf{0}\}$ is a subset of $V \times V$, and the set $F \times \{\mathbf{0}\}$ is a subset of $F \times V$. Let σ be the restriction of $\boldsymbol{+}$ to $\{\mathbf{0}\} \times \{\mathbf{0}\}$, and let τ be the restriction of $\cdot$ to $F \times \{\mathbf{0}\}$.
   a. Show that σ is an operation on $\{\mathbf{0}\}$.
   b. Show that τ is an operation of F on $\{\mathbf{0}\}$.
   c. Show that $\{\mathbf{0}\}, \sigma, \tau$ is a vector space over $F, +, \cdot$.
   d. Compare $\{\mathbf{0}\}, \sigma, \tau$ with X, σ, τ of the previous exercise.
   Thus, $\{\mathbf{0}\}$ is a vector space with respect to the (restrictions of) the operations of V. This is at least a partial justification of our notation $V^{\varnothing} = \{\mathbf{0}\}$. For now V^S is a vector space (over F, of course) for *every set S*.

3 / VECTOR SUBSPACES, SUBSPACE SUMS, AND SUBSPACE PRODUCTS

3.1 Definitions and Elementary Properties

Definition 3.5

Let $V, \boldsymbol{+}, \boldsymbol{\cdot}$ be a vector space over a field $F, +, \cdot$, and let U be a nonempty subset *of V.*

We say that U is closed with respect to the operations $\boldsymbol{+}$ and $\boldsymbol{\cdot}$ of V, if and only if for all $\mathbf{u}_1$ and $\mathbf{u}_2$ in U and all a in F,

$$\mathbf{u}_1 + \mathbf{u}_2 \in U$$

$$a \cdot \mathbf{u}_1 \in U.$$

We may also express this property more directly in terms of the functions —i.e. operations— $+ : V \times V \to V$ and $\cdot : F \times V \to V$. Note that $U \times U$ is a nonempty subset of $V \times V$ and $F \times U$ is a nonempty subset of $F \times V$. Consider the restrictions $+ \mid U \times U$ and $\cdot \mid F \times U$. The above, property, then, can be put as follows: *the ranges of* $+ \mid U \times U$ *and* $\cdot \mid F \times U$ *are both subsets of* U. The reader should be sure that he understands why this formulation is equivalent to the preceding one.

According to the second formulation, if U is closed with respect to $+$ and $\cdot$, then we may regard $+ \mid U \times U$ as a function $U \times U \to U$—that is, $+ \mid U \times U$ is an operation on U—and we may regard $\cdot \mid F \times U$ as a function $F \times U \to U$—that is $\cdot \mid F \times U$ is an operation of F on U.**

In Exercises 3.3. **4a**, **b**, the reader showed, essentially, that $\{\mathbf{0}\}$ is closed with respect to the operations $+$ and $\cdot$ of V. Moreover, it is easy to verify that V itself is closed with respect to $+$ and $\cdot$.

Proposition 3.1

Let $V, +, \cdot$ *be a vector space over* $F, +, \cdot$, *and let* U *be a nonempty subset of* V. *If* U *is closed with respect to* $+$ *and* $\cdot$, *then* $U, + \mid U \times U, \cdot \mid F \times U$ *is a vector space over* $F, +, \cdot$.

Proof

We must show that the operations $+ \mid U \times U$ and $\cdot \mid F \times U$ satisfy the conditions of Definition 3.4. Now, conditions (c)–(f) involve equalities which must be satisfied for all $\mathbf{u}_1, \mathbf{u}_2, \ldots$ in U and all $a_1, a_2, \ldots$ in F. But, since the operations of U are just those of V restricted to U, and since the operations of V do satisfy the equalities in question, in conditions (c)–(f), for *all* $\mathbf{v}_1, \mathbf{v}_2, \ldots$ *in* V (hence, certainly, for all $\mathbf{u}_1, \mathbf{u}_2, \ldots$ in U) and all $a_1, a_2, \ldots$ in F, the operations $+ \mid U \times U$ and $\cdot \mid F \times U$ satisfy conditions (c)–(f). A similar argument shows that $+ \mid U \times U$ is associative and commutative.

It remains, then, to show that U has a $+ \mid U \times U$-identity and that every $\mathbf{u} \in U$ has a $+ \mid U \times U$-inverse in U.

Now, suppose that $\mathbf{0}$, the $+$-identity of V, belongs to U. Then, for every $\mathbf{u} \in U$, $\mathbf{u} + \mathbf{0} = \mathbf{u}$, so that $\mathbf{0}$ is a $+ \mid U \times U$ identity. Thus, it suffices to show that $\mathbf{0} \in U$. Since U is nonempty, there is some vector, say $\mathbf{u}$, belonging to U. According to Definition 3.5, $a \cdot \mathbf{u} \in U$, for all $a \in F$. In particular, choose $a = 0$, *the* $+$-identity of F. Then, $0 \cdot \mathbf{u} \in U$. But, according to Exercises 3.2.3.**e**, $0 \cdot \mathbf{u} = \mathbf{0}$, Thus, $\mathbf{0} \in U$, as desired.

To show that every $\mathbf{u} \in U$ has a $+ \mid U \times U$-inverse in U, it suffices to show that it has a $+$-inverse in U (since the operation $+ \mid U \times U$ is the same as $+$ applied only to vectors in U). But, according to Exercises 2.3.3.**f**, $(-1) \cdot \mathbf{u}$ is

** The converse of this statement, of course, also holds. For to say that, for example, $+ \mid U \times U$ is an operation on U means that it is a function from $U \times U$ *to* U, that is, with codomain U, and, hence, with range contained in U. A similar comment applies to $\cdot \mid F \times U$.

a $+$-inverse of $\mathbf{u}$, and according to Definition 3.5, above, $(-1) \cdot \mathbf{u}$ belongs to U. Thus, $+ \mid U \times U$ satisfies condition (b) of Definition 3.4. Q.E.D.

Notice that the above proof shows that if U is nonempty and closed with respect to $+$ and $\cdot$, then $\mathbf{0} \in U$.

Definition 3.6

Let V, $+$ $\cdot$ be vector space over F, $+$, $\cdot$, and let U be a nonempty subset of V, closed with respect to $+$ and $\cdot$. Then, we say that (the vector space over F, $+$, $\cdot$) U, $+ \mid U \times U$, $\cdot \mid F \times U$ is a vector subspace of V, $+$, $\cdot$. More concisely, we say that U, or U, $+$, $\cdot$, is a vector subspace of V, it being understood that the operations of U are those of V restricted to U.

Next, we show how to construct new subspaces from given ones.

Proposition 3.2

Let V, $+$, $\cdot$ be a vector space over F, $+$, $\cdot$, and let $\mathscr{S}$ be a (nonempty) collection of vector subspaces of V. Then, $\bigcap\mathscr{S}$ (the intersection set of $\mathscr{S}$) is a vector subspace of V, $+$, $\cdot$

Proof

We must show that $\bigcap\mathscr{S}$ is closed with respect to $+$ and $\cdot$.**

Choose any $\mathbf{u}_1$ and $\mathbf{u}_2$ in $\bigcap\mathscr{S}$ and any $a \in F$. Since $\mathbf{u}_1$ and $\mathbf{u}_2$ belong to $\bigcap\mathscr{S}$, they belong to *every* member of $\mathscr{S}$. Since $\mathscr{S}$ consists of vector subspaces of V, the members of $\mathscr{S}$ are all closed with respect to $+$ and $\cdot$. Thus, $\mathbf{u}_1 + \mathbf{u}_2$ and $a \cdot \mathbf{u}_1$ belong to *every* member of $\mathscr{S}$. This means that $\mathbf{u}_1 + \mathbf{u}_2 \in \bigcap\mathscr{S}$ and $a \cdot \mathbf{u}_1 \in \bigcap\mathscr{S}$. Therefore, $\bigcap\mathscr{S}$ is closed with respect to $+$ and $\cdot$. Q.E.D.

In general, it is *not* true that the *union* of a nonempty family of vector subspaces of V is a vector subspace of V. (cf. Exercises 3.4.**11**). However, there is—in a sense that we make precise—a *smallest* vector subspace of V containing this union. We now demonstrate this fact.

Let X be any *subset* of V, and let $\mathscr{F}$ be the collection of all vector subspaces of V containing X. Since the set V is closed with respect to $+$ and $\cdot$, V is a vector subspace of V. Moreover, V contains X. Therefore, $V \in \mathscr{F}$, so that $\mathscr{F}$ is not empty. According to the preceding proposition, $\bigcap\mathscr{F}$ is a vector subspace of V. $\bigcap\mathscr{F}$ has the following two properties:

1. $X \subset \bigcap\mathscr{F}$
2. If a vector subspace U of V contains X, then U contains $\bigcap\mathscr{F}$.

These properties are easily verified. To verify 1., observe that every member of X is also a member of every subspace in $\mathscr{F}$, and hence it is a member of

** $\bigcap\mathscr{S}$ is nonempty because $\mathbf{0}$ (the $+$-identity of V) belongs to every vector subspace of V, hence to every member of $\mathscr{S}$, hence to $\bigcap\mathscr{S}$.

$\bigcap\mathscr{F}$. Therefore, $X \subset \bigcap\mathscr{F}$. To verify 2. notice that, if a vector subspace U of V contains X, then $U \in \mathscr{F}$. By definition, if $\mathbf{v} \in \bigcap\mathscr{F}$, then $\mathbf{v}$ belongs to *every* member of $\mathscr{F}$. In particular, $\mathbf{v} \in U$. Thus, $\bigcap\mathscr{F} \subset U$

It is also easy to show that *the properties above completely characterize* $\bigcap\mathscr{F}$. That is, *if* W is a vector subspace of V satisfying: 1. $X \subset W$; and 2. if a vector subspace U of V contains X, then U contains W; *then* $W = \bigcap\mathscr{F}$.

To see this, let W be such a subspace. Then, $W \supset X$. But, according to 2., satisfied by $\bigcap\mathscr{F}$, this means that W contains $\bigcap\mathscr{F}$, or $W \supset \bigcap\mathscr{F}$. On the other hand, $\bigcap\mathscr{F} \supset X$. Therefore, according to 2., satisfied by W, this means that $\bigcap\mathscr{F}$ contains W, or $\bigcap\mathscr{F} \supset W$. Combining these two relations, we get $\bigcap\mathscr{F} = W$.

The above discussion shows that *there is one and only one subspace of V satisfying conditions* 1. *and* 2. *This fact can be conveniently summarized as follows:* $\bigcap\mathscr{F}$ *is the smallest vector subspace of V containing X.*

Definition 3.7

Let X and $\mathscr{F}$ be as above. Then, $\bigcap\mathscr{F}$, *the smallest vector subspace of V containing X, is called the vector subspace generated by X, or the vector subspace of V spanned by X. Henceforth, we denote* $\bigcap\mathscr{F}$ *as* $\text{span}_V(X)$, *or simply span* (X).** *(We discuss various properties of span(X) later in this chapter.)*

If $\mathscr{S}$ *is a nonempty family of vector subspaces of V, then* $\bigcup\mathscr{S}$ *is a subset of V, and span*($\bigcup\mathscr{S}$) *is the smallest vector subspace of V containing* $\bigcup\mathscr{S}$. *For reasons that become clear later, we call span*($\bigcup\mathscr{S}$) *the sum of the vector subspaces in* $\mathscr{S}$, *and we denote it by* $\Sigma\mathscr{S}$. *Alternatively, if* $\mathscr{S}$ *is finite, consisting, say, of vector subspaces* $U_1, U_2, \ldots, U_n$ *then we may write* $\Sigma\mathscr{S}$ *as* $U_1 + U_2 + \cdots + U_n$ *(the order of appearance being irrelevant).*

The summation notation introduced above is, at this point, a complete formality, a notational convention. The "+" occuring in "$U_1 + U_2 + \cdots + U_n$" is not (yet) to be construed as bearing any relation to the vector-space operation +. Later, we show that there actually is a close relationship, so that our choice of notation will be justified.

Proposition 3.3

Let $n > 2$ *be any natural number, let* $V_1, V_2, \ldots, V_n$ *be vector spaces over* $F, +, \cdot$, *and let* U_1 *be a vector subspace of* V_1, U_2 *a vector subspace of* $V_2, \ldots,$ *and* U_n *a vector subspace of* V_n. *Then,* $U_1 \times U_2 \times \cdots \times U_n$ *is a vector subspace of* $V_1 \times V_2 \times \cdots \times V_n$. *(The product of vector subspaces is a vector subspace of the product.)*

We leave the proof of this result to the reader. He must show that $U_1 \times U_2 \times \cdots \times U_n$ is closed with respect to the operations + and $\cdot$ defined on

** We shall also refer to $\text{span}_V(X)$ as the *linear span* of X.

$V_1 \times V_2 \times \cdots \times V_n$ in Construction 1 of Section 2. Note that there are vector subspaces of $V_1 \times V_2 \times \cdots \times V_n$ that are *not* products of subspaces U_1, $U_2, \ldots, U_n$, as above.

3.2 Some Examples of Vector Subspaces and One Counterexample

Note that all of the following examples of vector subspaces are, *a fortiori*, examples of vector spaces.

(a) Given any vector space $V, +, \cdot$ over $F, +, \cdot$, it itself is a vector subspace of V. Every other vector subspace of V is called a *proper* subspace.

(b) Given any vector space $V, +, \cdot$ over $F, +, \cdot$, the set consisting of the zero vector alone, $\{\mathbf{0}\}$, is closed with respect to $+$ and $\cdot$, so that $\{\mathbf{0}\}$ is a vector subspace of V. It is called *the trivial subspace* of V.

Given any vector subspace U of V, the vector $\mathbf{0}$ belongs to U, as we showed in the proof of Proposition 3.1. Thus, $\{\mathbf{0}\} \subset U$, or: every subspace of V contains the trivial subspace of V.

(c) Let $\mathscr{P}$ be the vector space over $\mathbf{R}$ of polynomials, described in Example 1.2(d). Let $\mathscr{P}^n$ be the subset of $\mathscr{P}$ consisting of all polynomials of degree $\leqq n$, and define addition and real multiplication of such polynomials as in Exercises 3.2.**2**. Note that we define these operations there to be the "same as" the operations defined for $\mathscr{P}$: that is, they are the restrictions of the operations of $\mathscr{P}$ to $\mathscr{P}^n$. Furthermore, note that adding two polynomials of degree $\leqq n$, or multiplying a polynomial of degree $\leqq n$ by a real number, results in a polynomial of degree $\leqq n$. That is, $\mathscr{P}^n$ is closed with respect to the operations of $\mathscr{P}$.

Thus, for every $n \in \mathbf{N}$, $\mathscr{P}^n$ is a vector subspace of $\mathscr{P}$.

The reader should be able to show that for every $n \in \mathbf{N}$, and every $m \in \mathbf{N}$ such that $m \geqq n$, $\mathscr{P}^n$ is a vector subspace of $\mathscr{P}^m$.

(d) Let a and b be any two real numbers, $a < b$, and let $[a, b] = \{x \mid x \in \mathbf{R}$ and $a \leqq x \leqq b\}$. Then, $\mathbf{R}^{[a,b]}$, the $[a, b]$th power of $\mathbf{R}$ is a vector space over $\mathbf{R}$, as described in Construction 2 of Section 2. Let $\mathscr{C}[a, b]$ be, as in Chapter 1, the set of all continuous, real-valued functions on $[a, b]$; let $\mathscr{D}[a, b]$ be, as in Chapter 1, the set of all real-valued functions defined on $[a, b]$ possessing a first derivative that belongs to $\mathscr{C}[a, b]$ (i.e., it is continuous). We define $\mathscr{D}^n[a, b]$, by induction, as follows:

1. Let $\mathscr{D}^1[a, b] = \mathscr{D}[a, b]$.
2. If $\mathscr{D}^n[a, b]$ is defined, let $\mathscr{D}^{n+1}[a, b]$ be the set of all real-valued functions defined on $[a, b]$ possessing a first derivative that belongs to $\mathscr{D}^n[a, b]$.

This inductive definition defines $\mathscr{D}^n[a, b]$ for all n. (It is easy to see that $\mathscr{D}^n[a, b]$ consists of all real-valued functions on $[a, b]$ possessing a continuous nth derivative.)

Now, it is a well-known result of calculus, that a differentiable function is continuous. Therefore, $\mathscr{D}[a, b] \subset \mathscr{C}[a, b]$. Moreover, clearly $\mathscr{C}[a, b] \subset \mathbf{R}^{[a,b]}$. Furthermore, the operations of addition and real multiplication defined on $\mathscr{C}[a, b]$ and $\mathscr{D}[a, b]$ are precisely the restrictions of the corresponding operations of $\mathbf{R}^{[a,b]}$, (cf. Construction 2 of Section 2, this chapter, and Examples (d), (e), (f), of Chapter 1). It was shown in Chapter 1 that $\mathscr{C}[a, b]$ and $\mathscr{D}[a, b]$ are closed with respect to these operations. Thus $\mathscr{D}[a ,b]$ is a vector subspace of $\mathscr{C}[a, b]$ and $\mathbf{R}^{[a,b]}$, and $\mathscr{C}[a, b]$ is a vector subspace of $\mathbf{R}^{[a,b]}$.

We shall have more to say about $\mathscr{D}^n[a, b]$ later.

(e) Recall Example (b) of Chapter 1: A line ℓ in $\mathbf{R}^2$, through the origin of $\mathbf{R}^2$. As was shown in Chapter 1, ℓ is closed with respect to the operations of $\mathbf{R}^2$. Hence, ℓ is a vector subspace of $\mathbf{R}^2$.

It is easy to show that if ℓ has positive slope, ℓ is not the product of vector subspaces, $U_1 \times U_2$, where U_1 and U_2 are vector subspaces of $\mathbf{R}$. For, suppose first that either U_1 or U_2 consisted of more than one member: Say U_1 consists of at least two distinct members $\mathbf{u}$ and $\mathbf{u}'$. Then, for any $\mathbf{v} \in U_2$, $(\mathbf{u}, \mathbf{v})$ and $(\mathbf{u}', \mathbf{v})$ belong to $U_1 \times U_2$. But, if ℓ has positive slope, no two ordered pairs in ℓ have the same second member. Thus, U_1 cannot have more than one member. Similarly, U_2 cannot have more than one member. But this means that $U_1 \times U_2$ cannot have more than one member. Since ℓ has an uncountable number of members (the function sending each $x \in \mathbf{R}$ to the ordered pair of ℓ lying over it in $\mathbf{R}^2$—thinking of $\mathbf{R}$ as the X-axis—is a 1-1 correspondence between $\mathbf{R}$ and ℓ), ℓ cannot equal $U_1 \times U_2$. Thus, although the product of subspaces is a subspace of the product, it is not always true that a subspace of a product is a product of subspaces.

(f) Recall that in Chapter 1, we discussed systems of linear equations: Say n equations and k indeterminates. The set of solutions to a homogeneous system of equations of this type, obviously a subset of $\mathbf{R}^k$, was shown to be closed with respect to the operations of $\mathbf{R}^k$. Therefore, this solution set is a vector subspace of $\mathbf{R}^k$. (It is, of course nonempty, since every such system has the zero solution.)

The question arises as to whether there exist vector spaces V_1 and V_2, over a field F, such that $V_1 \subset V_2$, but V_1 is *not* a vector subspace of V_2. The answer is *yes* as the following (counter-) example shows.

(g) Consider the vector space $\mathbf{R}^+ \setminus \{0\}$, $\oplus$, $\otimes$ over $\mathbf{R}$ described in 1.2(c). Clearly, $\mathbf{R}^+ \setminus \{0\} \subset \mathbf{R}$. But, because the operations $\oplus$ and $\otimes$ do not coincide with the vector space operations of $\mathbf{R}$ (ordinary $+$ and $\cdot$), we cannot say that $\mathbf{R}^+ \setminus \{0\}$ is a vector subspace of $\mathbf{R}$.

Indeed, $\mathbf{R}^+ \setminus \{0\}$ is not closed with respect to the operation $\cdot$. To see this, choose any $r \in \mathbf{R}^+ \setminus \{0\}$. Since $(-1) \cdot r = -r$, and $-r$ is negative, $(-1) \cdot r \notin \mathbf{R}^+ \setminus \{0\}$.

This example illustrates the following point:

A subset U of a vector space V may itself be a vector space with respect to certain operations. But unless these operations are (the restrictions of) those of V, we do not call U a vector subspace of V.

EXERCISES / 3.4

1. Consider the following subsets of $\mathbf{R}^2, +, \cdot$:

$$\begin{aligned}
A &= \{(x, y) \mid (x, y) \in \mathbf{R}^2 \quad \text{and} \quad x^2 + y^2 = 1\}, \\
B &= \{(x, y) \mid (x, y) \in \mathbf{R}^2 \quad \text{and} \quad 2x = 3y + 1\}, \\
C &= \{(x, y) \mid (x, y) \in \mathbf{R}^2 \quad \text{and} \quad x^2 = y\}, \\
D &= \{(0, 0)\}, \\
E &= \{(1, 0)\}
\end{aligned}$$

Which of these sets are closed with respect to $+$ and $\cdot$ and which are not? Justify your answers.

2.* Consider the following two systems of equations (one equation and two indeterminates):

$$3x_1 - x_2 = 1 \tag{1}$$

and

$$3x_1 - x_2 = 0 \tag{2}$$

(Recall that we call system (2) the *homogeneous system* associated with (1).) Let S_1 be the set of all solutions to system (1), and let S_2 be the set of all solutions to system (2). (See Chapter 1 for a definition of "solution.")

a. Prove that S_2 is a vector subspace of $\mathbf{R}^2$.
b. Prove that S_1 is *not* closed with respect to the operations of $\mathbf{R}^2$.
c. Prove that each member of S_2 is the difference of two members of S_1.
d. Prove that each member of S_1 is the sum of some fixed member of S_1 and some member of S_2.
e. Compute S_1 and S_2.

3.* Consider the following two systems of equations:

$$\begin{aligned}
4x_1 - 5x_2 + x_3 &= 1 \\
2x_1 - 5x_2 + x_3 &= -3
\end{aligned} \tag{1}$$

and

$$\begin{aligned}
4x_1 - 5x_2 + x_3 &= 0 \\
2x_1 - 5x_2 + x_3 &= 0
\end{aligned} \tag{2}$$

Let S_1 be the set of all solutions to (1) and S_2 be the set of all solutions to (2).

a. Show that S_2 is a vector subspace of $\mathbf{R}^3$ but that S_1 is not.
b. Compute S_1 and S_2.

4.* Let $F, +, \cdot$ by any one of the fields **Q**, **R**, **C**. Consider the following system of equations:

$$ax_1 + bx_2 = e$$

$$cx_1 + dx_2 = f,$$

where a, b, c, d, e, f belong to F.

a. Suppose that $a \cdot d - b \cdot c \neq 0$ and solve for x_1 and x_2 in terms of a, b, c, d, e, f.

b. Show that the solutions x_1 and x_2 belong to F, hence, that $(x_1, x_2) \in F^2$.

5. **a.** Consider the set **R** as a vector space over itself. Is the subset **Q** a vector subspace of **R**? Justify your answer.

b. Consider the set **R** as a vector space over **Q**. Is the subset **Q** a vector subspace of **R** (over **Q**)? Justify your answer.

6. Consider the set $X = \{x \mid x = r + s\sqrt{2}$, for $r \in \mathbf{Q}$ and $s \in \mathbf{Q}\}$. Clearly, $\mathbf{Q} \subset X$ and $X \subset \mathbf{R}$.

a. Is X closed with respect to the operations of ordinary addition and ordinary multiplication by members of **R**? Justify your answer.

b. Prove that X is closed with respect to the operations of ordinary addition and ordinary multiplication by members of **Q**.

Thus, regarding **R** as a vector space over **Q**, X is a vector subspace of **R** (over **Q**).

c. Prove that X is a field with respect to the operations of ordinary addition and ordinary multiplication.

Thus, X is a vector space over itself.

d. Multiplication of members of **R** by members of X results in an operation of X on **R**. Prove that, with respect to this operation and the operation of ordinary addition, **R** is a vector space over X.

e. Finally, regarding **R** as a vector space over X, show that X is a vector subspace of **R** (over X).

The reader should study Exercises **5.** and **6.** until he is sure of the various interrelationships.

7. Let $V, +, \cdot$ be a vector space (over a field $F, +, \cdot$), and let U be a vector subspace of V. For any set S (empty or not) we have defined V^S in Construction 2 of Section 2. If $S = \varnothing$, let $U^S = \{\mathbf{0}\}$, where $\mathbf{0}$ is the zero vector of V; if $S \neq \varnothing$, then U^S has been defined as the set of all functions from S to U. In any case, U^S is a subset of V^S. Show that U^S is closed with respect to the operations of V^S defined in Construction 2 of Section 2.

8. Let $V, +, \cdot$ be any vector space over a field F, and let U be a vector subspace of V. Then, of course, U is a vector space, over F. Let W be a vector subspace of U.

Prove that W is a vector subspace of V.

This result may be summarized by: the relation of being a vector subspace of a vector space over F is transitive.

9.* Let $V, +, \cdot$ be any vector space and let U_1 and U_2 be any vector subspace of V. We have defined $U_1 + U_2$ to be $\text{span}_V(U_1 \cup U_2)$, the smallest vector subspace of V containing $U_1 \cup U_2$.

a. If $\mathbf{u}_1 \in U_1$ and $\mathbf{u}_2 \in U_2$, show that $\mathbf{u}_1 + \mathbf{u}_2 \in U_1 + U_2$.
b. Let $X = \{\mathbf{v} \mid \mathbf{v} \in V \text{ and } \mathbf{v} = \mathbf{u}_1 + \mathbf{u}_2 \text{ for some } \mathbf{u}_1 \in U_1 \text{ and } \mathbf{u}_2 \in U_2\}$. That is, X is the set of all possible sums of the form $\mathbf{u}_1 + \mathbf{u}_2$, where $\mathbf{u}_1$ ranges over U_1 and $\mathbf{u}_2$ ranges over U_2. According to **a.**, each such sum belongs to $U_1 + U_2$. Thus $X \subset U_1 + U_2$.
Show that $U_1 \cup U_2 \subset X$. (Thus, X is nonempty.)
c. Show that X is closed with respect to the vector-space operations of $U_1 + U_2$ (i.e., $+$ and $\cdot$ of V restricted to $U_1 + U_2$). Thus, X is a vector subspace of $U_1 + U_2$. Since $U_1 + U_2$ is a vector subspace of V, Exercise **8**, above, implies that X is a vector subspace of V. But, $X \supset U_1 \cup U_2$. Therefore, since $U_1 + U_2$ is the *smallest* vector subspace of V containing $U_1 \cup U_2$, $U_1 + U_2 \subset X$.
Hence, since X is a subspace of $U_1 + U_2$, $X = U_1 + U_2$.
This exercise shows that $U_1 + U_2$ is the set of all sums of the form $\mathbf{u}_1 + \mathbf{u}_2$, where $\mathbf{u}_1$ ranges over U_1 and $\mathbf{u}_2$ ranges over U_2. This justifies the notation "$U_1 + U_2$."
We amplify this point later in this chapter.

10. Let $V, +, \cdot$ be a vector space over F.
a. For any vector subspace U of V, prove that $\text{span}_V(U) = U$.
b. If X is the empty set, prove that $\text{span}_V(X) = \{\mathbf{0}\}$.

11. Let ℓ_1 and ℓ_2 be any two distinct lines through the origin in $\mathbf{R}^2$. These are both vector subspaces of $\mathbf{R}^2$. Show that $\ell_1 \cup \ell_2$ is *not* a vector subspace of $\mathbf{R}^2$. What is $\ell_1 + \ell_2$?

4† / HYPERPLANES AND QUOTIENTS OF VECTOR SPACES

4.1 Definitions and Elementary Results

Let $V, +, \cdot$ be a vector space over $F, +, \cdot$, and let U be a vector subspace of V.

Definition 3.8

We define a relation on V, called congruence modulo U, *as follows:*
Vectors $\mathbf{v}_1$ and $\mathbf{v}_2$ are said to be congruent modulo U, written $\mathbf{v}_1 \equiv \mathbf{v}_2 (\text{mod } U)$ if and only if

$$\mathbf{v}_1 - \mathbf{v}_2 \in U$$

Proposition 3.4

Congruence modulo U is an equivalence relation on V.

Proof

(1) *Reflexivity.* Choose any $\mathbf{v} \in V$. Since $\mathbf{v} - \mathbf{v} = \mathbf{0}$, and $\mathbf{0} \in U$, $\mathbf{v} \equiv \mathbf{v} \pmod U$.
(2) *Symmetry.* Choose any $\mathbf{v}_1 \in V$ and $\mathbf{v}_2 \in V$ such that $\mathbf{v}_1 \equiv \mathbf{v}_2 \pmod U$.

Then $\mathbf{v}_1 - \mathbf{v}_2 \in U$. Since U is closed with respect to multiplication by members of F, $(-1) \cdot (\mathbf{v}_1 - \mathbf{v}_2) \in U$. But $(-1) \cdot (\mathbf{v}_1 - \mathbf{v}_2)$, it is easily verified, equals $\mathbf{v}_2 - \mathbf{v}_1$. Therefore, $\mathbf{v}_2 - \mathbf{v}_1 \in U$, so that $\mathbf{v}_2 \equiv \mathbf{v}_1 \pmod{U}$.

(3) *Transitivity*. Choose any $\mathbf{v}_1, \mathbf{v}_2, \mathbf{v}_3$ in V such that $\mathbf{v}_1 \equiv \mathbf{v}_2 \pmod{U}$ and $\mathbf{v}_2 \equiv \mathbf{v}_3 \pmod{U}$. Then, $\mathbf{v}_1 - \mathbf{v}_2 \in U$ and $\mathbf{v}_2 - \mathbf{v}_3 \in U$. Since U is closed with respect to $+$, $(\mathbf{v}_1 - \mathbf{v}_2) + (\mathbf{v}_2 - \mathbf{v}_3) \in U$. But,

$$\begin{aligned}(\mathbf{v}_1 - \mathbf{v}_2) + (\mathbf{v}_2 - \mathbf{v}_3) &= [\mathbf{v}_1 + (-\mathbf{v}_2)] + [\mathbf{v}_2 + (-\mathbf{v}_3)] \\ &= ([\mathbf{v}_1 + (-\mathbf{v}_2)] + \mathbf{v}_2) + (-\mathbf{v}_3) \\ &= (\mathbf{v}_1 + [(-\mathbf{v}_2) + \mathbf{v}_2]) - \mathbf{v}_3 \\ &= (\mathbf{v}_1 + \mathbf{0}) - \mathbf{v}_3 = \mathbf{v}_1 - \mathbf{v}_3\end{aligned}$$

The second and third steps in this sequence involve applications of the associative law for $+$.

Thus, $\mathbf{v}_1 - \mathbf{v}_3 \in U$ so that $\mathbf{v}_1 \equiv \mathbf{v}_3 \pmod{U}$. Q.E.D.

Since congruence modulo U is an equivalence relation, it determines a *partition* of V in the standard way. That is, the sets of the partition are the equivalence classes of the relation: each class consists of all those vectors of V congruent modulo U to some given vector of V. This "given" vector can be any one of the vectors in the class, that is, any representative of the class (see Chapter 2. 1.7).

Definition 3.9

We denote the partition of V determined by congruence modulo U by "V/U" and call it V mod U, or the quotient of V by U, or the quotient space determined by U. We call each member of the partition—that is each equivalence class of the relation of congruence modulo U—a hyperplane (determined by U).

The remainder of this section is devoted to describing these two notions—that of a quotient and that of a hyperplane—more fully.

Definition 3.10

Let U and V be as above, and choose any vector $\mathbf{v} \in V$. We denote by "$\mathbf{v} + U$" the set consisting of all sums of vectors of the form $\mathbf{v} + \mathbf{u}$, where $\mathbf{v}$ is fixed and $\mathbf{u}$ ranges over U. We call this set the translate of U by $\mathbf{v}$.

Proposition 3.5

Let U and V be as above, and choose any vector $\mathbf{v} \in V$. Then, the hyperplane (determined by U) containing $\mathbf{v}$ is precisely $\mathbf{v} + U$.

Proof

Let the hyperplane containing $\mathbf{v}$ be (temporarily) denoted by "$[\mathbf{v}]$."

If $\mathbf{w} \in [\mathbf{v}]$, then by definition, $\mathbf{w} \equiv \mathbf{v} \pmod{U}$, whence $\mathbf{w} - \mathbf{v} \in U$. But

$\mathbf{w} = \mathbf{v} + (\mathbf{w} - \mathbf{v})$, and so is of the form $\mathbf{v} + \mathbf{u}$, where $\mathbf{u} \in U$ is just $\mathbf{w} - \mathbf{v}$. Therefor $\mathbf{w} \in \mathbf{v} + U$, which implies that $[\mathbf{v}] \subset \mathbf{v} + U$.

On the other hand, if $\mathbf{w} \in \mathbf{v} + U$, $\mathbf{w} = \mathbf{v} + \mathbf{u}$, for some $\mathbf{u} \in U$. Therefore, $\mathbf{w} - \mathbf{v} = \mathbf{u} \in U$, and so $\mathbf{w} \equiv \mathbf{v}$ (mod U). This means, precisely, that $\mathbf{w} \in [\mathbf{v}]$, from which it follows that $\mathbf{v} + U \subset [\mathbf{v}]$. Q.E.D.

Corollary to Proposition 3.5

The following properties hold for translates of U

(1) $\mathbf{v}_1 + U = \mathbf{v}_2 + U$, *if and only if* $\mathbf{v}_1 - \mathbf{v}_2 \in U$;
(2) $\mathbf{v} \in \mathbf{v} + U$, *for every* $\mathbf{v} \in V$;
(3) *if* $\mathbf{v}_1 \in \mathbf{v}_2 + U$, *then* $\mathbf{v}_2 \in \mathbf{v}_1 + U$;
(4) *if* $\mathbf{v}_1 \in \mathbf{v}_2 + U$, and $\mathbf{v}_2 \in \mathbf{v}_3 + U$, *then* $\mathbf{v}_1 \in \mathbf{v}_3 + U$.

Proof

(1) Since $\mathbf{v} + U$ is the equivalence class of $\mathbf{v}$ determined by congruence modulo U, the equality $\mathbf{v}_1 + U = \mathbf{v}_2 + U$ states simply that the equivalence class of $\mathbf{v}_1$ is equal to the equivalence class of $\mathbf{v}_2$. This is the same as saying that $\mathbf{v}_1$ and $\mathbf{v}_2$ are equivalent (i.e., congruent modulo U), which is the same as saying $\mathbf{v}_1 - \mathbf{v}_2 \in U$ by definition of congruence modulo U.

Conditions (2)–(4) follow easily from the above remarks, together with the fact that congruence modulo U is reflexive, symmetric, and transitive [which is all that (2), (3) and (4) say, respectively]. Q.E.D.

A concrete example at this point will be revealing.

Let $V = \mathbf{R}^2$, considered as a vector space over $\mathbf{R}$ and let U be the line through the origin given by the equation $y = 2x$. U and V are pictured in Figure 14:

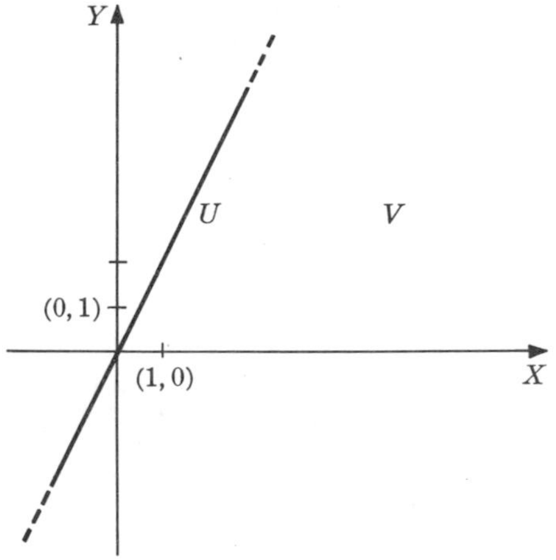

FIGURE 14

Now, consider the equivalence relation of congruence modulo U:

$$(x_1, y_1) \equiv (x_2, y_2) \text{ (mod } U\text{), if and only if}$$

$$(x_1 - y_2, y_1 - y_2) = (x_1, y_1) - (x_2, y_2) \in U$$

An ordered pair (x, y) belong to U, if and only if $y = 2x$. Thus, $(x_1, y_2) \equiv (x_2, y_2)$ (mod U) if and only if $y_1 - y_2 = 2(x_1 - x_2)$.

Choose any pair $(x_1, y_1) \in \mathbf{R}^2$ and hold it fixed. It belongs to a unique equivalence class of the relation of congruence modulo U: namely, to the class of all $(x, y) \in \mathbf{R}^2$ satisfying $(x, y) \equiv (x_1, y_1)$(mod U); equivalently, according to the preceding paragraph, this class consists of all (x, y) such that $(y - y_1) = 2(x - x_1)$. But, this is well known to be the straight line through (x_1, y_1) of slope 2.

On the other hand, by definition the translate of U by (x_1, y_1) is the set of all sums of the form $(x_1, y_1) + (x', y') = (x_1 + x', y_1 + y')$, where (x', y') ranges over U. That is, $(x_1, y_1) + U$ consists of all vectors of the form $(x_1 + x', y_1 + 2x')$, where x' ranges over $\mathbf{R}$. (This is obtained from the previous sentence by noting that, for (x', y') ranging over U, x' ranges over $\mathbf{R}$ and $y = 2x'$.) Now, set $y = y_1 + 2x'$ and set $x = x_1 + x'$. Then, the pair $(x_1 + x', y_1 + 2x')$ is just (x, y), and this pair satisfies the above equation: namely $y - y_1 = 2(x - x_1)$. Therefore, all such pairs [and, hence, all of $(x_1, y_1) + U$] lie on the straight line of slope 2 through (x_1, y_1). In a similar way, we can show that all points on this line belong to $(x_1, y_1) + U$. Therefore, $(x_1, y_1) + U$ is precisely the line through (x_1, y_1) of slope 2. Of course, this fact is also an immediate consequence of the result of the preceding paragraph, together with the fact, proved in Proposition 3.5, that $(x_1, y_1) + U$ is the hyperplane containing (x_1, y_1). Nevertheless, it is desirable to see the result proved directly in the concrete case.

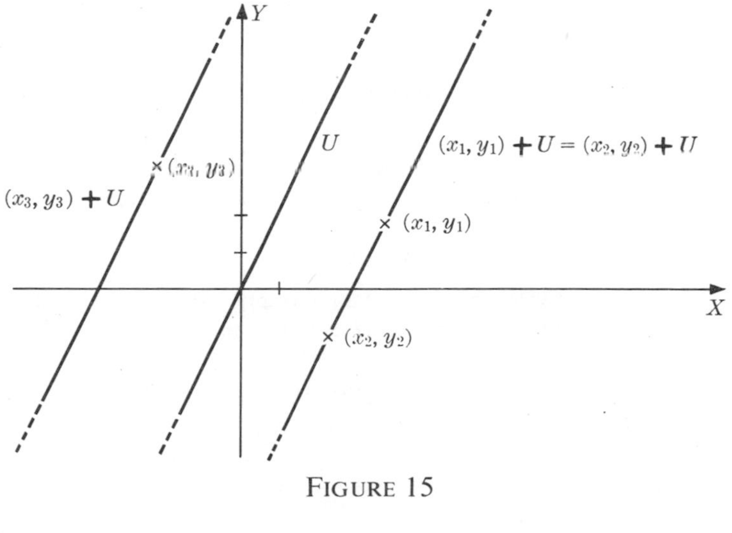

FIGURE 15

In any case, the translates of U by vectors of $\mathbf{R}^2$, *or, equivalently, the hyperplanes determined by U, are just the straight lines in* $\mathbf{R}^2$ *of slope* 2.

The reader should, as an exercise, prove *directly*** (for the specific U given above) that if vectors (x_1, y_1) and (x_2, y_2) both belong to the same line of slope 2, then $(x_1, y_1) + U = (x_2, y_2) + U$. Figure 15 illustrates the situation.

EXERCISES / 3.5

1. Let V be any vector space over a field F, and let U be any vector subspace of V.

a. Prove that, if $\mathbf{v}$ is any vector of V, $\mathbf{v} + V = V$.

b. Prove that, if $\mathbf{v}$ is any vector of U, $\mathbf{v} + U = U$.

c. Prove that, if $\mathbf{v}$ is any vector of V, and if $\mathbf{v} \notin U$, then $\mathbf{v} + U$ is *not* a vector subspace of V.

d. Prove that $\mathbf{v} + U \subset \text{span}_V(\{\mathbf{v}\} \cup U)$. (Recall that if X is a subset of V, then $\text{span}_V(X)$ is the smallest vector subspace of V containing U.)

2. Consider Exercises 3.4.**2.** and **3**. There, we consider two systems of equations, (1) and (2). Let S_1 be the set of solutions to (1) and S_2 the set of solution to (2). In **2.** and **3.**, the reader proved that S_2 is a vector subspace of $\mathbf{R}^2$ (in **2**) or $\mathbf{R}^3$ (in **3**). Prove that in each case, S_1 is a translate of S_2 (or hyperplane determined by S_2).

3. Let $p_{a,b,c}$ be the plane in $\mathbf{R}^3$, going through the origin of $\mathbf{R}^3$, determined by the equation

$$ax + by + cz = 0$$

where a, b, c are any real numbers such that $a \neq 0$.

a. Prove that $p_{a,b,c}$ is a vector subspace of $\mathbf{R}^3$ (over $\mathbf{R}$, of course).

b. Let d be any real number and let $p_{a,b,c,d}$ be the set of all (x, y, z) satisfying the equation

$$ax + by + cz + d = 0$$

Prove that $p_{a,b,c,d}$ is the translate of $p_{a,b,c}$ by $(-d/a, 0, 0)$.

4. Let V be any vector space over a field F and let H be a nonempty *subset* of V with the following property: The set of all vectors of the form $\mathbf{v}_1 - \mathbf{v}_2$, where $\mathbf{v}_1$ and $\mathbf{v}_2$ range over H, is closed with respect to the vector-space operations of V. Call this set U.

Prove: H is a translate of U.

5. Let V be any vector over $\mathbf{R}$, and let H be a nonempty subset of V with the following property: For any $\mathbf{v}_1$ and $\mathbf{v}_2$ in H and for any $r \in \mathbf{R}$, $r \cdot \mathbf{v}_1 + (1 - r) \cdot \mathbf{v}_2$ belongs to H.

Let U be the set of all vectors of the form $\mathbf{v}_1 - \mathbf{v}_2$, where $\mathbf{v}_1$ and $\mathbf{v}_2$ range over H. Clearly U is nonempty.

** I.e., without recourse to Proposition 3.5 or its corollary.

a. If $\mathbf{u} \in U$ and $r \in \mathbf{R}$ show that $r \cdot \mathbf{u} \in U$. (*Hint:* $r \cdot \mathbf{v}_1 + (1-r) \cdot \mathbf{v}_2 = r \cdot (\mathbf{v}_1 - \mathbf{v}_2) + \mathbf{v}_2$.)

b. If $\mathbf{v}_1$, $\mathbf{v}_2$, $\mathbf{v}_3$ belong to H, show that

$$(\mathbf{v}_1 - \mathbf{v}_2) + \mathbf{v}_3 \in H$$

(*Hint*: $(\mathbf{v}_1 - \mathbf{v}_2) + \mathbf{v}_3 = 2 \cdot (1/2 \cdot \mathbf{v}_1 + 1/2 \cdot \mathbf{v}_3) + (-1) \cdot \mathbf{v}_2$.)

c. Use **b** to show that if $\mathbf{u}_1$ and $\mathbf{u}_2$ belong to U, then $\mathbf{u}_1 + \mathbf{u}_2$ belongs to U.

Thus, U is closed with respect to $+$ and $\cdot$, and so, by **4.**, above, H is a translate of U.

d. Let W be any vector subspace of V, and let K be any translate of W. Prove that K has the property of H described above.

This exercise shows that hyperplanes (in vector spaces over **R**) are completely characterized by the property of H, above (which makes no reference to vector subspaces of V).

This property has a simple geometric interpretation. Let $V = \mathbf{R}^3$ and the $\mathbf{v}_1$ and $\mathbf{v}_2$ be any two distinct vectors of V. Then, the set of all vectors of the form $t \cdot \mathbf{v}_1 + (1-t) \cdot \mathbf{v}_2$, where t ranges over **R**, is precisely the *straight line through* $\mathbf{v}_1$ *and* $\mathbf{v}_2$. The property of H then (for $\mathbf{v} = \mathbf{R}^3$) can be expressed as follows: *For any two vectors* $\mathbf{v}_1$ *and* $\mathbf{v}_2$ *in* H, *the line through* $\mathbf{v}_1$ *and* $\mathbf{v}_2$ *lies in* H.

With this characterization of hyperplanes in mind, the reader is now invited to try to enumerate the different kinds of hyperplanes in $\mathbf{R}^3$. Since every subspace of $\mathbf{R}^3$ is a hyperplane (the translate of itself by **0**), this list will include the different kinds of subspaces of $\mathbf{R}^3$.

4.2 Addition and Scalar Multiplication of Hyperplanes

Let V, $+$, $\cdot$ be any vector space over F, $+$, $\cdot$, and let U be a vector subspace of V. We consider the set V/U of congruence classes modulo U, or hyperplanes determined by U, and we attempt to use the operations $+$ and $\cdot$ to define operations on it. Given two hyperplanes $\mathbf{v}_1 + U$ and $\mathbf{v}_2 + U$, we tentatively define their *sum* by

$$(\mathbf{v}_1 + U) \oplus (\mathbf{v}_2 + U) = (\mathbf{v}_1 + \mathbf{v}_2) + U \tag{1}$$

Given any scalar $a \in F$ and any hyperplane $\mathbf{v}_1 + U$, we tentatively define the product of a and $\mathbf{v}_1 + U$ by

$$a \otimes (\mathbf{v}_1 + U) = (a \cdot \mathbf{v}_1) + U \tag{2}$$

The trouble, *a priori*, with these definitions is that they may be ambiguous. For example, in (1) above, the sum of $\mathbf{v}_1 + U$ and $\mathbf{v}_2 + U$ is defined using the vectors $\mathbf{v}_1$ and $\mathbf{v}_2$. But, it is quite possible that the hyperplane $\mathbf{v}_1 + U = \mathbf{v}_3 + U$, where $\mathbf{v}_1 \neq \mathbf{v}_3$. Indeed, just choose any $\mathbf{v}_3$ such that $\mathbf{v}_3 - \mathbf{v}_1 \in U$ (cf. Corollary to Proposition 3.5). Moreover, according to equation (1),$(\mathbf{v}_3 + U) \oplus (\mathbf{v}_2 + U) = (\mathbf{v}_3 + \mathbf{v}_2) + U$. Now, if (1) is to make sense, it had better be true that $(\mathbf{v}_3 + \mathbf{v}_2) + U = (\mathbf{v}_1 + \mathbf{v}_2) + U$; for, otherwise, we would be adding equal things to the same thing and getting unequal answers. Similar comments apply to (2).

The next proposition shows that such ambiguity never occurs.

Proposition 3.6

Let V, $+$, $\cdot$, F, and U be as above and choose any $\mathbf{v}_1 \in V$, $\mathbf{v}_2 \in V$, and $a \in F$. *If $\mathbf{v}_1' \equiv \mathbf{v}_1$ (mod U) and $\mathbf{v}_2' \equiv \mathbf{v}_2$ (mod U), then*

$$(1) \qquad (\mathbf{v}_1 + \mathbf{v}_2) + U = (\mathbf{v}_1' + \mathbf{v}_2') + U$$

and

$$(2) \qquad (a \cdot \mathbf{v}_1) + U = (a \cdot \mathbf{v}_1') + U$$

Proof

(1) According to the Corollary to Proposition 3.5, it suffices to show that $(\mathbf{v}_1 + \mathbf{v}_2) - (\mathbf{v}_1' + \mathbf{v}_2') \in U$. Since $\mathbf{v}_1' \equiv \mathbf{v}_1$ (mod U) and since $\mathbf{v}_2' \equiv \mathbf{v}_2$ (mod U), then $\mathbf{v}_1 - \mathbf{v}_1' \in U$ and $\mathbf{v}_2 - \mathbf{v}_2' \in U$. Thus, since U is closed with respect to $+$,

$$(\mathbf{v}_1 - \mathbf{v}_1') + (\mathbf{v}_2 - \mathbf{v}_2') \in U.$$

The result now follows from the equality $(\mathbf{v}_1 - \mathbf{v}_1') + (\mathbf{v}_2 - \mathbf{v}_2') = (\mathbf{v}_1 + \mathbf{v}_2) - (\mathbf{v}_1' + \mathbf{v}_2')$.

(2) It suffices to show that $a \cdot \mathbf{v}_1 - a \cdot \mathbf{v}_1' \in U$. Since, as in (1), $\mathbf{v}_1 - \mathbf{v}_1' \in U$, it follows that $a \cdot (\mathbf{v}_1 - \mathbf{v}_1') \in U$, because U is closed with respect to $\cdot$. The result now follows from the equality $a \cdot (\mathbf{v}_1 - \mathbf{v}_1') = a \cdot \mathbf{v}_1 - a \cdot \mathbf{v}_1'$. Q.E.D.

Thus, our tentative definitions, equations (1) and (2) are unambiguous, so that $\oplus$ is an operation on V/U and $\otimes$ is an operation of F on V/U.

Proposition 3.7

V/U, $\oplus$, $\otimes$ is a vector space over F.

The proof involves verifying that $\oplus$ and $\otimes$ satisfy the appropriate conditions of Definition 3.4. This will be left to the reader. In the next chapter we present a simple proof of this result.

Henceforth, we shall refer to V/U *as the quotient vector space* obtained from V and U, and we shall use the usual symbols "$+$" and "$\cdot$" for its operations. These operations are always those defined as above, in equations (1) and (2). We call them the operations *determined by* (*those of*) V or *induced by* (*those of*) V. We shall find it convenient sometimes to write the members of V/U as equivalence classes. Thus, instead of $\mathbf{v} + U$ we may write $[\mathbf{v}]$.

With these alterations, the definitions, equations (1) and (2) become:

$$[\mathbf{v}_1] + [\mathbf{v}_2] = [\mathbf{v}_1 + \mathbf{v}_2] \qquad (1')$$

or

$$(\mathbf{v}_1 + U) + (\mathbf{v}_2 + U) = (\mathbf{v}_1 + \mathbf{v}_2) + U$$

and

$$a \cdot [\mathbf{v}_1] = [a \cdot \mathbf{v}_1] \qquad (2')$$

or

$$a \cdot (\mathbf{v}_1 + U) = (a \cdot \mathbf{v}_1) + U$$

EXERCISES / 3.6

1. Let V be a vector space over F. Describe the vector spaces V/V and $V/\{\mathbf{0}\}$.

2. Let V be as in **1**, and let U be a vector subspace of V. Show that U is a member of V/U and that it is the $+$-identity of V/U.

3. Let $F = \mathbf{R}$, $V = \mathbf{R}^2$, and $U = \ell$, the line given by the equation $y = 3x - 2$.
   a. Show that the lines $\ell_1 : y - x = 2x + 4$ and $\ell_2 : 3x - y = 6$ are translates of U.
   b. $\ell_1 + \ell_2$ is a line parallel to ℓ. What is its equation?
   c. What is the equation of $-\ell_1$? Of $5 \cdot \ell_2$?
   d. Let ℓ_3 be a line through the origin distinct from ℓ. Choose any $\mathbf{v}_1, \mathbf{v}_2 \in \ell_3$, $\mathbf{v}_1 \neq \mathbf{v}_2$. These lie on the intersection of ℓ_3 with $\mathbf{v}_1 + \ell$ and $\mathbf{v}_2 + \ell$, respectively. Show that $\mathbf{v}_1 + \mathbf{v}_2$ lies on the intersection of ℓ_3 with $(\mathbf{v}_1 + \ell) + (\mathbf{v}_2 + \ell)$.

5 / LINEAR DEPENDENCE AND INDEPENDENCE, BASES AND DIMENSION

At this point, our knowledge of vector spaces is still qualitative and abstract. Vector spaces are, for us, still mysterious, unexplored objects, often comprising uncountably many vectors. What is needed is, on the one hand, a method of comparing vectors more precisely (or, *quantitatively*, if we are dealing with vector spaces over **Q**, **R**, or **C**), and, on the other hand, a method whereby questions about the entire vector space are reduced to questions about smaller (hopefully even finite) subsets of the vector space.

The key to such a method is the notion of vector-space bases, certain special subsets of a vector space. They play the role of coordinate systems (such as the X-axis and Y-axis in $\mathbf{R}^2$). The essential ingredients in the definition of this notion are the notions of (linear) dependence and independence, which we deal with in this section.

At this point the interesting work of linear algebra really begins. As evidence for this assertion, the reader will note that the ideas developed in the next few sections are crucial for the solution of systems of linear equations.

Throughout this section, $V, +, \cdot$ will be a vector space over $F, +, \cdot$

5.1 Linear Span and Linear Combinations

Let X be any subset of V (empty or not). In Subsection 3.1, we defined $\text{span}_V(X)$ to be the smallest vector subspace of V containing X, after showing that this notion was meaningful. In this section, we elaborate on this concept, giving some examples, some properties, and a useful characterization. First some examples.

(a) Let $X \neq \emptyset$ and let $\mathbf{0}$, as usual, be the zero vector of V. Then, as the reader showed in Exercises **3.4.10**, span $(X) = \{\mathbf{0}\}$. A proof of this fact is left to the reader.

(b) Let U be a vector subspace of V. Then, $\text{span}_V(U) = U$. This the reader was asked to prove in Exercises **3.4.10**. (The proof is easy: For U is a vector subspace of V, and $U \supset U$, so that $\text{span}_V(U)$, being the smallest vector subspace of V containing U satisfies $\text{span}_V(U) \subset U$; on the other hand, by definition, $\text{span}_V(U) \supset U$.)

(c) Let $\mathbf{v}$ be any non-zero vector of V. Then, $\text{span}_V(\{\mathbf{v}\})$ consists of precisely all the scalar multiples of $\mathbf{v}$.

To see this, notice that the set of such multiples is closed under $+$ and $\cdot$: $a \cdot \mathbf{v} + b \cdot \mathbf{v} = (a + b) \cdot \mathbf{v}$ and $c \cdot (a \cdot \mathbf{v}) = (c \cdot a) \cdot \mathbf{v}$. Thus, it is a vector subspace of V, and it contains $\mathbf{v}$, because $\mathbf{v} = 1 \cdot \mathbf{v}$. Therefore, $\text{span}_V(\{\mathbf{v}\})$ is contained in this set of multiples, because $\text{span}_V(\{\mathbf{v}\})$ is the *smallest* subspace of V containing $\mathbf{v}$. On the other hand, since $\mathbf{v} \in \text{span}_V(\{\mathbf{v}\})$, and $\text{span}_V(\{\mathbf{v}\})$ is closed under scalar multiplication $\text{span}_V(\{\mathbf{v}\})$ contains every scalar multiple of $\mathbf{v}$. In other words, $\text{span}_V(\{\mathbf{v}\})$ contains the set of all scalar multiples of $\mathbf{v}$.

Thus, $\text{span}_V(\{\mathbf{v}\})$ equals the set of multiples of $\mathbf{v}$.

If $V = \mathbf{R}^3$ and $F = \mathbf{R}$, then the set of such multiples is precisely the straight line determined by $\mathbf{v}$ and the origin.

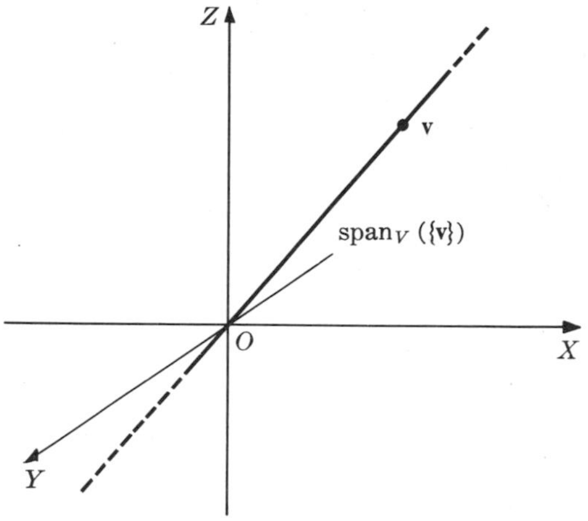

FIGURE 16

(d) Let $V = \mathbf{R}^3$, $F = \mathbf{R}$, and $X = \{(3, -1, 4), (2, 0, 0)\}$. Then, $\text{span}_V(X)$ is the plane $\not{p}$ determined by $(0, 0, 0)$, $(3, -1, 4)$, $(2, 0, 0)$.

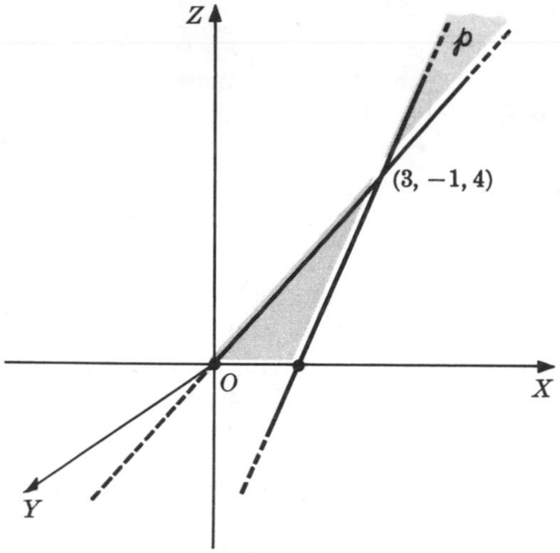

FIGURE 17

(e) Let $\mathscr{P}$ be the vector space over $\mathbf{R}$ of all polynomials in one variable x. [See Example 1.2(d)]. Let $X = \{x^0, x^1, x^2, x^3, \ldots\}$** Then, $\text{span}_{\mathscr{P}}(X) = \mathscr{P}$. We leave a verification of this fact to the reader.

Next, we list and prove the main properties of linear spans.

Proposition 3.8

Let X and Y be subsets of V, and let U be a vector subspace of V.

(1) *If $X \subset Y$, then $\text{span}_V(X) \subset \text{span}_V(Y)$.*
(2) *$\text{span}_V(U) = U$*
(3) *$\text{span}_V(X \cup Y) = \text{span}_V(X) + \text{span}_V(Y)$.*

Remarks: Note that we have already proved (2) above. Note also that, since $\text{span}_V(X)$ is a vector subspace of V, we get, letting $U = \text{span}_V(X)$,

$$\text{span}_V(\text{span}_V(X)) = \text{span}_V(X)$$

Note also that the right-hand side of (3) has two interpretations. On the one hand, by Definition 3.6, $\text{span}_V(X) + \text{span}_V(Y)$ equals $\text{span}_V(\text{span}_V(X) \cup \text{span}_V(Y))$. On the other hand, the reader showed, in Exercises 3.4.9, that if U_1 and U_2 are two vector subspaces of V, then $U_1 + U_2 =$ the set of all sums of the form $\mathbf{u}_1 + \mathbf{u}_2$, where $\mathbf{u}_1$ ranges over U_1 and $\mathbf{u}_2$ ranges over U_2. Thus, $\text{span}_V(X) + \text{span}_V(Y) =$ the set of all sums $\mathbf{u}_1 + \mathbf{u}_2$, where $\mathbf{u}_1$ ranges over $\text{span}_V(X)$ and $\mathbf{u}_2$ ranges over $\text{span}_V(Y)$.

** x^0 is the zeroth power of x, which is usually equated with 1; x^1 is the first power of x, usually equated with x. We follow these conventions, too, but sometimes use the above notation.

Proof

(1) By definition $Y \subset \text{span}_V(Y)$, and, since $X \subset Y$, it follows that $X \subset \text{span}_V(Y)$. Therefore, by the defining property of $\text{span}_V(X)$, $\text{span}_V(X) \subset \text{span}_V(Y)$.

(2) This has already been proved.

(3) The following inclusions are direct consequences of the definition of linear span:

$X \subset \text{span}_V(X)$, $Y \subset \text{span}_V(Y)$, $\text{span}_V(X) \cup \text{span}_V(Y) \subset \text{span}_V(\text{span}_V(X) \cup \text{span}_V(Y)) = \text{span}_V(X) + \text{span}_V(Y)$. It follows from the first two inclusions that $X \cup Y \subset \text{span}_V(X) \cup \text{span}_V(Y)$, and, then, from the third that $X \cup Y \subset \text{span}_V(\text{span}_V(X) \cup \text{span}_V(Y)) = \text{span}_V(X) + \text{span}_V(Y)$. Then, since $\text{span}_V(X \cup Y)$ is the smallest vector subspace containing $X \cup Y$, we have

$$\text{span}_V(X \cup Y) \subset \text{span}_V(X) + \text{span}_V(Y) \tag{1}$$

On the other hand, we have the inclusions

$$X \subset X \cup Y \quad \text{and} \quad Y \subset X \cup Y,$$

from which it follows, using (1), that $\text{span}_V(X) \subset \text{span}_V(X \cup Y)$ and $\text{span}_V(Y) \subset \text{span}_V(X \cup Y)$. Thus,

$$\text{span}_V(X) \cup \text{span}_V(Y) \subset \text{span}_V(X \cup Y)$$

Now, since $\text{span}_V(X) + \text{span}_V(Y)$ $[=\text{span}_V(\text{span}_V(X) \cup \text{span}_V(Y))]$ is the smallest vector subspace of V containing $\text{span}_V(X) \cup \text{span}_V(Y)$, we have

$$\text{span}_V(X) + \text{span}_V(Y) \subset \text{span}_V(X \cup Y) \tag{2}$$

Combining equations (1) and (2), we get the desired equality. Q.E.D.

Proposition 3.8 exposes some interesting and important properties of linear span, but it gives the student very little idea of (or feeling for) what these properties really mean. What is needed is a more direct, computationally-oriented description of linear span. This the following definition and proposition are designed to give. In addition the following definition introduces a new concept that plays a basic role in most of what will follow.

Definition 3.11

First, we introduce a modification of our notation. Until now, we have used "$\bullet$" to designate scalar multiplication in V and "$\cdot$" to designate the field multiplication. Henceforth, with minor exceptions, we eliminate these symbols and denote all multiplications by juxtaposition. Thus, "$a \cdot b$" becomes "ab" and "$a \bullet \mathbf{v}$" becomes "$a\mathbf{v}$." The only exceptions to this rule occur when we are using the actual numerical symbols for members of **Q**, **R**, *and* **C**, *or the numerical symbols "0" and "1" that designate the +-identity and $\cdot$-identity, respectively, of an arbitrary field F. When these symbols are used in connection with some multiplication of* *two elements of the above type we still use the symbol* "·". *Thus* "0 · 1" *remains the same,* "3 · 4" *remains the same,* "0 · **v**" *becomes* 0**v**, "2 · **v**" *becomes* "2**v**."

Let X be an arbitrary subset of V. We shall define what we mean by a linear combination of (some) members of X.

If X is empty, the only linear combination of members of X is **0**, *the zero vector of V.*

Suppose that X is not empty. Then, a linear combination of vectors of X is a vector $\mathbf{v} \in V$, *together with a finite number of members of the field F, say* $a_1, a_2, \ldots, a_k$, *and* distinct *vectors of X,* $\mathbf{x}_1, \mathbf{x}_2, \ldots, \mathbf{x}_k$, *such that*

$$\mathbf{v} = a_1\mathbf{x}_1 + \cdots + a_k\mathbf{x}_k$$

We call $a_1\mathbf{x}_1, a_2\mathbf{x}_2, \ldots, a_k\mathbf{x}_k$ *the* terms of the combination, $a_1, a_2, \ldots, a_k$ *the* coefficients of the combination, *and* $\mathbf{x}_1, \mathbf{x}_2, \ldots, \mathbf{x}_n$ *the* vectors of the combination. *The vector* **v** *is the* value of the combination, *but often, we shall abbreviate terminology and refer to it (or to the expression* $a_1\mathbf{x}_1 + \cdots + a_k\mathbf{x}_k$*) as the linear combination.*

A term with 0 coefficient is called *trivial.* If all the terms in the combination are trivial, then the combination is called trivial. If not, it is called nontrivial. It will be convenient, in the case of the empty set, to say that its (one and only) linear combination is trivial.**

We shall say that two linear combinations of vectors of *X* are *the same, or identical if they consist of the same nontrivial terms.* For example, let *X* consist of the three vectors $\mathbf{x}_1$, $\mathbf{x}_2$ and $\mathbf{x}_3$. Then $1\mathbf{x}_2$, $0\mathbf{x}_1 + 1\mathbf{x}_2$, $0\mathbf{x}_1 + 1\mathbf{x}_2 + 0\mathbf{x}_3$ are all to be considered identical linear combinations. Now, it may very well happen that two linear combinations of vectors of *X* are *not* identical, but they have *the same value.* We give an example of this below. In this case, we say that the two combinations *have the same value* or that they are *equal.* Clearly, if two combinations are identical, then they have the same value, or are equal.

It is clear that the identity of a linear combination is unchanged by the addition or deletion of trivial terms. From this it follows that if we are given two linear combinations of vectors of *X*, then we may suppose that these combinations consist of precisely the same vectors. For if the first combination has vectors that the second does not, add these vectors, with zero coefficients, to the second combination. The second combination remains the same and now has at least all the vectors that the first one has. If it has more than the first, adjoin these, with zero coefficients to the first. The resulting combinations have the same value as before and now consist of the same vectors. Clearly, this

** This supposition is made merely to simplify the language of some of the latter propositions, as is the earlier supposition that **0** is the only linear combination of $\varnothing$. The reader will recognize that the case of the empty set is a rather special one and, from a practical point of view, not too significant. From a logical viewpoint, however, it is desirable to include this case in our presentation. The conventions adopted concerning the empty set are aimed at making this inclusion as smooth and as painless as possible. They do not conflict with the definitions adopted for nonempty sets. Rather, they complement them.

process can be extended to situations involving more than two linear combinations. *Hence, the following assumption will be in force throughout the text: given a finite number of linear combinations of a set X, we shall assume that the same vectors occur in each (some, perhaps, with zero coefficients, of course).*

Note that the set X may be infinite but that *under all circumstances* a linear combination of vectors of X consists of only finitely many nontrivial terms.

Examples

(f) Let $\mathbf{v} \in V$ be any nonzero vector, and let $a \in F$ be any element distinct from 0 or 1. Let $X = \{\mathbf{v}, a\mathbf{v}\}$. Then,

$$\mathbf{0} = a\mathbf{v} + (-1)a\mathbf{v}$$

is a nontrivial linear combination of vectors of X, with coefficients a and -1 (reading from left to right), and with value $\mathbf{0}$.

Notice that the trivial linear combination $0\mathbf{v} + 0(a\mathbf{v})$ also has value $\mathbf{0}$ so that it *equals* the one above but is not *identical* with it.

(g) Consider the vector space $\mathbf{R}^3$. Let $X = \{(0, 0, 1), (-2, 3, 1), (-4, 6, 0)\}$. Then, $(-20, 30, 9)$ is (the value of) a linear combination of vectors of X, because

$$(-20, 30, 9) = 5(0, 0, 1) + 4(-2, 3, 1) + 3(-4, 6, 0)$$

(h) Let V be as in (b), and let $X = \{(1, 0, 0), (0, 1, 0), (0, 0, 1)\}$. Every vector in V is a linear combination of vectors of X. In particular, for any real numbers r_1, r_2, r_3,

$$(r_1, r_2, r_3) = r_1(1, 0, 0) + r_2(0, 1, 0) + r_3(0, 0, 1)$$

(i) Consider the following pictorial representation of $\mathbf{R}^3$.

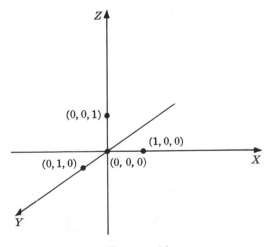

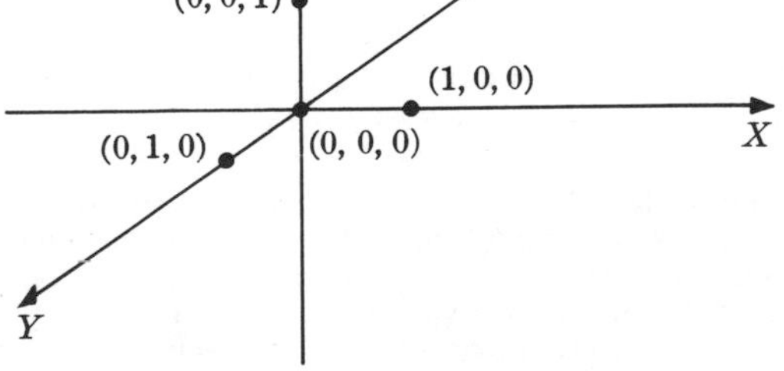

FIGURE 18

Let $X = \{(2, 0, 0), (3, -1, 4)\}$. The shaded area in the picture below represents one portion of the plane p determined by (0, 0, 0), (2, 0, 0) and (3, −1, 4). In Example (d) above, p is claimed to be $\text{span}_V(X)$. We shall show here that *p can also be described as the set of all linear combinations of vectors of X.*

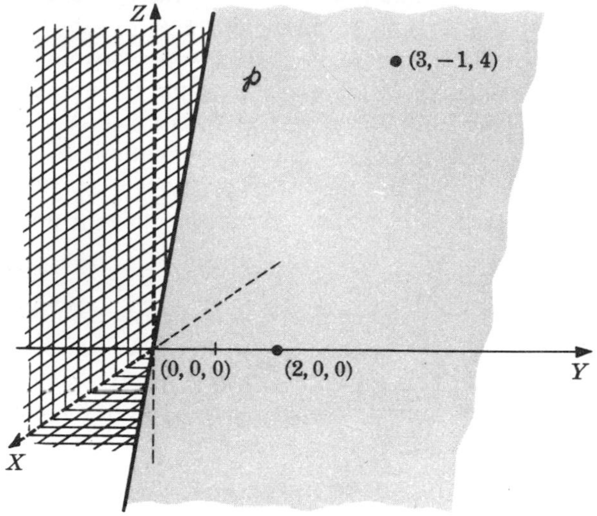

FIGURE 19

To see that any vector **v** in the plane p is a linear combination of (3, −1, 4) and (2, 0, 0), locate the vector as a point on p and draw lines through it parallel to the two heavy lines indicated in Figure 20. These lines will intersect the heavy ones, as indicated, in vectors $\mathbf{v}_1$ and $\mathbf{v}_2$. Since $\mathbf{v}_1$ is on the same line through the origin as (3, −1, 4), Example (c), above, implies that $\mathbf{v}_1$ is a

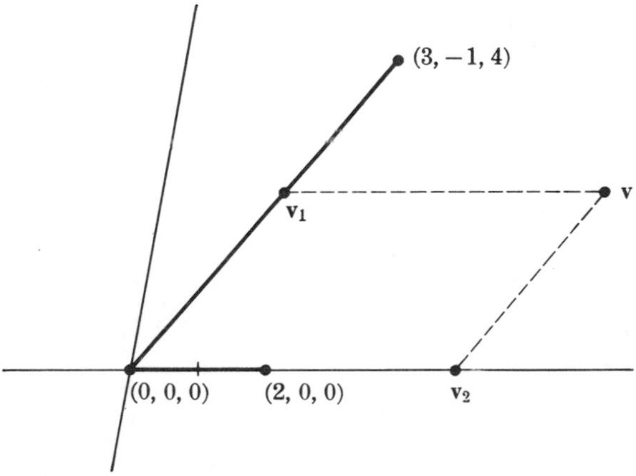

FIGURE 20

multiple of $(3, -1, 4)$, say $\mathbf{v}_1 = r_1(3, -1, 4)$. Similarly, $\mathbf{v}_2 = r_2(2, 0, 0)$. Now by the parallelogram rule for vector addition (see Exercises 1.1.**5**), it is easy to see that $\mathbf{v} = \mathbf{v}_1 + \mathbf{v}_2$. Thus, $\mathbf{v} = r_1(3, -1, 4) + r_2(2, 0, 0)$.

Thus, every $\mathbf{v} \in \not{p}$ is a linear combination of $(3, -1, 4)$ and $(2, 0, 0)$. The reverse argument shows that the converse is true: namely, every linear combination of $(3, -1, 4)$ and $(2, 0, 0)$ lies in the plane $\not{p}$.

Thus, the set of all linear combinations of $X = \not{p} = \text{span}_V(X)$.

(j) Consider the vector space $\mathscr{P}$, as in Example (e) above, and let $X = \{x^0, x^1, x^2, x^3, \ldots\}$. We claim in (e) that $\text{span}_{\mathscr{P}}(X) = \mathscr{P}$. We show here that $\text{span}_{\mathscr{P}}(X)$ = the set of all (values of) linear combinations of members of X. More precisely, we show that this set of combinations $= \mathscr{P}$.

Clearly, it is contained in $\mathscr{P}$, so that it remains only to prove the reverse inclusion.

Choose any polynomial $P(x) \in \mathscr{P}$. $P(x) = a_0x^0 + a_1x^1 + \cdots + a_nx^n$, for some integer n, $n \geqq 0$. But this expression is obviously a linear combination of members of X. Thus, $P(x)$ belongs to the set of (values of) linear combinations of members of X. This proves the desired reverse inclusion.

The above examples all point to a relationship between the notions of linear span and linear combinations. This is no accident, as we now show.

Proposition 3.9

Let X be an arbitrary subset of V. Then the set of all (values of) linear combinations of vectors of X is precisely $\text{span}_V(X)$.

Proof

Let $\overline{X}$ be the set of all (values of) linear combinations of vectors of X. Suppose first that $X \neq \varnothing$. Notice that, by definition, for any $\mathbf{x} \in X$, $1\mathbf{x}$ is a linear combination of vectors of X. Since $\mathbf{x} = 1\mathbf{x}$, this means that $\mathbf{x}$ is a value of a linear combination of vectors of X. Thus $\mathbf{x} \in \overline{X}$, and so, $X \subset \overline{X}$.

Next, choose any two vectors $\mathbf{v}_1 \in \overline{X}$ and $\mathbf{v}_2 \in \overline{X}$. They are both linear combinations of vectors of X, and we may assume that these combinations consist of the same vectors. Thus,

$$\mathbf{v}_1 = a_1\mathbf{x}_1 + a_2\mathbf{x}_2 + \cdots + a_k\mathbf{x}_k$$

and

$$\mathbf{v}_2 = b_1\mathbf{x}_1 + b_2\mathbf{x}_2 + \cdots + b_k\mathbf{x}_k, \quad \text{where} \quad \mathbf{x}_1, \mathbf{x}_2, \ldots, \mathbf{x}_k \in X,$$

so that $\mathbf{v}_1 + \mathbf{v}_2 = (a_1 + b_1)\mathbf{x}_1 + (a_2 + b_2)\mathbf{x}_2 + \cdots + (a_k + b_k)\mathbf{x}_k$. Thus, $\mathbf{v}_1 + \mathbf{v}_2 \in \overline{X}$. Also, for any $a \in F$

$$a\mathbf{v}_1 = (aa_1)\mathbf{x}_1 + \cdots + (aa_k)\mathbf{x}_k,$$

so that $a\mathbf{v}_1 \in \overline{X}$. Therefore, $\overline{X}$ is closed with respect to the operations of V and is, therefore, a vector subspace of V.

Thus, $\text{span}_V(X) \subset \bar{X}$, because $\text{span}_V(X)$ is the *smallest* subspace of V containing X.

On the other hand, $X \subset \text{span}_V(X)$ and, therefore, since $\text{span}_V(X)$ is closed with respect to the operations of V, every linear combination of vectors of X is also contained in $\text{span}_V(X)$. (Clearly, each such combination is formed from vectors of X by repeatedly applying the operations of V.) Therefore, $\bar{X} \subset \text{span}_V(X)$.

Combining this with the previous inclusion, we conclude that if $X \neq \varnothing$, then $\bar{X} = \text{span}_V(X)$.

If $X = \varnothing$, then, as we claim in the examples above,

$$\text{span}_V(X) = \{\mathbf{0}\} = \bar{X}$$

Thus, in this case, too, we have equality. Q.E.D.

Notice that this proposition accomplishes two things: 1. It gives an algebraic characterization of linear span. That is, $\text{span}_V(X)$ is the set of all vectors obtainable by applying the (algebraic) operations of V to the set X. This means that it is possible to compute $\text{span}_V(X)$ in special cases. For example, let $X = \{(1, 2, 3), (0, 0, 1)\} \subset \mathbf{R}^3$; then $\text{span}_{\mathbf{R}^3}(\{(1, 2, 3), (0, 0, 1)\})$ is the set of all combinations

$$r(1, 2, 3) + s(0, 0, 1),$$

where r and s range over $\mathbf{R}$, that is, the set of all vectors of the form $(r, 2r, 3r + s)$, where r and s range over $\mathbf{R}$.

2. It shows that the set of all linear combinations of vectors of a set $X \subset V$ is a vector subspace of V. Indeed, it is the smallest vector subspace of V containing X.

Observation 1 allows us to interpret the relation $\text{span}_V(X \cup Y) = \text{span}_V(X) + \text{span}_V(Y)$ as follows: The set of all linear combinations of vectors selected from $X \cup Y$ is equal to the set of sums of the form $\mathbf{u}_1 + \mathbf{u}_2$, where $\mathbf{u}_1$ is a linear combination of vectors of X and $\mathbf{u}_2$ is a linear combination of vectors of Y. Put this way, the equality should be evident, for, given any linear combination of vectors of $X \cup Y$, it is clearly possible—by rearranging terms, if necessary, so that the terms involving vectors of X are together and the terms involving vectors of Y are together—to break this combination up into a sum of combinations, one of vectors of X, the other of vectors of Y. Conversely, given any two such linear combinations, one of vectors of X, the other of vectors of Y, their sum is obviously a linear combination of vectors of $X \cup Y$.

Observation 1 also permits the following interpretation of the relation $\text{span}_V(\text{span}_V(X)) = \text{span}_V(X)$:

Suppose that we are given a number of linear combinations of vectors of X, say,

$$\begin{aligned} \mathbf{v}_1 &= a_1\mathbf{x}_1 + \cdots + a_{1k}\mathbf{x}_k \\ &\vdots \\ \mathbf{v}_n &= a_{nk}\mathbf{x}_1 + \cdots + a_{nk}\mathbf{x}_k, \end{aligned}$$

and we then form the linear combination $b_1\mathbf{v}_1 + \cdots + b_n\mathbf{v}_n$. This combination is, by definition, a member of $\text{span}_V(\text{span}_V(X))$. The equality $\text{span}_V(\text{span}_V(X)) = \text{span}_V(X)$, then, implies that the combination is a member of $\text{span}_V(X)$. This can, of course, be seen directly, by the following algebraic manipulation:

$$\begin{aligned} b_1\mathbf{v}_1 + \cdots + b_n\mathbf{v}_n &= b_1(a_{11}\mathbf{x}_1 + \cdots + a_{1k}\mathbf{x}_k) + \cdots + b_n(a_{n1}\mathbf{x}_1 + \cdots + a_{nk}\mathbf{x}_k) \\ &= (b_1a_{11} + \cdots + b_na_{n1})\mathbf{x}_1 + \cdots + (b_1a_{1k} + \cdots + b_na_{nk})\mathbf{x}_k \end{aligned}$$

Thus, every linear combination of linear combinations of vectors of X is a linear combination of vectors of X.

Perhaps, at this point, it is worthwhile to remind the reader of our objective in these sections and to explain the extent of our progress in achieving this objective. We are attempting to remove some of the complexity and abstractness of dealing with vector spaces by reducing problems and properties of the entire vector space to those of "small" subsets of the space. Of course, it must be possible to go back the other way. That is, given a special subset, of the type we have in mind, we must be able to "obtain" the entire vector space again. What do we mean by "obtain"? Well, the word implies that the vector space is the end-product of some process that we may apply to the subset. What process? Well, the only vector-space *processes* that we have at our disposal: namely, the vector-space operations. Thus, we are interested in those subsets of V that yield the entire vector space V as the result of applying the operations of V. But, we have already developed precise terminology for this situation: namely, we are interested in sets $X \subset V$, such that the set of all linear combinations of vectors of X is V, that is $\text{span}_V(X) = V$. In Definition 3.7 we described this situation by saying that V is *generated by* X. We elaborate on this and say that X is a *generating set of* (*or for*) V, or that X is *a set of generators of* (*or for*) V.

The key fact about sets of generators of V is that every vector of V can be written as a linear combination of vectors of the generating set. Thus, it would seem that many questions about V could be reduced to questions about generating sets of V.

And this is indeed true. Our problems, in general, however, are by no means solved by this conclusion. For, given a vector space V, we have, at this point, only *one* sure-fire candidate for a generating set of V: namely, V itself! [Recall that $\text{span}_V(V) = V$.] And we certainly gain no advantage by "restricting" our attention to this generating set.

It is clear, that V is too big to be an interesting generating set. Moreover, it is obvious that many of the vectors of V are unnecessary, or redundant, for the purposes of generating. For example, the zero vector of V is, clearly, unnecessary. For it can be obtained as a (trivial) linear combination of any set of nonzero vectors. Indeed, in general, any vector in V that is (the value of) a linear combination of other vectors in V is, by itself, redundant for the purposes of generating. Given any $\mathbf{v} \in V$, then, all of its scalar multiples (except $1\mathbf{v}$) are redundant, for each of them is a linear combination of $\mathbf{v}$.

It is clear, therefore, that, from the viewpoint of efficiency and usefulness, the truly desirable generating sets are those that are, in some sense, *irredundant*. We develop this notion in the next section.

Irredundancy is desirable for yet another reason. Suppose that X is a generating set of V, that $\mathbf{v}$ is a vector of V, and that $\mathbf{v}$ is the value of more than one linear combination of vectors of X. If we are supposed to deduce facts about $\mathbf{v}$ from one such combination, we must be sure that such facts *are actually about* $\mathbf{v}$ and not merely about the particular coefficients and vectors at hand. Such assurance, however, would be present, only if each vector in V is the value of precisely one linear combination of vectors of X, that is, only if X is irredundant. For example, if the reader were given vectors $\mathbf{x}_1$ and $\mathbf{x}_2$ of $X \subset \mathbf{R}^3$, and the coefficients r_1 and r_2 (in $\mathbf{R}$) and were told only that these vectors and coefficients were non-zero, he would not be entitled to conclude that the (value of) the linear combination $r_1\mathbf{x}_1 + r_2\mathbf{x}_2$ was nonzero! (For example, let $\mathbf{x}_1 = (2, 1, -1)$, $\mathbf{x}_2 = (-4, 2, -2)$, $r_1 - 2$, $r_2 = 1$; then $r_1\mathbf{x}_1 + r_2\mathbf{x}_2 = 2(2, 1, -1) + 1(-4, -2, 2) = (0, 0, 0)$.)

These comments motivate the considerations of the next section.

EXERCISES / 3.7

1. Describe the vectors of $\text{span}_V(X)$, where S, V, and F are as follows:
   a. $F = \mathbf{R}$, $V = \mathbf{R}^3$, $X = \{(0, 0, 0), (1, 0, 0)\}$.
   b. $F = \mathbf{R}$, $V = \mathbf{R}^3$, $X = \{(1, 0, 0)\}$.
   c. $F = \mathbf{R}$, $V = \mathbf{R}^3$, $X = \{(1, 0, 0), (0, 1, 0)\}$.
   d. F any field, $V = F$, $X = \{1\}$.
   e. $F = \mathbf{R}$, $V = \mathbf{R}$, $X = \{2\}$.
   f. $F = \mathbf{Q}$, $V = \mathbf{R}$, $X = \{1\}$.
   g. $F = \mathbf{C}$, $V = \mathbf{C}$, $X = \{i\}$.
   h. $F = \mathbf{R}$, $V = \mathbf{C}$, $X = \{i\}$.
   i. $F = \mathbf{R}$, $V = \mathcal{P}^n$ (polynomials of degree $\leqq n$), $X = \{x^0, x^1, \ldots, x^n\}$.

2. Let $F = \mathbf{R}$ and $V = \mathbf{R}^3$. Is $(2, 1, -3)$ a linear combination of vectors of $\{(1, 4, 1), (2, 2, 2), (-1, 0, 0)\}$? If not, why not? If so, exhibit the combination.

3.* Let V be any vector space over F. Let X be any subset of V. Show that $\text{span}_V(X \cup \{\mathbf{0}\}) = \text{span}_V(X)$.

4. Let $V = \mathbf{R}^3$, $F = \mathbf{R}$, and let X be any nonempty subset of V.
   Let $\mathcal{F}$ be the family of all subsets Y of V with the following two properties:
   a. $X \subset Y$

b. If $\mathbf{v}_1$ and $\mathbf{v}_2$ belong to Y, then the (infinite) straight line joining $\mathbf{v}_1$ and $\mathbf{v}_2$ belongs to Y.

- **i.** Show that $\mathscr{F}$ is nonempty.
- **ii.** Show that $X \subset \bigcap \mathscr{F}$.
- **iii.** Show that $\bigcap \mathscr{F} \in \mathscr{F}$.
- **iv.** Show that $\bigcap \mathscr{F}$ is a hyperplane in V (cf. Exercises **3.6.5**).
- **v.** If $\mathbf{0} \in X$, show that $\bigcap \mathscr{F} = \text{span}_V(X)$.

This exercise allows us to characterize $\text{span}_V(X)(V = \mathbf{R}^3,\ X \subset \mathbf{R}^3)$ in the following way. First, notice that, by **3** above, $\text{span}_V(X) = \text{span}_V(X \cup \{\mathbf{0}\})$. Let $X \cup \{\mathbf{0}\} = X'$. Then, by **1** above, $\text{span}_V(X) = \text{span}_V(X') = \bigcap \mathscr{F}$, where $\mathscr{F}$ is the family described above (for X' instead of X). Thus, we may call $\text{span}_V(X)$ the smallest subset of V containing $X \cup \{\mathbf{0}\}$ having property **4.a** above (which we may express as being closed under the operation of drawing lines determined by its points). Thus, pictorially, if X consists of the three points pictured below, we first draw all lines determined by points X and $\mathbf{0}$, obtaining a set X_1. We then apply this procedure to X_1, obtaining a set X_2. We imagine this process continued indefinitely until no new points are added. The result is $\text{span}_V(X)$.

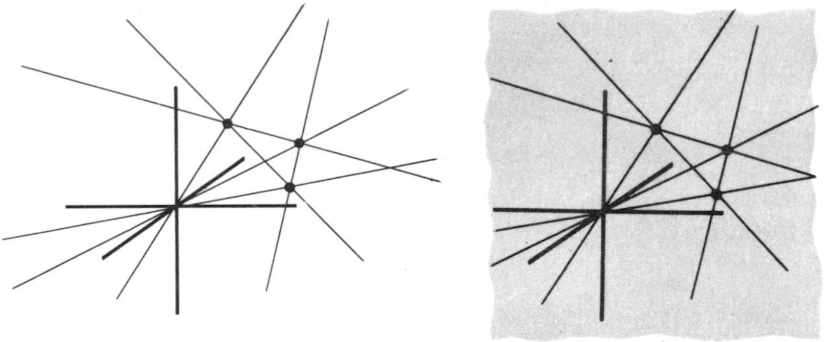

Step 1 Step 2

(a) $\text{span}_V(X) = \mathbf{R}^2$

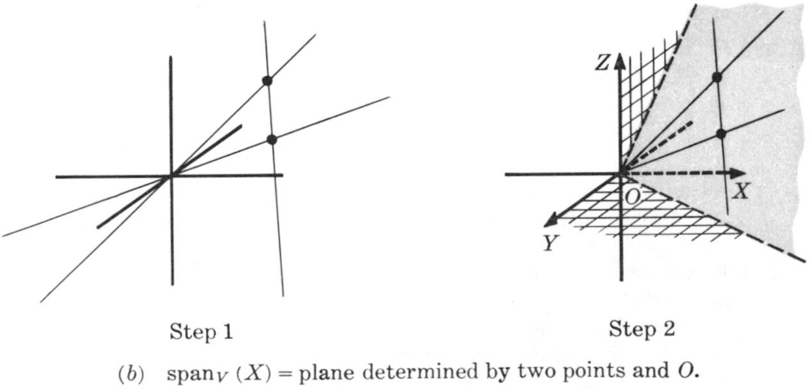

Step 1 Step 2

(b) $\text{span}_V(X)$ = plane determined by two points and O.

FIGURE 21

c. Is it possible for a set X consisting of fewer than three points to satisfy $\text{span}_{\mathbf{R}^3}(X) = \mathbf{R}^3$? Justify your answer on intuitive grounds.

5. For V, F, and X as below, which of the following X are generating sets of V? Which are irredundant? Which are redundant?

a. $F =$ any field, $V = \{0\}$ ($0 =$ the $+$-identity for F), $X = \varnothing$
b. $F =$ any field, $V = \{0\}$, $X = \{0\}$
c. $F = \mathbf{R}$, $V = \mathbf{R}$, $X = \{2\}$
d. $F = \mathbf{R}$, $V = \mathbf{R}$, $X = \{0\}$
e. $F = \mathbf{R}$, $V = \mathbf{R}$, $X = \{1, 0\}$
f. $F = \mathbf{R}$, $V = \mathbf{R}^3$, $X = \{(3, 1, 1), (-1, 2, 4), (2, 3, 5)\}$
g. $F = \mathbf{R}$, $V = \mathbf{C}$, $X = \{1, i\}$
h. $F = \mathbf{C}$, $V = \mathbf{C}$, $X = \{1, i\}$
i. $F = \mathbf{Q}$, $V = \mathbf{R}$, $X = \{1\}$
j. $F = \mathbf{Q}$, $V = \mathbf{Q}$, $X = \{1\}$
k. $F = \mathbf{R}$, $V = \mathbf{R}^2$, $X = \{(0, 1), (1, 0)\}$

6. Let $\mathscr{P}^n \subset \mathscr{P}$ be as in **1.i.**, above. Show that $\{x^0, x^1, \ldots, x^n\}$ generates $\mathscr{P}^n$.

5.2 Linear Dependence and Independence

In this section we develop the notions of redundance (linear dependence) of generating sets and irredundance (linear independence), informally introduced in Subsection 5.1. Throughout this section, $V, +, \cdot$ will denote a vector space over $F, +, \cdot$

Definition 3.12

*A subset X of V is linearly dependent if and only if there is a proper subset Y of X (i.e., $Y \subset X$ but $Y \neq X$)** such that $\text{span}_V(Y) = \text{span}_V(X)$.*

X is linearly independent, if and only if it is not linearly dependent.

Remarks: 1. Notice that linear dependence coincides with the notion of redundance mentioned above in 5.1. For to say that X is linearly dependent means that there is a strictly "smaller" set Y that generates the same linear span as X. The set $X \setminus Y$, therefore, is nonempty, and it consists of unnecessary or redundant vectors—they are not needed for the generation of $\text{span}_V(X)$.

Similarly, the notion of independence coincides with the notion of irredundance mentioned above.

2. Since the empty set has no proper subsets, it is linearly independent.

3. Let $\mathbf{v} \in V$ be any nonzero vector. The set $\{\mathbf{v}\}$ is linearly independent, for its only proper subset is $\varnothing$, and $\text{span}_V(\varnothing) = \{\mathbf{0}\}$, which does not equal $\text{span}_V(\{\mathbf{v}\})$.

4. Let X be any subset of V such that $\mathbf{0} \in X$. Then X is linearly dependent. For, let $Y = X \setminus \{\mathbf{0}\}$. Y is clearly a proper subset of X. Moreover, $X = Y \cup \{\mathbf{0}\}$.

** Thus, $Y \subset X$, and there is at least one $\mathbf{x} \in X$ such that $\mathbf{x} \notin Y$.

Thus, $\text{span}_V(X) = \text{span}_V(Y \cup \{\mathbf{0}\}) = \text{span}_V(Y)$, by Exercises 3.7.3. The reader is urged to verify this fact now, if he has not already done so.

(Clearly, as indicated in the discussion at the end of 5.1, the vector $\mathbf{0}$ is always redundant.)

The following two propositions are important because they provide computational criteria for deciding when a set is linearly dependent or linearly independent.

Proposition 3.9

Let X be a subset of V. The following four statements are logically equivalent.

(1) *X is linearly dependent.*
(2) *There is a nontrivial linear combination of vectors of X with value $\mathbf{0}$.*
(3) *Some vector $\mathbf{x} \in X$ is the value of a linear combination of vectors of $X \setminus \{\mathbf{x}\}$ (i.e. vectors of X not equal to $\mathbf{x}$).*
(4) *Some vector in $\text{span}_V(X)$ is the value of more than one linear combination of vectors of X.*

Proposition 3.10

Let X be a subset of V. The following four statements are logically equivalent.

(1) *X is linearly independent.*
(2) *Every linear combination of vectors of X with value $\mathbf{0}$ is trivial.*
(3) *No vector $\mathbf{x} \in X$ is the value of a linear combination of vectors of $X \setminus \{\mathbf{x}\}$. That is, for each $\mathbf{x} \in X$, we have $\mathbf{x} \notin \text{span}_V(X \setminus \{\mathbf{x}\})$.*
(4) *Every vector in $\text{span}_V(X)$ is the value of precisely one linear combination of vectors of X.*

Note that each of the statements (1), (2), (3), (4) of Proposition 3.10 is the negation of the corresponding statement in Proposition 3.9. Thus, the logical equivalence of the statements of Proposition 3.9 is logically equivalent to the logical equivalence of the statements of Proposition 3.10. It suffices, therefore, to prove only Proposition 3.9.

Before doing so, however, we present three examples of how to apply the result.

(a) Let $V = \mathbf{R}^3$, $F = \mathbf{R}$, and $X = \{(2, 1, 1), (1, 0, 0), (5, 1, 1)\}$. We show that X is linearly dependent by showing that $(0, 0, 0)$ is the value of a nontrivial linear combination of vectors of X [cf. Proposition 3.9(2)]. Clearly,

$$(0, 0, 0) = 1(2, 1, 1) + 3(1, 0, 0) + (-1)(5, 1, 1)$$

(b) Let $V = F^3$, $F =$ any field, and $X = \{(1, 0, 0), (0, 1, 0), (0, 0, 1)\}$, where $1 \in F$ is the $\cdot$-identity. We show that X is linearly independent by showing that every linear combination of vectors of X with value $(0, 0, 0)$ is trivial [cf. Proposition 3.10, (2)].

Suppose then that a_1, a_2, and a_3 belong to F and that

$$a_1(1, 0, 0) + a_2(0, 1, 0) + a_3(0, 0, 1) = (0, 0, 0)$$

By definition, $a_1(1, 0, 0) + a_2(0, 1, 0) + a_3(0, 0, 1) = (a_1, a_2, a_3)$. Then, the equation $(a_1, a_2, a_3) = (0, 0, 0)$ implies that $a_1 = 0$, $a_2 = 0$, and $a_3 = 0$, so that the combination is trivial.

(c) Let $V = \mathbf{R}^2$, $F = \mathbf{R}$, $X = \{(2, 1), (3, -2)\}$. We use the technique of (b) to show that X is linearly independent.

Suppose, then, that r_1 and r_2 belong to $\mathbf{R}$ and that

$$r_1(2, 1) + r_2(3, -2) = (0, 0)$$

This equation is equivalent to $(2r_1 + 3r_2, r_1 - 2r_2) = (0, 0)$, which, in turn, is equivalent to the system of two equations

$$2r_1 + 3r_2 = 0$$
$$r_1 - 2r_2 = 0$$

Using the second equation, we conclude that $r_1 = 2r_2$, and using the first, we conclude that $0 = 2r_1 + 3r_2 = 4r_2 + 3r_2 = 7r_2$, so that $r_1 = r_2 = 0$.

Thus, the combination is trivial, as desired.

This example should suggest to the reader that the notions of linear dependence and independence are closely related to questions about solutions of systems of linear equations.

Proof of Proposition 3.9

We shall prove that (1) implies (3), (3) implies (4), (4) implies (2), and (2) implies (1). This will prove the desired equivalence.

(1) *implies* (3). Assume that (1) is true, letting Y be a proper subset of X such that $\text{span}_V(Y) = \text{span}_V(X)$. Since $Y \subset X$ but $Y \neq X$, there is a vector $\mathbf{x} \in X$ such that $\mathbf{x} \notin Y$. Thus, we have the inclusions $Y \subset X \setminus \{\mathbf{x}\} \subset X$. The second of these is obvious; the first follows from the observation that Y is a subset of X and that, since $\mathbf{x} \notin Y$, the withdrawal of $\mathbf{x}$ from X leaves Y unaffected. Thus, by Proposition 3.8,

$$\text{span}_V(X) = \text{span}_V(Y) \subset \text{span}_V(X \setminus \{\mathbf{x}\}) \subset \text{span}_V(X)$$

Therefore, $\text{span}_V(X) = \text{span}_V(X \setminus \{\mathbf{x}\})$. Since $\mathbf{x} \in X$ and $X \subset \text{span}_V(X)$, this equality implies that $\mathbf{x} \in \text{span}_V(X \setminus \{\mathbf{x}\})$, which means that $\mathbf{x}$ is a linear combination of vectors of $X \setminus \{\mathbf{x}\}$.

Thus, (3) is true, so that (1) implies (3).

(3) *implies* (4). Consider the vector $\mathbf{x}$ above, under the assumption that (3) is true. Clearly, $\mathbf{x} = 1\mathbf{x}$. Moreover, by (3), $\mathbf{x}$ is a linear combination of vectors of $X \setminus \{\mathbf{x}\}$. Such a combination must differ from $1\mathbf{x}$ because it does not contain $\mathbf{x}$, whereas $1\mathbf{x}$ does. Thus, $\mathbf{x}$ is the value of at least two distinct linear combinations of vectors of X. Since $\mathbf{x} \in X$ and $X \subset \text{span}_V(X)$, $\mathbf{x}$ is the desired vector, so that (4) is true.

(4) *implies* (2). Suppose that (4) is true, and let $\mathbf{v} \in \operatorname{span}_V(X)$ be the value of distinct linear combinations of vectors of X. We may assume that these combinations consist of the same vectors; since they are *distinct* combinations, they differ at least in one term, which, without losing generality, we may assume is the first term. Thus,

$$\mathbf{v} = a_1\mathbf{x}_1 + \cdots + a_n\mathbf{x}_n$$

and

$$\mathbf{v} = b_1\mathbf{x}_1 + \cdots + b_n\mathbf{x}_n,$$

where $a_1 \neq b_1$. Subtracting the second equation from the first, we obtain

$$\mathbf{0} = (a_1 - b_1)\mathbf{x}_1 + \cdots + (a_n - b_n)\mathbf{x}_n$$

Since $a_1 \neq b_1$, $a_1 - b_1 \neq 0$. Moreover, the vectors $\mathbf{x}_1, \ldots, \mathbf{x}_n$ are, by choice, distinct. Thus, $(a_1 - b_1)\mathbf{x}_1 + \cdots + (a_n - b_n)\mathbf{x}_n$ is a nontrivial linear combination of vectors of X with value $\mathbf{0}$.

Thus, (2) is true, so that (4) implies (2).

(2) *implies* (1). Suppose that (2) is true and consider a linear combination of vectors of X with value $\mathbf{0}$, the first term of which is nontrivial. (Given any nontrivial combination, we may, by rearranging terms, always assume that the first term is nontrivial.) Thus, $\mathbf{0} = a_1\mathbf{x}_1 + a_2\mathbf{x}_2 + \cdots + a_n\mathbf{x}_n$, where $a_1 \neq 0$. We subtract $a_1\mathbf{x}_1$ from both sides of the equation and multiply both sides by $-1/a_1$. We get

$$\begin{aligned}\mathbf{x}_1 &= -1/a_1(a_2\mathbf{x}_2 + \cdots + a_n\mathbf{x}_n)\\ &= \left(\frac{-a_2}{a_1}\right)\mathbf{x}_2 + \cdots + \left(\frac{-a_n}{a_1}\right)\mathbf{x}_n\end{aligned}$$

Let $Y = X \setminus \{\mathbf{x}_1\}$. *Clearly, Y is a proper subset of X*, and $\operatorname{span}_V(Y) \subset \operatorname{span}_V(X)$. Now, $\mathbf{x}_2, \ldots, \mathbf{x}_n$, above, belong to Y, so that $\mathbf{x}_1 \in \operatorname{span}_V(Y)$, by the equation above. Since $Y \subset \operatorname{span}_V(Y)$, it follows that $Y \cup \{\mathbf{x}_1\} \subset \operatorname{span}_V(Y)$. But $Y \cup \{\mathbf{x}_1\} = (X \setminus \{\mathbf{x}_1\}) \cup \{\mathbf{x}_1\} = X$, so that $X \subset \operatorname{span}_V(Y)$. By Proposition 3.8, $\operatorname{span}_V(X) \subset \operatorname{span}_V(\operatorname{span}_V(Y)) = \operatorname{span}_V(Y)$. Combining this with the reverse inclusion, obtained above, *we conclude that $\operatorname{span}_V(X) = \operatorname{span}_V(Y)$.*

Thus, (1) is true, so that (2) implies (1). Q.E.D.

Henceforth, we shall feel free to use any of the statements of Proposition 3.9 as equivalent to the definition of linear dependence in Definition 3.12. Similarly, we shall feel free to use any of the statements of Proposition 3.10 as equivalent to the definition of linear independence in Definition 3.12.

All the statements are important. Of particular interest, however, is statement (4) of Proposition 3.10. This implies that if X is a linearly independent generating set for V [i.e., if $\operatorname{span}_V(X) = V$], then every vector in $\mathbf{V}$ can be obtained in *precisely one way* from X via the operations of V; that is, it is the value of precisely one linear combination of vectors of X. The discovery of such a set $X \subset V$ would then represent a genuine step forward in reducing the complexity of V. We shall show, in the next section, that every vector space has such sets.

First, however, we prove some propositions that will assist us in constructing linearly independent sets. Then, we present some more examples.

Proposition 3.11

Let X and Y be subsets of V such that $X \subset Y$.

(1) *If X is linearly dependent, then so is Y.*
(2) *If Y is linearly independent, then so is X.*

Statements (1) and (2) are contrapositives of one another, and, hence, they are logically equivalent. We shall prove (2). It can be paraphrased as: *Any subset of a linearly independent set is linearly independent.*

Proof

The key to this proof is the observation that, since $X \subset Y$, every linear combination of vectors of X is, *a fortiori*, a linear combination of vectors of Y. Let us assume that Y is linearly independent; we must prove that X is. Of course, if $X = \varnothing$, it is linearly independent, by Remark 2, above. Suppose then that $X \neq \varnothing$, and that $a_1\mathbf{x}_1 + \cdots + a_n\mathbf{x}_n$ is a linear combination of vectors of X with value $\mathbf{0}$. It is then also a linear combination of vectors of Y with value $\mathbf{0}$, and, since Y is linearly independent, the combination must be trivial.

Thus, X is linearly independent, by criterion (2) of Proposition 3.10. Q.E.D.

Proposition 3.12

Let X and Y be linearly independent subsets of V. The set $X \cup Y$ is linearly independent, if and only if $\mathrm{span}_V(X) \cap \mathrm{span}_V(Y) = \mathrm{span}_V(X \cap Y)$.

This result is important when it comes to piecing together (i.e., forming the union of) "small" linearly independent sets to form "larger" ones.

Proof

Notice that under all circumstances (i.e., with no conditions on X and Y), $X \subset \mathrm{span}_V(X)$, $Y \subset \mathrm{span}_V(Y)$, so that $X \cap Y \subset \mathrm{span}_V(X) \cap \mathrm{span}_V(Y)$, and, therefore,

$$\mathrm{span}_V(X \cap Y) \subset \mathrm{span}_V(\mathrm{span}_V(X) \cap \mathrm{span}_V(Y)).$$

Since $\mathrm{span}_V(X)$ and $\mathrm{span}_V(Y)$ are vector subspaces of V, so is $\mathrm{span}_V(X) \cap \mathrm{span}_V(Y)$, so that $\mathrm{span}_V(\mathrm{span}_V(X) \cap \mathrm{span}_V(Y)) = \mathrm{span}_V(X) \cap \mathrm{span}_V(Y)$. Thus, under all circumstances, we have

$$\mathrm{span}_V(X \cap Y) \subset \mathrm{span}_V(X) \cap \mathrm{span}_V(Y)$$

The condition of equality in the above statement of the proposition, therefore, tells us only one thing new: namely, the reverse inclusion holds (under suitable circumstances).

(1) Suppose then that X and Y are linearly independent subsets of V, such that $X \cup Y$ is linearly independent. We shall prove that

$$\text{span}_V(X \cap Y) \supset \text{span}_V(X) \cap \text{span}_V(Y),$$

which is equivalent, by the above remark, to proving that equality holds.

First, we introduce some temporary notation. Members of X that do not belong to Y, that is, members of $X \setminus Y$, will be denoted by "$\mathbf{x}$", together with some subscript, say "$\mathbf{x}_1$," "$\mathbf{x}_2$," and so on; members of Y but not X, that is, members of $Y \setminus X$, will be denoted by "$\mathbf{y}$," together with some subscript; finally, members of X and Y, that is, members of $X \cap Y$, will be denoted by "$\mathbf{w}$," together with some subscript.

If $X = \varnothing$, or if $Y = \varnothing$, then $X \cap Y = \varnothing$, and $\text{span}_V(X \cap Y) = \{\mathbf{0}\} = \text{span}_V(X) \cap \text{span}_V(Y)$, so that the desired relation holds. Let us assume, therefore, that $X \neq \varnothing$ and $Y \neq \varnothing$. We also assume, temporarily, that $X \cap Y \neq \varnothing$.

Choose any $\mathbf{v} \in \text{span}_V(X) \cap \text{span}_V(Y)$. Since $\mathbf{v} \in \text{span}_V(X)$, $\mathbf{v}$ is a linear combination of vectors of X. Thus, $\mathbf{v} = a_1\mathbf{x}_1 + \cdots + a_k\mathbf{x}_k + b_1\mathbf{w}_1 + \cdots + b_\ell\mathbf{w}_\ell$, some of the coefficients possibly being zero. Similarly, $\mathbf{v} = c_1\mathbf{y}_1 + \cdots + c_m\mathbf{y}_m + d_1\mathbf{w}_1 + \cdots + d_\ell\mathbf{w}_\ell$. We may, of course, assume that the same $\mathbf{w}$'s occur in both expressions. Subtracting the second equation from the first, we get

$$\mathbf{0} = a_1\mathbf{x}_1 + \cdots + a_k\mathbf{x}_k + (b_1 - d_1)\mathbf{w}_1 + \cdots + (b_\ell - d_\ell)\mathbf{w}_\ell + (-c_1)\mathbf{y}_1 + \cdots + (-c_m)\mathbf{y}_m$$

This is clearly a linear combination of (distinct) vectors of $X \cup Y$ with value $\mathbf{0}$. Since $X \cup Y$ is linearly independent, it follows that the combination is trivial, so that $a_1 = a_2 = \cdots = a_k = 0 = c_1 = c_2 = \cdots = c_m$, $b_1 = d_1, \ldots, b_\ell = d_\ell$. Therefore,

$$\mathbf{v} = b_1\mathbf{w}_1 + \cdots + b_\ell\mathbf{w}_\ell,$$

because, $a_1, a_2, \ldots, a_k$ being zero, the other terms drop out. Therefore, $\mathbf{v} \in \text{span}_V(X \cap Y)$, which proves the desired inclusion.

If $X \cap Y = \varnothing$, the proof proceeds as above, only there are no terms $b_1\mathbf{w}_1, \ldots, b_\ell\mathbf{w}_\ell, d_1\mathbf{w}_1, \ldots, d_\ell\mathbf{w}_\ell$. Thus, the concluding equation for $\mathbf{v}$ is $\mathbf{v} = \mathbf{0}$. This means that $\text{span}_V(X) \cap \text{span}_V(Y) \subset \{\mathbf{0}\} = \text{span}_V(\varnothing) = \text{span}_V(X \cap Y)$, as desired.

(2) We now prove the converse of part (1). That is, we assume that $\text{span}_V(X \cap Y) = \text{span}_V(X) \cap \text{span}_V(Y)$ (and that X and Y are linearly independent), and we shall show that $X \cup Y$ is linearly independent. We may, of course, assume that $X \neq \varnothing$ and that $Y \neq \varnothing$, for if either of them are empty, the result is obvious. We also assume, temporarily, that $X \cap Y \neq \varnothing$, and we use the notation introduced in (1).

Suppose that

$$a_1\mathbf{x}_1 + \cdots + a_k\mathbf{x}_k + b_1\mathbf{w}_1 + \cdots + b_\ell\mathbf{w}_\ell + c_1\mathbf{y}_1 + \cdots + c_m\mathbf{y}_m$$

is a linear combination of vectors of $X \cup Y$ with value $\mathbf{0}$. Then,

$$a_1\mathbf{x}_1 + \cdots + a_k\mathbf{x}_k + b_1\mathbf{w}_1 + \cdots + b_\ell\mathbf{w}_\ell = (-c_1)\mathbf{y}_1 + \cdots + (-c_m)\mathbf{y}_m$$

The left-hand expression is a vector in $\text{span}_V(X)$; the right-hand vector belongs to $\text{span}_V(Y)$. Since they are equal, they both belong to $\text{span}_V(X) \cap \text{span}_V(Y)$, and, hence, by the equation assumed, they both belong to $\text{span}_V(X \cap Y)$. Thus,

$$(-c_1)\mathbf{y}_1 + \cdots + (-c_m)\mathbf{y}_m = d_1\mathbf{w}_{\ell+1} + \cdots + d_n\mathbf{w}_{\ell+n},$$

where the vectors $\mathbf{w}_{\ell+1}, \ldots, \mathbf{w}_{\ell+n}$ may or may not coincide with the vectors $\mathbf{w}_1, \ldots, \mathbf{w}_\ell$, above (it does not matter). This equation implies that

$$(-c_1)\mathbf{y}_1 + \cdots + (-c_m)\mathbf{y}_m + (-d_1)\mathbf{w}_{\ell+1} + \cdots + (-d_n)\mathbf{w}_{\ell+n}\mathbf{x}_k = \mathbf{0}$$

This is a linear combination of vectors of Y. Since Y is linearly independent, $-c_1 = \cdots = -c_m = -d_1 = \cdots = -d_n = 0$, or $c_1 = \cdots = c_m = 0 = d_1 = \cdots = d_n$.

In a similar way, we show that $a_1 = \cdots = a_k = 0$. For, since $a_1\mathbf{x}_1 + \cdots + a_k\mathbf{x}_k + b_1\mathbf{w}_1 + \cdots + b_\ell\mathbf{w}_\ell = e_1\mathbf{w}_1 + \cdots + e_\ell\mathbf{w}_\ell$, (we may assume that the same $\mathbf{w}$'s appear on both sides by adding terms with zero coefficients to each side, if necessary), we get $a_1\mathbf{x}_1 + \cdots + a_k\mathbf{x}_k + (b_1 - e_1)\mathbf{w}_1 + \cdots + (b_\ell - e_\ell)\mathbf{w}_\ell = \mathbf{0}$. This is a linear combination of vectors of X, so that, since X is linearly independent, the combination is trivial. That is $a_1 = \cdots = a_k = 0$, $b_1 = e_1, \ldots, b_\ell = e_\ell$.

Therefore, all the a's and c's are zero in the original combination. We are, thus, left with the combination $b_1\mathbf{w}_1 + \cdots + b_\ell\mathbf{x}_\ell$ with value $\mathbf{0}$. Since this is a linear combination of vectors of $X \cap Y$, and $X \cap Y \subset X$, then $X \cap Y$ is linearly independent, because X is [Proposition 3.11(2)], and the combination must be trivial. That is $b_1 = \cdots = b_\ell = 0$.

Therefore, we have proved that the entire original combination must be trivial, so that $X \cup Y$ is linearly independent.

If $X \cap Y = \varnothing$, the proof proceeds as above, only, again, there are no terms $b_1\mathbf{w}_1, \ldots, b_\ell\mathbf{w}_\ell$, etc.: these may easily be omitted from the argument, however, the only change being notational and linguistic. The reader should reread the above proof of (2) under the assumption that $X \cap Y = \varnothing$ and be able to state what changes must be made. Q.E.D.

Corollary 1 to Proposition 3.12

Let X and Y be linearly independent subsets of V, such that $X \cap Y = \varnothing$. Then, $X \cup Y$ is linearly independent, if and only if $\text{span}_V(X) \cap \text{span}_V(Y) = \{\mathbf{0}\}$.

The proof here should be obvious and will be omitted.

The next corollary can be obtained directly from the definition of linear independence. Nevertheless, we find it convenient to state it and prove it in the context of Proposition 3.12.

Corollary 2 to Proposition 3.12

Let X be any linearly independent subset of V, and let $\mathbf{v}$ be any vector of V such that $\mathbf{v} \notin X$. Then, $X \cup \{\mathbf{v}\}$ is linearly independent if and only if $\mathbf{v} \notin \text{span}_V(X)$.

Proof

Suppose that $\mathbf{v} \notin \text{span}_V(X)$. Then, $\text{span}_V(\{\mathbf{v}\}) \cap \text{span}_V(X) = \{\mathbf{0}\}$. For, since the intersection of these two subspaces is a vector subspace of V, $\mathbf{0}$ belongs to it. On the other hand, every vector belonging to the intersection must be both a multiple of $\mathbf{v}$ and a member of $\text{span}_V(X)$. Suppose this multiple be $a\mathbf{v}$, $a \neq 0$. Then, $\mathbf{v} = (1/a)(a\mathbf{v}) \in \text{span}_V(X)$, which is impossible. Thus, $a = 0$, and $a\mathbf{v} = \mathbf{0}$. This proves the equality $\text{span}_V(\{\mathbf{v}\}) \cap \text{span}_V(X) = \{\mathbf{0}\}$. Moreover, since $\mathbf{v} \notin X$, $\{\mathbf{v}\} \cap X = \varnothing$, so that, by the previous corollary, $X \cup \{\mathbf{v}\}$ is linearly independent.

On the other hand, suppose that $X \cup \{\mathbf{v}\}$ is linearly independent. Notice that $X = (X \cup \{\mathbf{v}\}) \setminus \{\mathbf{v}\}$. Then, by statement (3) of Proposition 3.10, $\mathbf{v} \notin \text{span}_V((X \cup \{\mathbf{v}\}) \setminus \{\mathbf{v}\}) = \text{span}_V(X)$. Q.E.D.

Examples

(d) Let F be any field and n be any natural number, $n \geqq 2$. Let $\mathbf{e}_i^{(n)}$. be the ordered n-tuple in F^n consisting of a 1 in the ith place and 0's elsewhere. Thus, $\mathbf{e}_1^{(n)}$ is the n-tuple $(1, 0, \ldots, 0)$, $\mathbf{e}_2^{(n)}$ is the n-tuple $(0, 1, 0, \ldots, 0)$, and so on.

Let $X = \{\mathbf{e}_1^{(n)}, \mathbf{e}_2^{(n)}, \ldots, \mathbf{e}_n^{(n)}\}$. Then, X is a linearly independent subset of F^n.

To prove this assertion we consider any linear combination $a_1\mathbf{e}_3^{(n)} + \cdots + a_n\mathbf{e}_n^{(n)}$ with value $\mathbf{0} = (0, 0, \ldots, 0)$. It is easy to verify that

$$a_1\mathbf{e}_1{}^{(n)} + \cdots + a_n\mathbf{e}_n{}^{(n)} = (a_1, \ldots, a_n) \tag{1}$$

Thus, if $a_1\mathbf{e}_1^{(n)} + \cdots + a_n\mathbf{e}_n^{(n)} = \mathbf{0}$, then $(a_1, \ldots, a_n) = (0, 0, \ldots, 0)$, so that $a_1 = a_2 = \cdots = a_n = 0$, and the combination is trivial.

Notice that equality (1) above implies that every n-tuple $(a_1, a_2, \ldots, a_n)$ in F^n is a linear combination of vectors of X.

Thus, X is a linearly independent generating set for V.

(e) Let $V = \mathbf{R}^3$ and $F = \mathbf{R}$. We apply Corollary 2, above, to prove that $\{(2, 0, 0), (8, 1, 0), (-1, 0, 1)\}$ is linearly independent.

Start with $X = \varnothing$. Since $(2, 0, 0) \notin \varnothing$ and $(2, 0, 0) \notin \text{span}_V(\varnothing) = \{\mathbf{0}\} = \{(0, 0, 0)\}$, Corollary 2 implies that $X \cup \{(2, 0, 0)\} = \{(2, 0, 0)\}$ is linearly independent.

Now, let $X = \{(2, 0, 0)\}$. The set $\text{span}_{\mathbf{R}^3}(X)$ consists of all real multiples of $(2, 0, 0)$. Clearly, then $(8, 1, 0) \notin X$ and $(8, 1, 0) \notin \text{span}_{\mathbf{R}^3}(X)$ so that $X \cup \{(8, 1, 0)\} = \{(2, 0, 0), (8, 1, 0)\}$ is linearly independent.

Finally, let $X = \{(2, 0, 0), (8, 1, 0)\}$. Notice that every linear combination $r(2, 0, 0) + s(8, 1, 0) = (2r + 8s, s, 0)$ has a 0 in the third place. Thus, $(-1, 0, 1) \notin \text{span}(X)$, so that $X \cup \{(-1, 0, 1)\} = \{(2, 0, 0), (8, 1, 0), (-1, 0, 1)\}$ is linearly independent.

This example shows how Corollary 2 to Proposition 3.12 can be used to build up linearly independent sets. Moreover, it points out a simple but useful Corollary to Corollary 2, which we now state and prove.

Corollary to Corollary 2

Let $\{\mathbf{v}_1, \mathbf{v}_2, \ldots, \mathbf{v}_k\}$ be a set of nonzero vectors of V. Then, $\{\mathbf{v}_1, \mathbf{v}_2, \ldots, \mathbf{v}_k\}$ is linearly dependent if and only if one of the $\mathbf{v}_i$ is a linear combination of vectors in $\{\mathbf{v}_1, \mathbf{v}_2, \ldots, \mathbf{v}_k\}$ having smaller subscripts than it.

In other words, saying that, say, $\{\mathbf{v}_1, \mathbf{v}_2, \mathbf{v}_3, \mathbf{v}_4\}$ is linearly dependent is equivalent to saying that at least one of the following is true: $\mathbf{v}_2$ is a linear combination (i.e., multiple) of $\mathbf{v}_1$; $\mathbf{v}_3$ is a linear combination of $\mathbf{v}_1$ and $\mathbf{v}_2$; $\mathbf{v}_4$ is a linear combination of $\mathbf{v}_1$, $\mathbf{v}_2$, and $\mathbf{v}_3$.

Proof of the Corollary

Let the statement of the corollary be called P_k. We prove, by the inductive method, that P_k is true for all natural numbers k.

When $k = 1$, the set consists of one nonzero vector, say $\mathbf{v}_1$. Such a set is, of course, linearly independent. Moreover, there are no vectors in the set with subscripts smaller than 1. Thus, both portions of the proposition are false, and hence, they are logically equivalent. Therefore, P_1 is true, for it simply asserts the logical equivalence of the two portions.

Now, let S be the truth set for the sequence of propositions P_k (i.e., the set of natural numbers k for which P_k is true). We have just shown that $1 \in S$.

Assume that $n \in S$, and consider P_{n+1}. Let $\{\mathbf{v}_1, \mathbf{v}_2, \ldots, \mathbf{v}_n, \mathbf{v}_{n+1}\}$ be any set of nonzero vectors of V. *Suppose that it is dependent.* Now, either $\{\mathbf{v}_1, \mathbf{v}_2, \ldots, \mathbf{v}_n\}$ is dependent, or it is independent. If it is dependent, P_n, which we are assuming is true, implies that one of its vectors is a linear combination of vectors of $\{\mathbf{v}_1, \ldots, \mathbf{v}_n\}$ having smaller subscripts than it. Since $\{\mathbf{v}_1, \ldots, \mathbf{v}_n\} \subset \{\mathbf{v}_1, \ldots, \mathbf{v}_n, \mathbf{v}_{n+1}\}$, this means that one of the vectors of $\{\mathbf{v}_1, \ldots, \mathbf{v}_n, \mathbf{v}_{n+1}\}$ is a linear combination of vectors having subscripts smaller than it. On the other hand, if $\{\mathbf{v}_1, \ldots, \mathbf{v}_n\}$ is independent, then $\mathbf{v}_{n+1} \in \text{span}_V(\{\mathbf{v}_1, \ldots, \mathbf{v}_n\})$ for to deny this would imply, by Corollary 2 to Proposition 3.12, that $\{\mathbf{v}_1, \ldots, \mathbf{v}_n\} \cup \{\mathbf{v}_{n+1}\} = \{\mathbf{v}_1, \ldots, \mathbf{v}_n, \mathbf{v}_{n+1}\}$ is linearly independent, contradicting our initial assumption. Thus, if $\{\mathbf{v}_1, \ldots, \mathbf{v}_n, \mathbf{v}_{n+1}\}$ is linearly dependent, then one of its vectors is a linear combination of "earlier" ones. Clearly, the converse is true, by statement (3) of Proposition 3.9. Thus, P_{n+1} is true, so that $n + 1 \in S$.

This means that S is inductive, and so $S = \mathbf{N}$, as desired. Q.E.D.

(f) Consider $\mathscr{P}^n$, the vector space over $\mathbf{R}$, of all polynomials (one variable, real coefficients) of degree $\leqq n$. Let $X_n = \{x^0, x^1, x^2, x^3, \ldots, x^n\}$. In Exercises 3.7.**6** the reader showed that X_n generates $\mathscr{P}^n$. We now assert that X_n is linearly independent.

The proof is easy. For consider any linear combination $a_0x^0 + a_1x^1 + a_2x^2 + \cdots + a_nx^n$ with value $\mathbf{0}$. Recall that the zero vector of $\mathscr{P}^n$ is the identically zero polynomial. Thus, *for all real values of* x,

$$a_0x^0 + a_1x^1 + \cdots + a_nx^n = 0$$

This means that the polynomial $a_0x^0 + a_1x^1 + \cdots + a_nx^n$ has an infinite (indeed, uncountably infinite) number of roots. Moreover, the Polynomial Remainder Theorem tells us that a *nontrivial* polynomial of degree $\leqq n$ cannot have more than n roots. From these two assertions we conclude that $a_0x^0 + a_1x^1 + \cdots + a_nx^n$ must be trivial; that is, $a_0 = a_1 = \cdots = a_n = 0$. Thus, only the trivial combination of vectors of X_n has value $\mathbf{0}$, so that X_n is linearly independent.

EXERCISES / 3.8

1. Which of the following subsets of $\mathbf{R}^4$ are linearly dependent and which are not?
  a. $\{(1, 0, 0, 0), (2, 0, 0, 0)\}$
  b. $\{(1, 0, 0 ,0), (0, 2, 0, 0)\}$
  c. $\{(1, 1, 0, 0), (0, 0, 1, 1), (1, 0, 0, 1), (0, 1, 1, 0)\}$
  d. $\{(1, 2, 3, 4), (1, 4, 9, 16), (1, 8, 27, 64)\}$
  e. $\{(0, 0, 0, 0)\}$
  f. $\{(1, 0, 0, 0), (0, 1, 0, 0), (0, 0, 0, 1), (1, 0, 1, 0)\}$

2.* **a.** Let V be a vector space over any field F and let $X_1, X_2, X_3, \ldots$, be a countable sequence of linearly independent subsets of V such that $X_1 \subset X_2 \subset X_3 \subset \cdots$. Let X be the union of these sets. Prove that X is linearly independent.
  b. Apply Exercise 2 **a** and Example (f), above, to show that $\{x^0, x^1, x^2, \ldots\}$ is a linearly independent subset of $\mathscr{P}$.

3. Considering the field of complex numbers $\mathbf{C}$ as a vector space over $\mathbf{R}$ show that the set $\{1, i\}$ is linearly independent. Consider $\mathbf{C}$ as a vector space over itself and show that $\{1, i\}$ is dependent.

4. **a.** Consider $\mathbf{R}$ as a vector space over $\mathbf{Q}$ and show that the set $\{1, \sqrt{2}\}$ is linearly independent. Consider $\mathbf{R}$ as a vector space over itself and show that $\{1, \sqrt{2}\}$ is dependent.
  b. Can $\mathbf{R}$ (considered as a vector space over $\mathbf{Q}$) have a finite generating set? (To answer this question, the reader must know the following fact about countable sets: The union of a countable number of sets each of which has a countable number of members is countable.)

5.* Let X be a subset of a vector space V such that every finite subset of X is linearly independent. Prove that X is linearly independent.

Conversely, if X is linearly independent, prove that every finite subset of X is linearly independent.

5.3 Bases and Dimension

Definition 3.13

Let V be a vector space over F. Any linearly independent generating set of V is called a basis of V.

The important feature of a basis is this: If X is a basis of V, then every vector $\mathbf{v} \in V$ is the value of *precisely one* linear combination of vectors of X.

However, at this point, it is not at all clear that a given vector space has a basis. We shall see that every vector space does have a basis, but the proof of this fact is not easy. Indeed, we shall be able to prove only a special case of this fact. First, however, we reintroduce certain special vector spaces and some bases.

Examples of bases

(a) Let V be any vector space over F, and let $\mathbf{0} \in V$ be the $+$-identity. The vector subspace $\{\mathbf{0}\}$ has, as a basis, the empty set, $\varnothing$. For, $\text{span}_V(\varnothing) = \{\mathbf{0}\}$, and $\varnothing$ is linearly independent.

(b) Let F be any field. The set $\{\mathbf{e}_1^{(n)}, \mathbf{e}_2^{(n)}, \ldots, \mathbf{e}_n^{(n)}\} \subset F^n$ is a basis of F^n [cf. Example (d) of the previous section].

This basis is important: we call it the *standard basis* of F^n.

Perhaps a concrete special case would be helpful here. Let $n = 2$ and $F = \mathbf{R}$. Then, $F^n = \mathbf{R}^2$, and the standard basis is $\{(1, 0), (0, 1)\}$.

This example shows how a basis of a vector space plays the role of a coordinate system. Let us consider $\mathbf{R}^2$ and its standard representation in analytic geometry, as pictured in Figure 22.

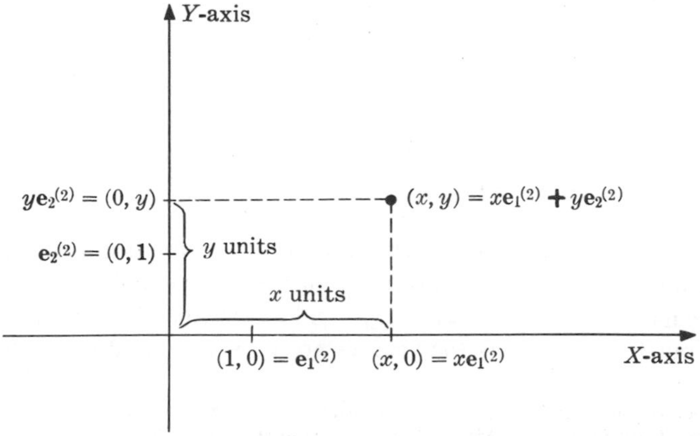

FIGURE 22

The coordinate system consists of perpendicular axes on which directed distances can be measured. *Every point on the plane can be uniquely determined by two numbers: namely, its directed distance from the Y-axis* ($=x$) *and its directed distance from the X-axis* ($=y$). This fact lies at the heart of the notion of a coordinate system (of this type).

The relation $(x, y) = x\mathbf{e}_1^{(2)} + y\mathbf{e}_2^{(2)}$ allows us to interpret this property of coordinate systems in terms of the vectors $\mathbf{e}_1{}^{(2)}$ and $\mathbf{e}_2{}^{(2)}$ as follows:

Every vector in $\mathbf{R}^2$ *can be uniquely expressed as a linear combination of* $\mathbf{e}_1^{(2)}$ *and* $\mathbf{e}_2^{(2)}$. This, of course, is merely another way of saying that $\{\mathbf{e}_1^{(2)}, \mathbf{e}_2^{(2)}\}$ is a basis.

Thus, the basis $\{\mathbf{e}_1^{(2)}, \mathbf{e}_2^{(2)}\}$ plays the role of a coordinate system of $\mathbf{R}^2$. In general, it will be useful to think of a basis of a vector space in this way.

(c) Let $\mathscr{P}$ be the vector space over $\mathbf{R}$ of polynomials in one variable x, as before, and let $\mathscr{P}^n$ be the vector subspace of $\mathscr{P}$ consisting of polynomials of degree $\leqq n$, as before.

Then, $\{x^0, x^1, x^2, \ldots\}$ is a basis of $\mathscr{P}$, and $\{x^0, x^1, \ldots, x^n\}$ is a basis of $\mathscr{P}^n$.

The following proposition exhibits one of the most important properties of bases.

Proposition 3.13

Let V be a vector space over F, let Z be a generating set of V, and let X be a linearly independent subset of Z. Then, there exists a basis Y of V such that $X \subset Y \subset Z$.

Although this proposition is true in the generality stated, we shall be able to prove it only in the case that $\bar{\bar{Z}} \leqq \mathbf{N}$ (i.e., Z is finite or countable).** Thus, suppose that Z is finite or countable; since $X \subset Z$, it follows that X, also, is finite or countable.

Proof

The idea of the proof is to enlarge X carefully, step by step, adjoining at most one new vector of Z at each step. Care must be taken in the choice of these new vectors so that the enlarged sets are linearly independent and so that X, together with all these newly adjoined vectors, is a generating set for V.

Let X be called X_1. The successive enlargements of X_1 will be called X_2, $X_3, \ldots, X_n, \ldots$, and so on. We define the sets X_n inductively. For $n = 1$, we have already defined X_n to be X.

Consider the set of vectors of Z that are not in X, that is $Z \setminus X$. This set may be empty, it may be nonempty and finite, or it may be countable.‡ If it is nonempty, use natural numbers 1, 2, 3, . . . , and so on, to index the vectors in some arbitrary but fixed way: say the vectors are $\mathbf{v}_1, \mathbf{v}_2, \ldots$ and so on. (Of course,

** In other words, there is a 1–1 correspondence between Z and a subset of $\mathbf{N}$.
‡ That is, if not finite, it will be in 1–1 correspondence with $\mathbf{N}$.

if $Z \setminus X$ is finite, only finitely many indices will be used; if $Z \setminus X$ is countable, then all of **N** will be used.)

Now, suppose that X_k has been defined for some $k \in \mathbf{N}$. We define X_{k+1} as follows. If $Z \setminus X \subset \text{span}_V(X_k)$, let $X_{k+1} = X_k$. If $Z \setminus X \not\subset \text{span}_V(X_k)$, then some of the vectors $\mathbf{v}_i$ do not belong to $\text{span}_V(X_k)$. This means that the set S of all natural numbers i such that $\mathbf{v}_i \notin \text{span}_V(X_k)$ is not empty. Thus, by the *Fact about* **N** of Chapter 2, S has a smallest member, say n_{k+1}. In this case, let $X_{k+1} = X_k \cup \{\mathbf{v}_{n_{k+1}}\}$. Clearly, $\mathbf{v}_{n_{k+1}} \notin \text{span}_V(X_k)$, because $n_{k+1} \in S$.

This completes our inductive definition of the X_n.

Next, we give an informal proof that each X_n has the following properties: 1. $X \subset X_n \subset X_{n+1} \subset Z$; 2. X_n is linearly independent; 3. if $Z \setminus X$ has at least n distinct members, then $\{\mathbf{v}_1, \ldots, \mathbf{v}_n\} \subset \text{span}_V(X_{n+1})$; if not, then $Z \setminus X \subset \text{span}_V(X_{n+1})$.

Property 1 is easy to prove. For at no stage in the enlargement process did we use vectors other than those in Z. Moreover, each of the X_n is an enlargement of X, and X_{n+1} either equals X_n or is an enlargement of it.

Property 2 is verified as follows. We start with a linearly independent set X_1 and start enlarging it, step by step. Every time we adjoin a new vector, we are careful that it does not lie in the linear span of the set to which we are adjoining it. Corollary 2 to Proposition 3.12 assures us, then, that this adjunction procedure never results in a dependent set. Thus, all the X_n are independent.

Finally, Property 3 is proved by a careful examination of the enlargement procedure. At each step, the procedure involves scanning those vectors of $Z \setminus X$ not already engulfed in the linear span of the set constructed in the previous step. The scanning is done *in order*, starting with the lowest possible subscripts and working up. The first vector scanned that is not already engulfed is adjoined to the set at hand to form the next set. Notice that the only vectors skipped over are those already engulfed by previous steps. At each step, a new vector is engulfed, unless all of $Z \setminus X$ has already been engulfed in the previous step. From this model of the procedure, the reader should be able to deduce property 3, noting that the set X_{n+1} is formed after the nth scanning step.

We point out to the reader that the above is not a completely rigorous proof. A rigorous proof would use the inductive method. For expository purposes, however, the above sketch is preferable.

Now, *let* Y *be the union of the increasing sequence of sets* $X_1 \subset X_2 \subset \cdots \subset X_n \subset \cdots$. Since each X_n is linearly independent, so is Y, by Exercises 3.8.**2.a**.

Next, choose any vector $\mathbf{v} \in Z$. If $\mathbf{v} \in X = X_1$, then, clearly, $\mathbf{v} \in Y \subset \text{span}_V(Y)$. If $\mathbf{v} \in Z \setminus X$, then $\mathbf{v} = \mathbf{v}_n$, for some $n \in \mathbf{N}$. According to property 3 above, $\mathbf{v}_n \in \text{span}_V(X_{n+1})$. Since $X_{n+1} \subset Y$, by definition, $\text{span}_V(X_{n+1}) \subset \text{span}_V(Y)$, so that $\mathbf{v}_n \in \text{span}_V(Y)$. Thus, in every case, $\mathbf{v} \in \text{span}_V(Y)$, so that $Z \subset \text{span}_V(Y)$.

But, by hypothesis $\text{span}_V(Z) = V$. Thus, $\text{span}_V(Y) = \text{span}_V(\text{span}_V(Y)) \supset \text{span}_V(Z) = V$. Since, obviously, $\text{span}_V(Y) \subset V$, we conclude that $\text{span}_V(Y) = V$. Thus, Y is a generating set for V.

Therefore, Y is the desired basis of V. Q.E.D.

Corollary 1 to Proposition 3.13

Let V be a vector space over a field F. Then, V has a basis.

Proof

Let $X = \varnothing$ and $Z = V$. Clearly, $X \subset Z$, X is linearly independent, and Z is a set of generators of V. Thus, Proposition 3.13 applies and yields a basis Y of V, satisfying the not very interesting relation $\varnothing \subset Y \subset V$. Q.E.D.

Corollary 2 to Proposition 3.13

Let V be a vector space over a field F, and let U be a vector subspace of V. Suppose that X is a basis of U. Then X may be enlarged to form a basis of V. That is, there is a basis Y of V, such that $X \subset Y$.

Proof

Let $Z = V$. Then, X and Z satisfy the hypotheses of Proposition 3.13, so that there is a basis Y of V, satisfying $X \subset Y \subset V$. Q.E.D.

The above corollary implies that, in general, a vector space has very many bases. Indeed, choose any nonzero vector $\mathbf{v} \in V$ (if such exist). The set of all multiples of $\mathbf{v}$ is a vector subspace U of V, of which the set $\{\mathbf{v}\}$ is easily shown to be a basis. The above corollary then implies that V has a basis Y such that $\{\mathbf{v}\} \subset Y$. In other words, *given any nonzero vector $\mathbf{v} \in V$, there is a basis Y of V such that $\mathbf{v} \in Y$.*

Despite the great diversity of bases of a given vector space, however, they all have the same cardinality. (see Definition 2.25.) This general fact is of great importance. Its proof, however, lies beyond the scope of this text. However, we are able to prove an important special case of this fact; it is to this end that the following two propositions are dedicated. We then state the main result as a corollary.

Lemma**

Let V be any vector space over F, and let $\{\mathbf{v}_1, \ldots, \mathbf{v}_n\}$ be a linearly independent subset of V, $n \geqq 2$. Choose any $n - 1$ members of F (zero or nonzero), and label them "a_2", "a_3," ..., "a_n." Then, the set $\{\mathbf{v}_1, \mathbf{v}_2 - a_2\mathbf{v}_1, \mathbf{v}_3 - a_3\mathbf{v}_1, \ldots, \mathbf{v}_n - a_n\mathbf{v}_1\}$ is linearly independent.

Proof

Let $\mathbf{v}_1, \mathbf{v}_2, \ldots, \mathbf{v}_n$ and $a_2, \ldots, a_n$ be as above. To show that $\{\mathbf{v}_1, \mathbf{v}_2 - a_2\mathbf{v}_1, \mathbf{v}_3 - a_3\mathbf{v}_1, \ldots, \mathbf{v}_n - a_n\mathbf{v}_1\}$ is linearly independent, we take an arbitrary linear combination of vectors of this set with value zero and show that it is trivial:

$$b_1\mathbf{v}_1 + b_2(\mathbf{v}_2 - a_2\mathbf{v}_1) + \cdots + b_n(\mathbf{v}_n - a_n\mathbf{v}_1) = \mathbf{0}$$

** The word "lemma" is applied to those propositions whose importance is not intrinsic but resides in their contributions toward the proofs of other propositions.

Collecting terms rather differently, we get,

$$(b_1 - b_2a_2 - \cdots - b_na_n)\mathbf{v}_1 + b_2\mathbf{v}_2 + \cdots + b_n\mathbf{v}_n = \mathbf{0}.$$

Since $\{\mathbf{v}_1, \ldots, \mathbf{v}_n\}$ is linearly independent, this combination is trivial. Thus, $b_2 = 0$, $b_3 = 0$, $\ldots$, $b_n = 0$, and $b_1 - b_2a_2 - \cdots - b_na_n = 0$. From the first $n - 1$ equations and the last, it follows that $b_1 = 0$ also. Thus, the coefficients, b_i, of the original combination are zero. Q.E.D.

Proposition 3.14

Let V be any vector space over F, let X be any linearly independent subset of V, and let Y be any generating set of V. Then $X \leqq Y$.‡

We shall be able to prove this result only in case V has a finite set of generators, although it is true in general.

Proof

Let P_n be the following statement: *If V is a vector space over F having a generating set with $\leqq n$ members, if X is any linearly independent subset of V, and if Y is any set of generators of V, then $X \leqq Y$.*

We shall prove that P_n holds for all $n \in \mathbf{N}$. Let S be the truth set for the sequence of P_n.

(1) $1 \in S$. Let V be a vector space having a generating set with $\leqq 1$ member, let X be linearly independent, as above, and let Y be a set of generators of V. If V has a generating set with <1 member (i.e., if $\varnothing$ generates V), then V consists only of the zero vector: $V = \{\mathbf{0}\}$. The only linearly independent subset of $\{\mathbf{0}\}$ is $\varnothing$ (so that $X = \varnothing$) which has no members. Thus, no matter what Y is, $X \leqq Y$. If V does not have the empty set as generating set, that is, if V does not have a generating set with <1 member, then it has a generating set of precisely one element. Moreover, this element is nonzero: For were it zero, then $V = \{\mathbf{0}\}$ and $\varnothing$ is a generating set of this. In the case of one nonzero generator, V consists precisely of all multiples of this nonzero vector. Clearly, any set consisting of more than one such multiple is dependent. Thus, if X is independent, then X has no more than one member. On the other hand, no generating set of V can have <1 member. Thus, $X \leqq Y$, equality occuring if they both have one member.

Thus, P_1 is true.

(2) *Assuming that $k \in S$, then $k + 1 \in S$.*

Let X and Y be as before. Let Z be a generating set of V with $\leqq k + 1$ members. If Z has $\leqq k$ members, then, because P_k holds, $X \leqq Y$, and we are done. Therefore, we may assume that Z has precisely $k + 1$ members.

‡ The reader will recall that, given two sets A and B, we write $A \leqq B$ to indicate that there is a 1–1 correspondence between A and a subset of B. If A and B are finite sets, this means, simply, that A does not have more members than B.

Now, if Y has $\leqq k$ members, then, since it is a generating set of V and P_k holds, we conclude again that $X \leqq Y$. Therefore, we may assume that Y has at least $k + 1$ members. That is, we may assume that $Z \leqq Y$.

We shall prove that $X \leqq Y$ indirectly: namely, we show that $X \leqq Z$ and then use the fact that $Z \leqq Y$ and the fact that $\leqq$ is transitive to conclude that $X \leqq Y$. (See Proposition 2.14.)

Thus, the stage is set. Let $Z = \{\mathbf{z}_1, \mathbf{z}_2, \ldots, \mathbf{z}_{k+1}\}$. Of course, if $X = \varnothing$, then $X \leqq Z$, and we are done. Thus, we shall assume that $X \neq \varnothing$. Choose any $\mathbf{x} \in X$ (note that X may, *a priori*, be infinite). If $X = \{\mathbf{x}\}$, then we are finished, for clearly, in that case X does not have more members than Z (i.e., $X \leqq Z$). Assume, then, that X has at least one member distinct from $\mathbf{x}$.

Since Z generates V, every member of X is a linear combination of members of Z. In particular $\mathbf{x}$ is, so that $\mathbf{x} = a_1\mathbf{z}_1 + \cdots + a_{k+1}\mathbf{z}_{k+1}$. Moreover, $\mathbf{x} \neq \mathbf{0}$ (because X is linearly independent) so that at least one of the terms $a_i\mathbf{z}_i$ is nonzero. Without loss of generality we may assume, for convenience, that $a_1\mathbf{z}_1 \neq 0$, since the indexing can always be rearranged so that this is so.

We form a set X' as follows. Choose any $\mathbf{x}' \in X$ so that $\mathbf{x}' \neq \mathbf{x}$. This vector $\mathbf{x}'$ is the value of a linear combination of vectors of Z: Say $\mathbf{x}' = b_1\mathbf{z}_1 + b_2\mathbf{z}_2 + \cdots + b_{k+1}\mathbf{z}_{k+1}$. Consider the vector $\mathbf{x}' - b_1/a_1\mathbf{x}$. The set X' is defined to be composed of all such vectors $\mathbf{x}' - b_1/a_1\mathbf{x}$, precisely one such corresponding to each $\mathbf{x}' \in X \setminus \{\mathbf{x}\}$. Clearly this set is in 1-1 correspondence with $X \setminus \{\mathbf{x}\}$. Moreover, because of the subtraction process, each of these vectors can be written as a linear combination of vectors $\mathbf{z}_2, \ldots, \mathbf{z}_{k+1}$ (Note: $\mathbf{x}' - b_1/a_1\mathbf{x} = (b_2 - (b_1/a_1)a_2)\mathbf{z}_2 + \cdots + (b_{k+1} - (b_1/a_1)a_{k+1})\mathbf{z}_{k+1}$, the term containing $\mathbf{z}_1$ dropping out). Finally, the preceding Lemma, together with Exercises 3.8.5, implies that X' is linearly independent.

Now, $\text{span}_V(\{\mathbf{z}_2, \ldots, \mathbf{z}_{k+1}\})$ is a vector space over F with a generating set having $\leqq k$ members, X' is a linearly independent subset of $\text{span}_V(\{\mathbf{z}_2, \ldots, \mathbf{z}_{k+1}\})$ and $\{\mathbf{z}_2, \ldots, \mathbf{z}_{k+1}\}$ is a generating set of $\text{span}_V(\{\mathbf{z}_2, \ldots, \mathbf{z}_{k+1}\})$. Therefore, since P_k is assumed true, we may conclude that $X' \leqq \{\mathbf{z}_2, \ldots, \mathbf{z}_{k+1}\}$. Since, as we stated above, $X \setminus \{\mathbf{x}\} \approx X'$ (i.e., since there is a 1-1 correspondence between $X \setminus \{\mathbf{x}\}$ and X') we conclude that $X \setminus \{\mathbf{x}\} \leqq \{\mathbf{z}_2, \ldots, \mathbf{z}_{k+1}\}$. But $\{\mathbf{z}_2, \ldots, \mathbf{z}_{k+1}\}$ has k members. Thus, $X \setminus \{\mathbf{x}\}$ has $\leqq k$ members, so that $X = (X \setminus \{\mathbf{x}\}) \cup \{\mathbf{x}\}$ has $\leqq k + 1$ members. Thus, $X \leqq Z$, as desired.

This means that S is inductive; therefore, $S = \mathbf{N}$, and P_n is true for all $n \in \mathbf{N}$. Q.E.D.

The following corollary is the main result, mentioned above, about cardinality of bases of a vector space.

Corollary 1 to Proposition 3.14

Let V be any vector space over F, and let X and Y be any bases of V. Then, $X \approx Y$ (i.e., they have the same cardinality, or, there is a 1-1 *correspondence from X to Y).*

If either X or Y is finite, then the above result means that the other one is finite and that, indeed, they have the same number of members.

Proof of the Corollary

Since X and Y are bases of V, X is linearly independent and Y is a generating set of V. Thus, by Proposition 3.14, $X \leqq Y$. But, also, X is a generating set of V and Y is linearly independent. Thus, by the same result, $Y \leqq X$.

Then, by the Schröder-Bernstein Theorem (Proposition 2.15), $X \overset{\#}{=} Y$. Q.E.D.

Corollary 1 to Proposition 3.13 assures us that every vector space has at least one basis. The above corollary assures us that all the bases of a vector space have the same cardinality. Thus, the cardinality of a basis of a vector space is actually a property of the entire vector space itself and not specific to any single basis of the vector space.

Definition 3.14

Let V be a vector space over F. The cardinality of any given basis of V will be called the dimension of V, referred to more briefly as dim V.

Given any two vector spaces V and W with bases X and Y, we write dim $V <$ dim W, dim $V =$ dim W, dim $V >$ dim W, according as $X < Y$, $X \overset{\#}{=} Y$, or $X > Y$, respectively. Recall that we say $X < Y$ if $X \leqq Y$ and if there is no 1–1 correspondence between X and Y. When X and Y are finite, then $X < Y$ means, simply, that X has (strictly) fewer members than Y.

If dim V is finite, then we use the usual natural-number notation to indicate the cardinality of a basis of V. That is, if such a basis has n members, then we may write dim $V = n$ and say that V is n-dimensional. If dim V is finite, then we may say that V is finite-dimensional. If not, we may say that it is infinite-dimensional (perhaps distinguishing at times between countably infinite and uncountably infinite).

The reader should pay attention to the role of F in this definition of dimension. For example, the set of real numbers **R**, considered as a vector space *over itself*, has dimension one, whereas, if it is considered as a vector space *over* **Q**, it is infinite-dimensional [cf. Examples (h), (i), below, and Exercises 3.8.4 above].**

Corollary 2 to Proposition 3.14

Let V be a vector space over F, and let X be a basis for V. Let Y be a subset of V.

(1) *If $X < Y$, then Y is linearly dependent.*

(2) *If X is finite, Y is linearly independent, and $X \overset{\#}{=} Y$, then Y is a basis of V.*

** This should not be too surprising. The idea of dimension is founded on the notions of linear independence and linear combination, and these are strongly linked to the scalar field via the operation of scalar multiplication. The "bigger" the scalar field, the "smaller" need be a generating set.

Proof

(1) X is, among other things, a set of generators for V. If Y were linearly independent, then $Y \leqq X$, by Proposition 3.14. Since, by hypothesis, $X < Y$, Y must be dependent.

(2) Suppose that X is finite and $X \not\gtrless Y$, Y being linearly independent. We must show that Y generates V. Choose any $\mathbf{v} \in V$. If $\mathbf{v} \in Y$, then $\mathbf{v} \in \text{span}_V(Y)$. Suppose that $\mathbf{v} \notin Y$. Then, $Y \cup \{\mathbf{v}\}$ has one more member than Y. Since $X \not\gtrless Y$ and X (and Y) is (are) finite, $X < Y \cup \{\mathbf{v}\}$. Thus, by part (1), $Y \cup \{\mathbf{v}\}$ is linearly dependent.

Now, we claim that $\mathbf{v} \in \text{span}_V(Y)$. For if $\mathbf{v} \notin \text{span}_V(Y)$, then, by Corollary 2 to Proposition 3.12, $Y \cup \{\mathbf{v}\}$ would be linearly independent, which we have just shown to be impossible.

Thus, every $\mathbf{v} \in V$ belongs to $\text{span}_V(Y)$. Clearly, this implies that Y is a generating set for V. Q.E.D.

Corollary 3 to Proposition 3.14

Let V be a vector space and U be a vector subspace of V. Then, $\dim U \leqq \dim V$. If $\dim V$ is finite and if $\dim U = \dim V$, then $U = V$. If $\dim V$ is infinite, then there are many vector subspaces U of V such that $\dim U = \dim V$ but $U \neq V$.

Proof

Let U be any vector subspace of V. By Corollary 1 to Proposition 3.13, U has a basis, say X. By Corollary 2 to Proposition 3.13, V has a basis Y such that $X \subset Y$. Clearly then $X \leqq Y$, so that, by Definition 3.13, $\dim U \leqq \dim V$.

Suppose that $\dim V$ is finite, and let X and Y be as above. If $\dim U = \dim V$, then, by definition, $X \not\gtrless Y$. But Y is a basis of V, and X, of course, is linearly independent, being a basis of U. Then, by Corollary 2 to Proposition 3.14, statement (2), X is a basis of V. That is, X generates V. But, X was given as a generating set of U. Therefore, $U = \text{span}(X) = V$.

Finally, suppose that Y is a basis of V, and that Y is infinite. Choose any $\mathbf{y} \in Y$. The reader should be able to show that $Y \setminus \{\mathbf{y}\} \not\gtrless Y$.** Moreover, $Y \setminus \{\mathbf{y}\} \subset Y$, so that $Y \setminus \{\mathbf{y}\}$ is linearly independent (since Y is). Let $U = \text{span}_V(Y \setminus \{\mathbf{y}\})$. Note that $\mathbf{y} \notin \text{span}_V(Y \setminus \{\mathbf{y}\})$, for if $\mathbf{y}$ did belong to $\text{span}_V(Y \setminus \{\mathbf{y}\})$, the union $(Y \setminus \{\mathbf{y}\}) \cup \{\mathbf{y}\} = Y$ would be linearly dependent (by Corollary 2 to Proposition 3.12). Therefore, $\mathbf{y} \notin U$, so that U cannot equal all of V. On the other hand, $\dim U =$ cardinality of $Y \setminus \{\mathbf{y}\} =$ cardinality of $Y = \dim V$. Q.E.D.

Next, we present some familiar examples and look at the concept of dimension in connection with them.

(d) Let V be any vector space over F, and let $\mathbf{0} \in V$ be the $+$-identity. Then, the empty set $\varnothing$ is a basis for $\{\mathbf{0}\}$. Thus, $\dim \{\mathbf{0}\} = 0$.

** A proof is outlined in Exercises 3.9.4.

If U is a vector subspace of V such that $\dim U = 0$, then $U = \{\mathbf{0}\}$. For $\{\mathbf{0}\}$ is a vector subspace of U; moreover, U can have no nonzero vector, for if it did, according to the remark after Corollary 2 to Proposition 3.13, this nonzero vector can be made a member of a basis of V, and then $\dim U \geqq 1$.

(e) Let V be as above, and let $\mathbf{v} \in V$ be a nonzero vector. Let $U = \text{span}_V(\{\mathbf{v}\})$. It is not hard to see that $\{\mathbf{v}\}$ is a basis of U, so that $\dim U = 1$.

(f) Let F be any field and let $V = F^n$, for some $n \in \mathbf{N}$. F^n has a standard basis, $\{\mathbf{e}_1^{(n)}, \ldots, \mathbf{e}_n^{(n)}\}$, so that $\dim F^n = n$.

If $F = \mathbf{R}$ and $n = 2$, then $F^n = \mathbf{R}^2$, and $\dim \mathbf{R}^2 = 2$. Happily, this coincides with out intuitive notion of the dimension of $\mathbf{R}^2$. (And it is not hard to see why. Independent sets of vectors are sets of vectors, each of which "points" in a direction essentially different from the directions in which the others "point." $\mathbf{R}^2$ is determined by two such directions; hence its dimension is two.)

(g) Let $\mathscr{P}$ be the usual vector space over $\mathbf{R}$ of polynomials and $\mathscr{P}^n \subset \mathscr{P}$ the vector space over $\mathbf{R}$ of polynomials of degree $\leqq n$.

Since $\{x^0, x^1, x^2, \ldots\}$ is a basis of $\mathscr{P}$, the dimension of $\mathscr{P}$ is countably infinite. On the other hand, $\{x^0, x^1, \ldots, x^n\}$ is a basis of $\mathscr{P}^n$, so that $\dim \mathscr{P}^n = n + 1$.

(h)† Let X be any nonempty set and let F be any field. Then, F^X is, as constructed in Section 2, Construction 2, a vector space over F.

For each $x \in X$, let f_x be the function from X to F defined as follows:

$$f_x(x') = \begin{cases} 0, & \text{if} \quad x \neq x' \\ 1, & \text{if} \quad x = x' \end{cases}$$

Then, $f_x \in F^X$.

In a sense, the function f_x can be thought of as favoring x (in the sense that a king favors a subject). For f_x ignores all other $x' \in X$, sending them to 0, and singles out x alone, assigning to it the number 1.

There is, clearly a 1–1 correspondence between X and $\{f_x \mid x \in X\}$: namely, x corresponds to f_x.

Claim: *$\{f_x \mid x \in X\}$ is a linearly independent subset of F^X.*

Proof

Suppose $a_1 f_{x_1} + \cdots + a_n f_{x_n} = \bar{0}$, where $\bar{0}$ is the function $X \to F$ identically zero. Then, evaluate the functions on both sides of the equation at x_1. By definition, $f_{x_1}(x_1) = 1$, whereas $f_{x_i}(x_1) = 0$, $i > 1$, so that

$$(a_1 f_{x_1} + \cdots + a_n f_{x_n})(x_1) = a_1 \cdot 1 + 0 + \cdots + 0 = a_1$$

On the other hand, $\bar{0}(x_1) = 0$. Thus, $a_1 = 0$. Similarly, by evaluating the above equation at $x_2, \ldots, x_n$, we can prove that $a_2 = 0$, $a_3 = 0, \ldots, a_n = 0$. Therefore, the combination is trivial, and the claim is verified. Q.E.D.

Denote by $F(X)$ the vector subspace of F^X, $\text{span}(\{f_x \mid x \in X\})$.

Then, $F(X)$ is a vector space over F with a basis in 1–1 correspondence with X (i.e., its basis is $\{f_x \mid x \in X\}$).

This example shows that given a field F, there are vector spaces of any given dimension over F.

Notice that since $F(X) \subset F^X$, the cardinality of X is less than or equal to $\dim F^X$.

Now, it is not hard to show (a bit too hard for this presentation, however) that *if X is infinite and $F \leqq X$, then the cardinality of any basis of F^X is the same as the cardinality of F^X.*

Next, recall that $\mathscr{P}(X)$ is the set of all subsets of X. We showed (Proposition 2.17) that $X < \mathscr{P}(X)$ and (Exercises 2.17.**1**) that $\mathscr{P}(X) \approx \{0, 1\}^X$, where 0 and 1 are the ordinary real numbers. Now, let us think of 0 and 1 as elements of F. Then, $\{0, 1\} \subset F$ and $\{0, 1\}^X \subset F^X$. Thus, we have the chain of relations $X < \mathscr{P}(X) \approx \{0, 1\}^X \leqq F^X$, *from which we conclude that $X < F^X$.*

Combining this result with that of the preceding paragraph, we conclude that if Y is a basis of F^X, if X is infinite, and if $F \leqq X$, then $X < Y$.

In particular, since $X \approx \{f_x \mid x \in X\}$, $\{f_x \mid x \in X\} < Y$. That is, if X is infinite and $F \leqq X$, then $\dim F(X) < \dim F^X$.

This implies most strongly that $F(X) \neq F^X$, (for if $F(X) = F^X$, their bases would have the same cardinality). This inequality, however, can be seen directly, assuming, here, only that X is infinite. Let $f\colon X \to F$ be the function constantly equal to $1 \in F$. Since $1 \neq 0$ and since X is infinite, f has nonzero values at infinitely many elements. Consider, on the other hand, *any* member of $\operatorname{span}_V(\{f_x \mid x \in X\}) = F(X)$. It can be written as $a_1 f_{x_1} + \cdots + a_n f_{x_n}$. At any $x \in X$ not equal to x_1 thru x_n, this linear combination has, by definition of f_{x_1} thru f_{x_n}, value zero. *Thus, the combination has nonzero values at most at n members of X (i.e., at $x_1, \ldots, x_n$).* This combination, clearly, cannot equal f.

Therefore, $f \in F^X$, but $f \notin F(X)$, showing that $F(X) \neq F^X$ when X is infinite.

(i)† In Example (f) above, let $F = \mathbf{R}$ and $n = 1$. Then $F^n = \mathbf{R}^1 = \mathbf{R}$, and $\dim \mathbf{R} = 1$. Notice that, here, we are considering $\mathbf{R}$ as a vector space over $\mathbf{R}$.

Next, consider $\mathbf{R}$ as a vector space over $\mathbf{Q}$. Suppose that $\mathbf{R}$ has a finite basis (as a vector space over $\mathbf{Q}$). That is, suppose that there are real numbers $r_1, r_2, \ldots, r_n$, such that every $r \in \mathbf{R}$ is the value of precisely one linear combination of $r_1, r_2, \ldots, r_n$, with rational coefficients (i.e. coefficients in $\mathbf{Q}$). We shall show that this is impossible.

Recall that $\mathbf{Q}$ is countable. That is, it can be indexed by $\mathbf{N}$: Thus, $\mathbf{Q}$ consists of the numbers $q^{(1)}, q^{(2)}, q^{(3)}, \ldots$, and so on, where we have chosen an arbitrary but fixed indexing (we use superscripts, here, to avoid confusion with the subscripts of the r_i). Consider any linear combination of $r_1, \ldots, r_n$ with rational coefficients: It can be written in the general form $q^{(i_1)}r_1 + q^{(i_2)}r_2 + \cdots + q^{(i_n)}r_n$. We arrange these combinations in *lexicographical order*. That is: given any two such combinations c_1 and c_2, we compare their coefficients of r_1. If one coefficient has a smaller superscript than the other, then we call the corresponding combination smaller than the other; if not—that is, if both combinations have equal coefficients of r_1—then, we compare their coefficients of r_2. If one coefficient has smaller superscript than the other, then we call the corresponding combination smaller than the other. If not, we proceed to the next coefficient and continue similarly. This procedure stops after at most n steps (n being the number of r_i), by which time we have established either that one combination is "smaller" than the other or that both consist of the same coefficients and are identical.

This defines a precise ordering of the combinations $q^{(i_1)}r_1 + \cdots + q^{(i_n)}r_n$. For example, the *first* in order is $q^{(1)}r_1 + q^{(1)}r_2 + \cdots + q^{(1)}r_n$; the *second* is $q^{(1)}r_1 + q^{(1)}r_2 + \cdots + q^{(1)}r_{n-1} + q^{(2)}r_n$. Label the first combination c_1, the second c_2, the third c_3, and so on. In this way, we establish an indexing of all the possible combinations by **N**. Thus, the set of all such combinations is *countable*. That is span($\{r_1, \ldots, r_n\}$) (combinations with rational coefficients) is countable. Since **R** is uncountable, span($\{r_1, \ldots, r_n\}$) $\neq$ **R**.

Thus, **R** (over **Q**) does not have a finite basis. In a similar but more elaborate way, we can show that **R** (over **Q**) does not even have a countable basis (as does, say $\mathscr{P}$ over **R**). Thus, the dimension of **R** over **Q** is uncountably infinite.

(j) In Example (f), above, let $F = \mathbf{C}$ and $n = 1$. Then, $F^n = \mathbf{C}$ and dim $\mathbf{C} = 1$ (**C** considered as a vector space over itself).

By previous work, however, we know that the set $\{1, i\}$ is a linearly independent generating set of **C** considered as a vector space over **R**. Thus, dim **C** (over **R**) = 2.

EXERCISES / 3.9

1. Prove that the following set is a basis of $\mathbf{R}^3$ (over **R**): $\{(2, 0, 1), (3, 5, 2), (-1, 1, 1)\}$.

2. Prove that if r_1, r_2, s_1, and s_2 are real numbers, then $\{(r_1, r_2), (s_1, s_2)\}$ is a basis of $\mathbf{R}^2$ (over **R**) if and only if $r_1s_2 - r_2s_1 \neq 0$.

   What are the possible values of dim $[\mathrm{span}_{\mathbf{R}^2}(\{(r_1, r_2), (s_1, s_2)\})]$ if $r_1s_2 - r_2s_1 = 0$? Under what circumstances are each of these values realized?

3.* Let a_1 and a_2 be any two nonzero members of a field $F, +, \cdot$. Consider the expression $a_1x_1 + a_2x_2$. By a *solution* of the equation $a_1x_1 + a_2x_2 = 0$, we mean an ordered pair $(c_1, c_2) \in F^2$ such that $a_1c_1 + a_2c_2 = 0$.

   a. Show that the equation $a_1x_1 + a_2x_2 = 0$ has at least one solution distinct from $(0, 0)$.

   b. Suppose that (c_1, c_2) and (d_1, d_2) are solutions of the equation in **a**. Show that there exists an $e \in F$ such that $c_1 = ed_1$ and $c_2 = ed_2$, so that $(c_1, c_2) = e(d_1, d_2)$.

   c. Let $S \subset F^2$ be the set of all solutions of the equation $a_1x_1 + a_2x_2 = 0$. Show that S is a vector subspace of F^2.

   Use **a** and **b** to show that dim $S = 1$.

4. a. Let Y be a countable set, consisting of, say, $y_1, y_2, \ldots$, and so on. Define a 1–1 correspondence between Y and $Y \setminus \{y_1\}$, that is, between $\{y_1, y_2, y_3, \ldots\}$ and $\{y_2, y_3, y_4, \ldots\}$.
   b. Let Z be any infinite set, and choose any $z \in Z$. Use the fact that Z contains a countable subset, together with part **a** above, to prove that Z is in 1–1 correspondence with $Z \setminus \{z\}$.

5. Let V be a vector space over a field F, and let U_1 and U_2 be vector subspaces of V, with bases X_1 and X_2 respectively.
   a. Show that $X_1 \cup X_2$ generates $U_1 + U_2$.
   b. Prove that if X_1 and X_2 are finite, then $\dim(U_1 + U_2) \leqq \dim(U_1) + \dim(U_2)$.
   c. Under what circumstances will equality occur?
   (*Hint*: Consult Proposition 3.8 and Proposition 3.12, Corollary 1.)

5.4 Products, Subspace Sums, Quotients

This section poses and answers the following three questions, in all of which $F, +, \cdot$ is any field and $V, +, \cdot$ is any vector space over $F, +, \cdot$:

1. If W is a vector space over F, then what is the relationship between bases of V and W and bases of $V \times W$?
2. If U_1 and U_2 are vector subspaces of V, then how are bases of U_1 and U_2 related to bases of $U_1 + U_2$?
3. If U is a vector subspace of V, then what is the relationship between bases of U, V, and V/U?

The answers to these questions will naturally imply certain important results about the relationships among the dimensions of the various vector spaces in question. A generalization of question 1 and material related to a generalization of question 2 will be described in the exercises below.

(a) *Products*

Let V and W be as above, let X be a basis of V and let Y be a basis of W. Let "$\mathbf{0}$" denote both the $+$-identity (zero vector) of V and that of W. Then, $X \times \{\mathbf{0}\} \subset V \times W$ and $\{\mathbf{0}\} \times Y \subset V \times W$, so that $X \times \{\mathbf{0}\} \cup \{\mathbf{0}\} \times Y \subset V \times W$.

Proposition 3.15

$X \times \{\mathbf{0}\} \cup \{\mathbf{0}\} \times Y$ is a basis of $V \times W$.

Proof

Every vector of $V \times W$ can be written uniquely as $(\mathbf{v}, \mathbf{w})$, where $\mathbf{v} \in V$ and $\mathbf{w} \in W$. Since X is a basis of V and Y a basis of W** we obtain equations

$$\mathbf{v} = a_1\mathbf{x}_1 + \cdots + a_k\mathbf{x}_k$$

** We assume that X and Y are nonempty, to avoid considering an easy special case. The reader should fill in this case.

and

$$\mathbf{w} = b_1\mathbf{y}_1 + \cdots + b_n\mathbf{y}_n,$$

$$\mathbf{x}_1, \ldots, \mathbf{x}_k \in X \quad \text{and} \quad \mathbf{y}_1, \ldots, \mathbf{y}_n \in Y$$

By definition of the operations of $V \times W$,

$$(\mathbf{v}, \mathbf{w}) = (\mathbf{v}, \mathbf{0}) + (\mathbf{0}, \mathbf{w})$$

Thus,

$$\begin{aligned}(\mathbf{v}, \mathbf{w}) &= (a_1\mathbf{x}_1 + \cdots + a_k\mathbf{x}_k, \mathbf{0}) + (\mathbf{0}, b_1\mathbf{y}_1 + \cdots + b_n y_n) \\ &= a_1(\mathbf{x}_1, \mathbf{0}) + \cdots + a_k(\mathbf{x}_k, \mathbf{0}) + b_1(\mathbf{0}, \mathbf{y}_1) + \cdots + b_n(\mathbf{0}, \mathbf{y}_n),\end{aligned}$$

this second equation also following from the definition of the operations in $V \times W$. But, this second equation reveals that $(\mathbf{v}, \mathbf{w})$ is the value of a linear combination of vectors $(\mathbf{x}_1, \mathbf{0}), \ldots, (\mathbf{x}_n, \mathbf{0}), (\mathbf{0}, \mathbf{y}_1), \ldots, (\mathbf{0}, \mathbf{y}_n)$, all belonging to $X \times \{\mathbf{0}\} \cup \{\mathbf{0}\} \times Y$.

Therefore, $X \times \{\mathbf{0}\} \cup \{\mathbf{0}\} \times Y$ generates $V \times W$.

Notice, moreover, that $X \times \{\mathbf{0}\}$ generates $V \times \{\mathbf{0}\}$ and that $\{\mathbf{0}\} \times Y$ generates $\{\mathbf{0}\} \times W$. Thus,

$$\begin{aligned}\text{span}_{V\times W}(X \times \{\mathbf{0}\}) \cap \text{span}_{V\times W}(\{\mathbf{0}\} \times Y) &= V \times \{\mathbf{0}\} \cap \{\mathbf{0}\} \times W \\ &= \{\mathbf{0}\} \times \{\mathbf{0}\} = \{(\mathbf{0}, \mathbf{0})\} \\ &= \text{span}_{V\times W}(\{(\mathbf{0}, \mathbf{0})\}) \\ &= \text{span}_{V\times W}(X \times \{\mathbf{0}\} \cap \{\mathbf{0}\} \times Y).\end{aligned}$$

Thus, if we can show that $X \times \{\mathbf{0}\}$ and $\{\mathbf{0}\} \times Y$ are linearly independent, then it will follow by Proposition 3.12, that $X \times \{\mathbf{0}\} \cup \{\mathbf{0}\} \times Y$ is linearly independent.

We show that $X \times \{\mathbf{0}\}$ is linearly independent, the proof for $\{\mathbf{0}\} \times Y$ being similar.

Let $a_1(\mathbf{x}_1, \mathbf{0}) + \cdots + a_k(\mathbf{x}_k, \mathbf{0})$ be a linear combination of vectors of $X \times \{\mathbf{0}\}$ with value $(\mathbf{0}, \mathbf{0})$. That is, $(a_1\mathbf{x}_1 + \cdots + a_k\mathbf{x}_k, \mathbf{0}) = (\mathbf{0}, \mathbf{0})$. Since these are equal ordered pairs, their first members must be equal, so that $a_1\mathbf{x}_1 + \cdots + a_k\mathbf{x}_k = \mathbf{0}$. Now, because X is linearly independent, we conclude that $a_1 = a_2 = \cdots = a_k = 0$. Thus, the original combination is trivial, so that $X \times \{\mathbf{0}\}$ is linearly independent.

Therefore, $X \times \{\mathbf{0}\} \cup \{\mathbf{0}\} \times Y$ is a linearly independent generating set of $V \times W$. Q.E.D.

Corollary to Proposition 3.15

Let V and W be as above. Then dim $V \leq$ dim$(V \times W)$ and dim $W \leq$ dim$(V \times W)$. Moreover, dim$(V \times W)$ is finite if and only if dim V and dim W are finite, and in that case

$$\dim V + \dim W = \dim(V \times W)$$

Proof

Let X and Y be as above.** The first statement follows immediately from the facts that X and Y are in obvious 1–1 correspondence with $X \times \{\mathbf{0}\}$ and $\{\mathbf{0}\} \times Y$, respectively, and that $X \times \{\mathbf{0}\} \subset X \times \{\mathbf{0}\} \cup \{\mathbf{0}\} \times Y$ and $\{\mathbf{0}\} \times Y \subset X \times \{\mathbf{0}\} \cup \{\mathbf{0}\} \times Y$.

Clearly, $X \times \{\mathbf{0}\} \cup \{\mathbf{0}\} \times Y$ is finite, if and only if $X \times \{\mathbf{0}\}$ (and, hence, X) and $\{\mathbf{0}\} \times Y$ (and, hence, Y) are. Suppose that X consists of m members, $\mathbf{x}_1, \ldots, \mathbf{x}_m$, and Y consists of n members $\mathbf{y}_1, \ldots, \mathbf{y}_n$. Then, $X \times \{\mathbf{0}\} \cup \{\mathbf{0}\} \times Y$ consists of $(\mathbf{x}_1, \mathbf{0}), \ldots, (\mathbf{x}_m, \mathbf{0}), (\mathbf{0}, \mathbf{y}), \ldots, (\mathbf{0}, \mathbf{y}_n)$, precisely $m + n$ members. These considerations imply the second and last statements of the proposition. Q.E.D.

In the next chapter we show how to apply the above corollary to prove (differently from the way we have already proved) that $\dim F^n = n$.

(b) *Subspace Sums*

Let U_1, U_2, and V be as in question 2, above, and let $U = U_1 \cap U_2$. U is also a vector subspace of V. Indeed, U is a vector subspace of U_1 and of U_2. Let X be a basis of U. Then, by Proposition 3.13, X may be enlarged to form a basis X_1 of U_1. Moreover, X may be enlarged to form a basis X_2 of U_2. Clearly, the set $X_1 \cup X_2$ is contained in $U_1 \cup U_2$, and $U_1 \cup U_2 \subset \text{span}_V(U_1 \cup U_2) = U_1 + U_2$.

Proposition 3.16

$X_1 \cup X_2$ is a basis of $U_1 + U_2$.

Proof

By Proposition 3.8,

$$\text{span}_V(X_1 \cup X_2) = \text{span}_V(X_1) + \text{span}_V(X_2) = U_1 + U_2.$$

Moreover, $X_1 \cap X_2 = X$ and we have

$$\text{span}_V(X_1 \cap X_2) = \text{span}_V(X) = U = U_1 \cap U_2 = \text{span}_V(X_1) \cap \text{span}_V(X_2)$$

Thus, we may apply Proposition 3.12 (since X_1 and X_2 are, by construction, linearly independent). This proposition implies that $X_1 \cup X_2$ is linearly independent.

Thus, $X_1 \cup X_2$ is a linearly independent generating set of $U_1 + U_2$. Q.E.D.

Corollary to Proposition 3.16

$\dim(U_1)$ and $\dim(U_2)$ are finite if and only if $\dim(U_1 + U_2)$ is. If this is the case, then

$$\dim(U_1 + U_2) = \dim(U_1) + \dim(U_2) - \dim(U_1 \cap U_2)$$

** See the previous footnote.

Proof

Let $U = U_1 \cap U_2$, and let X, X_1, X_2 be as in the proof above. Clearly X_1 and X_2 are finite, if and only if $X_1 \cup X_2$ is finite. This corresponds to (and, thus, proves) the first statement of the corollary, in view of the fact that $X_1 \cup X_2$ is a basis of $U_1 + U_2$.

Suppose that $X_1 \cup X_2$ is finite, and count the number of vectors in it. Every vector in X_1 will be counted, and so will every member of X_2. However, there may be overlap between X_1 and X_2 (the overlap being X). If we count the number of vectors in X_1, then we count the vectors in this overlap portion. When we count the number of vectors in X_2, separately, then we are counting the same overlap portion again.

Thus, if our counts of X_1 and X_2 separately are added, the sum exceeds our count of $X_1 \cup X_2$ precisely by the number of vectors in X. This number must, therefore, be subtracted from the sum to arrive at equality: Number in $X_1 \cup X_2$ = number in X_1 + number in X_2 − number in X. This yields the desired equality of dimensions. Q.E.D.

Corollary to the Previous Corollary

Let U_1 and U_2 be as above. If $U_1 \cap U_2 = \{\mathbf{0}\}$, then

$$dim(U_1 + U_2) = dim(U_1) + dim(U_2)$$

For reasons that become clear only later, the case of vector subspaces with trivial intersection is of special interest. Thus, we devote some attention to it now.

Proposition 3.17

Let U_1, U_2, be vector subspaces of V. The following two statements are equivalent. If $dim(U_1 + U_2)$ is finite, then (3) *is equivalent to* (1) *and* (2).

(1) $U_1 \cap U_2 = \{\mathbf{0}\}$
(2) *Every $\mathbf{v} \in U_1 + U_2$ can be expressed in precisely one way as a sum $\mathbf{u}_1 + \mathbf{u}_2$, where $\mathbf{u}_1 \in U_1$ and $\mathbf{u}_2 \in U_2$.***
(3) $dim(U_1 + U_2) = dim(U_1) + dim(U_2)$

Proof

In the above corollary, we proved that (1) implies (3). Suppose that (3) is true. Then, by the Corollary to Proposition 3.16,

$$\dim(U_1 \cap U_2) = \dim(U_1) + \dim(U_2) - \dim(U_1 + U_2).$$

** In other words, if two sums $\mathbf{u}_1 + \mathbf{u}_2$ and $\mathbf{u}_1' + \mathbf{u}_2'$ have the same value, then $\mathbf{u}_1 = \mathbf{u}_1'$ and $\mathbf{u}_2 = \mathbf{u}_2$.

Applying equality (3), we get

$$\dim(U_1 \cap U_2) = 0,$$

from which we may conclude that $U_1 \cap U_2 = \{\mathbf{0}\}$. Thus, (3) implies (1).

Therefore, (1) and (3) are equivalent.

Next, we prove that (2) implies (1). Suppose that (2) holds. Choose any $\mathbf{v} \in U_1 \cap U_2 \subset U_1 + U_2$. Since $\mathbf{v} \in U_1$ and $\mathbf{0} \in U_2$, we may write $\mathbf{v} = \mathbf{v} + \mathbf{0}$, which is in the form $\mathbf{u}_1 + \mathbf{u}_2$, for $\mathbf{u}_1 \in U_1$, $\mathbf{u}_2 \in U_2$ (i.e., $\mathbf{u}_1 = \mathbf{v}$ and $\mathbf{u}_2 = \mathbf{0}$). On the other hand, we may also write $\mathbf{v} = \mathbf{0} + \mathbf{v}$, which is in the form $\mathbf{u}_1' + \mathbf{u}_2'$, $\mathbf{u}_1' \in U_1$ and $\mathbf{u}_2' \in U_2$ (i.e., $\mathbf{u}_1' = \mathbf{0}$, $\mathbf{u}_2' = \mathbf{v}$).

But, since $\mathbf{v} \in U_1 + U_2$, and (2) holds, we conclude that $\mathbf{v}$ can be written only in one way as a sum of the above form. This means that the sums $\mathbf{u}_1 + \mathbf{u}_2$ and $\mathbf{u}_1' + \mathbf{u}_2'$ must consist of the same vectors in order: That is, $\mathbf{u}_1 = \mathbf{u}_1'$ and $\mathbf{u}_2 = \mathbf{u}_2'$. But $\mathbf{v} = \mathbf{u}_1$ and $\mathbf{0} = \mathbf{u}_1'$. Therefore, $\mathbf{v} = \mathbf{0}$.

This means that $U_1 \cap U_2$ consists only of $\mathbf{0}$; that is $U_1 \cap U_2 = \{\mathbf{0}\}$. Thus, (2) implies (1).

Finally, suppose that (1) is true, and consider two sums $\mathbf{u}_1 + \mathbf{u}_2$ and $\mathbf{u}_1' + \mathbf{u}_2'$ such that $\mathbf{u}_1, \mathbf{u}_1' \in U_1$, $\mathbf{u}_2, \mathbf{u}_2' \in U_2$, and $\mathbf{u}_1 + \mathbf{u}_2 = \mathbf{u}_1' + \mathbf{u}_2'$. Then, $\mathbf{u}_1 - \mathbf{u}_1' = \mathbf{u}_2 - \mathbf{u}_2'$. The left-hand side of this equation is a vector in U_1, the right side is a vector in U_2. Since they are equal, "they" are one and the same and so belong to $U_1 \cap U_2 = \{\mathbf{0}\}$. Thus, $\mathbf{u}_1 - \mathbf{u}_1' = \mathbf{0}$ and $\mathbf{u}_2 - \mathbf{u}_2' = \mathbf{0}$, from which we conclude that $\mathbf{u}_1 = \mathbf{u}_1'$ and $\mathbf{u}_2 = \mathbf{u}_2'$, as desired. Q.E.D.

Definition 3.15

Let V be a vector space over F and let U_1 and U_2 be vector subspaces of V. We say that V is the (internal) direct sum of U_1 and U_2 if and only if (1) $U_1 + U_2 = V$, and (2) $U_1 \cap U_2 = \{\mathbf{0}\}$. In this case we write $V = U_1 \oplus U_2$.

If $V = U_1 \oplus U_2$, then we say that U_1 is a complement (or complementary subspace) to U_2 and vice versa.

The following corollary is an immediate consequence of the definition and the preceding result.

Corollary to Proposition 3.17

If $V = U_1 \oplus U_2$, then:

(1) *Every $\mathbf{v} \in V$ can be written in precisely one way as a sum $\mathbf{u}_1 + \mathbf{u}_2$, where $\mathbf{u}_1 \in U_1$ and $\mathbf{u}_2 \in U_2$.*
(2) *If $\dim V$ is finite, then $\dim(V) = \dim(U_1) + \dim(U_2)$.*

Proposition 3.18

Let V be any vector space over F and let U_1 be any vector subspace of V. Then, there is a vector subspace U_2 of V such that $U_1 \oplus U_2 = V$.

Proof

Let X be a basis of U_1, and let Y be a basis of V such that $X \subset Y$. Let $U_2 = \text{span}_V(Y \setminus X)$.

Since $Y = X \cup (Y \setminus X)$, $V = \text{span}_V(Y) = \text{span}_V(X \cup (Y \setminus X)) = U_1 + U_2$. We leave to the reader the remaining task of showing that $U_1 \cap U_2 = \{\mathbf{0}\}$. Q.E.D.

The following example may clarify the notion of an internal direct sum. Let V and W be vector spaces. Then, $V \times \{\mathbf{0}\}$ and $\{\mathbf{0}\} \times W$ are vector subspaces of $V \times W$. Moreover, $V \times \{\mathbf{0}\} \cap \{\mathbf{0}\} \times W = \{(\mathbf{0}, \mathbf{0})\}$ and $V \times \{\mathbf{0}\} + \{\mathbf{0}\} \times W = V \times W$, as we showed in the proof in the previous section.

Therefore, $V \times W = V \times \{\mathbf{0}\} \oplus \{\mathbf{0}\} \times W$.

If $V = \mathbf{R} = W$, then $V \times W = \mathbf{R}^2$ = the Cartesian plane. Moreover, $\mathbf{R} \times \{0\}$ consists of those points of $\mathbf{R}^2$ that lie on the X-axis, and $\{0\} \times \mathbf{R}$ consists of those points of $\mathbf{R}^2$ that lie on the Y-axis. Thus, roughly speaking, we may say that the Cartesian plane is the internal direct sum of its X-axis and Y-axis.

Notice that in the proof of the above result, the basis Y of V was chosen almost entirely arbitrarily, subject only to the condition that $X \subset Y$. Thus, $Y \setminus X$ is by no means necessarily determined by the "given" of the proposition: namely, U_1 and V. From this we conclude that a given subspace $U_1 \subset V$ may very well have many distinct complementary subspaces. In the exercises at the end of this section, we provide some examples of different complements to a given subspace.

(c)† *Quotients*

Let V be a vector space over F, and let U be a vector subspace of V. Choose any basis X of U and any basis Y of V such that $X \subset Y$. For every $\mathbf{y} \in Y \setminus X$, form the hyperplane $\mathbf{y} + U$ (i.e., the translate of U by $\mathbf{y}$). Denote this hyperplane by $[\mathbf{y}]$. Let Z be the set of all $[\mathbf{y}]$ formed in this way: $Z = \{[\mathbf{y}] \mid \mathbf{y} \in Y \setminus X\}$. Clearly, $Z \subset V/U$, since this latter set consists of *all* translates of U.

Proposition 3.19

Z is a basis of V/U.

Proof

First, we show that span(Z) = V/U. Choose any $[\mathbf{v}] \in V/U$. The hyperplane $[\mathbf{v}]$ can be written as $\mathbf{v} + U$.

Denote vectors of X by "$\mathbf{x}$," together with some subscript, denote vectors of $Y \setminus X$ by "$\mathbf{y}$," together with some subscript. (Assume, for the moment, that $Y \setminus X$ is not empty.) We may write $\mathbf{v}$ as a linear combination of $\mathbf{x}$'s and $\mathbf{y}$'s:

$$\mathbf{v} = a_1\mathbf{x}_1 + \cdots + a_n\mathbf{x}_n + b_1\mathbf{y}_1 + \cdots + b_k\mathbf{y}_k$$

Since $\text{span}_V(X) = U$, $a_1\mathbf{x}_1 + \cdots + a_n\mathbf{x}_n \in U$, so that

$$\mathbf{v} \in (b_1\mathbf{y}_1 + \cdots + b_k\mathbf{y}_k) + U$$

We now use the definition of addition and scalar multiplication of hyperplanes defined in Section 4 of this chapter:

$$\mathbf{v} \in b_1(\mathbf{y}_1 + U) + \cdots + b_k(\mathbf{y}_k + U)$$

Therefore, $[\mathbf{v}] = b_1[\mathbf{y}_1] + \cdots + b_k[\mathbf{y}_k]$. This equation follows immediately from the previous line: the right hand side is just a rewrite of the right-hand side of the previous line; the previous line says that $\mathbf{v}$ belongs to the hyperplane on the right-hand side; thus, this is the hyperplane through $\mathbf{v}$, that is, it equals $[\mathbf{v}]$.

Therefore, $[\mathbf{v}] \in \text{span}_{V/U}(Z)$, as desired.

Next we show that Z is linearly independent. Let $a_1[\mathbf{y}] + \cdots + a_k[\mathbf{y}_k]$ be any linear combination of vectors in V/U with value zero: the zero vector of V/U is $[\mathbf{0}]$. Thus,

$$[a_1\mathbf{y}_1 + \cdots + a_k\mathbf{y}_k] = [\mathbf{0}].$$

But $[\mathbf{0}]$ is the translate of U containing $\mathbf{0}$: This is U itself. Therefore, the above equation implies that

$$a_1\mathbf{y}_1 + \cdots + a_k\mathbf{y}_k \in U = \text{span}_V(X)$$

Thus,

$$a_1\mathbf{y}_1 + \cdots + a_k\mathbf{y}_k = b_1\mathbf{x}_1 + \cdots + b_n\mathbf{x}_n,$$

for some vectors $\mathbf{x}_1, \ldots, \mathbf{x}_n \in X$ and field elements $b_1, \ldots, b_n \in F$.**

Then, $(-b_1)\mathbf{x}_1 + \cdots + (-b_n)\mathbf{x}_n + a_1\mathbf{y}_1 + \cdots + a_k\mathbf{y}_k = \mathbf{0}$. Since this is a linear combination of vectors of Y with value $\mathbf{0}$, and since Y is linearly independent, the coefficients are zero: $-b_1 = 0, \ldots, -b_n = 0$, $a_1 = 0, \ldots, a_k = 0$. Since the a's are zero, the original combination $a_1[\mathbf{y}_1] + \cdots + a_k[\mathbf{y}_k]$ is trivial.

Thus, Z is linearly independent.

The case $Y \setminus X = \varnothing$ can be easily treated by the reader. Q.E.D.

Corollary to Proposition 3.19

dim(U) *and dim*(V/U) *are finite if, and only if, dim*(V) *is finite. In this case,*

$$\mathit{dim}(U) + \mathit{dim}(V/U) = \mathit{dim}(V)$$

Proof

The first statement is obvious.

Next, note that if $Y \setminus X = \varnothing$, then $Z = \varnothing$, by definition of Z. If $Y \setminus X \neq \varnothing$, then let $f\colon Y \setminus X \to Z$ be given by $f(\mathbf{y}) = [\mathbf{y}]$. Clearly, f is onto. To show that f is 1–1, we select any two distinct $\mathbf{y}$'s, say $\mathbf{y}_1$ and $\mathbf{y}_2$ and we claim that they lie on different translates of U. For if not, then $\mathbf{y}_1 - \mathbf{y}_2 \in U = \text{span}_V(X)$ and we get the following nontrivial linear combination:

$$\mathbf{y}_1 - \mathbf{y}_2 - a_1\mathbf{x}_1 - \cdots - a_n\mathbf{x}_n = \mathbf{0},$$

contradicting the linear independence of Y. Thus, $[\mathbf{y}_1] \neq [\mathbf{y}_2]$, so that f is 1–1.

** The "$\mathbf{y}_i$'s," "$\mathbf{x}_j$'s" "a_i's," and "b_j's," here are not necessarily the same as those used in the first part of the proof.

Therefore, $Y \setminus X$ contains precisely the same number of members as does Z. The sum of the number of vectors in X and the number in $Y \setminus X$, clearly, equals the number in Y. Thus, the sum of the number in X and in Z equals the number in Y, from which the second statement of the corollary follows. Q.E.D.

EXERCISES / 3.10

1. Let $V = \mathbf{R}^3$ and $F = \mathbf{R}$. Any plane through the origin and any line through the origin of V are vector subspaces of V. Let $\wp$ be one such plane and ℓ be one such line. Prove that if ℓ does not lie in $\wp$, then $\ell \oplus \wp = \mathbf{R}^3$.

   Prove that if ℓ_1 and ℓ_2 are any two distinct lines through the origin of $\mathbf{R}^2$, then $\ell_1 \oplus \ell_2 = \mathbf{R}^2$.

2. Let V be any vector space over F, and let $U_1, U_2, \ldots, U_n$ be any distinct vector subspaces of V.

   a.* Recall that $U_1 + \cdots + U_n$ is defined to be $\text{span}_V(U_1 \cup \cdots \cup U_n)$. Prove that $U_1 + \cdots + U_n$ equals the set of all sums of the form $\mathbf{u}_1 + \cdots + \mathbf{u}_n$, where $\mathbf{u}_i$ ranges over U_i, $i = 1, \ldots, n$.

   b.* Let us introduce some notation. $U_1 + \cdots + \hat{U}_i + \cdots + U_n$ will denote the sum of all the subspaces $U_1, \ldots, U_n$ *except* U_i. Thus, for example, $\hat{U}_1 + U_2 + \cdots + U_n$ is simply $U_2 + \cdots + U_n$.
   We say that V is the (*internal*) *direct sum of $U_1, \ldots, U_n$ if and only if:* (i) $U_1 + \cdots + U_n = V$; (ii) *for each* $i = 1, 2, \ldots, n$, $U_i \cap (U_1 + \cdots + \hat{U}_i + \cdots + U_n) = \{\mathbf{0}\}$. In this case, we write $V = U_1 \oplus \cdots \oplus U_n$.
   Let X_i be a basis of U_i, $i = 1, \ldots, n$, and suppose that $V = U_1 \oplus \cdots \oplus U_n$. Prove that $X_1 \cup \cdots \cup X_n$, is a basis of V.

   c.* Suppose that $V = U_1 \oplus \cdots \oplus U_n$ and that V is finite-dimensional. Prove that $\dim V = \dim U_1 + \cdots + \dim U_n$.

   d. Suppose $V = U_1 \oplus \cdots \oplus U_n$. Show that every $\mathbf{v} \in V$ can be written in precisely one way as a sum of the form $\mathbf{u}_1 + \cdots + \mathbf{u}_n$, where $\mathbf{u}_i \in U_i$, $i = 1, \ldots, n$. Prove the converse of this result.

   e. Let U_1 and W be complementary vector subspaces of V, and let U_2 and U_3 be complementary vector subspaces of W. Prove that $V = U_1 \oplus U_2 \oplus U_3$.

   f. Let $W_1, \ldots, W_n$ be vector subspaces of V such that $W_1 \oplus \cdots \oplus W_n = V$. Let $k_1, \ldots, k_n$ be integers satisfying $1 \leq k_1 < k_2 < \cdots < k_n$, and let $U_1, \ldots, U_{k_n}$ be vector subspaces of V such that

   $$\begin{aligned} W_1 &= U_1 \oplus \cdots \oplus U_{k_1} \\ W_2 &= U_{k_1+1} \oplus \cdots \oplus U_{k_2} \\ &\vdots \\ W_n &= U_{k_{n-1}+1} \oplus \cdots \oplus U_{k_n}. \end{aligned}$$

   Prove that $V = U_1 \oplus \cdots \oplus U_{k_n}$.

3. Let $V_1, \ldots, V_n$ be vector spaces over F with bases $X_1, \ldots, X_n$ respectively.
Let

$$\bar{X}_i = \underbrace{\{0\} \times \cdots \times \{0\} \times \overset{i\text{th place}}{X_i} \times \{0\} \times \cdots \times \{0\}}_{n\text{-fold}}$$

Clearly $\bar{X}_i \subset V_1 \times V_2 \times \cdots \times V_n$, so that $\bar{X}_1 \cup \cdots \cup \bar{X}_n \subset V_1 \times V_2 \times \cdots \times V_n$.

a. Prove that $\bar{X}_1 \cup \cdots \cup \bar{X}_n$ is a basis of $V_1 \times \cdots \times V_n$.

b. Prove that if $\dim(V_1 \times \cdots \times V_n)$ is finite, then, $\dim(V_1 \times \cdots \times V_n) = \dim(V_1) + \cdots + \dim(V_n)$.

c. Prove that

$$\operatorname{span}(\bar{X}_i) = \underbrace{\{0\} \times \cdots \times \{0\} \times \overset{i\text{th place}}{V_i} \times \{0\} \times \cdots \times \{0\}}_{n\text{-fold}}$$

Call the right-hand side $\bar{V}_i$.

d. Prove that $V_1 \times \cdots \times V_n = \bar{V}_1 \oplus \cdots \oplus \bar{V}_n$.

4. Let $F = \mathbf{R}$ and let $V = \mathbf{R}^{\mathbf{R}}$. That is, V is the vector space of *all* real-valued functions of a real variable.

a. Let $U_1 \subset V$ consist of all functions $f: \mathbf{R} \to \mathbf{R}$ satisfying $f(-x) = -f(x)$ (odd functions), for all $x \in \mathbf{R}$.
Show that U_1 is closed with respect to the operations of V.

b. Let $U_2 \subset V$ consist of all functions $g: \mathbf{R} \to \mathbf{R}$ satisfying $g(-x) = g(x)$ (even functions), for all $x \in \mathbf{R}$.
Show that U_2 is closed with respect to the operations of V.

c. Show that $U_1 \cap U_2 = \{\bar{0}\}$, where $\bar{0}: \mathbf{R} \to \mathbf{R}$ is the function identically 0 to $\mathbf{R}$.

d. Let f be any function in V. Define f_o and f_e in V as follows:

$$f_o(x) = (1/2)\,[f(x) - f(-x)],\; f_e(x) = (1/2)\,[f(x) + f(-x)],$$

for all $x \in \mathbf{R}$.
Show that f_o is odd and f_e is even. Show that f is a linear combination of f_o and f_e.

e. Prove that $V = U_1 \oplus U_2$.

5. Let $V = \mathbf{R}^4$, $F = \mathbf{R}$, and let $U_1 = \operatorname{span}(X_1)$, $U_2 = \operatorname{span}(X_2)$, where $X_1 = \{(1, 0, 0, 0), (2, 3, 1, 0)\}$, $X_2 = \{(0, 0, 1, 0), (1, 0, 0, 0), (4, 2, 1, 6)\}$.
Obtain a basis for $U_1 \cap U_2$ and $U_1 + U_2$.

6. Let $\mathscr{P}$ be, as usual, the set of all polynomials in one variable, x, with real coefficients. Let $U =$ the set of all polynomials in $\mathscr{P}$ of the form $(x^2 + 1)\,q(x)$, where $q(x) \in \mathscr{P}$. That is, U consists of all polynomials in $\mathscr{P}$ that have $x^2 + 1$ as a factor.

a. Prove that U is a vector subspace of $\mathscr{P}$.

b. Define a function $t: \mathscr{P} \to \mathbf{C}$ as follows:
Choose any $p(x) \in \mathscr{P}$ and divide it by $x^2 + 1$; there will be a certain remainder of the form $ax + b$, where $a, b \in \mathbf{R}$. Let $t(p(x)) = ai + b$.
Prove that two polynomials $p(x)$ and $q(x)$ lie on the same translate of U, if and only if $t(p(x)) = t(q(x))$.
Thus, the relation determined by U is the same as that determined by t [cf. Chapter 2.2.5(f)].

c. Define a function $\mathscr{P}/U \xrightarrow{\tau} \mathbf{C}$ as follows:

$$\tau([p(x)]) = t(p(x))$$

Prove that τ is well-defined (i.e., if $[p(x)] = [q(x)]$, then $\tau([p(x)]) = \tau([q(z)])$, and that it is 1–1 and onto.

Thus τ is a 1–1 correspondence between $\mathscr{P}/U$ and $\mathbf{C}$.

Later we show that there is a very close relationship between $\mathscr{P}/U$ and $\mathbf{C}$.

7. Let $V = \mathbf{R}^2$, $F = \mathbf{R}$, and $U = \mathbf{R} \times \{\mathbf{0}\}$. Let $p_2 : \mathbf{R}^2 \to \mathbf{R}$ be the second coordinate projection ($p_2((x, y)) = y$).
   a. Prove that two pairs (x, y) and (x', y') lie in the same translate of U, if and only if $p_2((x, y)) = p_2((x', y'))$.
   b. Use a. to show that there is a 1–1 correspondence between $\mathbf{R}^2/U$ and $\mathbf{R}$.

CHAPTER 4

LINEAR TRANSFORMATIONS

Let V and W be two vector spaces over a field F. Recall that W^V is the set of all functions from V to W and that it has the structure of a vector space with respect to the operations defined in Construction 2 of Section 2, Chapter 3. From this collection W^V, we single out a special *subset*: namely, we single out the subset of all functions that are linear, as intuitively described in Chapter 1 and as will be made precise below. Functions such as these arise often in concrete problems. Moreover, they are useful for comparing the vector space V with the vector space W.

1 / BASIC DEFINITIONS AND RESULTS

Definition 4.1

Let V and W be as above. A function $f: V \to W$ is called a linear transformation from V to W, if and only if, for any $\mathbf{v}_1, \mathbf{v}_2 \in V$ and $a \in F$,

$$f(\mathbf{v}_1 + \mathbf{v}_2) = f(\mathbf{v}_1) + f(\mathbf{v}_2) \tag{1}$$

$$f(a\mathbf{v}_1) = af(\mathbf{v}_1) \tag{2}$$

If $V = W$, then we may call f a linear operator on V. If $W = F$, then we may call f a linear functional or linear form on V. We denote the collection of all linear transformations from V to W, "Trans(V, W)."

1.1 Remarks

(a) In equations (1) and (2), above, the reader should note that the vector-space operations on the left are operations of V, whereas the operations on the right are operations of W.

(b) Let $f: V \to W$ be any linear transformation. Since $\mathbf{0} = 0\mathbf{v}$, for any $\mathbf{v} \in V$, and since $\mathbf{0} = 0\mathbf{w}$, for any $\mathbf{w} \in W$, we have, by equation (2), above,

$$f(\mathbf{0}) = f(0\mathbf{v}) = 0f(\mathbf{v}) = \mathbf{0}$$

In this sequence of equations, the $\mathbf{0}$ on the left is the zero vector of V, the $\mathbf{0}$ on the right is the zero vector of W. We see, therefore, that *every linear transformation from V to W carries the zero vector of V to the zero vector of W.*

(c) Equation (1) can be put thus verbally: f preserves (or respects) the addition operations of V and W.

Schematically, we have:

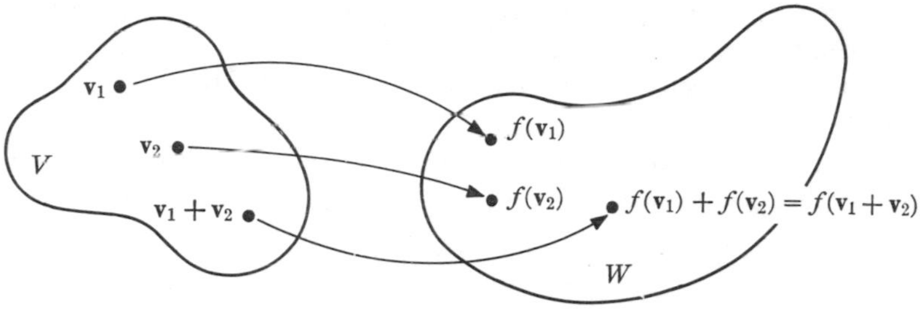

FIGURE 23

Actually, this schematic diagram can be made quite precise in a special case.

Let $F = \mathbf{R}$ and $V = \mathbf{R}^2$. Suppose that f is a linear operator on $\mathbf{R}^2$; that is, f takes $\mathbf{R}^2$ to $\mathbf{R}^2$. Suppose also, for pictorial convenience, that f is 1–1. Consider Figure 24.

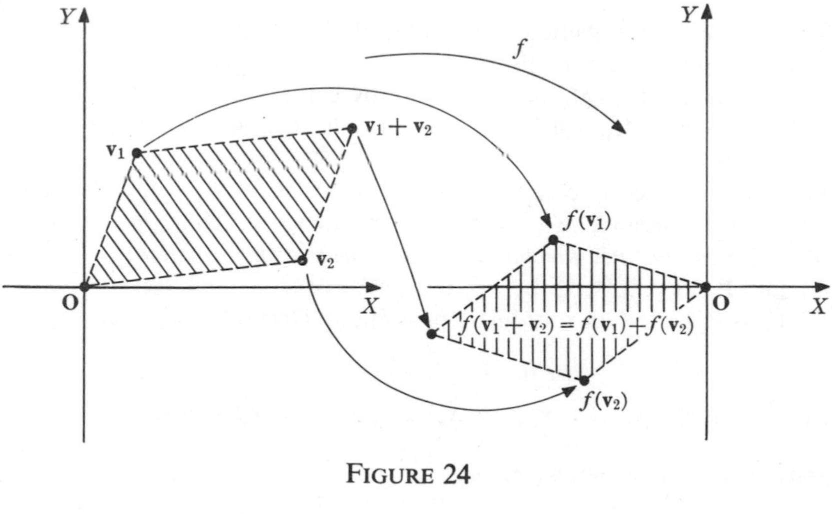

FIGURE 24

The sum of vectors $\mathbf{v}_1$, $\mathbf{v}_2$ is represented by the fourth vertex of a parallelogram whose other three vertices are $\mathbf{0}$, $\mathbf{v}_1$, and $\mathbf{v}_2$. Similarly, the sum of the vectors $f(\mathbf{v}_1)$ and $f(\mathbf{v}_2)$ is represented by the fourth vertex as a parallelogram whose other three vertices are $\mathbf{0}, f(\mathbf{v}_1), f(\mathbf{v}_2)$. The fact that f preserves the addition of $\mathbf{R}^2$ now can be interpreted as follows: f takes the fourth vertex of the parallelogram on the left to the fourth vertex of the parallelogram on the right. (Indeed, we shall be able to show more than this: We shall be able to show that f takes the entire shaded parallelogram on the left to the shaded parallelogram on the right. The function f clearly behaves in a very "rigid" manner.)

Similar comments apply to the behavior of f with respect to the multiplicative structure of V and W.

1.2 Examples and Counterexamples

(a) The reader should verify that the functions described in Examples (g)–(j) of Chapter 1 are all linear transformations.

(b) Let V be any vector space over a field F, and let a be chosen to be any member of F.

Define $M_a: V \to V$ as follows: For any $\mathbf{v} \in V$, $M_a(\mathbf{v}) = a\mathbf{v}$. Briefly, we describe M_a as multiplication by a.

Claim: *$M_a: V \to V$ is a linear transformation.*

Proof

Choose any $\mathbf{v}_1, \mathbf{v}_2 \in V$ and $b \in F$. Then,

$$M_a(\mathbf{v}_1 + \mathbf{v}_2) = a(\mathbf{v}_1 + \mathbf{v}_2) = a\mathbf{v}_1 + a\mathbf{v}_2 = M_a(\mathbf{v}_1) + M_a(\mathbf{v}_2),$$

and

$$M_a(b\mathbf{v}_1) = a(b\mathbf{v}_1) = (ab)\mathbf{v}_1 = (ba)\mathbf{v}_1 = b(a\mathbf{v}_1) = bM_a(\mathbf{v}_1)$$

Thus, M_a satisfies equations (1) and (2) of Definition 4.1.

Two special cases are worthy of note.

If $a = 0$, then $M_a = M_0$ is the constantly $\mathbf{0}$ function, for $M_0(\mathbf{v}) = 0\mathbf{v} = \mathbf{0}$, for all $\mathbf{v} \in V$. Thus, $M_0 = \bar{\mathbf{0}}$.** The above result, then, implies that $\bar{\mathbf{0}}$ is a linear transformation.

For another special case, let $a = 1$. Then, $M_a = M_1 = I_V$, the identity function of V, because $M_1(\mathbf{v}) = 1\mathbf{v} = \mathbf{v}$, for all $\mathbf{v} \in V$. Thus, *the above result implies that the identity function of V is a linear transformation.*

(c) Let $V_1, V_2, \ldots, V_n$ be vector spaces over F, and let $p_i: V_1 \times V_2 \times \cdots \times V_n \to V_i$ be the ith coordinate projection: That is,

$$p_i(\mathbf{v}_1, \ldots, \mathbf{v}_i, \ldots, \mathbf{v}_n) = \mathbf{v}_i,$$

for every n-tuple $(\mathbf{v}_1, \ldots, \mathbf{v}_i, \ldots, \mathbf{v}_n) \in V_1 \times \cdots \times V_n$, $i = 1, \ldots, n$.

** $\bar{\mathbf{0}}$ denotes the constantly $\mathbf{0}$ function.

We leave to the reader the task of showing that p_i is a linear transformation.

(d) Let V_1 and V_2 be vector spaces over F, and let $i_1 : V_1 \to V_1 \times V_2$ and $i_2 : V_2 \to V_1 \times V_2$ be given by:

$$i_1(\mathbf{v}_1) = (\mathbf{v}_1, \mathbf{0})$$

$$i_2(\mathbf{v}_2) = (\mathbf{0}, \mathbf{v}_2)$$

The reader should be able to show that i_1 and i_2 are 1–1. We show that i_1 is a linear transformation; the proof that i_2 is a linear transformation is similar.

Choose any $\mathbf{v}, \mathbf{v}' \in V_1$ and any $a \in F$. Then,

$$i_1(\mathbf{v} + \mathbf{v}') = (\mathbf{v} + \mathbf{v}', \mathbf{0}) = (\mathbf{v}, \mathbf{0}) + (\mathbf{v}', \mathbf{0}) = i_1(\mathbf{v}) + i_2(\mathbf{v}'),$$

and

$$i_1(a\mathbf{v}) = (a\mathbf{v}, \mathbf{0}) = a(\mathbf{v}, \mathbf{0}) = ai_1(\mathbf{v})$$

Thus, i_1 satisfies equations (1) and (2) of Definition 4.1.

(e) Let V be a vector space over F and let $\Sigma : V \times V \to V$ be the operation of addition on V. That is, $\Sigma(\mathbf{v}, \mathbf{v}') = \mathbf{v} + \mathbf{v}'$, for every pair $(\mathbf{v}, \mathbf{v}') \in V \times V$.

Claim. *Σ is a linear transformation.*

Proof

Choose any pairs $(\mathbf{v}, \mathbf{v}') \in V \times V$ and $(\mathbf{w}, \mathbf{w}') \in V \times V$ and any $a \in F$. Then,

$$\begin{aligned}\Sigma((\mathbf{v}, \mathbf{v}') + (\mathbf{w}, \mathbf{w}')) &= \Sigma(\mathbf{v} + \mathbf{w}, \mathbf{v}' + \mathbf{w}') \\ &= (\mathbf{v} + \mathbf{w}) + (\mathbf{v}' + \mathbf{w}') = (\mathbf{v} + \mathbf{v}') + (\mathbf{w} + \mathbf{w}') \\ &= \Sigma(\mathbf{v}, \mathbf{v}') + \Sigma(\mathbf{w}, \mathbf{w}'),\end{aligned}$$

and

$$\begin{aligned}\Sigma[a(\mathbf{v}, \mathbf{v}')] = \Sigma(a\mathbf{v}, a\mathbf{v}') = a\mathbf{v} + a\mathbf{v}' &= a(\mathbf{v} + \mathbf{v}') \\ &= a\Sigma(\mathbf{v}, \mathbf{v}') \qquad \text{Q.E.D.}\end{aligned}$$

(f) Let V be any vector space over F, and let $\Delta_V : V \to V \times V$ be given by the equation $\Delta_V(\mathbf{v}) = (\mathbf{v}, \mathbf{v})$, for all $\mathbf{v} \in V$ (cf. 2.2 (e), Chapter 2).

Claim. *Δ_V is a linear transformation.*

Proof

Choose any $\mathbf{v}_1, \mathbf{v}_2 \in V$ and any $a \in F$. Then,

$$\begin{aligned}\Delta_V(\mathbf{v}_1 + \mathbf{v}_2) &= (\mathbf{v}_1 + \mathbf{v}_2, \mathbf{v}_1 + \mathbf{v}_2) \\ &= (\mathbf{v}_1, \mathbf{v}_1) + (\mathbf{v}_2, \mathbf{v}_2) = \Delta_V(\mathbf{v}_1) + \Delta_V(\mathbf{v}_2),\end{aligned}$$

and

$$\Delta_V(a\mathbf{v}_1) = (a\mathbf{v}_1, a\mathbf{v}_1) = a(\mathbf{v}_1, \mathbf{v}_1) = a\Delta_V(\mathbf{v}_1) \qquad \text{Q.E.D.}$$

(g) Let $V = \mathbf{R}^2$ and $F = \mathbf{R}$. Let $A: \mathbf{R}^2 \to \mathbf{R}^2$ be defined as follows: For any $(x_1, x_2) \in \mathbf{R}^2$, $A(x_1, x_2) = (b_1, b_2)$, where b_1 and b_2 are given by the following equations:

$$b_1 = 3x_1 + x_2$$

$$b_2 = x_1 - x_2$$

The reader may verify that A is a linear transformation and that it is 1–1 and onto $\mathbf{R}^2$.

(h) Let θ be a fixed angle between 0 and $\pi/2$. Let us suppose that the vectors in $\mathbf{R}^2$ are represented by directed line segments issuing from (0, 0). We define a function $R_\theta : R^2 \to R^2$ as follows:

$$R_\theta(0, 0) = (0, 0);$$

$$R_\theta(x, y) = \text{the vector obtained by rotating } (x, y) \text{ through the angle } \theta, \text{ when } (x, y) \neq (0, 0).$$

The effect of R_θ on a nonzero pair (x, y) is illustrated:

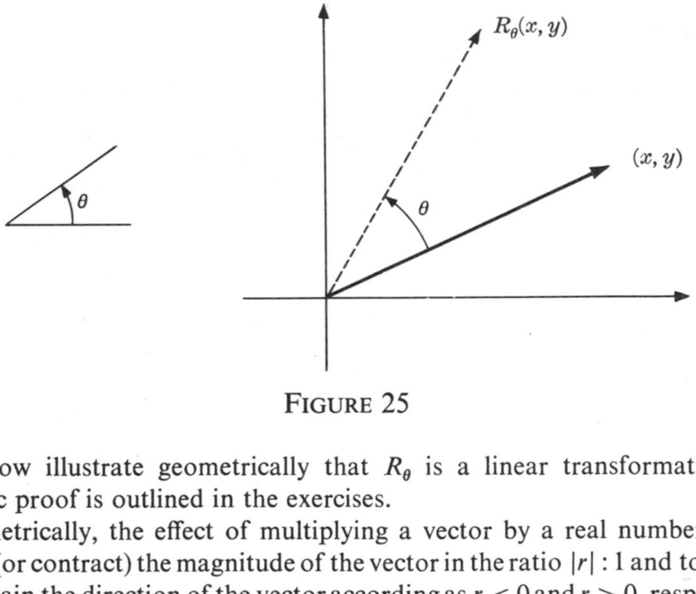

FIGURE 25

We now illustrate geometrically that R_θ is a linear transformation. An algebraic proof is outlined in the exercises.

Geometrically, the effect of multiplying a vector by a real number r is to expand (or contract) the magnitude of the vector in the ratio $|r| : 1$ and to reverse or maintain the direction of the vector according as $r < 0$ and $r > 0$, respectively. Notice that rotation does not alter the magnitude of vectors. We now compare $R_\theta(r(x, y))$ and $rR_\theta(x, y)$ in Figure 26. To fix ideas, we have assumed there that $r > 1$. The reader should draw separate diagrams to cover the cases: $0 < r \leqq 1$, $r = 0$, $r < 0$.

Corresponding line segments and angles in both diagrams clearly coincide, so that $R_\theta(r(x, y)) = rR_\theta(x, y)$.

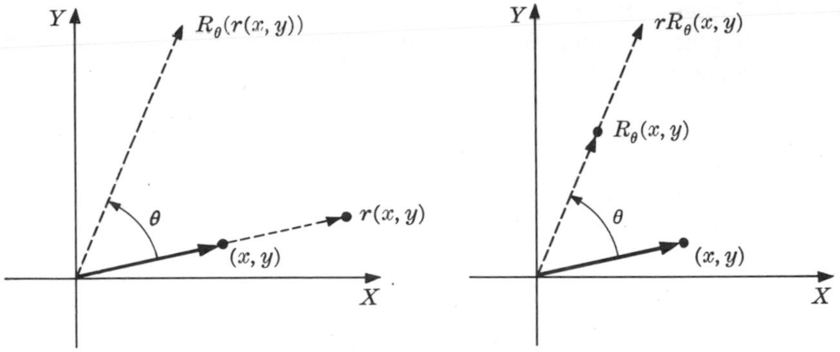

FIGURE 26

Let (x', y') be any other vector in $\mathbf{R}^2$, as in Figure 27. We compare $R_\theta((x, y) + (x', y'))$ and $R_\theta(x, y) + R_\theta(x', y')$.

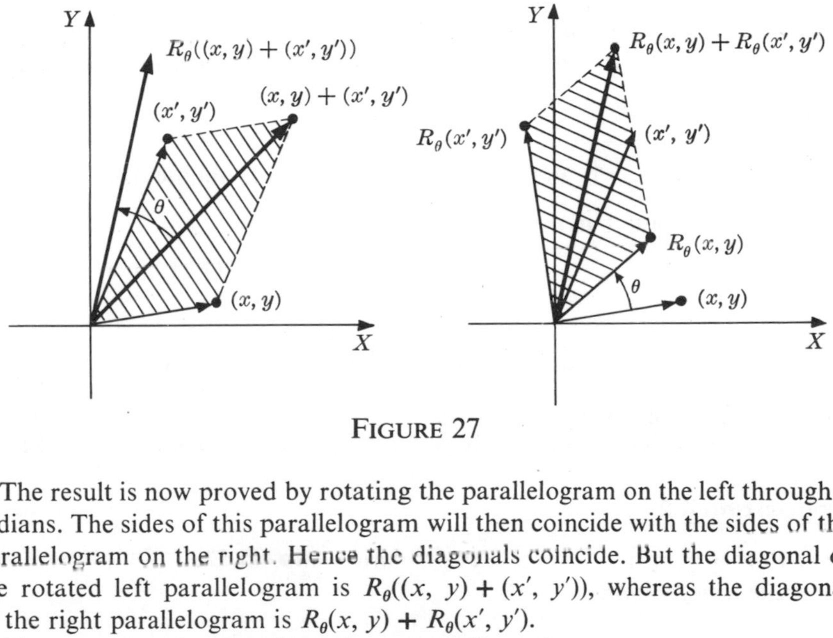

FIGURE 27

The result is now proved by rotating the parallelogram on the left through θ radians. The sides of this parallelogram will then coincide with the sides of the parallelogram on the right. Hence the diagonals coincide. But the diagonal of the rotated left parallelogram is $R_\theta((x, y) + (x', y'))$, whereas the diagonal of the right parallelogram is $R_\theta(x, y) + R_\theta(x', y')$.

Thus, rotation through θ is a linear transformation.

(i) Finally, we remind the reader that linear transformations make some of their most common appearances in systems of linear equations. He should look at the last portion of Chapter 1, where this is discussed. We shall have much more to say about it in Chapter 5.

Lest the reader be misled into thinking that linear transformations form a "majority" in the set W^V, we list below some common examples of functions in $\mathbf{R}^{\mathbf{R}}$ *that are not linear*, with respect to the ordinary operations of $\mathbf{R}$.

(j) *The Exponential Function.*

To see that the function $f: \mathbf{R} \to \mathbf{R}$ given by $f(x) = e^x$ is not linear, notice that $f(0) = e^0 = 1 \neq 0$.

(k) *Any Trigonometric Function*

This includes the sine, cosine, and tangent functions. Indeed, the fact that, say, the sine function is not linear follows from the well-known trigonometric identity, $\sin(x + y) = \sin x \cos y + \cos x \sin y$.

(l) *Any Polynomial Function of Degree Greater than One*

We leave a proof of this fact to the enthusiastic reader.

For more counterexamples, the reader should consult Exercises 1.2.**1** and **2**.

1.3 New Linear Transformations from Old

Proposition 4.1

Let $T: V \to W$ be a linear transformation, and let U be a vector subspace of V. Then, the restriction of T to U, $(T \mid U): U \to W$, is a linear transformation.

Proof

Choose any $\mathbf{u}_1, \mathbf{u}_2 \in U$ and $a \in F$. Then, $\mathbf{u}_1 + \mathbf{u}_2 \in U$ and $a\mathbf{u}_1 \in U$, and

$$(T \mid U)(\mathbf{u}_1 + \mathbf{u}_2) = T(\mathbf{u}_1 + \mathbf{u}_2) = T(\mathbf{u}_1) + T(\mathbf{u}_2)$$
$$= (T \mid U)(\mathbf{u}_1) + (T \mid U)(\mathbf{u}_2),$$

and

$$(T \mid U)(a\mathbf{u}_1) = T(a\mathbf{u}_1) = aT(\mathbf{u}_1) = a(T \mid U)(\mathbf{u}_1)$$

In this chain of equalities we are making repeated use of the equation $(T \mid U)(\mathbf{u}) = T(\mathbf{u})$, which, by definition of $T \mid U$, holds for all $\mathbf{u} \in U$. Q.E.D.

Proposition 4.2

Let $T: V \to W$ be a 1–1 *linear transformation onto W. Then, $T^{-1}: W \to V$ is a* 1–1 *linear transformation onto V.*

Proof

Since $T: V \to W$ is a 1–1, onto function, so is $T^{-1}: W \to V$. It suffices, then, to prove that T^{-1} is a linear transformation. Recall that, by definition of inverse, $T(\mathbf{v}) = \mathbf{w}$, if and only if $T^{-1}(\mathbf{w}) = \mathbf{v}$.

Choose any $\mathbf{w}_1, \mathbf{w}_2 \in W$ and $a \in F$. Let $\mathbf{v}_1 = T^{-1}(\mathbf{w}_1)$, $\mathbf{v}_2 = T^{-1}(\mathbf{w}_2)$. Then, $\mathbf{w}_1 = T(\mathbf{v}_1)$ and $\mathbf{w}_2 = T(\mathbf{v}_2)$, so that

$$\mathbf{w}_1 + \mathbf{w}_2 = T(\mathbf{v}_1) + T(\mathbf{v}_2) = T(\mathbf{v}_1 + \mathbf{v}_2)$$

This implies that $T^{-1}(\mathbf{w}_1 + \mathbf{w}_2) = \mathbf{v}_1 + \mathbf{v}_2 = T^{-1}(\mathbf{w}_1) + T^{-1}(\mathbf{w}_2)$. Moreover,

$$a\mathbf{w}_1 = aT(\mathbf{v}_1) = T(a\mathbf{v}_1),$$

so that $T^{-1}(a\mathbf{w}_1) = a\mathbf{v}_1 = aT^{-1}(\mathbf{w}_1)$.

Therefore, T^{-1} is a linear transformation. Q.E.D.

Proposition 4.3

Let $S: U \to V$ and $T: V \to W$ be linear transformations. Then, $T \circ S: U \to W$ is a linear transformation.

Proof

Choose any $\mathbf{u}_1, \mathbf{u}_2 \in U$ and $a \in F$. Then,

$$\begin{aligned}(T \circ S)(\mathbf{u}_1 + \mathbf{u}_2) &= T(S(\mathbf{u}_1 + \mathbf{u}_2)) \\ &= T(S(\mathbf{u}_1) + S(\mathbf{u}_2)) = T(S(\mathbf{u}_1)) + T(S(\mathbf{u}_2)) \\ &= (T \circ S)(\mathbf{u}_1) + (T \circ S)(\mathbf{u}_2)\end{aligned}$$

and

$$\begin{aligned}(T \circ S)(a\mathbf{u}_1) &= T(S(a\mathbf{u}_1)) = T(aS(\mathbf{u}_1)) \\ &= aT(S(\mathbf{u}_1)) = a(T \circ S)(\mathbf{u}_1) \qquad \text{Q.E.D.}\end{aligned}$$

Proposition 4.4

Let V_1, V_2, W_1, W_2 be vector spaces over F, and let $T_1: V_1 \to W_1$ and $T_2: V_2 \to W_2$ be linear transformations. Then, $T_1 \times T_2: V_1 \times V_2 \to W_1 \times W_2$ is a linear transformation.

Proof

Choose any $(\mathbf{v}_1, \mathbf{v}_2), (\mathbf{v}'_1, \mathbf{v}'_2) \in V_1 \times V_2$ and $a \in F$. Then,

$$\begin{aligned}(T_1 \times T_2)((\mathbf{v}_1, \mathbf{v}_2) + (\mathbf{v}'_1, \mathbf{v}'_2)) &= (T_1 \times T_2)(\mathbf{v}_1 + \mathbf{v}'_1, \mathbf{v}_2 + \mathbf{v}'_2) \\ &= (T_1(\mathbf{v}_1 + \mathbf{v}'_1), T_2(\mathbf{v}_2 + \mathbf{v}'_2)) \\ &= (T_1(\mathbf{v}_1) + T_1(\mathbf{v}'_1), T_2(\mathbf{v}_2) + T_2(\mathbf{v}'_2)) \\ &= (T_1(\mathbf{v}_1), T_2(\mathbf{v}_2)) + (T_1(\mathbf{v}'_1), T_2(\mathbf{v}'_2)) \\ &= (T_1 \times T_2)(\mathbf{v}_1, \mathbf{v}_2) + (T_1 \times T_2)(\mathbf{v}'_1, \mathbf{v}'_2),\end{aligned}$$

and

$$\begin{aligned}(T_1 \times T_2)(a(\mathbf{v}_1, \mathbf{v}_2)) &= (T_1 \times T_2)(a\mathbf{v}_1, a\mathbf{v}_2) \\ &= (T_1(a\mathbf{v}_1), T_2(a\mathbf{v}_2)) = (aT_1(\mathbf{v}_1), aT_2(\mathbf{v}_2)) \\ &= a(T_1(\mathbf{v}_1), T_2(\mathbf{v}_2)) \\ &= a(T_1 \times T_2)(\mathbf{v}_1, \mathbf{v}_2) \qquad \text{Q.E.D.}\end{aligned}$$

Let V and W be any vector spaces over F. Recall that for any $f_1, f_2 \in W^V$ and any $a \in F$, the sum $f_1 + f_2$ and the product af_1 are defined by the equations $(f_1 + f_2)(\mathbf{v}) = f_1(\mathbf{v}) + f_2(\mathbf{v})$ and $(af_1)(\mathbf{v}) = a(f_1(\mathbf{v}))$, for all $\mathbf{v} \in V$, and that W^V is a vector space over F with respect to these operations.

Proposition 4.5

Let $T_1: V \to W$ and $T_2: V \to W$ be any linear transformations and let a be any member of F. Then, $T_1 + T_2$ and aT_1 are also linear transformations.

Proof

Let $\Sigma: W \times W \to W$ be the operation of addition in W. In Example (e), above, we showed that Σ is a linear transformation. Let $\Delta_V: V \to V \times V$ be the "diagonal" function, which we showed, in Example (f), above, to be a linear transformation.

Claim: $T_1 + T_2 = \Sigma \circ (T_1 \times T_2) \circ \Delta_V$.

Proof

Choose any $\mathbf{v} \in V$. Then, $\Sigma \circ (T_1 \times T_2) \circ \Delta_V(\mathbf{v}) = \Sigma \circ (T_1 \times T_2)(\mathbf{v}, \mathbf{v}) = \Sigma(T_1(\mathbf{v}), T_2(\mathbf{v})) = T_1(\mathbf{v}) + T_2(\mathbf{v}) = (T_1 + T_2)(\mathbf{v})$, as desired.

Since $T_1 \times T_2$ is a linear transformation and Δ_V is, then so is $T_1 \times T_2 \circ \Delta_V$ by Proposition 4.4, above. Applying Proposition 4.4, again, $\Sigma \circ T_1 \times T_2 \circ \Delta_V$ is a linear transformation—that is, $T_1 + T_2$ is a linear transformation, by the claim just verified.

In Example (b), above, we showed that $M_a: W \to W$ is a linear transformation. Thus, so is $M_a \circ T_1$, by Proposition 4.4. But, for any $\mathbf{v} \in V$

$$(M_a \circ T_1)(\mathbf{v}) = a(T_1(\mathbf{v})) = (aT_1)(\mathbf{v}),$$

so that $M_a \circ T_1 = aT_1$. Therefore, aT_1 is a linear transformation. Q.E.D.

Corollary to Proposition 4.5

Trans (V, W) is a vector subspace of W^V.

Proof

Proposition 4.5 says, simply, that Trans (V, W) is closed with respect to the vector space operations of W^V. Q.E.D.

EXERCISES / 4.1

1.* Let $T: V \to W$ be a linear transformation, and let $a_1\mathbf{v}_1 + \cdots + a_n\mathbf{v}_n$ be any linear combination of vectors of V. Then, prove that

$$T(a_1\mathbf{v}_1 + \cdots + a_n\mathbf{v}_n) = a_1 T(\mathbf{v}_1) + \cdots + a_n T(\mathbf{v}_n).$$

2. Prove that the function $f: \mathbf{R} \to \mathbf{R}$ given by $f(x) = ax + b$, for all $x \in \mathbf{R}$, is a linear transformation if and only if $b = 0$.

3. Prove that the tangent function given by $y = \tan x$, is not a linear transformation.

4. Let $f: \mathbf{R} \to \mathbf{R}$ and $g: \mathbf{R} \to \mathbf{R}$ be functions such that $g \circ f$ is a linear transformation. Are g and f linear transformations? If so, why? If not, give an example to show why not.

5. Define $f: \mathbf{R}^2 \to \mathbf{R}^2$ and $g: \mathbf{R}^2 \to \mathbf{R}^2$ as follows:

$$f(x, y) = (x + y, xy), \qquad \text{for all} \quad (x, y) \in \mathbf{R}^2$$
$$g(x, y) = (x, 0), \qquad \text{for all} \quad (x, y) \in \mathbf{R}^2$$

a. Prove that g is a linear transformation and that $g \circ f$ is a linear transformation, but that f is not a linear transformation.

b. Using only the results stated in the previous sentence, and the propositions of the text, and *not* using the particular definitions of f and g above, show that it is impossible for g to be 1–1 and onto $\mathbf{R}^2$.

c. Prove that, if V, W, Z are vector spaces over F, and if $S: V \to W$ and $T: W \to Z$ are functions, such that T is 1–1 and onto Z and a linear transformation, and $T \circ S$ is a linear transformation, then S must also be a linear transformation.

6. Let $\mathbf{R}^+ \backslash \{0\}$, the set of positive real numbers, be denoted, here, by "P." Recall that P is a vector space over $\mathbf{R}$ with respect to the operations $\oplus$ and $\otimes$ defined in Exercises 3.1.4. These operations are defined as follows: for all $p_1, p_2 \in P$ and every $r \in \mathbf{R}$,

$$p_1 \oplus p_2 = p_1 p_2$$

and

$$r \otimes p_1 = p_1{}^r$$

a. Consider the exponential function $e^x: \mathbf{R} \to P$. Prove that e^x is a linear transformation from $\mathbf{R}, +, \cdot$ to $P, \oplus, \otimes$.

b. Consider the natural logarithm function $\log_e: P \to \mathbf{R}$. Prove that $\log_e$ is a linear transformation from $P, \oplus, \otimes$ to $\mathbf{R}, +, \cdot$.

c. Show that $\log_e$ and e^x are inverses of one another.

7. Let T be any linear transformation from V to W (both vector spaces over F). Recall that, by definition of a function, T is the set of all ordered pairs of the form $(\mathbf{v}, T(\mathbf{v}))$, where $\mathbf{v}$ ranges over V. Thus, T may be considered to be a subset of $V \times W$ (which the reader may think of as the "graph" of T).

a. Show that this subset is a vector subspace of $V \times W$.

b. Let U be a vector subspace of $V \times W$ with the property that every $\mathbf{v} \in V$ occurs exactly once as the first member of an ordered pair in U. Then, U is, by definition, a function from V to W. Show that U is a linear transformation from V to W.

8. In Chapter 1, Example (i), we showed that the definite integral

$$\int_a^b$$

is a linear transformation from the vector space $\mathscr{C}[a, b]$ to $\mathbf{R}$. Now, choose any fixed $g \in \mathscr{C}[a, b]$ [cf. Chapter 1, Example (e), for a description of $\mathscr{C}[a, b]$].

Define $L_g:\mathscr{C}[a, b] \to \mathbf{R}$ as follows:

$$L_g(f) = \int_a^b f(x)g(x)\,dx, \qquad \text{for all} \quad f \in \mathscr{C}[a, b]$$

a. Prove that L_g is a linear transformation.
b. Prove that $L_g(f) = 0$, for all $f \in \mathscr{C}[a, b]$, if and only if g is the identically zero function on $[a, b]$, that is, if and only if $g = \overline{0}$. [*Hint:* Look at $L_g(g)$.]
c. Prove that $L_{g_1}(f) = L_{g_2}(f)$, for all $f \in \mathscr{C}[a, b]$, if and only if $L_{g_1 - g_2}(f) = 0$, for all $f \in \mathscr{C}[a, b]$.
d. Let $L:\mathscr{C}[a, b] \to \text{Trans}\,(\mathscr{C}[a, b], \mathbf{R})$ be defined by $L(g) = L_g$. Use (c) and (b) to prove that L is 1–1.
e. Prove that L is a linear transformation.

9. We use the notation of **8** above. Let $\mathscr{L}:\mathscr{C}[a, b] \to \mathscr{C}[a, b]$ be defined as follows: for any $f \in \mathscr{C}[a, b]$, $\mathscr{L}(f)$ is the function whose value at any $x \in [a, b]$ is given by

$$\mathscr{L}(f)(x) = \int_a^x f(t)\,dt$$

a. Prove that $\mathscr{L}$ is a linear transformation.
b. Why is $\mathscr{L}(f)$ continuous? Prove that $\mathscr{L}(f)$ is differentiable. (*Hint:* Fundamental Theorem of Calculus). Thus, the range of $\mathscr{L}$ is a subset of $\mathscr{D}[a, b]$.
c. In Chapter 1, Example (j), we showed that the derivative d/dx is a linear transformation from $\mathscr{D}[a, b]$ to $\mathscr{C}[a, b]$ [cf. Chapter 1, Example (f) for a definition of $\mathscr{D}[a, b]$]. Let us denote d/dx by "$\mathscr{D}$."

Thus, according to Proposition 4.3, above, $\mathscr{D} \circ \mathscr{L}$ is a linear transformation from $\mathscr{C}[a, b]$ to $\mathscr{C}[a, b]$.

Prove that $\mathscr{D} \circ \mathscr{L} = I_{\mathscr{C}[a,b]}$, *the identity function of* $\mathscr{C}[a, b]$. (*Hint:* Fundamental Theorem of Calculus.)

Thus, by Proposition 2.7, $\mathscr{D}$ *is a left inverse of* $\mathscr{L}$, *and* $\mathscr{L}$ *is a right inverse of* $\mathscr{D}$, *so that* $\mathscr{L}$ *is* 1–1 *and D is onto.*

Show that $\mathscr{L} \circ D \neq I_{\mathscr{D}[a,b]}$. Thus, $\mathscr{D}$ is not a right inverse of $\mathscr{L}$, and, therefore, $\mathscr{D}$ is not 1–1 and $\mathscr{L}$ is not onto.

10. Consider the following three linear expressions (cf. Chapter 1, last portion):

$$x_1 + 2x_2 - x_3$$
$$x_1 - x_2$$
$$x_2 + 4x_3$$

Let $T:\mathbf{R}^3 \to \mathbf{R}^3$ be defined by $T(x_1, x_2, x_3) = (x_1 + 2x_2 - x_3, x_1 - x_2, x_2 + 4x_3)$, for all (x_1, x_2, x_3).
a. Prove that T is a linear transformation.
b. Prove that $\{T(1, 0, 0), T(0, 1, 0), T(0, 0, 1)\}$ is a linearly independent subset of $\mathbf{R}^3$.
c. Determine $(x_1, x_2, x_3) \in \mathbf{R}^3$ so that $T(x_1, x_2, x_3) = (1, 0, -1)$.

d. Show that $T(x_1, x_2, x_3) = (0, 0, 0)$, if and only if $(x_1, x_2, x_3) = (0, 0, 0)$.
e. Show that $T(x_1, x_2, x_3) = T(y_1, y_2, y_3)$, if and only if $(x_1, x_2, x_3) = (y_1, y_2, y_3)$. (Thus, T is 1–1).
f. Show that T is onto $\mathbf{R}^3$.

11. Let $M_2 : \mathbf{R} \to \mathbf{R}$ be multiplication by 2. Consider $\mathbf{R}$ as a vector space over $\mathbf{Q}$, and prove that M_2 is a linear transformation from $\mathbf{R}$ to $\mathbf{R}$ (over $\mathbf{Q}$).

12. Define $c : \mathbf{C} \to \mathbf{C}$ as follows:

$$c(a + bi) = a - bi,$$

(c is known as conjugation: The conjugate of a complex number z, $c(z)$, is usually denoted by "$\bar{z}$.")
a. Consider $\mathbf{C}$ as a vector space over $\mathbf{R}$, and show that c, in this case, is a linear transformation.
b. Consider $\mathbf{C}$ as a vector space over itself. Show, in this case, that c is *not* a linear transformation.

1.4 Isomorphisms of Vector Spaces

We have, as yet, no way of comparing two vector spaces. All we can say, so far, is whether or not a given vector space is the *same* as another, the two being the same, if and only if they consist of the same underlying set and have the same operations. Given a vector space, however, we have no criterion whereby we can identify those other vector spaces that are *similar*, in some sense, to the given one.

Now, such a concept of similarity arises most naturally and reasonably. For example, suppose that $V, +, \cdot$ is a given vector space, and that we replace one or more of the vectors of V by other distinct objects, agreeing to operate with these substitutes exactly as we did before with their predecessors. One feels, in such a case, that one has not really altered the essence of the vector-space structure of $V, +, \cdot$. One has merely altered something superficial: the particular identity of the elements replaced. The role filled by these elements, however, remains unchanged. It is, if one may be allowed a somewhat flamboyant analogy, as in a play in which, after some performances, new actors replace the old; the play is still the same. Clearly, in such a case, $V, +, \cdot$ should be considered to be similar to the vector space resulting from such replacements.

Let us examine this situation further. The crucial fact in the replacement, or substitution, procedure described above, is that we operate with the substitutes exactly as we did with their predecessors. This means that any linear combination of vectors of $V, +, \cdot$ containing the predecessor, now contains its substitute in its place. Moreover, every equation involving linear combinations in which some of the to-be-replaced-vectors appear must remain a valid equation when these vectors are replaced by their successor objects. Now, every linear combination of vectors in a vector space can be built up from the vectors of the vector space by applying, step by step, one or the other of the two vector-space operations. Thus, to check that the substitution procedure indeed preserves all valid equations involving linear combinations, all that one need do is check that the substitution procedure does so at each step in the construction of the linear combinations. Since each such step involves either only $+$ or $\cdot$, we need only check that if $\mathbf{v}$ is replaced by $\mathbf{x}$ and $\mathbf{v}'$ is replaced by $\mathbf{x}'$, then also the value of $\mathbf{v} + \mathbf{v}'$ is replaced by the value of $\mathbf{x} + \mathbf{x}'$ and the value of $a\,\mathbf{v}$ is replaced by the value of $a\mathbf{x}$; where a is any scalar: Schematically,

$$\left.\begin{array}{l}\mathbf{v} \rightarrow \mathbf{x} \\ \mathbf{v}' \rightarrow \mathbf{x}'\end{array}\right\} \Rightarrow \begin{array}{l}\mathbf{v} + \mathbf{v}' \rightarrow \mathbf{x} + \mathbf{x}' \\ a\mathbf{v} \rightarrow a\mathbf{x}\end{array}$$

Our investigation is, now, almost complete. All that we need do is to translate the informal remarks above into the more formal terminology introduced in Chapter 2 and in this chapter.

Let V' be the set of objects obtained at the end of the replacement procedure. We may express the replacement idea formally by saying that there is a 1–1 correspondence $f: V \rightarrow V'$. For each $\mathbf{v} \in V$, the object $f(\mathbf{v}) \in V'$ is either the successor of $\mathbf{v}$, if, indeed, $\mathbf{v}$ is replaced, or $f(\mathbf{v})$ is just $\mathbf{v}$ itself, if $\mathbf{v}$ is left untouched. It may, of course, happen that every $\mathbf{v} \in V$ is actually replaced, or it may happen that no $\mathbf{v} \in V$ is replaced. Such distinctions are unimportant, however. What is important is that there is a 1–1 correspondence, and this correspondence preserves the operations, as indicated schematically above. Indeed, with our new notation, we may express the above scheme as follows:

$$\left.\begin{array}{l}\mathbf{x} = f(\mathbf{v}) \\ \mathbf{x}' = f(\mathbf{v}')\end{array}\right\} \Rightarrow \begin{array}{l}f(\mathbf{v} + \mathbf{v}') = \mathbf{x} + \mathbf{x}' = f(\mathbf{v}) + f(\mathbf{v}') \\ f(a\mathbf{v}) = a\mathbf{x} = af(\mathbf{v})\end{array}$$

But, the reader will now notice that these equations are precisely the two requirements that a function must satisfy in order to be a linear transformation: This discussion motivates the following definition.

Definition 4.2

Let V, $+$, $\cdot$ and W, $+$, $\cdot$ be vector spaces over F. A vector-space isomorphism from V to W is a linear transformation $T: V \rightarrow W$ that is a 1–1 *correspondence between V and W.*

If there is a vector-space isomorphism from V to W, then we may say that V is isomorphic to W and write $V \cong W$.

The notion of *isomorphism* introduced here is clearly, according to the preceding discussion, the correct formalization of the notion of similarity between vector spaces.

One would expect, of course, that if V is isomorphic to W, then all of the properties of V that follow from the abstract definition of a vector space are transported by the isomorphism to corresponding properties of W. For example, one would expect that a linearly independent subset of V is taken to a linearly independent subset of W. Or, one would guess that a set of generators of V is taken to a set of generators of W.

Such suppositions, indeed, are true. Moreover, their validity follows from the general considerations already discussed above. For example, the replacement procedure must end with a zero vector that is the successor of the previous zero vector. For the previous zero vector $\mathbf{0}$ was characterized by the fact that it satisfied all equations of the form $\mathbf{v} + \mathbf{0} = \mathbf{v}$. Therefore, its replacement** must satisfy such equations, which means that it is the new zero vector. From this, it follows that any linear combination of successor vectors with value the new zero vector must have been obtained from a linear combination of original vectors with value the old vector. If the original vectors formed a linearly independent set, then that combination must be trivial. Thus, the corresponding combination of successor vectors must be trivial. This means that the set of successors of a linearly independent set must also be linearly independent.

We amplify these remarks shortly. First, however, we prove a more general result.

Proposition 4.6

Let $\mathscr{V}(F)$ be the set of all vector spaces over F.‡ Then, the relation of vector-space isomorphism is an equivalence relation on $\mathscr{V}(F)$. More specifically, let V, W, and Z be any vector spaces over F. Then: (1) $V \cong V$; (2) *if* $V \cong W$, *then* $W \cong V$; (3) *if* $V \cong W$ *and* $W \cong Z$, *then* $V \cong Z$. *That is,* $\cong$ *is reflexive, symmetric and transitive, respectively.*††

Proof

(1) The function $I_V: V \to V$ is a 1–1 correspondence, and it is a linear transformation, by Example (b) of Subsection 1.2.

(2) If $V \cong W$, then there is a vector-space isomorphism $T: V \to W$. According to Proposition 4.2, $T^{-1}: W \to V$ is a vector-space isomorphism. Thus, $W \cong V$.

(3) If $V \cong W$ and $W \cong Z$, then there are vector-space isomorphisms $T_1: V \to W$ and $T_2: W \to Z$. According to Proposition 4.3, $T_2 \circ T_1: V \to Z$ is a linear transformation, and according to Corollary to Proposition 2.6, $T_2 \circ T_1$ is a 1–1 correspondence. Therefore, it is a vector-space isomorphism. Q.E.D.

** If it is not replaced, then it becomes the new zero vector: we may regard it as replacing itself.

‡ Strictly speaking, $\mathscr{V}(F)$ is not a set: one runs into paradoxes or contradictions, similar to Russell's Paradox, if one insists on regarding it as a set. Thus, we use it here in a very limited way, merely as a convenient terminological device.

†† An equivalence relation is, simply, a reflexive, symmetric, transitive relation. Other examples of equivalence relations are the relation of equality and the relation of similarity-of-triangles. For more details, see Chapter 2, Section 1.7.

Our remarks in Chapter 2 concerning equivalence relations in general, now apply here. The totality of all vector spaces over F is broken up, or partitioned, into equivalence classes, or isomorphism classes. Each class consists of all those vector spaces that we want to consider similar to one another (i.e., isomorphic to one another). Such a class represents one level higher of abstraction than does the notion of vector space itself, as originally defined. For the original notion forced us to make superficial distinctions between vector spaces, distinctions that did not involve their structural "essence." The notion of isomorphism class of vector spaces (over F) involves a distillation away of these superficialities, and with it vector-space-hood reaches, perhaps, its purest expression.

Of course, the mere fact that we have an equivalence relation is, itself, not very interesting. There are literally infinitely many alternative ways to partition $\mathscr{V}(F)$. What is interesting, however, is that this particular relation, $\cong$, is an equivalence relation, because we have intuitive grounds for believing that $\cong$ represents a conceptually relevant and meaningful tie between distinct vector spaces. The following propositions add some substance to our intuitive judgment.

First, we introduce a new bit of notation. If $f: A \to B$ is any function, and if $X \subset A$, then we define $f(X)$, as follows:

$$f(X) = \begin{cases} \varnothing, & \text{if} \quad X = \varnothing \\ \{f(a) \mid a \in X\}, & \quad X \neq \varnothing \end{cases}$$

Or, to put it another way, if $X \neq \varnothing$, then $f(X)$ is just the range of $f \mid X$.

Proposition 4.7

Let $T: V \to W$ be a linear transformation, and let X be a subset of V. Then:

(1) $T(span_V(X)) = span_W(T(X))$.
(2) *If T is* 1–1 *and X is linearly independent, then $T(X)$ is linearly independent.*

Proof

(1) Choose any $\mathbf{w} \in T(\text{span}_V(X))$. By definition, $\mathbf{w} = T(\mathbf{v})$, where $\mathbf{v} \in \text{span}_V(X)$. If $X = \varnothing$, then $\text{span}_V(X) = \{\mathbf{0}\}$, so that $\mathbf{v} = \mathbf{0}$, and, therefore, $\mathbf{w} = T(\mathbf{0}) = \mathbf{0}$. Since $\text{span}_W(T(X))$ is a vector subspace of W, $\mathbf{0}$ belongs to it, so that in this case $\mathbf{w} \in \text{span}_W(T(X))$. If $X \neq \varnothing$, then $\mathbf{v} = a_1\mathbf{x}_1 + \cdots + a_k\mathbf{x}_k$, where $\mathbf{x}_1, \ldots, \mathbf{x}_k$ belong to $\text{span}_V(X)$. Therefore, $\mathbf{w} = T(\mathbf{v}) = T(a_1\mathbf{x}_1 + \cdots + a_k\mathbf{x}_k) = a_1T(\mathbf{x}_1) + \cdots + a_kT(\mathbf{x}_k)$, the last equality following from the fact that T is a linear transformation (see Exercises 4.1. **1**). But, $T(\mathbf{x}_1), \ldots, T(\mathbf{x}_k)$ belong to $T(X)$, so that $\mathbf{w}$ is a linear combination of vectors of $T(X)$. Thus, in this case, too, $\mathbf{w} \in \text{span}_W(T(X))$.

Therefore, $T(\text{span}_V(X)) \subset \text{span}_W(T(X))$.

The reverse inequality is proved similarly. If $X = \varnothing$, then $T(X) = \varnothing$, so that $\text{span}_V(T(X)) = \{\mathbf{0}\} = T(\{\mathbf{0}\}) = T(\text{span}_V(X))$. If $X \neq \varnothing$, then $T(X) \neq \varnothing$. Choose any $\mathbf{w} \in \text{span}_W(T(X))$, assuming, now, that $X \neq \varnothing$. Then, $\mathbf{w} = b_1T(\mathbf{x}_1') + \cdots + b_\ell T(\mathbf{x}_\ell')$, where $\mathbf{x}_1', \ldots, \mathbf{x}_1' \in X$. Again, using the linearity property of T,

$$\mathbf{w} = T(b_1\mathbf{x}_1' + \cdots + b_\ell \mathbf{x}_\ell')$$

Now, $b_1\mathbf{x}_1' + \cdots + b_\ell\mathbf{x}_\ell' \in \text{span}_V(X)$, so that $\mathbf{w} = T(b_1\mathbf{x}_\ell' + \cdots + b_1\mathbf{x}_\ell') \in T(\text{span}_V(X))$.

Thus, $\text{span}_W(T(X)) \subset T(\text{span}_V(X))$, which, together with the reverse inclusion proved above implies result (1).

(2) Suppose that X is linearly independent, $X \neq \varnothing$, and T is a 1–1 linear transformation. Consider any linear combination of vectors of $T(X)$ with value $\mathbf{0}$: $a_1T(\mathbf{x}_1) + \cdots + a_nT(\mathbf{x}_n) = \mathbf{0}$. The vectors $T(\mathbf{x}_i)$ are assumed to be distinct, so that, since T is a function, the $\mathbf{x}_i$ are all distinct. Moreover, $a_1T(\mathbf{x}_1) + \cdots a_nT(\mathbf{x}_n) = T(a_1\mathbf{x}_1 + \cdots + a_n\mathbf{x}_n)$. Thus, $T(a_1\mathbf{x}_1 + \cdots + a_n\mathbf{x}_n) = \mathbf{0}$.

Now, T is a linear transformation, so that $T(\mathbf{0}) = \mathbf{0}$. Since T is 1–1, the vectors $a_1\mathbf{x}_1 + \cdots + a_n\mathbf{x}_n$ and $\mathbf{0}$, both taken to $\mathbf{0}$ by T, must be the same.

Therefore, $a_1\mathbf{x}_1 + \cdots + a_n\mathbf{x}_n$ is a linear combination of vectors of X with value $\mathbf{0}$. Since X is linearly independent, the combination is trivial; thus, $a_1 = 0, \ldots, a_n = 0$. This means that the combination $a_1T(\mathbf{x}_1) + \cdots + a_nT(\mathbf{x}_n)$ is trivial. Therefore, $T(X)$ is linearly independent.

If $X = \varnothing$, then $T(X) = \varnothing$, so that $T(X)$ is independent in this case too. Q.E.D.

Corollary to Proposition 4.7

Let $T: V \to W$ be a vector-space isomorphism, and let X be a basis of V. Then, $T(X)$ is a basis of W.

Proof

Since X is linearly independent and T is 1–1, Proposition 4.7 (2) implies that $T(X)$ is linearly independent.

Notice, moreover, that since T is onto, the range of T is W. Therefore, by Proposition 4.7 (1), $\text{span}_W(T(X)) = T(\text{span}_V(X)) = T(V) = \text{range}(T \mid V) = \text{range } T = W$.

Therefore, $T(X)$ is a linearly independent generating set of W. Q.E.D.

Corollary to the Corollary to Proposition 4.7

If $V \cong W$, then $\dim(V) = \dim(W)$.

Proof

Since T is 1–1, for any (nonempty) subset $Y \subset V$, the correspondence $\mathbf{y} \to T(\mathbf{y})$ is a 1–1 correspondence between Y and $T(Y)$.

Let X be a basis of V; then $T(X)$ is a basis of W. By the preceding remark, if $X \neq \varnothing$, then $X \not\approx T(X)$ [i.e. X is in 1–1 correspondence with $T(X)$]. If $X = \varnothing$, then $T(X) = \varnothing$, so that, again, trivially, $X \not\approx T(X)$.

Therefore,

$$\dim(V) = \text{cardinality of } X = \text{cardinality of } T(X) = \dim(W) \qquad \text{Q.E.D.}$$

Later, we shall prove the converse of this result.

1.5 Examples of Vector-space Isomorphisms

(a) Let V and W be vector spaces over F, both consisting of only one vector. This must be the zero vector in each, since every vector space has a zero vector. Let $f: V \to W$ be the function that sends $\mathbf{0}$ to $\mathbf{0}$. Clearly, f is a 1–1 correspondence between V and W. Moreover, $f(\mathbf{0} + \mathbf{0}) = f(\mathbf{0}) = \mathbf{0} = \mathbf{0} + \mathbf{0} = f(\mathbf{0}) + f(\mathbf{0})$, and $f(a\mathbf{0}) = f(\mathbf{0}) = \mathbf{0} = a\mathbf{0} = af(\mathbf{0})$, for any $a \in F$, so that f is a linear transformation.

Therefore, $V \cong W$. Henceforth, we shall call any vector space over F in the isomorphism class of V or W *trivial*, and we shall denote it by $\{\mathbf{0}\}$.

(b) Let V be any vector space over F, and let $a \in F$ be any nonzero scalar. *Then, multiplication by a, $M_a: V \to V$, is a vector-space isomorphism.*

The proof of this fact is easy. First of all, M_a is a linear transformation, as was shown in Subsection 1.2, Example (b). Secondly, since $a \neq 0$, it has a -inverse, $1/a \in F$, and $M_{1/a}: V \to V$ is a linear transformation. Finally, notice that $M_a \circ M_{1/a} = M_1 = I_V = M_{1/a} \circ M_a$. This chain of equalities follows from:

$$(M_a \circ M_{1/a})(\mathbf{v}) = M_a((1/a)\mathbf{v}) = a((1/a)\mathbf{v}) = \mathbf{v} = I_V(\mathbf{v}) = 1/a(a\mathbf{v}) = (M_{1/a} \circ M_a)(\mathbf{v}),$$

for every $\mathbf{v} \in V$.

Therefore, $M_{1/a}$ is the inverse of M_a, so that M_a is 1–1 and onto.

In particular, notice that if $a = 1$, $M_a = M_1 = I_V$, so that the above result implies that I_V is a vector-space isomorphism—which we, of course, already know.

(c) Let V and W be any vector spaces over F. In Chapter 3, we constructed the product $V \times W$, and we showed that $V \times \{\mathbf{0}\}$ and $\{\mathbf{0}\} \times W$ are complementary vector subspaces of $V \times W$. We now claim that $V \cong V \times \{\mathbf{0}\}$ and $W \cong \{\mathbf{0}\} \times W$. We only exhibit the former isomorphism, the latter isomorphism being similar.

Define a function $f: V \to V \times \{\mathbf{0}\}$ as follows: $f(\mathbf{v}) = (\mathbf{v}, \mathbf{0})$, for all $\mathbf{v} \in V$. The reader should verify that f is a 1–1 onto linear transformation.

Thus, we may conclude that $V \times W$ is the internal direct sum of a copy of V (namely, $V \times \{\mathbf{0}\}$) and a copy of W (namely $\{\mathbf{0}\} \times W$).

(d) Let V be a vector space over F, and let U_1 and U_2 be complementary subspaces of V; that is, $U_1 \oplus U_2 = V$. *We show that* $U_1 \times U_2 \cong V$.

Let $T: U_1 \times U_2 \to V$ be defined as follows: for any $(\mathbf{u}_1, \mathbf{u}_2) \in U_1 \times U_2$, $T(\mathbf{u}_1, \mathbf{u}_2) = \mathbf{u}_1 + \mathbf{u}_2$.

Claim. *T is a linear transformation.*

Proof

Choose any pairs $(\mathbf{u}_1, \mathbf{u}_2), (\mathbf{u}_1', \mathbf{u}_2') \in U_1 \times U_2$ and any $a \in F$. Then,

$$\begin{aligned} T((\mathbf{u}_1, \mathbf{u}_2) + (\mathbf{u}_1', \mathbf{u}_2')) &= T(\mathbf{u}_1 + \mathbf{u}_1', \mathbf{u}_2 + \mathbf{u}_2') \\ &= (\mathbf{u}_1 + \mathbf{u}_1') + (\mathbf{u}_2 + \mathbf{u}_2') \\ &= (\mathbf{u}_1 + \mathbf{u}_2) + (\mathbf{u}_1' + \mathbf{u}_2') \\ &= T(\mathbf{u}_1, \mathbf{u}_2) + T(\mathbf{u}_1', \mathbf{u}_2'), \end{aligned}$$

and

$$\begin{aligned} T(a(\mathbf{u}_1, \mathbf{u}_2)) &= T(a\mathbf{u}_1, a\mathbf{u}_2) \\ &= a\mathbf{u}_1 + a\mathbf{u}_2 = a(\mathbf{u}_1 + \mathbf{u}_2) \\ &= aT(\mathbf{u}_1, \mathbf{u}_2) \qquad \text{Q.E.D.} \end{aligned}$$

Claim: *T is* 1–1 *and onto V.*

Proof

To see that T is onto, choose any $\mathbf{v} \in V$. Since $V = U_1 + U_2$, we may write $\mathbf{v} = \mathbf{u}_1 + \mathbf{u}_2$, where $\mathbf{u}_1 \in U_1$ and $\mathbf{u}_2 \in U_2$. Therefore, $T(\mathbf{u}_1, \mathbf{u}_2) = \mathbf{u}_1 + \mathbf{u}_2 = \mathbf{v}$, so that $\mathbf{v} \in$ range of T.

To see that T is 1–1, choose any two pairs $(\mathbf{u}_1, \mathbf{u}_2)$ and $(\mathbf{u}_1', \mathbf{u}_2')$ in $U_1 \times U_2$ and suppose that $T(\mathbf{u}_1, \mathbf{u}_2) = T(\mathbf{u}_1, \mathbf{u}_2)$. Then $\mathbf{u}_1 + \mathbf{u}_2 = \mathbf{u}_1' + \mathbf{u}_2'$, so that, since every vector in V can be written in *only one* way as a sum of two vectors, one from U_1 and one from U_2, we must have $\mathbf{u}_1 = \mathbf{u}_1'$ and $\mathbf{u}_2 = \mathbf{u}_2'$. Thus, $(\mathbf{u}_1, \mathbf{u}_2) = (\mathbf{u}_1', \mathbf{u}_2')$. This implies that if $(\mathbf{u}_1, \mathbf{u}_2)$ and $(\mathbf{u}_1', \mathbf{u}_2')$ had been chosen to be distinct from one another, then their T-images would have to be distinct. Thus, T is 1–1. Q.E.D.

Thus, our conclusion is that $U_1 \oplus U_2 \cong U_1 \times U_2$.

(e) Let V be any vector space over F, and let X be a basis of V. We suppose, to avoid an uninteresting case, that V is not trivial, so that $X \neq \varnothing$. Recall that F^X, the set of all functions $X \to F$, is a vector space over F with respect to the usual operations of addition and scalar multiplication of functions. Recall also that in Chapter 3, Subsection 5.3, Example (h), we defined a certain subset $\overline{X} \subset F^X$, and a 1–1 correspondence between X and $\overline{X}$, and we let $F(X) = \text{span}_{F^X}(\overline{X})$. The set $\overline{X}$ consists of all functions $X \to F$ that are constantly zero except at one member of X where they assume the value of 1. The 1–1 correspondence $X \to \overline{X}$ is defined by sending each $\mathbf{x} \in X$ to that function, $f_{\mathbf{x}} \in \overline{X}$, that sends $\mathbf{x}$ to 1 and all the other members of X to 0.

Claim: $V \cong F(X)$.

Proof

We define an isomorphism $T: V \to F(X)$ as follows:

Choose any $\mathbf{v} \in V$. Since X is a basis of V, there is precisely one linear combination of vectors of X with value $\mathbf{v}$: Say, $a_1\mathbf{x}_1 + \cdots + a_n\mathbf{x}_n = \mathbf{v}$. Define $T(\mathbf{v})$ to be $a_1 f_{\mathbf{x}_1} + \cdots + a_n f_{\mathbf{x}_n} \in \text{span}_{F^X}(\overline{X}) = F(X)$.

We leave to the reader the task of showing that T is an isomorphism.

Thus, every vector space over F is a replica of $F(X)$, for some appropriately chosen set X.

Notice that if X is finite, then $F(X) = F^X$. If X is empty, this is obvious. If X is not empty, then suppose $X = \{\mathbf{x}_1, \ldots, \mathbf{x}_n\}$. Every function $f: X \to F$ is, then, completely determined by its function values $f(\mathbf{x}_1), \ldots, f(\mathbf{x}_n)$. Let $f(\mathbf{x}_i) = a_i$, and consider the linear combination of functions of $\overline{X}$, $a_1 f_{\mathbf{x}_1} + \cdots + a_n f_{\mathbf{x}_n}$. This is a function from X to F with value at $\mathbf{x}_i$

$$\begin{aligned}(a_1 f_{\mathbf{x}_1} + \cdots + a_n f_{\mathbf{x}_n})(\mathbf{x}_i) &= a_1 f_{\mathbf{x}_1}(\mathbf{x}_i) + \cdots + a_i f_{\mathbf{x}_i}(\mathbf{x}_i) + \cdots + a_n f_{\mathbf{x}_n}(\mathbf{x}_i)\\ &= a_1 \cdot 0 + \cdots + a_i \cdot 1 + \cdots + a_n \cdot 0\\ &= a_i = f(\mathbf{x}_i)\end{aligned}$$

Therefore, $f \in \text{span}_{F^X}(\overline{X}) = F(X)$, so that $F(X) = F^X$.

(f) Let X be any finite set, and suppose that it contains n members. To keep matters interesting, we assume $n > 0$. Then, *the vector space F^X is isomorphic to F^n.*

To see this, notice that, if $X = \{\mathbf{x}_1, \ldots, \mathbf{x}_n\}$, then $\{f_{\mathbf{x}_1}, \ldots, f_{\mathbf{x}_n}\}$ is a basis of $F(X) = F^X$. Recall, also, that F^n has a standard basis $\{\mathbf{e}_1^{(n)}, \ldots, e_n^{(n)}\}$. Define a function $T: F^X \to F^n$ as follows:

$$T(a_1 f_{\mathbf{x}_1} + \cdots + a_n f_{\mathbf{x}_n}) = a_1\mathbf{e}_1^{(n)} + \cdots + a_n\mathbf{e}_n^{(n)}$$

Because the linear combination on the left is the only one with its particular value, T is unambiguously defined. We leave to the reader the task of showing that T is a vector-space isomorphism.

Combining results (e) and (f) we obtain the following important consequence.

Proposition 4.8

Let V be a vector space over F of finite dimension n. Then, $V \cong F^n$.

Proof

Again, to keep matters interesting, we assume $n > 0$, although the result holds for $n = 0$ as well.

Let X be any basis of V. It consists of n vectors. By (e), $V \cong F(X) = F^X$. By (f), $F^X \cong F^n$. Since $\cong$ is transitive, $V \cong F^n$. Q.E.D.

This result shows that every finite-dimensional vector space over F is a replica of F^n, for a suitable natural number n. Thus, the vector spaces F^n are paradigm examples of finite-dimensional vector spaces over F. Similarly, the vector spaces $F(X)$ are paradigm examples of all vector spaces over F.

The question now arises as to why we study general abstract vector spaces in the first place if they are all replicas of the particular vector spaces $F(X)$ or F^n. The answer is two-fold. First, $F(X)$ is more than a vector space over F (of a certain dimension). It has, *per definitionem*, additional structure. For example, it has a preferred basis: $\bar{X}$. In an abstract vector space any basis is as good as any other. In $F(X)$, $\bar{X}$ is better than others, or more natural, since there is such a nice relationship between the function values of a member of $F(X)$ and the coefficients in its expression as a linear combination of members of $\bar{X}$: namely, they are the same. There is, therefore, the very reasonable tendency to prefer $\bar{X}$ over other bases and to use $\bar{X}$ when making certain general definitions about $F(X)$. The trouble with such a procedure is that one may be misled into believing that one is talking about $F(X)$ when in reality one is talking only about $\bar{X}$. Such difficulties may occur when one is discussing determinants, for example, as we shall point out. Secondly—and this is an extension of the first point—$F(X)$ is only one special example of a certain general type. It is a vector space over F, but it is also *a certain set of functions from X to F*. How does one discuss other examples? What about subspaces of $F(X)$? It may not be apparent how to write these in the form $F(Y)$ for some Y; indeed, it may be impossible to do so. *True, other examples are replicas of F(X), but in order to see that they are replicas, one must do so in a universe (of vector spaces and linear transformations) in which these other examples are also allowed to exist in their own right as vector spaces.* The universe most convenient for this purpose turns out to be the universe of abstract vector spaces as we have defined them.

Similar comments apply to F^n.

(g) Let $F = \mathbf{R}$ and $V = \mathbf{R}^2$. Suppose that θ is an angle between 0 and $\pi/2$ radians and consider the linear transformation $R_\theta: R^2 \to \mathbf{R}^2$, rotation through the angle θ. R_θ is a vector-space isomorphism.

To see this, recall that in Subsection 1.2, Example (h), we showed that R_θ is a linear transformation. In a similar way, we can show that $R_{-\theta}$, rotation through $-\theta$, is a linear transformation. Finally, it is easy to see that $R_\theta \circ R_{-\theta} = R_{-\theta} \circ R_\theta = I_{\mathbf{R}^2}$, for the first transformation involves rotating through $-\theta$ and then back through θ, whereas the second involves rotating through θ and then back through $-\theta$. The end result in both cases is, clearly, not to have moved anything at all. That is, the end result is the identity map.

Therefore, $R_{-\theta} = R_\theta^{-1}$, so that R_θ is 1–1 and onto.

(h) Let $A: \mathbf{R}^3 \to \mathbf{R}^3$ be given by the following linear expressions

$$\begin{aligned} &3x_1 + x_2 + x_3 \\ &\qquad x_2 - x_3 \\ &x_1 - x_2 \end{aligned} \tag{1}$$

That is, for any $(x_1, x_2, x_3) \in \mathbf{R}^3$, $A(x_1, x_2, x_3) = (3x_1 + x_2 + x_3, x_2 - x_3, x_1 - x_2)$. We have shown already that such a function is a linear transformation. Let us now show that this one is 1–1 and onto.

Choose any $(y_1, y_2, y_3) \in \mathbf{R}^3$. We try to determine $(x_1, x_2, x_3) \in \mathbf{R}^3$ such that

$$A(x_1, x_2, x_3) = (y_1, y_2, y_3) \tag{2}$$

This amounts to solving the equation system

$$\begin{aligned} 3x_1 + x_2 + x_3 &= y_1 \\ x_2 - x_3 &= y_2 \\ x_1 - x_2 \quad\quad &= y_3 \end{aligned} \tag{3}$$

Add equations (1) and (2) and add twice equation (3) to the result. We obtain, as a new equation (1),

$$5x_1 = y_1 + y_2 + 2y_3 \tag{1'}$$

Thus, $x_1 = 1/5(y_1 + y_2 + 2y_3)$. Substituting this into equation (3), we get $x_2 = 1/5(y_1 + y_2 + 2y_3) - y_3 = 1/5(y_1 + y_2 - 3y_3)$. Finally, substituting this answer in equation (2), we get

$$x_3 = 1/5(y_1 + y_2 - 3y_3) - y_2 = 1/5(y_1 - 4y_2 - 3y_3).$$

Returning to the original system, the reader may check that the values $x_1 = 1/5(y_1 + y_2 + 2y_3)$, $x_2 = 1/5(y_1 + y_2 - 3y_3)$ and $x_3 = 1/5(y_1 - 4y_2 - 3y_3)$ do indeed constitute a solution of that system. Thus, A is onto.

Next, suppose that (c_1, c_2, c_3) and (c_1', c_2', c_3') are both solutions to the above system. Then, it is not hard to see that $(c_1 - c_1', c_2 - c_2', c_3 - c_3')$ is a solution to the system

$$\begin{aligned} 3x_1 + x_2 + x_3 &= 0 \\ x_2 - x_3 &= 0 \\ x_1 - x_2 \quad\quad &= 0 \end{aligned}$$

That is, substituting $c_1 - c_1'$ for x_1, $c_2 - c_2'$ for x_2, and $c_3 - c_3'$ for x_3, we get the actual equations

$$\begin{aligned} 3(c_1 - c_1') + (c_2 - c_2') + (c_3 - c_3') &= 0 \\ (c_2 - c_2') - (c_3 - c_3') &= 0 \\ (c_1 - c_1') - (c_2 - c_2') \quad\quad\quad &= 0 \end{aligned}$$

Now, go through the same procedure that we did above in solving for the x's in terms of the y's. We obtain, $c_1 - c_1' = 1/5(0 + 0 + 2 \cdot 0) = 0$, $c_2 - c_2' = 1/5(0 + 0 - 3 \cdot 0) = 0$, and $c_3 - c_3' = 1/5(0 - 4 \cdot 0 - 3 \cdot 0) = 0$, so that $c_1 = c_1'$, $c_2 = c_2'$, and $c_3 = c_3'$.

Thus, the first system of equations has one and *only one* solution, namely, the one obtained above. Since (y_1, y_2, y_3) was chosen arbitrarily in R^3, this means that for every $(y_1, y_2, y_3) \in \mathbf{R}^3$, there is one and only one (x_1, x_2, x_3) such that $A(x_1, x_2, x_3) = (y_1, y_2, y_3)$.

Thus, in addition to being onto, A is 1–1.

Thus, A is an isomorphism.

This example, it is hoped, points to the relation our abstract discussion bears to the concrete problems of solving systems of linear equations. We discuss this in more detail in Chapter 5.

1.6 Some standard isomorphisms

Proposition 4.9

Let V be a vector space over F. Then, the vector space Trans(F, V) is isomorphic to V.

Proof

Recall that Trans(F, V) consists of all linear transformations from F to V. We define a function E : Trans(F, V) $\to V$ as follows: given any $T \in$ Trans(F, V), $E(T) = T(1)$. Indeed, E is merely the *evaluation function* discussed in example (h) of Chapter 1; only now it is not defined on all of V^F but restricted to Trans(F, V) $\subset V^F$. E is evaluation at $1 \in F$.

We showed in example (h) of Chapter 1 that the evaluation function is a linear transformation; thus, by Proposition 4.1, its restriction to the subspace Trans(F, V) is a linear transformation.

We conclude by showing that E is 1–1 and onto.

Suppose that $T_1, T_2 \in$ Trans(F, V) and $T_1 \neq T_2$. By definition of equality of functions, this means that there is some $a \in F$ such that $T_1(a) \neq T_2(a)$. Clearly, $a \neq 0$, for, since T_1 and T_2 are both linear transformations, $T_1(0) = \mathbf{0} = T_2(0)$.

Therefore, a has a $\cdot$-inverse, $1/a$, and we get

$$\begin{aligned} E(T_1) &= T_1(1) = T_1(1/a \cdot a) = 1/aT_1(a) \neq 1/a\, T_2(a) = T_2(1/a \cdot a) \\ &= T_2(1) = E(T_2) \end{aligned}$$

Thus, E takes distinct members of Trans (F, V) to distinct vectors of V and is, therefore, 1–1.

To see that E is onto, choose any $\mathbf{v} \in V$. We shall show that there is a $T \in$ Trans(F, V) such that $E(T) = \mathbf{v}$.

Indeed, consider the function $T : F \to V$ defined as follows: for every $a \in F$, $T(a) = a\mathbf{v}$. Choosing any a_1, a_2 and b in F, we get

$$T(a_1 + a_2) = (a_1 + a_2)\mathbf{v} = a_1\mathbf{v} + a_2\mathbf{v} = T(a_1) + T(a_2)$$

and $T(ba_1) = (ba_1)\mathbf{v} = b(a_1\mathbf{v}) = bT(a_1)$. Therefore, T is a linear transformation from F to V, so that $T \in$ Trans(F, V). Moreover, $T(1) = 1\mathbf{v} = \mathbf{v}$, so that $E(T) = T(1) = \mathbf{v}$, as desired. Q.E.D.

Notice in the above proof that T is a linear transformation how importantly the distributive and associative laws featured.

Whereas Trans(F, V) is isomorphic to V for all vector spaces V over F, Trans(V, F) is isomorphic to V only for *finite-dimensional* V. A proof of this will be presented later in this chapter.

Proposition 4.10

Let V_1, V_2, W_1, and W_2 be vector spaces over F, such that $V_1 \simeq W_1$ and $V_2 \simeq W_2$. Then $V_1 \times V_2 \simeq W_1 \times W_2$.

Proof

Let $T_1 : V_1 \to W_1$ and $T_2 : V_2 \to W_2$ be isomorphisms. Then, by Proposition 4.4,

$$T_1 \times T_2 : V_1 \times V_2 \to W_1 \times W_2$$

is a linear transformation. We leave to the reader the proof that it is 1–1 and onto. Q.E.D.

Proposition 4.11

Let V_1, V_2, W_1 and W_2 be as above, and again suppose that $V_1 \simeq W_1$ and $V_2 \simeq W_2$. Then, Trans(V_1, V_2) $\simeq$ Trans(W_1, W_2).

Proof

Let $T_1 : V_1 \to W_1$ and $T_2 : V_2 \to W_2$ be isomorphisms. We define a function

$$\mathscr{T} : \text{Trans}(V_1, V_2) \to W_2{}^{W_1}$$

as follows: For any $T \in \text{Trans}(V_1, V_2)$, let $\mathscr{T}(T)$ be the function $T_2 \circ T \circ T_1{}^{-1}$: $W_1 \to W_2$. (Note: $T_1{}^{-1}$ takes W_1 to V_1, T takes V_1 to V_2, and T_2 takes V_2 to W_2. Therefore, $T_2 \circ T \circ T_1{}^{-1}$ takes W_1 to W_2.)

Next, we note that, by Proposition 4.2 and Proposition 4.3, $T_2 \circ T \circ T_1{}^{-1}$ is a linear transformation. Therefore $\mathscr{T}(T) \in \text{Trans}(W_1, W_2)$.

Claim: *$\mathscr{T}$ is* 1–1 *and onto Trans(W_1, W_2).*

To prove this we exhibit the inverse of $\mathscr{T}$, which we shall call $\mathscr{S}$. $\mathscr{S}$ will take Trans(W_1, W_2) to Trans(V_1, V_2). It is defined as follows: For any $S \in$ Trans(W_1, W_2), $\mathscr{S}(S)$ is the function $T_2{}^{-1} \circ S \circ T_1 : V_1 \to V_2$. By the same reasoning as above, $\mathscr{S}(S)$ is a linear transformation.

Now we evaluate $\mathscr{T} \circ \mathscr{S}$ at an arbitrary $S \in \text{Trans}(W_1, W_2)$.

$$\begin{aligned}(\mathscr{T} \circ \mathscr{S})(S) &= \mathscr{T}(\mathscr{S}(S)) = \mathscr{T}(T_2{}^{-1} \circ S \circ T_1) \\ &= T_2 \circ (T_2{}^{-1} \circ S \circ T_1) \circ T_1{}^{-1} \\ &= (T_2 \circ T_2{}^{-1}) \circ S \circ (T_1 \circ T_1{}^{-1}) \\ &= I_{W_2} \circ S \circ I_{W_1} = S = I_{\text{Trans}(W_1, W_2)}(S)\end{aligned}$$

Similarly, for any $T \in \text{Trans}(V_1, V_2)$,

$$\begin{aligned}(\mathscr{S} \circ \mathscr{T})(T) &= \mathscr{S}(\mathscr{T}(T)) = \mathscr{S}(T_2 \circ T \circ T_1^{-1}) = T_2^{-1} \circ (T_2 \circ T \circ T_1^{-1}) \circ T_1 \\ &= (T_2^{-1} \circ T_2) \circ T \circ (T_1^{-1} \circ T_1) = I_{V_2} \circ T \circ I_{V_1} = T \\ &= I_{\text{Trans}(V_1, V_2)}(T)\end{aligned}$$

Thus,

$$\mathscr{T} \circ \mathscr{S} = I_{\text{Trans}(W_1, W_2)}, \text{ and } \mathscr{S} \circ \mathscr{T} = I_{\text{Trans}(V_1, V_2)}$$

so that $\mathscr{S}$ and $\mathscr{T}$ are (two-sided) inverses of one another, and, hence, they are both 1–1 and onto.

Claim: *$\mathscr{T}$ is a linear transformation.*

Choose any $T, T' \in \text{Trans}(V_1, V_2)$ and any $a \in F$. Then, for every $\mathbf{v} \in V$,

$$\begin{aligned}(\mathscr{T}(T + T'))(\mathbf{v}) &= (T_2 \circ (T + T') \circ T_1^{-1})(\mathbf{v}) \\ &= T_2 \circ (T + T')(T_1^{-1}(\mathbf{v})) = T_2(T(T_1^{-1}(\mathbf{v})) + T'(T_1^{-1}(\mathbf{v}))) \\ &= T_2(T(T_1^{-1}(\mathbf{v}))) + T_2(T'(T_1^{-1}(\mathbf{v}))) \\ &= (T_2 \circ T \circ T_1^{-1})(\mathbf{v}) + (T_2 \circ T' \circ T_1^{-1})(\mathbf{v}) \\ &= ((T_2 \circ T \circ T_1^{-1}) + (T_2 \circ T' \circ T_2^{-1}))(\mathbf{v}) = (\mathscr{T}(T) + \mathscr{T}(T))(\mathbf{v})\end{aligned}$$

and

$$\begin{aligned}\mathscr{T}(aT))(\mathbf{v}) &= (T_2 \circ (aT) \circ T_1^{-1})(\mathbf{v}) = T_2 \circ (aT)(T_1^{-1}(\mathbf{v})) \\ &= T_2(aT(T_1^{-1}(\mathbf{v}))) = aT_2(T(T_1^{-1}(\mathbf{v})) = (a(T_2 \circ T \circ T_1^{-1}))(\mathbf{v}) \\ &= (a(T_2 \circ T \circ T_1^{-1}))(\mathbf{v}) = (a\mathscr{T}(T))(\mathbf{v}),\end{aligned}$$

so that $\mathscr{T}(T + T') = \mathscr{T}(T) + \mathscr{T}(T')$ and $\mathscr{T}(aT) = a\mathscr{T}(T)$. Q.E.D.

EXERCISES / 4.2

1.* Let θ be any angle between 0 and $\pi/2$. Let $R_\theta : \mathbf{R}^2 \to \mathbf{R}^2$ be rotation through θ.

a. Prove that for any $(x, y) \in \mathbf{R}^2$,

$$R_\theta(x, y) = (x \cos \theta - y \sin \theta,\ x \sin \theta + y \cos \theta).$$

b. Using only the equation in **a**, prove that R_θ is a linear transformation.

c. Using only the equation in **a**, prove that R_θ is 1–1 and onto $\mathbf{R}^2$. (You may use facts about trigonometric functions, of course.)

2.* Let $V_1, \ldots, V_n$ and $W_1, \ldots, W_n$ be vector spaces over F such that $V_i \simeq W_i$, $i = 1, \ldots, n$. Prove that $V_1 \times \cdots \times V_n \simeq W_1 \times \ldots \times W_n$.

3. Let U, V, W, be vector spaces over F. Form the vector spaces $U \times V$ and $V \times W$, and then form, from them and U and W, $(U \times V) \times W$ and $U \times (V \times W)$. These are vector spaces over F.

   Prove that $(U \times V) \times W \simeq U \times (V \times W) \simeq U \times V \times W$. This is a kind of associative law for vector-space products. How would you generalize it?

4. Which of the following systems of linear expressions determine vector-space isomorphisms (of vector spaces over **R**), in the way described in example (h), above? (Justify your answers.)

   a. $\begin{array}{l} 3x_1 + x_2 \\ \qquad x_2 \end{array}$

   b. $\begin{array}{l} x_1 \\ x_2 \\ x_3 \end{array}$

   c. $\begin{array}{l} x_1 + x_2 \\ \qquad x_2 + x_3 \\ \qquad\qquad x_3 + x_4 \\ x_1 + x_2 + x_3 + x_4 \end{array}$

   d. $\begin{array}{l} 2x_1 - x_2 \\ 9x_2 - 4x_1 \end{array}$

   e. $x_1 - x_2$

5. Let V be a vector space over **R**. Since the field of rational numbers **Q** is contained in **R**, there is well-defined a notion of scalar multiplication by members of **Q**. Using the addition of V and this scalar multiplication by members of **Q**, it is not hard to see that we may regard V as a vector space over **Q**, just as **R** has been so regarded. To emphasize when we are so regarding V, we call V, $V_{\mathbf{Q}}$.

   a. Let $T: V \to V$ be a linear transformation. Show that $T: V_{\mathbf{Q}} \to V_{\mathbf{Q}}$ is a linear transformation.

   b. Show that if $T: V \to V$ is an isomorphism, then so is $T: V_{\mathbf{Q}} \to V_{\mathbf{Q}}$.

6. Define $T: \mathbf{R}^2 \to \mathbf{C}$ as follows:

$$T(x, y) = x + iy, \text{ for all } (x, y) \in \mathbf{R}^2$$

   Regard **C** as a vector space over **R**, and prove that T is a vector-space isomorphism.

   Thus, $\mathbf{R}^2 \simeq \mathbf{C}$ when both are regarded as vector spaces over **R**.

7. Let $a + bi$ be any complex number such that $a^2 + b^2 = 1$, $a > 0$, $b > 0$. Show that $M_{a+bi}: \mathbf{C} \to \mathbf{C}$, multiplication by $a + bi$, is the same as rotation of **C** through a certain angle θ. What is θ in terms of a and b?

8. Let $\mathscr{P}^n$, as before, be the vector space, over **R**, of all polynomials in the variable x with real coefficients and degree $\leq n$.

   Prove that $\mathscr{P}^n \simeq \mathbf{R}^{n+1}$.

9. **a.** Let $T_1: V \to W$ and $T_2: V \to W$ be vector-space isomorphisms. Is $T_1 + T_2$ always a vector-space isomorphism between V and W? If so, prove it. If not, give an example to show why not.

   b. Let $T: V \to W$ be a vector-space isomorphism, and let $a \in F$ be any scalar. Is aT a vector-space isomorphism? Even when $a = 0$? What about when $a \neq 0$? Substantiate your answers.

   c. In view of **a** and **b**, is the set of vector-space isomorphisms from V to W closed with respect to the operations of Trans(V, W)?

10. Let V_1, V_2, and W be vector spaces over F. Let $G\colon \text{Trans}(V_1, W) \times \text{Trans}(V_2, W) \to \text{Trans}(V_1 \times V_2, W)$ be defined as follows: For any pair $(T_1, T_2) \in \text{Trans}(V_1, W) \times \text{Trans}(V_2, W)$, let $G(T_1, T_2)$ be the function from $V_1 \times V_2$ to W whose value at any pair $(\mathbf{v}_1, \mathbf{v}_2) \in V_1 \times V_2$ is given by

$$G(T_1, T_2)(\mathbf{v}_1, \mathbf{v}_2) = T_1(\mathbf{v}_1) + T_2(\mathbf{v}_2)$$

a. Prove that G is a linear transformation.
b. Prove that G is 1–1 and onto. (*Hint:* Given any $T\colon V_1 \times V_2 \to W$, let $T_1\colon V_1 \to W$ and $T_2\colon V_2 \to W$ be given by, $T_1(\mathbf{v}_1) = T(\mathbf{v}_1, \mathbf{0})$ and $T_2(\mathbf{v}_2) = T(\mathbf{0}, \mathbf{v}_2)$, for every $\mathbf{v}_1 \in V_1$ and $\mathbf{v}_2 \in V_2$. Show that $T = G(T_1, T_2)$.)
Thus, $\text{Trans}(V_1, W) \times \text{Trans}(V_2, W) \simeq \text{Trans}(V_1 \times V_2, W)$.

This result, together with Proposition 4.9, and other earlier results, allows us to conclude that

$$\textit{Trans}(F^2, F) \simeq F^2$$

To see this, note that the above result implies that

$$\text{Trans}(F^2, F) \simeq \text{Trans}(F, F) \times \text{Trans}(F, F)$$

Then, using Proposition 4.9, we get that $\text{Trans}(F, F) \simeq F$, so that, by Proposition 4.10

$$\text{Trans}(F, F) \times \text{Trans}(F, F) \simeq F \times F = F^2$$

Combining this with the previous isomorphism, we get the desired one above.

From this we may conclude that any 2-dimensional vector space V over F satisfies:

$$\text{Trans}(V, F) \simeq V$$

Proof

If V is two-dimensional, then $V \simeq F^2$. Thus, by Proposition 4.11, $\text{Trans}(V, F) \simeq \text{Trans}(F^2, F)$. By the above result, $\text{Trans}(F^2, F) \simeq F^2$, and of course, $F^2 \simeq V$. Since $\simeq$ is transitive, we get

$$\text{Trans}(V, F) \simeq V$$

A similar result applies to higher dimensional V. We prove the general fact slightly differently later in this chapter.

1.7 The Null Space and Range of a Linear Transformation

If $f\colon X \to Y$ is an arbitrary function, then the range of f is the subset of Y consisting of all f-images. In general, this is merely a subset of Y. If X and Y are vector spaces, however, and if f is a linear transformation, then we can say a little bit more.

Proposition 4.12

Let $V, +, \cdot$ be a vector space over F, and let W be a nonempty set on which are defined an operation $\oplus : W \times W \to W$ and an operation $\otimes : F \times W \to W$.
Let $f: V \to W$ be any function such that for any $\mathbf{v}_1, \mathbf{v}_2 \in V$ and any $a \in F$,

$$f(\mathbf{v}_1 + \mathbf{v}_2) = f(\mathbf{v}_1) \oplus f(\mathbf{v}_2)$$
$$f(a \cdot \mathbf{v}_1) = a \otimes f(\mathbf{v}_1)$$

Then: (1) *$\mathscr{R}_f$, the range of f, is closed with respect to $\oplus$ and $\otimes$. That is, for any $\mathbf{w}_1, \mathbf{w}_2 \in \mathscr{R}_f$ and any $a \in F$, $\mathbf{w}_1 \oplus \mathbf{w}_2$ and $a \otimes w_1$ belong to $\mathscr{R}_f$.*
(2) *$\mathscr{R}_f$ is a vector space over F with respect to these operations.*
(3) *$f: V \to \mathscr{R}_f$ is a linear transformation.*

Proof

The proof of (3) is trivial given the hypotheses on f. To verify (1), choose $\mathbf{w}_1, \mathbf{w}_2$ and a as above, and let $\mathbf{v}_1, \mathbf{v}_2 \in V$ be such that $f(\mathbf{v}_1) = \mathbf{w}_1, f(\mathbf{v}_2) = \mathbf{w}_2$. Then, by hypothesis, $\mathbf{w}_1 \oplus \mathbf{w}_2 = f(\mathbf{v}_1) \oplus f(\mathbf{v}_2) = f(\mathbf{v}_1 + \mathbf{v}_2) \in \mathscr{R}_f$, and $a \otimes \mathbf{w}_1 = a \otimes f(\mathbf{v}_1) = f(a \cdot \mathbf{v}_1) \in \mathscr{R}_f$. Thus, (1) is true. It remains to prove (2), which we do partially. Choose any $\mathbf{w}_1, \mathbf{w}_2, \mathbf{w}_3 \in \mathscr{R}_f$. Then, there are $\mathbf{v}_1, \mathbf{v}_2, \mathbf{v}_3 \in V$, such that $\mathbf{w}_i = f(\mathbf{v}_i)$, $i = 1, 2, 3$.

(1) *$\oplus$ is associative and commutative*

(i)
$$\begin{aligned}\mathbf{w}_1 \oplus (\mathbf{w}_2 \oplus \mathbf{w}_3) &= f(\mathbf{v}_1) \oplus (f(\mathbf{v}_2) \oplus f(\mathbf{v}_3)) \\ &= f(\mathbf{v}_1) \oplus f(\mathbf{v}_2 + \mathbf{v}_3) \\ &= f(\mathbf{v}_1 + (\mathbf{v}_2 + \mathbf{v}_3)) = f((\mathbf{v}_1 + \mathbf{v}_2) + \mathbf{v}_3) \\ &= f(\mathbf{v}_1 + \mathbf{v}_2) \oplus f(\mathbf{v}_3) \\ &= (f(\mathbf{v}_1) \oplus f(\mathbf{v}_2)) \oplus f(\mathbf{v}_3) \\ &= (\mathbf{w}_1 \oplus \mathbf{w}_2) \oplus \mathbf{w}_3\end{aligned}$$

(ii)
$$\begin{aligned}\mathbf{w}_1 \oplus \mathbf{w}_2 &= f(\mathbf{v}_1) \oplus f(\mathbf{v}_2) = f(\mathbf{v}_1 + \mathbf{v}_2) \\ &= f(\mathbf{v}_2 + \mathbf{v}_1) = f(\mathbf{v}_2) \oplus f(\mathbf{v}_1) = \mathbf{w}_2 \oplus \mathbf{w}_1\end{aligned}$$

(2) *$f(\mathbf{0})$ is a $\oplus$-identity.*

$$\mathbf{w}_1 \oplus f(\mathbf{0}) = f(\mathbf{v}_1) \oplus f(\mathbf{0}) = f(\mathbf{v}_1 + \mathbf{0}) = f(\mathbf{v}_1) = \mathbf{w}_1.$$

(3) *$f(-\mathbf{v}_1)$ is a $\oplus$-inverse of $\mathbf{w}_1$*

$$\mathbf{w}_1 \oplus f(-\mathbf{v}_1) = f(\mathbf{v}_1) \oplus f(-\mathbf{v}_1) = f(\mathbf{v}_1 + (-\mathbf{v}_1)) = f(\mathbf{0}), \text{ a } \oplus\text{-identity}$$

We leave verification of the remaining requirements to the reader. Q.E.D.

Corollary 1 to Proposition 4.12

Let V and W be vector spaces and let $f: V \to W$ be a linear transformation. Then, $\mathscr{R}_f$ is a vector subspace of W.

We leave a proof of this to the reader.

Corollary 2 to Proposition 4.12†

Let V be any vector space over F, and let U be any vector subspace of V. Then, V/U is a vector space over F with respect to addition and scalar multiplication of hyperplanes as defined in Chapter 3, Section 4.

Proof

For any $\mathbf{v} \in V$, let $[\mathbf{v}]$ be the hyperplane (or congruence class modulo U, or translate of U) to which $\mathbf{v}$ belongs. Addition and scalar multiplication of hyperplanes are defined by the unambiguous formulas

$$[\mathbf{v}_1] + [\mathbf{v}_2] = [\mathbf{v}_1 + \mathbf{v}_2]$$

and

$$a[\mathbf{v}_1] = [a\mathbf{v}_1]$$

Let $f: V \to V/U$ be defined by $f(\mathbf{v}) = [\mathbf{v}]$, for all $\mathbf{v} \in V$ (cf. Exercises 2.17.3). For any $\mathbf{v}_1, \mathbf{v}_2 \in V$ and $a \in F$,

$$f(\mathbf{v}_1 + \mathbf{v}_2) = [\mathbf{v}_1 + \mathbf{v}_2] = [\mathbf{v}_1] + [\mathbf{v}_2] = f(\mathbf{v}_1) + f(\mathbf{v}_2)$$

and

$$f(a\mathbf{v}_1) = [a\mathbf{v}_1] = a[\mathbf{v}_1] = af(\mathbf{v}_1)$$

Thus, f satisfies the requirements of Proposition 4.12, so that $\mathscr{R}_f$ is a vector space. But, f is *onto* V/U, since each hyperplane passes through at least one vector of V. Thus, V/U is a vector space over F with respect to the stated operations. Q.E.D.

Note that the function $f: V \to V/U$ defined in the above proof is a linear transformation. Henceforth, we call it the *natural projection* of V *onto* V/U *and denote it by* π_U. Thus, π_U is defined by the equation

$$\pi_U(\mathbf{v}) = [\mathbf{v}] = \mathbf{v} + U, \text{ for all } \mathbf{v} \in V$$

Proposition 4.13

Let V and W be vector spaces over F, and let $T: V \to W$ be a 1–1 linear transformation. Then, T is an isomorphism between V and $\mathscr{R}_T \subset W$.

Proof

T is a 1–1 linear transformation from V onto $\mathscr{R}_T$. Q.E.D.

Therefore, to say that there is a 1–1 linear transformation of V to W, means that V is isomorphic to a vector subspace of W, or that a replica of V is contained in W as a vector subspace. Clearly, V and this replica have the same dimension, by the Corollary to the Corollary to Proposition 4.7. Moreover, the dimension of the subspace is $\leqq$ the dimension of W.

Corollary to Proposition 4.13

If $T: V \to W$ is a 1–1 *linear transformation, then dim $V \leqq$ dim W. If T is onto, then equality holds. If T is not onto W and if dim W is finite, then we get dim $V <$ dim W.*

Proof

The first statement follows from the above remarks: dim $V =$ dim $\mathscr{R}_T \leqq$ dim W. If T is onto, then it is an isomorphism between V and W, so that $V \simeq W$, and, therefore, by Corollary to the Corollary to Proposition 4.7, dim $V =$ dim W. Finally, if T is not onto W, then $\mathscr{R}_T \neq W$. If dim W is finite, this nonequality means that a basis of $\mathscr{R}_T$ has strictly fewer members than a basis of W. (For if dim $W = n$, then any set of n linearly independent vectors in W is a basis of W.) Thus, dim $V =$ dim $\mathscr{R}_T <$ dim W, in this case. Q.E.D.

Definition 4.3

Let V and W be vector spaces over F and let $T: V \to W$ be a linear transformation. The null space of T, written $\mathscr{N}_T$, is the subset of V consisting of all $\mathbf{v} \in V$ sent to $\mathbf{0} \in W$ by T. That is $\mathscr{N}_T = \{\mathbf{v} \mid \mathbf{v} \in V$ and $T(\mathbf{v}) = \mathbf{0}\}$.

Proposition 4.14

Let T, V, and W be as in Definition 4.3. *Then, $\mathscr{N}_T$ is a vector subspace of V.*

Proof

It suffices to show that $\mathscr{N}_T$ is closed with respect to the vector-space operations of V and that $\mathscr{N}_T$ is nonempty. Since T is a linear transformation, $T(\mathbf{0}) = \mathbf{0}$, so that $\mathbf{0} \in \mathscr{N}_T$: It is not empty.

Choose any $\mathbf{v}_1, \mathbf{v}_2 \in N_T$ and any $a \in F$. Then, $T(\mathbf{v}_1 + \mathbf{v}_2) = T(\mathbf{v}_1) + T(\mathbf{v}_2) = \mathbf{0} + \mathbf{0} = \mathbf{0}$, so that $\mathbf{v}_1 + \mathbf{v}_2 \in \mathscr{N}_T$. Moreover, $T(a\mathbf{v}_1) = aT(\mathbf{v}_1) = a\mathbf{0} = \mathbf{0}$, so that $a\mathbf{v}_1 \in N_T$. Thus, $\mathscr{N}_T$ is closed, as desired. Q.E.D.

Proposition 4.15

Let $T: V \to W$ be a linear transformation. Then:

(1) *T is onto if and only if $\mathscr{R}_T = W$.*

(2) *T is* 1–1 *if and only if $\mathscr{N}_T = \{\mathbf{0}\}$.*

Proof

Statement (1) is obvious, since it is just another form of the definition of "onto". Statement (2) is the important one; statement (1) is presented merely to show the nice kind of symmetry between the statements.

Notice that since $\mathcal{N}_T$ is a vector subspace of V, $\mathbf{0} \in \mathcal{N}_T$, so that $\mathcal{N}_T \supset \{\mathbf{0}\}$, whether or not T is 1–1. Thus, the statement $\mathcal{N}_T = \{\mathbf{0}\}$, in this case, is equivalent to the statement $\mathcal{N}_T \subset \{\mathbf{0}\}$.

Suppose that T is 1–1, and choose any $\mathbf{v} \in \mathcal{N}_T$. Then, $T(\mathbf{v}) = \mathbf{0}$. Since $T(\mathbf{0}) = \mathbf{0}$, $\mathbf{v}$ cannot be distinct from $\mathbf{0}$, so that $\mathbf{v} = \mathbf{0}$. Thus, $\mathcal{N}_T \subset \{\mathbf{0}\}$.

If $\mathcal{N}_T = \{\mathbf{0}\}$, choose any distinct $\mathbf{v}_1, \mathbf{v}_2 \in V$. That is, $\mathbf{v}_1 - \mathbf{v}_2 \notin \mathcal{N}_T$ (because $\mathbf{v}_1 \neq \mathbf{v}_2$ implies that $\mathbf{v}_1 - \mathbf{v}_2 \neq \mathbf{0}$). Therefore, $T(\mathbf{v}_1 - \mathbf{v}_2) \neq \mathbf{0}$. But $T(\mathbf{v}_1 - \mathbf{v}_2) = T(\mathbf{v}_1) - T(\mathbf{v}_2)$, because T is a linear transformation. Therefore, $T(\mathbf{v}_2) - T(\mathbf{v}_2) \neq \mathbf{0}$, or $T(\mathbf{v}_1) \neq T(\mathbf{v}_2)$. Thus, if $\mathcal{N}_T = \{\mathbf{0}\}$, distinct members of V have distinct T-images: that is, T is 1–1. Q.E.D.

There are, therefore, associated with every linear transformation $T: V \to W$ two vector subspaces, $\mathcal{N}_T$, a subspace of V, and $\mathcal{R}_T$, a subspace of W.

Now, $\mathcal{R}_T$ measures, in a sense, the extent to which T is onto W. The bigger $\mathcal{R}_T$ (relative to W), the more nearly T is onto W. If $\mathcal{R}_f = W$, then, of course, T is actually onto W.

In a similar way $\mathcal{N}_T$ measures the extent to which T is 1–1. The smaller $\mathcal{N}_T$, the more nearly T is 1–1. If $\mathcal{N}_T = \{\mathbf{0}\}$, then, according to part (2) of the above proposition, T is actually 1–1.

Notice that we could have defined the null space of an arbitrary *function* from V to W in the same way that we defined $\mathcal{N}_T$: namely, the null space of the function is the subset of V consisting of all vectors sent to $\mathbf{0}$ by the function. Indeed, the range of an arbitrary function was defined. However, the definition of general null space, although possible, is for all of our purposes useless. For the main interest in the null space of a linear transformation is that it is a vector subspace of the domain that measures the 1–1-ness of the transformation. It does not, however, have this feature for more general functions. For example, let $f: \mathbf{R} \to \mathbf{R}$ be given by $f(x) = x^2$. f is emphatically *not* 1–1. For example, f takes both 1 and -1 to 1. However, the null space of f is $\{0\}$, since 0 is the only real number whose square is 0. Thus, the fact that the null space is $\{0\}$ does not give us much information in this case. Indeed, in general, the only information obtainable from the fact that the null space of a function (in general) is $\{0\}$ is that the function sends 0 and only 0 to 0. No conclusions can be drawn about what f does to other vectors.

These comments, then, serve to point out the remarkable rigidity of behavior of linear transformations. From information about the set of vectors sent to $\mathbf{0}$ by the transformation, we can deduce certain properties of the transformation on its entire domain (i.e., whether or not it is 1–1).

Now, although $\mathcal{N}_T$ and $\mathcal{R}_T$ are, in general, subspaces of different vector spaces ($\mathcal{N}_T \subset V$, $\mathcal{R}_T \subset W$), there is a very interesting connection between them, which we next state and prove. This connection, together with the comments above, should inspire the reader to suspect that the properties of being onto and 1–1, for linear transformations, are also connected. This is true. Wait and see.

Proposition 4.16†

Let V and W be vector spaces over F, and let $T: V \to W$ be a linear transformation. Then,

$$V/\mathcal{N}_T \simeq \mathcal{R}_T^{**}$$

Proof

We must define a function $V/\mathcal{N}_T \to \mathcal{R}_T$ and prove that it is a 1–1, onto linear transformation. Remember that "vectors" of $V/\mathcal{N}_T$ are just translates of $\mathcal{N}_T$ (or congruence classes modulo $\mathcal{N}_T$), which can all be written in the form $\mathbf{v} + \mathcal{N}_T$, $\mathbf{v}$ ranging over V. Two such translates $\mathbf{v}_1 + \mathcal{N}_T$ and $\mathbf{v}_2 + \mathcal{N}_T$ are equal, if and only if $\mathbf{v}_1 - \mathbf{v}_2 \in \mathcal{N}_T$.

We attempt to define a function $\overline{T}: V/\mathcal{N}_T \to \mathcal{R}_T$ as follows: for any $\mathbf{v} + \mathcal{N}_T$ in $V/\mathcal{N}_T$, let

$$\overline{T}(\mathbf{v} + \mathcal{N}_T) = T(\mathbf{v}) \in \mathcal{R}_T$$

We must first show that $\overline{T}$, so defined, is really a function. For this, we must show that the value of $\overline{T}$ at a translate of $\mathcal{N}_T$ is unambiguous—which the above definition, *a priori*, does not guarantee. For the above definition depends on a particular representation of a translate as $\mathbf{v} + \mathcal{N}_T$. A different representation $\mathbf{v}' + \mathcal{N}_T$ of the same translate is sent, by definition, to $T(\mathbf{v}')$ by $\overline{T}$. Thus, we must show that if $\mathbf{v} + \mathcal{N}_T = \mathbf{v}' + \mathcal{N}_T$, then $T(\mathbf{v}) = T(\mathbf{v}')$. But, the equation $\mathbf{v} + \mathcal{N}_T = \mathbf{v}' + \mathcal{N}_T$ is true, if and only if $\mathbf{v} - \mathbf{v}' \in \mathcal{N}_T$. Therefore, $T(\mathbf{v} - \mathbf{v}') = \mathbf{0}$, from which we deduce that $T(\mathbf{v}) - T(\mathbf{v}') = \mathbf{0}$; hence, $T(\mathbf{v}) = T(\mathbf{v}')$, as desired. Therefore $\overline{T}$ is a function.

Next we show that $\overline{T}$ is onto $\mathcal{R}_T$. This is easy. Choose any $\mathbf{w} \in \mathcal{R}_T$. By definition of $\mathcal{R}_T$, there is a $\mathbf{v} \in V$ such that $T(\mathbf{v}) = \mathbf{w}$. Therefore, by definition of $\overline{T}$, the translate $\mathbf{v} + \mathcal{N}_T$ is sent by $\overline{T}$ to $T(\mathbf{v}) = \mathbf{w}$.

Now we show that $\overline{T}$ is a linear transformation. Choose any two translates, say $\mathbf{v}_1 + \mathcal{N}_T$ and $\mathbf{v}_2 + \mathcal{N}_T$, and any $a \in F$. Recall that, by definition of addition of translates, $(\mathbf{v}_1 + \mathcal{N}_T) + (\mathbf{v}_2 + \mathcal{N}_T) = (\mathbf{v}_1 + \mathbf{v}_2) + \mathcal{N}_T$. Also, $a \cdot (\mathbf{v}_1 + \mathcal{N}_T) = a\mathbf{v}_1 + \mathcal{N}_T$. Therefore,

$$\begin{aligned}\overline{T}((\mathbf{v}_1 + \mathcal{N}_T) + (\mathbf{v}_2 + \mathcal{N}_T)) &= \overline{T}(\mathbf{v}_1 + \mathbf{v}_2 + \mathcal{N}_T) = T(\mathbf{v}_1 + \mathbf{v}_2)\\ &= T(\mathbf{v}_1) + T(\mathbf{v}_2) = \overline{T}(\mathbf{v}_1 + \mathcal{N}_T) + \overline{T}(\mathbf{v}_2 + \mathcal{N}_T),\end{aligned}$$

and

$$\overline{T}(a \cdot (\mathbf{v}_1 + \mathcal{N}_T)) = \overline{T}(a\mathbf{v}_1 + \mathcal{N}_T) = T(a\mathbf{v}_1) = aT(\mathbf{v}_1) = a\overline{T}(\mathbf{v}_1 + \mathcal{N}_T)$$

Therefore, $\overline{T}$ is a linear transformation.

Finally we show that $\overline{T}$ is 1–1. We do this by showing that $\mathcal{N}_T$ consists only of the zero vector of $V/\mathcal{N}_T$. Recall that this zero vector is the translate $\mathbf{0} + \mathcal{N}_T$.

** An equivalent result that does not involve the notion of quotients of vector spaces is developed in Exercises 4.3.**10**.

Suppose then that some translate $\mathbf{v} + \mathcal{N}_T$ is sent to $\mathbf{0}$ by $\overline{T}$. That is,

$$\overline{T}(\mathbf{v} + \mathcal{N}_T) = \mathbf{0}$$

By definition, $\overline{T}(\mathbf{v} + \mathcal{N}_T) = T(\mathbf{v})$, so that the previous equation implies that $T(\mathbf{v}) = \mathbf{0}$. Therefore, $\mathbf{v} \in \mathcal{N}_T$, and, since $\mathbf{v} - \mathbf{0} = \mathbf{v}$, we may conclude that $\mathbf{v} - \mathbf{0} \in \mathcal{N}_T$. But, this means that $\mathbf{v} + \mathcal{N}_T = \mathbf{0} + \mathcal{N}_T$, which is to say that $\mathbf{v} + \mathcal{N}_T$ is the zero vector of $V/\mathcal{N}_T$, as desired. Q.E.D.

The reader should compare the above result and proof with Chapter 2. 2.5(f), in which we discussed the equivalence relation determined by a function. It is, indeed, true, that the equivalence relation determined by a linear transformation T is precisely congruence modulo $\mathcal{N}_T$ (cf. Exercises 4.3.**12** below). Notice also that in addition to providing the desired result, the above proof also exhibits a particular isomorphism

$$\overline{T}: V/\mathcal{N} \to \mathcal{R}_T$$

We call $\overline{T}$ *the isomorphism induced by T*. We repeat its definition here for possible future reference:

$$\overline{T}(\mathbf{v} + \mathcal{N}_T) = T(\mathbf{v}), \text{ for all } \mathbf{v} \in V$$

Corollary to Proposition 4.16

Let $T: V \to W$ be a linear transformation, and suppose that dim V is finite. Then,

$$\textit{dim } V = \textit{dim } \mathcal{N}_T + \textit{dim } \mathcal{R}_T{}^{**}$$

Proof

According to Corollary to Proposition 3.19,

$$\dim V = \dim \mathcal{N}_T + \dim V/\mathcal{N}_T$$

By the above propositions and Corollary to the Corollary to Proposition 4.7,

$$\dim V/\mathcal{N}_T = \dim \mathcal{R}_T,$$

from which the result now follows. Q.E.D.

The result shows how $\mathcal{N}_T$ and $\mathcal{R}_T$ are related. We now apply this result to T itself.

Corollary to the Corollary to Proposition 4.16

Let $T: V \to W$ be a linear transformation, and suppose that dim V and dim W are finite and that dim V = dim W. Then, T is 1–1, if and only if T is onto W.

** A proof of this result not involving the notion of quotients of vector spaces is presented in Exercises 4.3.**11**.

Proof

T is 1–1, if and only if $\mathcal{N}_T = \{\mathbf{0}\}$. $\mathcal{N}_T = \{\mathbf{0}\}$ if and only if dim $\mathcal{N}_T = 0$. Dim $\mathcal{N}_T = 0$ if and only if dim $\mathcal{R}_T =$ dim $V =$ dim W. dim $\mathcal{R}_T =$ dim W, if and only if $\mathcal{R}_T = W$. $\mathcal{R}_T = W$, if and only if T is onto.

The reader is invited to supply the justification for each of the above statements. Together, they imply the desired result. Q.E.D.

This result is extremely useful for dealing with systems of linear equations in which the number of unknowns equals the number of equations. We illustrate this in part of an example below, and we treat the general case in Chapter 5.

Note that the above result does not hold when dim V and dim W are infinite. For example, let $V = W = \mathcal{P}$, the vector space of polynomials, and let $T : \mathcal{P} \to \mathcal{P}$ be defined as follows:

$$T(a_0x^0 + a_1x^1 + \cdots + a_nx^n) = a_0x^1 + a_1x^2 + \cdots + a_nx^{n+1},$$

for every $a_0x^0 + a_1x^1 + \cdots + a_nx^n \in \mathcal{P}$. It is not hard to show that T is a 1–1 linear transformation from $\mathcal{P}$ to $\mathcal{P}$. T is not, however, onto $\mathcal{P}$; for example, $x^0 \in \mathcal{P}$, but $x^0 \notin \mathcal{R}_T$.

Thus, the condition that dim V and dim W be finite is essential to the above result.

We now present some examples that illustrate the above results.

(a)† Let V be any vector space over F, and consider the trivial map $\bar{\mathbf{0}}$: $V \to V$. By definition, $\bar{\mathbf{0}}(\mathbf{v}) = \mathbf{0}$, for all $\mathbf{v} \in V$. Therefore, $\mathcal{N}_{\bar{\mathbf{0}}} = V$ and $\mathcal{R}_{\bar{\mathbf{0}}} = \{\mathbf{0}\}$.

Notice that in the vector space V there is only one translate of V (i.e., only one congruence class modulo V): namely, V itself. Thus, V/V consists of only one vector, and hence it is a trivial vector space over F. Since $\mathcal{R}_{\bar{\mathbf{0}}} = \{\mathbf{0}\}$, it, too, is trivial, and so, by Example (a) in Subsection 1.5 of this chapter, $V/V \simeq \mathcal{R}_{\bar{\mathbf{0}}}$, as expected, in view of Proposition 4.16.

(b)† Let V be as above and let $T : V \to W$ by any isomorphism. Then, T is 1–1 and onto so that $\mathcal{N}_T = \{\mathbf{0}\}$ and $\mathcal{R}_T = W$.

Consider $V/\mathcal{N}_T$. It consists of all translates of $\mathcal{N}_T = \{\mathbf{0}\}$. But any such translate $\mathbf{v} + \mathcal{N}_T = \mathbf{v} + \{\mathbf{0}\} = \{\mathbf{v}\}$: that is, each translate consists only of the vector by which one is translating. Clearly, the natural projection $\pi_{\{\mathbf{0}\}} : V \to V/_{\{\mathbf{0}\}} = V/\mathcal{N}_T$ is a 1–1 correspondence. Indeed, to see this, notice that $\pi_{\{\mathbf{0}\}}(\mathbf{v}) = \{\mathbf{v}\}$, by definition. If $\mathbf{v} \neq \mathbf{v}'$, then clearly the set $\{\mathbf{v}\}$ does not equal the set $\{\mathbf{v}'\}$, so that $\pi_{\{\mathbf{0}\}}(\mathbf{v}) \neq \pi_{\{\mathbf{0}\}}(\mathbf{v}')$. Therefore $\pi_{\{\mathbf{0}\}}$ is 1–1. The reader should easily be able to show that $\pi_{\{\mathbf{0}\}}$ is onto.

Therefore, $\pi_{\{\mathbf{0}\}}$ is an isomorphism from V to $V/\mathcal{N}_T$. Thus, $V \simeq V/\mathcal{N}_T$, and, of course, since $V \simeq W$, $V/\mathcal{N}_T \simeq W$, as expected.

(c)† Let U be a vector subspace of V, and let $\pi_U : V \to V/U$ be the natural projection determined by U. Then, $\mathcal{N}_{\pi_U} = U$ and $\mathcal{R}_{\pi_U} = V/U$.

To see the latter equality, note that every translate of U passes through some $\mathbf{v} \in V$, and for this $\mathbf{v}$, $\pi_U(\mathbf{v})$ is the given translate. To see the first equality, note that the zero vector of V/U is the translate of U by $\mathbf{0}$, which is just U itself. Thus, a vector in V is sent by π_U to the zero vector of V/U, if and only if this vector belongs to U.

(d) Let $a_1, \ldots, a_k$ be real numbers, and consider the linear expression $a_1x_1 + \cdots + a_kx_k$. As described in Chapter 1, it determines a function from $\mathbf{R}^k$ to $\mathbf{R}$ by sending every k-tuple $(x_1, \ldots, x_k) \in \mathbf{R}^k$ to $a_1x_1 + \cdots + a_kx_k \in \mathbf{R}$. This is a linear form (cf. Definition 4.1) on $\mathbf{R}^k$, which we shall call f. If $a_1 = a_2 = \cdots = a_k = 0$, then $f(x_1, \ldots, x_k) = 0x_1 + \cdots + 0x_k = 0$, for every $(x_1, \ldots, x_k) \in \mathbf{R}^k$. That is, in this case f is the trivial function. Therefore, $\mathcal{N}_f = \mathbf{R}^k$ and $\mathcal{R}_f = \{0\}$.

Suppose, now, that not all a_i are zero. Say $a_i \neq 0$, for some i between 1 and k. Consider $\mathbf{e}_i^{(k)}$, the ith vector in the standard basis of $\mathbf{R}^k$. $f(\mathbf{e}_i^{(k)}) = 0a_1 + \cdots + 1a_i + 0a_{i+1} + \cdots + 0a_k = a_i \neq 0$. Thus, in this case f is nontrivial.

Notice that for any real number r,

$$f((r/a_i)\mathbf{e}_i^{(k)}) = (r/a_i)(a_i) = r,$$

so that, in this case, f is onto. That is, $\mathcal{R}_f = \mathbf{R}$. Recall that $\dim \mathbf{R} = 1$.

Since, $\dim \mathbf{R}^k = \dim \mathcal{N}_f + \dim \mathcal{R}_f$, we get $k = \dim \mathcal{N}_f + 1$, or $\dim \mathcal{N}_f = k - 1$.

Therefore, given any linear expression $a_1x_1 + \cdots + a_kx_k$, either it determines the trivial transformation (when all $a_i = 0$), or it determines a nontrivial transformation f (when some $a_i \neq 0$) such that $\dim \mathcal{N}_f = k - 1$.

Now, let g be determined by another linear expression, $b_1x_1 + \cdots + b_nx_n$, and suppose that g is nontrivial. Notice that $\mathcal{N}_g \subset \mathbf{R}^k$, and $\mathcal{N}_f \subset \mathbf{R}^k$ so that $\mathcal{N}_g + \mathcal{N}_f \subset \mathbf{R}^k$. Therefore, applying Corollary to Proposition 3.16,

$$\dim \mathcal{N}_f + \dim \mathcal{N}_g - \dim (\mathcal{N}_f \cap \mathcal{N}_g) = \dim (\mathcal{N}_f + \mathcal{N}_g) \leqq \dim \mathbf{R}^k = k,$$

or $(k-1) + (k-1) \leqq \dim (N_f \cap N_g) + k$, from which we conclude that $\dim (\mathcal{N}_f \cap \mathcal{N}_g) \geqq k - 2$.

Suppose now that $k > 2$. Then,

$$\dim (\mathcal{N}_f \cap \mathcal{N}_g) \geqq k - 2 > 0,$$

so that $\mathcal{N}_f \cap \mathcal{N}_g$ is nontrivial. That is, there exists a k-tuple $(x_1, \ldots, x_k)$, belonging to both $\mathcal{N}_f$ and $\mathcal{N}_g$, such that at least one x_i is not 0. This k-tuple, therefore, satisfies $f(x_1, \ldots, x_k) = 0$ *and* $g(x_1, \ldots, x_k) = 0$ simultaneously. That is, it is a nontrivial solution to the homogeneous system of two linear equations

$$a_1x_1 + \cdots + a_kx_k = 0$$

$$b_1x_1 + \cdots + b_kx_k = 0$$

*We have, therefore, proved that any homogeneous system of two linear equations and more than two unknowns** has at least one nontrivial solution.*

** Actually, we were also assuming that both expressions are nontrivial (i.e., some $a_i \neq 0$ and some $b_i \neq 0$). The statement is still true in case either or both expression is trivial.

(e) Consider the following two general systems of linear equations:

$$\begin{aligned} a_{11}x_1 + a_{12}x_2 &= b_1 \\ a_{21}x_1 + a_{22}x_2 &= b_2 \end{aligned} \tag{1}$$

and

$$\begin{aligned} a_{11}x_1 + a_{12}x_2 &= 0 \\ a_{21}x_1 + a_{22}x_2 &= 0 \end{aligned} \tag{2}$$

The associated linear transformation $A:\mathbf{R}^2 \to \mathbf{R}^2$ is given by:

$$A(x_1, x_2) = (a_{11}x_1 + a_{12}x_2, a_{21}x_1 + a_{22}x_2), \text{ for all } (x_1, x_2) \in \mathbf{R}^2.$$

Systems (1) and (2), then, can be written as

$$A(x_1, x_2) = (b_1, b_2) \tag{1'}$$

and

$$A(x_1, x_2) = (0, 0) \tag{2'}$$

Notice that $\mathcal{N}_A$, the null space of A, consists precisely of all solutions to (2′). For such a solution is a pair $(x_1, x_2) \in R^2$ sent to (0, 0) by A; conversely, any vector in $\mathbf{R}^2$ sent to (0, 0) by A is, by definition, a solution of (2′).

Notice that $\mathcal{R}_A$, the range of A, consists precisely of all possible $(b_1, b_2) \in R^2$ for which (1′) has a solution.

The fact that $\mathcal{R}_A = \mathbf{R}^2$ if and only if $\mathcal{N}_A = \{(0, 0)\}$ (i.e. A is 1–1 if and only if A is onto), can, therefore, be interpreted in the following way:

System (1) *has at least one solution for every* $(b_1, b_2) \in \mathbf{R}^2$ *if and only if system* (2) *has only the trivial solution* (0, 0).

The fact that $\mathcal{N}_A = \{\mathbf{0}\}$ if and only if A is 1–1 can be interpreted as follows:

System (2) *has only the trivial solution* (0, 0) *if and only if system* (1) *has at, most one solution for every* $(b_1, b_2) \in \mathbf{R}^2$.

EXERCISES / 4.3

1.* Supply a proof of Corollary 1 to Proposition 4.12.

2.† **a.** Let V be a vector space over F, and let U be a vector subspace of V. Let $\pi_U: V \to V/U$ be the natural projection of V onto V/U (see the definition of π_U after the proof of Corollary 2 to Proposition 4.12). Note that π_U is a linear transformation (this was demonstrated in the above mentioned proof). Finally, suppose that W is a vector space over F.

Prove that a function $f:V/U \to W$ *is a linear transformation if and only if* $f \circ \pi_U$ *is a linear transformation.*

b. Let $T:V \to W$ be a linear transformation, and let $\bar{T}:V/\mathcal{N}_T \to \mathcal{R}_T$ be the isomorphism induced by T (see the definition of $\bar{T}$ following the proof of Proposition 4.16). Prove that $T = \bar{T} \circ \pi_{\mathcal{N}_T}$.

This proves that every linear transformation is the composition of an onto linear transformation (namely, $\pi_{\mathcal{N}_T}$) and a 1–1 linear transformation (namely, $\bar{T}$).

Moreover, comparing this result with part **a**, above, we obtain another proof that $\bar{T}$ is a linear transformation (assuming that the equation above can be obtained without referring to the linearity of $\bar{T}$—which it can).

For T is, by assumption, a linear transformation. Thus, $\bar{T} \circ \pi_{\mathcal{N}_T}$ is a linear transformation, so that, by **a**, $\bar{T}$ is.

3. According to solid analytic geometry, every plane in $\mathbf{R}^3$ through (0, 0, 0) is determined as the set of all solutions to an equation of the form $ax + by + cz = 0$ for some given real numbers a, b, c (depending on the plane). The expression $ax + by + cz$ is a *linear expression*, as we have used the term, and thus it determines a linear form $f:\mathbf{R}^3 \to \mathbf{R}$. The set of solutions to the above equation (i.e., the plane) is precisely $\mathcal{N}_f$. Thus, this shows that every plane through the origin in $\mathbf{R}^3$ (i.e. every 2-dimensional vector subspace of $\mathbf{R}^3$) is of the form $\mathcal{N}_f$ for some linear transformation $f:\mathbf{R}^3 \to \mathbf{R}$ (f depending on the subspace).

Prove that every 2-dimensional vector subspace of $\mathbf{R}^3$ *is of the form* $\mathcal{R}_T$ *for some linear transformation* $T:\mathbf{R}^2 \to \mathbf{R}^3$ (*T depending on the subspace*).

4. In Exercises 3.10.4, we considered the vector space $\mathbf{R}^{\mathbf{R}}$ of all real-valued functions of a real variable. We defined vector substances U_1 and U_2 of $\mathbf{R}^{\mathbf{R}}$ as follows:

$$U_1 = \{f \mid f \in \mathbf{R}^{\mathbf{R}} \text{ and } f(-x) = -f(x), \text{ for all } x \in \mathbf{R}\},$$

$$U_2 = \{f \mid f \in \mathbf{R}^{\mathbf{R}} \text{ and } f(-x) = f(x), \text{ for all } x \in \mathbf{R}\}$$

a. Let $T_1:\mathbf{R}^{\mathbf{R}} \to \mathbf{R}^{\mathbf{R}}$ be defined as follows: for any $f \in \mathbf{R}^{\mathbf{R}}$, $T_1(f)$ is the function from $\mathbf{R}$ to $\mathbf{R}$ whose value at any $x \in \mathbf{R}$ is given by

$$T_1(f)(x) = 1/2[f(x) + f(-x)]$$

Let $T_2:\mathbf{R}^{\mathbf{R}} \to \mathbf{R}^{\mathbf{R}}$ be defined as follows: For any $f \in \mathbf{R}^{\mathbf{R}}$, $T_2(f)$ is the function from $\mathbf{R}$ to $\mathbf{R}$ whose value at any $x \in \mathbf{R}$ is given by

$$T_2(f)(x) = 1/2[f(x) - f(-x)]$$

Prove that T_1 and T_2 are linear transformations.

b. Prove that $T_1 + T_2 = I_{\mathbf{R}^{\mathbf{R}}}$, the identity function of $\mathbf{R}^{\mathbf{R}}$.

c. Prove that $T_1 \circ T_1 = T_1$ and that $T_2 \circ T_2 = T_2$.

d. Prove that $\mathcal{R}_{T_1} = U_1$ and that $\mathcal{R}_{T_2} = U_2$.

e. Prove that $T_1 \circ T_2 = \bar{0}$ and that $T_2 \circ T_1 = 0$.

f. Prove that $\mathcal{N}_{T_1} = U_2$ and that $\mathcal{N}_{T_2} = U_1$.

We may draw the following conclusions from the above results. First, note that, because $U_1 \oplus U_2 = \mathbf{R}^{\mathbf{R}}$, $U_1 \times U_2 \simeq \mathbf{R}^{\mathbf{R}}$. Secondly, note that $U_1 = \mathcal{R}_{T_1}$ and $U_2 = \mathcal{N}_{T_1}$. Therefore $\mathbf{R}^{\mathbf{R}}/\mathcal{N}_{T_1} \simeq \mathcal{R}_{T_1} = U_1$, so that

$$(\mathbf{R}^{\mathbf{R}}/\mathcal{N}_{T_1}) \times \mathcal{N}_{T_1} \simeq \mathbf{R}^{\mathbf{R}}$$

Similarly, $(\mathbf{R}^{\mathbf{R}}/\mathcal{N}_{T_2}) \times \mathcal{N}_{T_2} \simeq \mathbf{R}^{\mathbf{R}}$.

This "cancellation law" holds in general, as we shall see. Moreover, we also get, from the above equations and isomorphisms, the following results, which also hold more generally (with $\mathbf{R}^{\mathbf{R}}$ replaced by the domain of the transformation):

$$\mathscr{R}_{T_1} \times \mathscr{N}_{T_1} \simeq \mathbf{R}^{\mathbf{R}}$$

and

$$\mathscr{R}_{T_2} \times \mathscr{N}_{T_2} \simeq \mathbf{R}^{\mathbf{R}}$$

5. Let a, b be two real numbers, and let $\mathscr{D}[a, b]$ be the vector space of all real-valued functions on the closed interval $[a, b]$ possessing a continuous first derivative. Let $D : \mathscr{D}[a, b] \to \mathscr{C}[a, b]$ be the linear transformation given by: $D(f)(x) = f'(x) = \left(\frac{df}{dx}\right)(x)$ [cf. Chapter 1, Example (j)].

a. Prove that $\mathscr{N}_D$ consists of all the constant functions on $[a, b]$. (To prove this you must know some calculus.)

b. Prove that $D(f) = D(g)$, if and only if f and g differ by a constant function.

c. Let V and W be any vector spaces over F, and let $T : V \to W$ be any linear transformation. Prove that $T(\mathbf{v}_1) = T(\mathbf{v}_2)$, if and only if $\mathbf{v}_1$ and $\mathbf{v}_2$ differ by a vector in $\mathscr{N}_T$.

6.* Let V and W be vector spaces over F such that $\{\mathbf{v}_1, \mathbf{v}_2\}$ is a basis of V and $\{\mathbf{w}_1, \mathbf{w}_2\}$ is a basis of W. Let $T : V \to W$ be a linear transformation such that $T(\mathbf{v}_1) = \mathbf{w}_1$ and $T(\mathbf{v}_2) = \mathbf{w}_2$. Prove that T is an isomorphism.

7. Consider any homogeneous system of three linear equations and *more* than three unknowns. Following the method of Example (d) above, show that the system has at least one nontrivial solution.

8. Let $\mathscr{P}$ be the vector space of polynomials with real coefficients. Define a function $g : \mathscr{P} \to \mathscr{P}$ as follows: for every

$$a_0x^0 + a_1x^1 + \cdots + a_nx^n \in \mathscr{P},$$

$$g(a_0x^0 + a_1x^1 + \cdots + a_nx^n) = a_1x^0 + a_2x^1 + \cdots + a_nx^{n-1}$$

Prove that g is a linear transformation onto $\mathscr{P}$, but not 1–1.

9. Let $\mathscr{P}$ be as in Exercise **8**, above, and let $U \subset \mathscr{P}$ consist of all polynomials of the form $(x^2 + 1)p(x)$, where $p(x)$ ranges over $\mathscr{P}$. In Exercises 3.10.**6**, the reader was asked to show that U is a vector subspace of $\mathscr{P}$. Moreover, a function $t : \mathscr{P} \to \mathbf{C}$ was defined, there, as follows. To determine $t(p(x))$, divide $p(x)$ by $x^2 + 1$; the remainder will be of the form $ax + b$, where a and b are real numbers. Let $t(p(x)) = ai + b$.

a. Let $p(x)$ and $g(x)$ be any polynomials in $\mathscr{P}$. Prove that if $ax + b$ is the remainder obtained by dividing $p(x)$ by $x^2 + 1$, and if $cx + d$ is the remainder obtained by dividing $g(x)$ by $x^2 + 1$, then $(a + c)x + (b + d)$ is the remainder obtained by dividing $p(x) + g(x)$ by $x^2 + 1$.

b. Prove that if $ax + b$ is the remainder obtained by dividing $p(x)$ by $x^2 + 1$, and if c is any real number, then $(ca)x + (cb)$ is the remainder obtained by dividing $cp(x)$ by $x^2 + 1$.

c. Consider **C** as a vector space over **R** in the usual way. Show that t is a linear transformation and that $\mathcal{N}_t = U$, $\mathcal{R}_t = \mathbf{C}$.
Thus, according to Proposition 4.16

$$\bar{t}: \mathcal{P}/U \to \mathbf{C}$$

is an isomorphism (the one induced by t) between vector spaces over **R**. In Exercises 3.10.6, we called $\bar{t}$, "τ."

Therefore, the real vector space of complex numbers can be obtained from $\mathcal{P}$ by forming the quotient space $\mathcal{P}/U$, where U consists of all polynomial multiples of $x^2 + 1$.

It is no coincidence, dear reader, that the polynomial $x^2 + 1$ has as its only zeros the imaginary quantities $\pm i$, precisely the quantities used to enlarge **R** to form **C**. Indeed, the procedure indicated above (of forming $\mathcal{P}/U$) is a way of enlarging **R** to form **C**. We say a little more about this in the exercises at the end of this chapter.

10.* Let V and W be any vector spaces over F, and let $T: V \to W$ be a linear transformation. Let U be any vector subspace of V complementary to $\mathcal{N}_T$. Prove that $T \mid U$ is an isomorphism from U to $\mathcal{R}_T$. (*Hint:* Show that $\mathcal{N}_{T|U} = \{\mathbf{0}\}$ and that $\mathcal{R}_{T|U} = \mathcal{R}_T$.)

11.* Let $T: V \to W$ be a linear transformation, and suppose that dim V is finite. Use **10**, the Corollary to the Corollary to Proposition 4.7, and the Corollary to Proposition 3.17 to prove that

$$\dim \mathcal{N}_T + \dim \mathcal{R}_T = \dim V$$

12.† Let $T : V \to W$ be a linear transformation.

a. Prove that $T(\mathbf{v}) = T(\mathbf{w})$, if and only if **V** is congruent to **w** modulo $\mathcal{N}_T$.

b. Deduce from **a.** that congruence modulo $\mathcal{N}_T$ is the equivalence relation determined by T [in the sense of Chapter 2, Section 2.5 (f)].

2 / CONSTRUCTION OF LINEAR TRANSFORMATIONS

We have already proved that if X is a basis of V and $T : V \to W$ is an isomorphism of vector spaces, then $T(X)$ is a basis of W. As a corollary we deduced that isomorphic vector spaces have the same dimension.

In this section we prove, among other things, the converse of these results. Our main method will be to present a general way of constructing linear transformations. For this, bases turn out to be essential. Indeed, just as the introduction of the notion of basis simplified problems of comparing vectors (since, once a basis was introduced, we could compare the corresponding "coordinates," or coefficients of vectors expressed as linear combinations of basis vectors), the introduction of bases, here, will help us in comparing linear transformations. We compare them by comparing their values at basis vectors. More about this later. First, our main result.

Proposition 4.17

Let V and W be vector spaces over F, and let X be a basis of V. Suppose that $f : X \to W$ is an arbitrary function. Then, there exists one and only one linear transformation $T : V \to W$ such that $T \mid X = f$.

Moreover, T is 1–1 if and only if f is 1–1 and $f(X)$ is linearly independent. T is onto if and only if $f(X)$ generates W.

Hence, T is an isomorphism if and only if f is 1–1 and $f(X)$ is a basis of W.

Before we prove this result, we want to make four points:

(a) The function f assigns to each basis vector in X some vector in W. The conclusion of the proposition tells us that such assignments completely and uniquely determine a linear transformation on V whose values at the basis vectors are the assigned ones. *Thus, to specify a linear transformation completely and uniquely, one need only specify its values at the basis vectors.*

This can be an enormous advantage, theoretically. For example, $\mathbf{R}^3$ has a basis consisting of three vectors. Thus, to describe completely a linear transformation from $\mathbf{R}^3$ to any other vector space over $\mathbf{R}$, one need only give *three bits of information*: namely, the values of the transformation at the basis vectors. Contrast this with the problem of specifying an *arbitrary function* from $\mathbf{R}^3$ to any other set. Since $\mathbf{R}^3$ contains an isomorphic copy of $\mathbf{R}$ as a vector subspace (any line through the origin), $\mathbf{R}^3$ is uncountably infinite so that one must, in general, give uncountably many bits of information.

In addition, the last part of the proposition shows how the most important general properties of a linear transformation are already revealed by its values on the basis.

(b) Note that f is completely arbitrary. This means that we may specify values at random (in W) and always be assured of getting a linear transformation that assumes these values at the appropriate basis vectors. Clearly, this means that there are many different linear transformations from one vector space to another.

(c) Note that *every* linear transformation $S : V \to W$ can be obtained from some $f : X \to W$ by the construction given in the proof below. For, given S, let $f = S/X$. The T constructed in the proof will be the *only* linear transformation from V to W whose restriction to X is f. Thus, it equals S, so that S can be obtained from f by the construction.

(d) Finally, when reading the following proof, the reader should pay attention not only to getting the desired result, but also (and especially) to the method of construction of the linear transformation from the given function f.

Proof

(1) *Construction of T*: To define $T : V \to W$, we need merely specify its value at every $\mathbf{v} \in V$. Now, every such $\mathbf{v}$ is the value of precisely one linear combination of vectors of X:

$$\mathbf{v} = a_1\mathbf{x}_1 + \cdots + a_n\mathbf{x}_n \tag{1}$$

where $\mathbf{x}_1, \ldots, \mathbf{x}_n \in X$. The value $T(\mathbf{v})$ is, then, defined by the following equation.

$$T(\mathbf{v}) = a_1 f(\mathbf{x}_1) + \cdots + a_n f(\mathbf{x}_n) \tag{2}$$

Thus, given any $\mathbf{v} \in V$, there is unambiguously determined a vector $T(\mathbf{v}) \in W$, given by equation (2), so that $T : V \to W$ is a well-defined function.

(2) *T is a linear transformation*: Choose any $\mathbf{v}', \mathbf{v} \in V$, and any $a \in F$. Suppose, for convenience sake, that $\mathbf{v}$ is given by (1), above. We may suppose that $\mathbf{v}'$ is the value of a linear combination of the same vectors that appear in the combination (1) (by adding or deleting terms with zero coefficients, if necessary):

$$\mathbf{v}' = b_1\mathbf{x}_1 + \cdots + b_n\mathbf{x}_n \tag{3}$$

Then, we have:

$$\mathbf{v} + \mathbf{v}' = (a_1 + b_1)\mathbf{x}_1 + \cdots + (a_n + b_n)\mathbf{x}_n \tag{4}$$

and

$$a\mathbf{v} = (aa_1)\mathbf{x}_1 + \cdots + (aa_n)\mathbf{x}_n \tag{5}$$

Therefore, by equation (2) above,

$$\begin{aligned} T(\mathbf{v} + \mathbf{v}') &= (a_1 + b_1)f(\mathbf{x}_1) + \cdots + (a_n + b_n)f(\mathbf{x}_n) \\ &= [a_1 f(\mathbf{x}_1) + \cdots + a_n f(\mathbf{x}_n)] + [b_1 f(\mathbf{x}_1) + \cdots + b_n f(\mathbf{x}_n)] \\ &= T(\mathbf{v}) + T(\mathbf{v}'), \end{aligned}$$

and

$$\begin{aligned} T(a\mathbf{v}) &= (aa_1)f(\mathbf{x}_1) + \cdots + (aa_n)f(\mathbf{x}_n) \\ &= a[a_1 f(\mathbf{x}_1) + \cdots + a_n f(\mathbf{x}_n)] \\ &= aT(\mathbf{v}) \end{aligned}$$

Therefore, T is a linear transformation.

(3) $T \mid X = f$: If $\mathbf{v} \in X$, then (1) reduces to

$$\mathbf{v} = 1\mathbf{v},$$

so that $T(\mathbf{v}) = 1f(\mathbf{v}) = f(\mathbf{v})$. Thus, $T \mid X = f$.

(4) *T is the only linear transformation from V to W satisfying* (3): Suppose that $S: V \to W$ is any linear transformation satisfying $S \mid X = f$. Then, for $\mathbf{v}$ as in (1), above,

$$\begin{aligned} S(\mathbf{v}) &= S(a_1\mathbf{x}_1 + \cdots + a_n\mathbf{x}_n) \\ &= a_1 S(\mathbf{x}_1) + \cdots + a_n S(\mathbf{x}_n) \text{ (because } S \text{ is linear)} \\ &= a_1 f(\mathbf{x}_1) + \cdots + a_n f(\mathbf{x}_n) \text{ (because } S \mid X = f) \\ &= T(\mathbf{v}) \text{ (by definition of } T) \end{aligned}$$

(5) *T is 1–1, if and only if f is 1–1 and $f(X)$ is linearly independent.*

Since $T \mid X = f$, $T(X) = f(X)$.

Suppose that T is 1–1. Then, $T \mid X$ is 1–1. Therefore, f is 1–1. Moreover, by Proposition 4.7, since T is 1–1 and X is linearly independent, then $T(X) = f(X)$ is linearly independent.

Now, suppose that f is 1–1 and $f(X)$ is linearly independent. We shall show that T is 1–1 by showing that $\mathcal{N}_T = \{\mathbf{0}\}$.

Choose any $\mathbf{v} \in \mathcal{N}_T$. We may write $\mathbf{v} = a_1\mathbf{x}_1 + \cdots + a_n\mathbf{x}_n$, for some $\mathbf{x}_1, \ldots, \mathbf{x}_n \in X$. Then,

$$\mathbf{0} = T(\mathbf{v}) = a_1 f(\mathbf{x}_1) + \cdots + a_n f(\mathbf{x}_n)$$

Since f is 1–1, the vectors $f(\mathbf{x}_1), \ldots, f(\mathbf{x}_n)$ are distinct vectors of W. Therefore, $a_1 f(\mathbf{x}_1) + \cdots + a_n f(\mathbf{x}_n)$ is a linear combination of vectors of $f(X)$ with value $\mathbf{0}$. Since $f(X)$ is linearly independent, the combination must be trivial. Therefore,

$$a_1 = 0, a_2 = 0, \ldots, a_n = 0, \text{ so that } \mathbf{v} = a_1\mathbf{x}_1 + \cdots + a_n\mathbf{x}_n = \mathbf{0}$$

Thus, $\mathcal{N}_T = \{\mathbf{0}\}$ and T is 1–1.

(6) *T is onto if and only if $f(X)$ generates W*: Recall that $T(X) = f(X)$. The results follows from the chain of equalities,

$$\mathcal{R}_T = T(V) = T(\text{span}_V(X)) = \text{span}_W(T(X)) = \text{span}_W(f(X))$$

For T is onto, if and only if $\mathcal{R}_T = W$; $\mathcal{R}_T = W$, if and only if $\text{span}_W(f(X)) = W$; $\text{span}_W(f(X)) = W$, if and only if $f(X)$ generates W.

The last statement of the proposition follows immediately from (5) and (6). Q.E.D.

Corollary to Proposition 4.17

Let V and W be vector spaces over F. Then, $V \simeq W$ if and only if $\dim V = \dim W$.

Proof

If $V \simeq W$, then according to Corollary to the Corollary to Proposition 4.7, $\dim V = \dim W$.

Now, suppose that $\dim V = \dim W$. Then, there are bases X of V and Y of W, and a 1–1 correspondence between X and Y. If X is empty, then so is Y, and both V and W are trivial, hence, isomorphic. If X is not empty, then let $f: X \to Y$ be a 1–1 correspondence. Let T be the linear transformation from V to W determined by f. Since f is 1–1 and $f(X) = Y$ is a basis of W, the last statement of Proposition 4.17, above, tells us that T is an isomorphism. Thus, $V \simeq W$. Q.E.D.

An immediate consequence of this result is the fact (that we already know) that *every n-dimensional vector space over F is isomorphic to F^n.*

Proposition 4.17 gives us a useful, quick way to establish isomorphisms between vector spaces. As an application, we prove the following result.

Proposition 4.18

Let V be a vector space over F. Let U_1 and U_2 be vector subspaces of V such that $U_1 \oplus U_2 = V$. Then, there exists a linear transformation $T: V \to U_2$ such that $\mathcal{R}_T = U_2$ and $\mathcal{N}_T = U_1$.

On the other hand, if $S: V \to W$ is any linear transformation and U is any vector subspace of V complementary to $\mathcal{N}_S$, then $U \simeq \mathcal{R}_S$.

Proof

Let X be a basis of U_1 and Y a basis of U_2 such that $X \cup Y$ is a basis of V. This is possible, according to Corollary to Proposition 3.13. Define a function $f: X \cup Y \to U_2$ as follows:

$$f(\mathbf{x}) = \mathbf{0}, \text{ for every } \mathbf{x} \in X, f(\mathbf{y}) = \mathbf{y}, \text{ for every } \mathbf{y} \in Y$$

Thus, $f(X \cup Y) = Y$. Let T be the linear transformation determined by f. Clearly, since $f(X \cup Y)$ generates U_2, T is onto U_2. Moreover,

$$T(U_1) = T(\text{span}_V(X)) = \text{span}_{U_2}(T(X)) = \text{span}_{U_2}(\{\mathbf{0}\}) = \{\mathbf{0}\},$$

so that $U_1 \subset N_T$. Notice that $T | U_2$ is a linear transformation sending the basis Y in a 1–1 fashion onto the basis Y. Thus, $T | U_2$ is 1–1. If $\mathbf{v} \in \mathcal{N}_T$, then $\mathbf{v} = \mathbf{u}_1 + \mathbf{u}_2$, $\mathbf{u}_1 \in U_1$ and $\mathbf{u}_2 \in U_2$. Since $U_1 \subset \mathcal{N}_T$, $\mathbf{u}_1 \in \mathcal{N}_T$, so that $T(\mathbf{u}_1) = \mathbf{0}$. Therefore, $\mathbf{0} = T(\mathbf{v}) = T(\mathbf{u}_1 + \mathbf{u}_2) = T(\mathbf{u}_1) + T(\mathbf{u}_2) = T(\mathbf{u}_2) = (T | U_2)(\mathbf{u}_2)$. This means, in view of the fact that $T | U_2$ is 1–1, that $\mathbf{u}_2 = \mathbf{0}$. Thus, $\mathbf{v} = \mathbf{u}_1 \in U_1$. Since $\mathbf{v}$ was chosen to be any vector of $\mathcal{N}_T$, it follows that $\mathcal{N}_T = U_1$.

This concludes the proof of the first part of the proposition.

The second part of the proposition was proved in Exercises 4.3.**10**. Q.E.D.

Corollary to Proposition 4.18

Let $T: V \to W$ be any linear transformation. Then, $\mathcal{R}_T \times \mathcal{N}_T \simeq V$, or, equivalently $V/\mathcal{N}_T \times \mathcal{N}_T \simeq V$.

Thus, again, if dim V is finite, so are dim $\mathcal{R}_T$ and dim $\mathcal{N}_T$ and

$$\dim \mathcal{R}_T + \dim \mathcal{N}_T = \dim V$$

Proof

According to Proposition 3.18, there is a vector subspace U of V complementary to $\mathcal{N}_T$. According to Subsection 1.5 Example (d), $U \times \mathcal{N}_T \simeq U + \mathcal{N}_T = V$. Proposition 4.18 implies that $U \simeq \mathcal{R}_T$ (or $V/\mathcal{N}_T$). Thus, applying Proposition 4.10,

$$\mathcal{R}_T \times \mathcal{N}_T \simeq V/\mathcal{N}_T \times \mathcal{N}_T \simeq U \times \mathcal{N}_T \simeq V.$$

The last statement now follows from the Corollary to Proposition 3.15. Q.E.D.

EXERCISES / 4.4

1. Let $F=\mathbf{R}$, $V=\mathbf{R}^3$, and $X=\{(1,0,0),(0,1,0),(0,0,1)\}$, the standard basis of $\mathbf{R}^3$. Let $f:X\to W$ be any function with $f(1,0,0)=\mathbf{v}_1$, $f(0,1,0)=\mathbf{v}_2$, $f(0,0,1)=\mathbf{v}_3$. Let T be the linear transformation from $\mathbf{R}^3$ to W determined by f. For which of the following sets $\{\mathbf{v}_1,\mathbf{v}_2,\mathbf{v}_3\}=f(X)\subset W$ is T 1–1? For which is T onto?
   a. $W=\mathbf{R}^3$, $\{\mathbf{v}_1,\mathbf{v}_2,\mathbf{v}_3\}=\{(1,0,0),(0,1,0),(0,0,1)\}$
   b. $W=\mathbf{R}^3$, $\mathbf{v}_1=(2,0,1)$, $\mathbf{v}_2=(1,3,-2)$, $\mathbf{v}_3=(2,-6,6)$
   c. $W=\mathbf{R}^2$, $\mathbf{v}_1=(1,-8)$, $\mathbf{v}_2=(6,0)$, $\mathbf{v}_3=(0,3)$
   d. $W=\mathbf{R}^4$, $\mathbf{v}_1=(1,2,3,0)$, $\mathbf{v}_2=(0,2,3,0)$, $\mathbf{v}_3=(0,0,3,0)$
   e. $W=\mathbf{R}^3$, $\mathbf{v}_1=(3,0,-1)$, $\mathbf{v}_2=(1,2,4)$, $\mathbf{v}_3=(2,0,0)$

2. Let V be any vector space over F, and let U_1 and U_2 be complementary vector subspaces of V, such that $\dim U_1=1$. Prove that there is an $f\in \text{Trans}(V,F)$ such that $\mathcal{N}_f=U_2$.

3.† Let $S:U\to V$ and $T:U\to W$ be linear transformations such that $\mathcal{N}_S\subset\mathcal{N}_T$. Let X be a basis of $\mathcal{N}_S$, Y a basis of $\mathcal{N}_T$ and Z a basis of U, such that $X\subset Y\subset Z$. Recall that $\pi_{\mathcal{N}_S}$ is the natural projection of U onto $U/\mathcal{N}_S$, that $\bar{S}:U/\mathcal{N}_S\to\mathcal{R}_S$ is the isomorphism determined by S, and that $\bar{S}\circ\pi_{\mathcal{N}_S}=S$.
   a. Prove that $S(Z\setminus X)$ is a basis of $\mathcal{R}_S$ and that $S\,|\,Z\setminus X$ is 1–1. (*Hint:* Use the established fact that $\pi_{\mathcal{N}_S}(Z\setminus X)$ is a basis of $U/\mathcal{N}_S$.)
   b. Let Y' be a basis of V such that $S(Z\setminus X)\subset Y'$. Define $f:Y'\to W$ as follows:

$$f(\mathbf{v})=\begin{cases}\mathbf{0}, & \text{if } \mathbf{v}\notin S(Z\setminus X)\\ T(\mathbf{u}), & \text{if } \mathbf{v}=S(\mathbf{u}),\ \mathbf{u}\in Z\setminus X\end{cases}$$

   Show that f is unambiguously defined.
   Let $R:V\to W$ be the linear transformation determined by f.
   Prove that $R\circ S=T$. (*Hint:* Prove that $R\circ S|Z=T\,|\,Z$ and apply Proposition 4.17.)
   c. Prove that every $T\in\text{Trans}(F,F)$ is of the form M_a, for some $a\in F$. That is, prove that for each $T\in\text{Trans}(F,F)$ there is an $a\in F$ such that $T(x)=ax$, for all $x\in F$.
   d. Let $f:V\to F$ and $g:V\to F$ be two linear transformations such that $N_g\subset N_f$. Prove that there is an $a\in F$ such that $f=ag$. [*Hint:* Apply (b) and (c).]

4. Let U, V, W be vector spaces over F, and let X be a basis of U. For any function $f:X\to V$, let $T_f:U\to V$ be the linear transformation determined by f, as in Proposition 4.17.
   a. Show that the association $f\to T_f$ is a 1–1 correspondence between V^X and Trans(U, V).
   b. Call the correspondence in **a**, $\mathcal{G}$. Both V^X and Trans(U, V) are vector spaces over F. Show that $\mathcal{G}$ is an isomorphism of vector spaces.
   c. Suppose that X has n members. Prove that $V^X\simeq V^n$.

d. Prove that if $\dim V = k$, then $\dim V^n = nk$.
Thus, combining **b**, **c**, and **d**, if $\dim U = n$ and $\dim V = k$, then

$$\dim \operatorname{Trans}(U, V) = nk.$$

e. Let $S: V \to W$ be any linear transformation, and let $f: X \to V$ be any function. Then, $S \circ f: X \to W$ is a function. Let $T_{S \circ f}: V \to W$ be the corresponding linear transformation. Prove that $S \circ T_f = T_{S \circ f}$.

f. Let Y be a basis of V, and let $f: X \to Y \subset V$ and $g: Y \to W$ be functions. Let T_f and T_g be the linear transformations corresponding to f and g, respectively, and let $T_{g \circ f}$ be the *trans*formation corresponding to $g \circ f: X \to W$.
Prove that $T_{g \circ f} = T_{T_g \circ f} = T_g \circ T_f$.

3 / DUALITY IN VECTOR SPACES

3.1 Introduction and Basic Results

In many mathematical systems, one is often struck by certain general, logical or structural symmetries. These symmetries often involve a pairing of concepts that are considered, in some sense, to be opposite in meaning.

For example, in set theory, one might consider the relation $A \subset B$ to be opposite to the relation $A \supset B$. Or one might consider the notion of set union, $A \cup B$, to be opposite to the notion of set intersection, $A \cap B$. With respect to functions, we might consider 1–1 functions to be, in some sense, opposite to onto functions. Or we might consider a function $f: A \to B$ to be opposite to a function $g: B \to A$.

However, more than a simple pairing is usually involved. What often happens is that in any true statement involving some of these concepts, if we replace each concept by its symmetric opposite, then we obtain a true statement involving the opposites.

Indeed, this is the case with the set theoretic notions involved above. Any universally true statement involving only sets A, B, relations $\subset$, $\supset$, and operations $\cup$, and $\cap$, remains true when the concepts are replaced by their opposites. For example,

$$\text{“}A \subset B, \text{ if and only if} \quad A \cap B = A\text{”}$$

is a true statement. Now, replace $\subset$ and $\cap$ by $\supset$ and $\cup$, respectively. We obtain the following true statement:

$$\text{“}A \supset B \text{ if and only if} \quad A \cup B = A\text{”}$$

Similar symmetries can be observed in many other areas of mathematics: mathematical logic, projective geometry, abstract algebra, and topology.

This symmetry of opposing concepts is known as *duality*.

It is only natural, then, to look for such symmetry in linear algebra. But it is more than merely “natural.” For, in addition to being aesthetically pleasing, such symmetry is often enlightening and useful.

Before we state precise definitions and results, however, let us present two more concepts and what we would expect their opposites to be. The set-theoretic and function-theoretic opposites have already been listed above. In addition, we might expect the notions of null space and range to be opposites, as might also be the notion of entire vector space and trivial subspace.

We now get to definitions and propositions.

Definition 4.4

(1) *Let V be any vector space over F. We call Trans(V, F) the vector space over F dual to V and denote it, henceforth, by V^*. Recall that the members of Trans$(V, F) = V^*$ are linear transformations, called linear forms or linear functionals.*

(2) *Let U be any vector subspace of V. The set of all $f \in V^*$ such that $f \mid U$ is constantly 0 will be called the annihilator of U and denoted by U^0. Symbolically,*

$$U^0 = \{f \mid f \in V^* \text{ and } f(\mathbf{u}) = 0, \text{ for all } \mathbf{u} \in U\}$$

Proposition 4.19

Let U and V be as above. Then, U^0 is a vector subspace of V^*.

Proof

The constantly 0 linear form is clearly constantly 0 when restricted to U. Thus, it belongs to U^0, so that U^0 is not empty. Choose f_1 and f_2 in U^0 and $a \in F$. Then, for any $\mathbf{u} \in U$,

$$(f_1 + f_2)(\mathbf{u}) = f_1(\mathbf{u}) + f_2(\mathbf{u}) = 0 + 0 = 0,$$

and

$$(af_1)(\mathbf{u}) = a[f_1(\mathbf{u})] = a \cdot 0 = 0,$$

so that $f_1 + f_2 \in U^0$ and $af_1 \in U^0$. Q.E.D.

Proposition 4.20

Let V be a vector space over F, and let U_1 and U_2 be vector subspaces of V.

Then:

(1) $U_1 \subset U_2$ *if and only if* $U_1{}^0 \supset U_2{}^0$.

(2) $U_1{}^0 + U_2{}^0 \subset (U_1 \cap U_2)^0$.

(3) $(U_1 + U_2)^0 = U_1{}^0 \cap U_2{}^0$.

Proof

(1) Suppose that $U_1 \subset U_2$ and that $f \in U_2{}^0$. Then, $f \mid U_2$ is constantly 0, so that f/U_1 is constantly 0. Thus, $f \in U_1{}^0$, so that $U_1{}^0 \supset U_2{}^0$.

Suppose that $U_1 \not\subset U_2$. Let X be a basis of U_1, Y a basis of U_2, and Z a basis of V such that $X \subset Y \subset Z$. Since $U_1 \not\subset U_2$, there must be a $\mathbf{y} \in Y$ such that $\mathbf{y} \notin X$. Define a linear form $f: V \to F$ by specifying its values on Z as follows:

$$f(\mathbf{z}) = 0, \quad \text{if} \quad \mathbf{z} \neq \mathbf{y}$$
$$= 1, \quad \text{if} \quad \mathbf{z} = \mathbf{y}$$

Since $\mathbf{y} \notin X$, it follows that $f \mid X$ is constantly 0, so that $f \mid U_1$ is constantly 0. Thus, $f \in U_1{}^0$. However, since $f(\mathbf{y}) = 1 \neq 0$ and $\mathbf{y} \in Y \subset U_2$, $f \mid U_2$ is not constantly 0, so that $f \notin U_2{}^0$. This means that $U_2{}^0 \not\subset U_1{}^0$.

(2) Choose any $f \in U_1{}^0 + U_2{}^0$. Then, we may write $f = g + h$, $g \in U_1{}^0$ and $h \in U_2{}^0$. Thus, $g \mid U_1$ and $h \mid U_2$ are constantly zero. Since $U_1 \cap U_2 \subset U_1$ and $U_1 \cap U_2 \subset U_2$, it follows that $g \mid U_1 \cap U_2$ and $h \mid U_1 \cap U_2$ are constantly 0. Therefore, $g \in (U_1 \cap U_2)^0$ and $h \in (U_1 \cap U_2)^0$. Since $(U_1 \cap U_2)^0$ is a vector space, this means that

$$f = g + h \in (U_1 \cap U_2)^0$$

Thus, $U_1{}^0 + U_2{}^0 \subset (U_1 \cap U_2)^0$, as desired. Q.E.D.

(3) Since $U_1 \subset U_1 + U_2$ and $U_2 \subset U_1 + U_2$, it follows from (1) that

$$(U_1 + U_2)^0 \subset U_1{}^0 \quad \text{and} \quad (U_1 + U_2)^0 \subset U_2{}^0$$

Therefore, $(U_1 + U_2)^0 \subset U_1{}^0 \cap U_2{}^0$.

Now, $U_1{}^0 \cap U_2{}^0 \subset U_1{}^0$ and $U_1{}^0 \cap U_2{}^0 \subset U_2{}^0$, so that any f in $U_1{}^0 \cap U_2{}^0$ belongs both to $U_1{}^0$ and to $U_2{}^0$. Therefore, such an f satisfies:

$$f \mid U_1 \text{ is constantly 0, and } f \mid U_2 \text{ is constantly 0}$$

Now, choose any $\mathbf{v} \in U_1 + U_2$. We may write $\mathbf{v} = \mathbf{u}_1 + \mathbf{u}_2$, where $\mathbf{u}_1 \in U_1$ and $\mathbf{u}_2 \in U_2$. Then,

$$f(\mathbf{v}) = f(\mathbf{u}_1 + \mathbf{u}_2) = f(\mathbf{u}_1) + f(\mathbf{u}_2) = 0 + 0 = 0$$

Since this holds for every $\mathbf{v} \in U_1 + U_2$, it follows that

$$f \in (U_1 + U_2)^0$$

Thus, $U_1{}^0 \cap U_2{}^0 \subset (U_1 + U_2)^0$, as desired. Q.E.D.

Notice that the operation of taking the annihilator of a subspace provides us with a mapping

$$\begin{array}{ccc} \text{subspaces of } V & \to & \text{subspaces of } V^* \\ U & \to & U^0 \end{array}$$

It is not clear, yet, that this mapping is 1–1 or onto. However, it does have nice duality properties. These are presented by (1), (2), (3) above. Notice that when we are dealing with vector spaces, it is useful to consider the operations of + and ∩ as symmetric opposites rather than ∪ and ∩.

Next we prove that the pairing is 1–1 but that it need not be onto.

Corollary to Proposition 4.20

Let V be a vector space over F, let $\mathscr{S}$ be the set of all vector subspaces of V, and let $\mathscr{S}^*$ be the set of all vector subspaces of V^*. The association $U \to U^0$, for every $U \in \mathscr{S}$ defines a 1–1 function from $\mathscr{S}$ to $\mathscr{S}^*$.

Proof

Call the function N. Thus, for $U \in \mathscr{S}$, $N(U) = U^0 \in \mathscr{S}^*$. Clearly, this function is well-defined.

Choose any $U_1, U_2 \in \mathscr{S}$ and suppose that $N(U_1) = N(U_2)$; that is, ${U_1}^0 = {U_2}^0$.

Therefore, ${U_1}^0 \subset {U_2}^0$ and ${U_1}^0 \supset {U_2}^0$, so that, applying (1), we get $U_1 \supset U_2$ and $U_1 \subset U_2$, respectively. That is, $U_1 = U_2$.

Thus, if U_1 and U_2 had been chosen to be distinct at the outset, we would have to conclude that $N(U_1)$ and $N(U_2)$ also were distinct. Q.E.D.

The function $N: \mathscr{S} \to \mathscr{S}^*$ need not be onto. A proof of this statement involves, merely, presenting an example of a field F and a vector space V over F for which N is not onto.

Let $F = \mathbf{R}$ and $V = \mathscr{C}[a, b]$ where a and b are real numbers $a < b$. $V^* =$ Trans($\mathscr{C}[a, b]$, $\mathbf{R}$). In Exercises 4.1.**8**, we defined certain members $L_g \in$ Trans($\mathscr{C}[a, b]$, $\mathbf{R}$), where g ranged over $\mathscr{C}[a, b]$. Specifically, for any $g \in \mathscr{C}[a, b]$, L_g is a linear functional whose value at any $f \in \mathscr{C}[a, b]$ is given by

$$L_g(f) = \int_a^b f(x)g(x)dx$$

Consider, now, only those L_g for which g is a polynomial function. Call the collection of such L_g, $L(\mathscr{P})$.

$$\text{Let } W = \text{span}_{V^*}(L(\mathscr{P}))$$

First, we claim that $W \neq V^*$. To prove this, we remind the reader that the function from $\mathscr{C}[a, b] \to$ Trans($\mathscr{C}[a, b]$, $\mathbf{R}$) given by $g \to L_g$ is a 1–1 linear transformation (which we called L in Exercises 4.1.**8**). Now, choose any $w \in W$. This is a linear combination of L_g's, where each g is a polynomial function:

$$w = a_1 L_{g_1} + \cdots + a_k L_{g_k}$$

Therefore,

$$w = a_1 L(g_1) + \cdots + a_k L(g_k) = L(a_1 g_1 + \cdots + a_k g_k)$$
$$= L_{a_1 g_1 + \cdots + a_k g_k}$$

Clearly, $a_1 g_1 + \cdots + a_k g_k$ is also a polynomial function. Now, choose any $g \in \mathscr{C}[a, b]$ that is not a polynomial function. Then, $g \neq a_1 g_1 + \cdots + a_k g_k$, so that since L is 1–1, $L_g \neq L_{a_1 g_1 + \cdots + a_k g_k} = w$. Since w is any arbitrary member of W, this means that $L_g \notin W$. Thus, $W \neq V^*$.

Now, *we claim that there is no vector subspace $U \subset V$ such* that $W = U^0$.

For, suppose that there were. Choose any $f \in U$. Then, by definition of $U^0(=W)$,

$$\int_a^b f(x)g(x) = L_g(f) = 0, \qquad \text{for all} \quad L_g \in W$$

Now we must appeal to a result of advanced calculus:

If $L_g(f) = 0$ for all polynomial functions g, then $L_f(f) = 0$.

Thus,

$$\int_a^b [f(x)]^2 dx = 0$$

Now, $[f(x)]^2 \geqq 0$, for all $x \in [a, b]$. If $[f(x)]^2 > 0$, for some such $x = x_0$, it would be possible, by the continuity of f, to find an $\epsilon > 0$ and a $\delta > 0$ so that

$$[f(x)]^2 > \epsilon, \qquad \text{for all} \quad x \in (x_0 - \delta, x_0 + \delta)$$

Consider Figure 28.

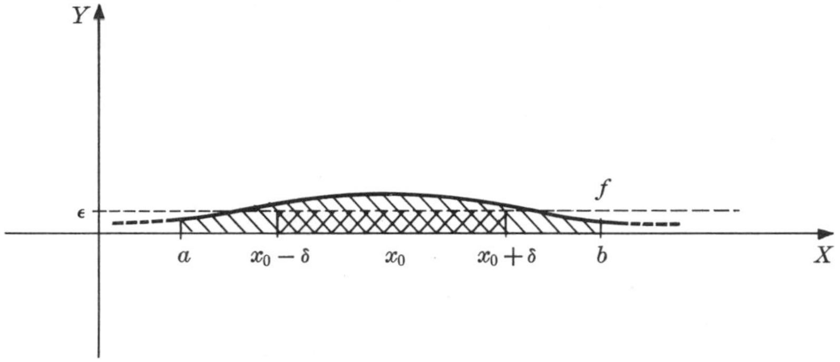

FIGURE 28

Clearly,

$$\int_a^b [f(x)]^2 \, dx \geqq 2\delta\epsilon > 0,$$

in this case. Since this is impossible, we conclude that $[f(x)]^2$ is constantly 0 on $[a, b]$ and, hence, that $f = \bar{0}$.

Thus, since f was chosen arbitrarily in U,

$$U = \{\bar{0}\}$$

But, *every* member of Trans($\mathscr{C}[a, b]$, $\mathbf{R}$) sends $\bar{0}$ to 0, since these members are linear transformations. That is, every $h \in V^*$ satisfies: $h \mid U$ is constantly zero. Therefore,

$$U^0 = V^* \neq W,$$

a contradiction. This concludes the example.

Next, we extend our discussion of duality to vector-space bases.

Let V be a vector space, and let X be any basis of V.** For each $\mathbf{x} \in X$, define a function $f_{\mathbf{x}}: X \to F$, as follows:

$$f_{\mathbf{x}}(\mathbf{x}') = \begin{cases} 0, & \text{if} \quad \mathbf{x}' \neq \mathbf{x} \\ 1, & \text{if} \quad \mathbf{x}' = \mathbf{x} \end{cases}$$

We have discussed such functions before in Chapter 3. Let $\mathbf{x}^*: V \to F$ be the linear form determined by $f_{\mathbf{x}}$, as in Proposition 4.17. Let X^* be the set of all $\mathbf{x}^*$, as $\mathbf{x}$ ranges over X. The association $\mathbf{x} \to \mathbf{x}^*$ is clearly a 1–1 correspondence from X to X^*. Note that, of course, $X^* \subset V^*$.

Proposition 4.21

Let X and V be as above. Then X^* is a linearly independent subset of V^*. It is a basis of V^* if and only if V is finite-dimensional.

Proof

We shall be making use of the following easy result. Choose any $\mathbf{x}_1, \ldots, \mathbf{x}_k \in X$ and $a_1, \ldots, a_k \in F$, and consider the linear combination $a_1\mathbf{x}_1^* + \cdots + a_k\mathbf{x}_k^*$. Recall that $\mathbf{x}_i^*$ satisfies, for all $\mathbf{x} \in X$,

$$\mathbf{x}_i^*(\mathbf{x}) = \begin{cases} 0, & \text{if} \quad \mathbf{x} \neq \mathbf{x}_i \\ 1, & \text{if} \quad \mathbf{x} = \mathbf{x}_i \end{cases} \tag{1}$$

for all i between 1 and k. Using (1) it is easy to show that

$$(a_1\mathbf{x}_1^* + \cdots + a_k\mathbf{x}_k^*)(\mathbf{x}_j) = a_j, \tag{2}$$

for all j between 1 and k, since $\mathbf{x}_i = \mathbf{x}_j$, if and only if $i = j$.

To show that X^* is linearly independent, we choose any linear combination, as above, and assume that it has value $\bar{0}$. That is, we assume that

$$a_1\mathbf{x}_1^* + \cdots + a_k\mathbf{x}_k^* = \bar{0} \tag{3}$$

Clearly, $\bar{0}(\mathbf{x}_j) = 0$, for all j between 1 and k. Hence, combining this with (2) and (3), we conclude that $a_j = 0$, for all j between 1 and k. Therefore, the combination is trivial, so that X^* is independent.

If V is finite-dimensional, suppose that $X = \{\mathbf{x}_1, \ldots, \mathbf{x}_k\}$, and choose any $f \in V^*$. Let

$$f(\mathbf{x}_j) = a_j, \qquad j = 1, \ldots, k \tag{4}$$

Consider the linear combination $a_1\mathbf{x}_1^* + \cdots + a_k\mathbf{x}_k^*$. According to (2), its values at $\mathbf{x}_j$, $j = 1, \ldots, k$, coincide with those of f. Since $\{\mathbf{x}_1, \ldots, \mathbf{x}_k\}$ is a basis of V, and since the values of a linear transformation on a basis determine the transformation entirely, by Proposition 4.17,

$$f = a_1\mathbf{x}_1^* + \cdots + a_k\mathbf{x}_k^*,$$

** We ignore the case $X = \varnothing$, since it is not interesting.

so that $f \in \text{span}_{V^*}(X^*)$. Since f was chosen arbitrarily, this means that $V^* = \text{span}_{V^*}(X^*)$, so that X^* is a basis of V^*.

Finally, suppose that V is not finite-dimensional; that is, X is infinite. Let $a_1\mathbf{x}_1^* + \cdots + a_k\mathbf{x}_k^*$ be any linear combination of vectors of X^*. Since X is infinite, there is an $\mathbf{x} \in X$ such that $\mathbf{x} \neq \mathbf{x}_i$, $i = 1, \ldots, k$. Therefore, for this $\mathbf{x}$, using (1),

$$(a_1\mathbf{x}_1^* + \cdots + a_k\mathbf{x}_k^*)(\mathbf{x}) = 0 \tag{5}$$

Now, define a function $f: X \to F$ as follows:

$$f(\mathbf{x}) = 1, \qquad \text{for all} \quad \mathbf{x} \in X$$

Let $T_f: V \to F$ be the linear transformation corresponding to f. Clearly,

$$T_f(\mathbf{x}) = f(\mathbf{x}) = 1, \qquad \text{for all} \quad \mathbf{x} \in X \tag{6}$$

Comparing (5) and (6), we conclude that no linear combination of vectors of X^* can equal T_f.

But, of course, $T_f \in V^*$. Thus, if X is infinite, $\text{span}_{V^*}(X^*) \neq V^*$. Q.E.D.

Corollary to Proposition 4.21

Let V be any vector space over F. Then, there is a 1–1 *linear transformation from V to V^*. If dim V is finite, then this transformation is onto.*

Thus, it is always true that dim $V^* \geqq$ dim V. If dim V is finite, then $V^* \simeq V$ so that dim V^* = dim V.

This corollary is an immediate consequence of the preceding proposition, and so we omit a proof.

Note that in our proof of Proposition 4.21, we showed that when dim V is infinite, X^* is not a basis of V^*, although it is linearly independent. We did *not* prove that V^* cannot have a basis with the same cardinality as that of X^*. This statement, however, is true, although a proof of it is beyond the scope of this text. We state the result. A proof of a special case of this result is sketched in the exercises.

Proposition 4.22

If dim V is infinite, then dim $V^* >$ dim V. That is, every basis of V^* has cardinality strictly greater than that of X^*.

In our proof of Proposition 4.21, the only fact we needed in order to show that X^* was linearly independent was that X was linearly independent. Thus, the proof really gives us a slightly more general result: namely, *if X is any linearly independent subset of V, then X^*, as defined above, is a linearly independent subset of V^*; if X is a finite basis of V, then X^* is a finite basis of V^*.*

Henceforth, *given any linearly independent subset X of V, we call X^* the set dual to X; if X is a finite basis of V, we call X^* the basis of V^* dual to X.*

We now show how dual bases relate to subspaces and their annihilators.

Proposition 4.23

Let V be a vector space over F, U a vector subspace of V, and X a basis of U. Let Y be any basis of the annihilator U^0. Then, $X^* \cap Y = \varnothing$ and $X^* \cup Y$ is a linearly independent subset of V^*. It is a basis of V^* if and only if dim U is finite.

Note that if $U = V$, then this proposition reduces to Proposition 4.21.

Proof

First, we show that $\text{span}_{V^*}(X^*) \cap U^0 = \{\bar{0}\}$. To see this, choose any linear combination of vectors of X^*, $a_1\mathbf{x}_1^* + \cdots + a_k\mathbf{x}_k^*$. If it is nontrivial, then some $a_i \neq 0$. Then, for this i,

$$(a_1\mathbf{x}_1^* + \cdots + a_k\mathbf{x}_k^*)(\mathbf{x}_i) = a_i \neq 0$$

Since $\mathbf{x}_i \in U$, the above relation implies that $a_1\mathbf{x}^*_1 + \cdots + a_k\mathbf{x}_k^* \notin U^0$. Thus, $\text{span}_{V^*}(X^*) \cap U^0$ have no nonzero vectors in common.

Since $X^* \subset \text{span}_{V^*}(X^*)$ and $Y \subset U^0$, and since neither contains the zero vector, we conclude that $X^* \cap Y = \varnothing$. Thus,

$$\begin{aligned}\text{span}_{V^*}(X^* \cap Y) &= \text{span}_{V^*}(\varnothing)\\ &= \{\bar{0}\} = \text{span}_{V^*}(X^*) \cap \text{span}_{V^*}(Y),\end{aligned}$$

so that by Proposition 3.12, $X^* \cup Y$ is linearly independent.

Now, suppose that X is finite. We show that $\text{span}(X^* \cup Y) = \text{span}(X^*) + \text{span}(Y) = V^*$.

Let $X = \{\mathbf{x}_1, \ldots, \mathbf{x}_k\}$, and choose any $f \in V^*$.

Let a_i, $i = 1, \ldots, k$, be given by

$$a_i = f(\mathbf{x}_i), \qquad i = 1, \ldots, k,$$

and let $g = a_1\mathbf{x}_1^* + \cdots + a_k\mathbf{x}_k^*$. Clearly, $g(\mathbf{x}_i) = f(\mathbf{x}_i)$, $i = 1, \ldots, k$, so that $g \mid U = f \mid U$. Hence,

$$(f - g) \mid U$$

is constantly 0, or, $f - g \in U^0$. Let $f - g = h \in U^0$. Then, $f = g + h \in \text{span}_{V^*}(X^*) + U^0 = \text{span}_{V^*}(X^*) + \text{span}_{V^*}(Y)$, as desired.

Finally, suppose that X is infinite. Then, an argument similar to the one in the proof of Proposition 4.21, shows that $X^* \cup Y$ does not generate V^*. In particular, let Z be a basis of V such that $X \subset Z$, and define a linear form $g : V \to F$ satisfying

$$g(\mathbf{z}) = 1, \quad \text{for all} \quad \mathbf{z} \in Z$$

In particular, $g(\mathbf{x}) = 1$, for all $\mathbf{x} \in X$, since $X \subset Z$.

Now, every $f \in \text{span}(X^* \cup Y) = \text{span}(X^*) + U^0$ has the property that $f(\mathbf{x}) \neq 0$ for only finitely many $\mathbf{x} \in X$. To see this note that $f = f_1 + f_2$, where $f_1 \in \text{span}(X^*)$, $f_2 \in U^0$. By definition $f_2(\mathbf{x}) = 0$, for $\mathbf{x} \in X$. On the other hand,

f_1 is a linear combination, say $f_1 = a_1\mathbf{x}_1^* + \cdots + a_k\mathbf{x}_k^*$. Thus, for any $\mathbf{x} \neq \mathbf{x}_i$, for all $i = 1, \ldots, k$,

$$f_1(\mathbf{x}) = 0$$

Thus, unless $\mathbf{x}$ is equal to $\mathbf{x}_1$, or $\mathbf{x}_2, \ldots$, or $\mathbf{x}_k$,

$$f(\mathbf{x}) = f_1(\mathbf{x}) + f_2(\mathbf{x}) = 0$$

Since $g(\mathbf{x}) = 1$ for all $\mathbf{x} \in X$, g cannot equal f. But f was chosen to be any member of $\text{span}_{V^*}(X^* \cup Y)$. Thus, $g \notin \text{span}_{V^*}(X^* \cup Y)$, and, hence, $V^* \neq \text{span}_{V^*}(X^* \cup Y)$. Q.E.D.

Corollary to Proposition 4.23

Let V be an n-dimensional vector space over F, and let U be any vector subspace of V. Then,

$$\dim U^0 = n - \dim U$$

We leave the proof to the reader.

We now pause to present an example, and some exercises.

3.2 An Important Example

Let F be any field, and let $V = F^n$. We shall call the standard basis $\{\mathbf{e}_1^{(n)}, \ldots, \mathbf{e}_n^{(n)}\}$ of F^n, X. Recall that every n-tuple $(b_1, \ldots, b_n) \in F^n$ satisfies:

$$(b_1, \ldots, b_n) = b_1\mathbf{e}_1^{(n)} + \cdots + b_n e_n^{(n)} \tag{1}$$

We use this relation to help us describe V^* and X^*. According to Proposition 4.21, X^* is a basis of V^*. It consists of the linear functionals $(\mathbf{e}_1^{(n)*}, \ldots, (\mathbf{e}_n^{(n)})^*$, which are characterized by the equalities

$$(\mathbf{e}_i^{(n)})^*(\mathbf{e}_j^{(n)}) = \begin{cases} 0, & \text{if } i \neq j \\ 1, & \text{if } i = j \end{cases} \tag{2}$$

Thus, combining (1) and (2), for any $(b_1, \ldots, b_n) \in F^n$,

$$(\mathbf{e}_i^{(n)})^*(b_1, \ldots, b_n) = b_1(\mathbf{e}_i^{(n)})^*(\mathbf{e}_1^{(n)}) + \cdots + b_n(\mathbf{e}_i^{(n)})^*(\mathbf{e}_n^{(n)}) = b_i \cdot 1 = b_i \tag{3}$$

Thus, $(\mathbf{e}_i^{(n)})^*$ is precisely the ith coordinate projection of F^n onto F.

Now, choose any $f \in (F^n)^*$. It is a linear combination of vectors of X^*: say

$$f = a_1(\mathbf{e}_1^{(n)})^* + \cdots + a_n(\mathbf{e}_n^{(n)})^* \tag{4}$$

Combining (3) and (4), we get, for any $(b_1, \ldots, b_n)$,

$$f(b_1, \ldots, b_n) = a_1 b_1 + \cdots + a_n b_n \tag{5}$$

If we think of $(b_1, \ldots, b_n)$ as an indeterminate variable ranging over F^n, then equation (5) tells us that f is precisely *the function determined by the linear expression in n indeterminates, with coefficients $a_1, \ldots, a_n \in F$.*

Such linear expressions, of course, are the building blocks of systems of linear equations. Thus, our interest in dual vector spaces is more than aesthetically motivated. Indeed, the elements of dual vector spaces, as we have just shown, lie at the heart of much of what is interesting and useful about linear algebra.

EXERCISES / 4.5

1.* Let V be an n-dimensional vector space over F.

a. If $f: V \to F$ is any nontrivial linear form, prove that $\dim \mathscr{R}_f = 1$ and

$$\dim \mathscr{N}_f = n - 1.$$

b. Let $f_1, \ldots f_k$ be nontrivial linear forms in V^*. Prove that

$$\dim(\mathscr{N}_{f_1} \cap \ldots \cap \mathscr{N}_{f_k}) \geqq n - k.$$

[*Hint:* see example (d) in 1.7].

c. Let $\mathscr{F}$ be any nonempty subset of V^*, and consider the collection of all subspaces $\mathscr{N}_f$, where $f \in \mathscr{F}$: say $\{\mathscr{N}_f \mid f \in \mathscr{F}]$. Prove that

$$\text{span}_{V^*}(\mathscr{F}) = (\cap \{\mathscr{N}_f \mid f \in \mathscr{F}\})^0$$

This generalizes Proposition 4.20 (b). [*Hint:* First show that $\text{span}_{V^*}(\mathscr{F}) \subset (\cap\{\mathscr{N}_f \mid f \in \mathscr{F}\})^0$, and then use previous results including **b.**, above, to show that both of these subspaces have the same dimension.]

d. Let $V = F^n$. Then, according to the example presented above, $f_1, \ldots, f_k$ are linear expressions in n indeterminates with coefficients in F. The subspace $\mathscr{N}_{f_1} \cap \cdots \cap \mathscr{N}_{f_k}$ consists of all n-tuples in F^n sent to 0 simultaneously by $f_1, \ldots, f_k$. That is, it consists of all solutions to the homogeneous system** of k linear equations determined by $f_1, \ldots, f_k$.

What does **b.** tell us about the set of solutions to such a system? This is a generalization of 1.7 Example (d).

e. Let $f, f_1, \ldots, f_k$ be linear functionals with the following property: for every $\mathbf{v} \in V$ such that, simultaneously, $f_1(\mathbf{v}) = 0, f_2(\mathbf{v}) = 0, \ldots, f_k(\mathbf{v}) = 0$, it happens that also $f(\mathbf{v}) = 0$.

Prove that there are scalars $a_1, \ldots, a_k \in F$ such that

$$f = a_1 f_1 + \cdots + a_k f_k$$

[*Hint:* Show that $f \in (\mathscr{N}_{f_1} \cap \cdots \cap \mathscr{N}_{f_k})^0$ and then use (**c**).]

f. Prove that if $f_1, f_2, \ldots, f_k$ are linear functionals satisfying

$$f = a_1 f_1 + \cdots + a_k f_k,$$

then, for any $\mathbf{v} \in V$ such that, simultaneously, $f_1(\mathbf{v}) = 0, \ldots, f_k(\mathbf{v}) = 0$, it happens that, also, $f(\mathbf{v}) = 0$.

** We defined this term in the last part of Chapter 1. Roughly speaking, in a homogeneous system, we look for values of the indeterminates that make the linear expressions equal zero.

g. These last two results have a useful application when they are interpreted in terms of linear expressions and linear equations. The reader is invited to supply the interpretation.

2. Let V be any vector space over F with countable dimension.** Let

$$Y = \{f_1, f_2, f_3, \ldots\}$$

be any countable linearly independent subset of V^*.

a. Show that there is some $\mathbf{x}_1 \in V$ such that $f_1(\mathbf{x}_1) = 1$.

b. Show that there is some $\mathbf{x}_2 \in V$ such that $f_2(\mathbf{x}_2) = 1$, but $f_1(\mathbf{x}_2) = 0$. [*Hint:* Use **1.e** and the fact that Y is linearly independent to find $\mathbf{x} \in \mathcal{N}_{f_1}$ so that $f_2(\mathbf{x}) \neq 0$.]

c. Suppose that you have found $\mathbf{x}_1, \ldots, \mathbf{x}_k$ satisfying **i.** $f_i(\mathbf{x}_i) = 1$, $i = 1, \ldots, k$; **ii.** $f_j(\mathbf{x}_i) = \mathbf{0}$, if $j < i$, $i = 1, \ldots, k$. Then, find an $\mathbf{x}_{k+1}$, so that $f_{k+1}(\mathbf{x}_{k+1}) = 1$ and $f_j(\mathbf{x}_{k+1}) = \mathbf{0}$, $j < k+1$. (*Hint:* Use **1.e** and the fact that Y is linearly independent to find $\mathbf{x} \in \mathcal{N}_{f_1} \cap \cdots \cap \mathcal{N}_{f_k}$, so that $f_{k+1}(\mathbf{x}) \neq 0$).

d. Let $X = \{\mathbf{x}_1, \mathbf{x}_2, \mathbf{x}_3, \ldots\}$ be the set constructed inductively in **a–c**. Prove that X is linearly independent. (*Hint:* Let $a_1\mathbf{x}_{i_1} + \cdots + a_k\mathbf{x}_{i_k}$ be any linear combination with value $\mathbf{0}$, where $\mathbf{x}_{i_1}, \mathbf{x}_{i_2}, \ldots, \mathbf{x}_{i_k} \in X$, and $i_1 < \cdots < i_k$. Evaluate $f_{i_1}(a_1\mathbf{x}_{i_1} + \cdots + a_k\mathbf{x}_{i_k})$, then $f_{i_2}(a_1\mathbf{x}_{i_1} + \cdots + a_k\mathbf{x}_{i_k})$, and so on, and use the results to show that $a_1, a_2, \ldots, a_k$ are zero).

e. Let Z be a basis for V such that $X \subset Z$. Suppose that there is a $\mathbf{z} \in Z$ such that $\mathbf{z} \notin X$. Show that $\mathbf{z}^*$ is not a linear combination of members of Y. (*Hint:* Proceed by obtaining a contradiction: Suppose $\mathbf{z}^* = a_1 f_{i_1} + \cdots + a_k f_{i_k}$, where all terms with zero coefficients have been eliminated and $i_1 < i_2 < \cdots < i_k$. Evaluate both sides at x_{i_k}.)

f. Suppose that X itself is a basis of V. Let $g\colon X \to F$ be the function constantly equal to 1, and let $T_g\colon V \to F$ be the corresponding linear functional. Prove that T_g is not a linear combination of members of Y.

Thus, in any case, Y is not a basis of V^*. The above results show, therefore, that V^* does not have a countable basis. Thus, dim $V^* >$ dim V.

3. a. Prove that $\{(1, 0, 2), (3, -1, 0), (0, 0, 2)\}$ is a basis of $\mathbf{R}^3$.

b. Compute the basis of $(\mathbf{R}^3)^*$ dual to $\{(1, 0, 2), (3, -1, 0), (0, 0, 2)\}$. Exhibit these basis members as linear expressions of the form $a_1x_1 + a_2x_2 + a_3x_3$ (i.e., determine the numbers a_1, a_2, a_3).

4. Define $T : F^n \to (F^n)^*$ as follows: for every $(a_1 \ldots, a_n) \in F^n$, let $T(a_1, \ldots, a_n)$ be the linear form whose value at every $(x_1, \ldots, x_n)$ is given by

$$T(a_1, \ldots, a_n)(x_1, \ldots, x_n) = a_1x_1 + \cdots + a_nx_n$$

Prove that T is an isomorphism. Prove that $T(\mathbf{e}_i^{(n)})^* = (\mathbf{e}_i^{(n)})^*$, $i = 1, \ldots, n$.

5. a. Prove that $\{(1, 2), (3, 5)\}$ is a basis of $\mathbf{R}^2$. Locate these vectors as points in the standard representation of the Cartesian plane.

b. Compute the dual basis of $(\mathbf{R}^2)^*$, $\{(1, 2)^*, (3, 5)^*\}$.

** Recall that V has countable dimension if and only if V has a countable basis: a basis that is in 1–1 correspondence with the set of natural numbers.

c. Let $T:\mathbf{R}^2 \to (\mathbf{R}^2)^*$ be as in **4**, above. Locate $T^{-1}((1,2)^*)$ and $T^{-1}((3,5)^*)$ on the Cartesian plane.

d. Show that the line joining (1, 2) to the origin is perpendicular to the line joining $T^{-1}((1,2)^*)$ to the origin. Explain why this is not a coincidence.

6. Let $X \subset \mathbf{R}^3$ be given by: $X = \{(1, 2), (3, 0)\}$.
Let $U = \text{span}_{\mathbf{R}^3}(X)$. What is dim U^0?

Determine a basis of U^0. Let $T:\mathbf{R}^3 \to (\mathbf{R}^3)^*$ be as in **4**, above. Prove that $T^{-1}(U^0)$ is a vector subspace of $\mathbf{R}^3$. Prove that $U \oplus T^{-1}(U^0) = \mathbf{R}^3$. Sketch pictures of U and $T^{-1}(U^0)$ in the standard pictorial representation of $\mathbf{R}^3$.

7. Let V be any finite-dimensional vector space over F, and let U be a vector subspace of V. Let X be a basis of U and Y a basis of V such that $X \subset Y$. Let Y^* be the corresponding basis of V^* dual to Y, and let $T: V \to V^*$ be the isomorphism determined by the 1–1 correspondence from Y to Y^* given by $y \leftrightarrow y^*$. Prove that $T^{-1}(U^0)$ is a vector subspace of V complementary to U (i.e., $U \oplus T^{-1}(U^0) = V$).

Would this same relation be valid if T is any arbitrary isomorphism between V and V^*? Justify your answer?

8. Show that in Proposition 4.20(b), the inclusion cannot, in general, be replaced by an equality.

3.3 Duality and Linear Transformations

Definition 4.5

Let V and W be vector spaces over F, and let $T: V \to W$ be a linear transformation. Choose any $f \in W^* = Trans(W, F)$. The composition $f \circ T$ is a linear transformation from V to F. That is, $f \circ T \in Trans(V, F) = V^*$. We now define a function $T^*: W^* \to V^*$ as follows:

For every $f \in W^*$, $T^*(f) = f \circ T \in V^*$.

T^* is called the adjoint (or dual) of T.

Proposition 4.24

Let T, V, and W be as above. The adjoint of T, $T^*: W^* \to V^*$, is a linear transformation.

Proof

Choose any $f_1, f_2 \in W^*$ and any $a \in F$. Then, for every $\mathbf{v} \in V$

$$\begin{aligned} T^*(f_1 + f_2)(\mathbf{v}) = (f_1 + f_2)(T(\mathbf{v})) &= f_1(T(\mathbf{v})) + f_2(T(\mathbf{v})) \\ &= T^*(f_1)(\mathbf{v}) + T^*(f_2)(\mathbf{v}) \\ &= (T^*(f_1) + T^*(f_2))(v) \end{aligned}$$

and

$$\begin{aligned} T^*(af_1)(\mathbf{v}) = (af_1)(T(\mathbf{v})) &= a(f_1(T(\mathbf{v})) \\ &= a(T^*(f_1)(\mathbf{v})) \\ &= (aT^*(f_1))(\mathbf{v}) \end{aligned}$$

Thus,

$$T^*(f_1 + f_2) = T^*(f_1) + T^*(f_2), \text{ and } T^*(af_1) = aT^*(f_1). \qquad \text{Q.E.D.}$$

Notice that the dual or adjoint of a linear transformation $T : V \to W$ does go in the direction opposite to that of T, in some sense (i.e., from W^* to V^*). We next present some more symmetric opposites.

Proposition 4.25

Let $T : V \to W$ be a linear transformation with adjoint $T^* : W^* \to V^*$. Then:

(1) $\mathscr{R}_{T^*} = (\mathscr{N}_T)^0$.
(2) $\mathscr{N}_{T^*} = (\mathscr{R}_T)^0$.

Proof

(1) Choose any $f \in \mathscr{R}_{T^*}$. Then, there is a $g \in W^*$ such that $g \circ T = T^*(g) = f$. For any $\mathbf{v} \in \mathscr{N}_T$, therefore,

$$f(\mathbf{v}) = (T^*(g))(\mathbf{v}) = (g \circ T)(\mathbf{v}) = g(T(\mathbf{v}))$$
$$= f(\mathbf{0}) = 0$$

This means that $f \in (\mathscr{N}_T)^0$. Thus, $\mathscr{R}_{T^*} \subset (\mathscr{N}_T)^0$.

Now, choose any $f \in (\mathscr{N}_T)^0$. Then, $f(\mathbf{v}) = 0$ for every $\mathbf{v} \in \mathscr{N}_T$, or, to put it another way,

$$\mathscr{N}_T \subset \mathscr{N}_f$$

We now apply Exercises **4.4.3** to obtain a linear transformation $g: W \to F$ satisfying

$$g \circ T = f$$

(c.f. Exercises **4.4.3b.**)
But, $g \in W^*$, and $g \circ T = T^*(g) \in \mathscr{R}_{T^*}$. Therefore, $f \in \mathscr{R}_{T^*}$. This means that $(\mathscr{N}_T)^0 \subset \mathscr{R}_{T^*}$.

Combining this inclusion with that of the first paragraph, we get $\mathscr{R}_{T^*} = (\mathscr{N}_T)^0$.

(2) Choose any $f \in \mathscr{N}_{T^*}$, and choose any $\mathbf{w} \in \mathscr{R}_T$. Then, $\mathbf{w} = T(\mathbf{v})$, for some $\mathbf{v} \in V$. Thus,

$$f(\mathbf{w}) = f(T(\mathbf{v})) = (f \circ T)(\mathbf{v}) = T^*(f)(\mathbf{v})$$
$$= \upsilon(\mathbf{v}) = 0$$

Since this holds for any $\mathbf{w} \in \mathscr{R}_T$, we conclude that $f \in (\mathscr{R}_T)^0$. Therefore, $\mathscr{N}_{T^*} \subset (\mathscr{R}_T)^0$.

Finally, choose any $f \in (\mathscr{R}_T)^0$. This f satisfies $f(\mathbf{w}) = 0$, for all $\mathbf{w} \in \mathscr{R}_T$. Now, consider $T^*(f)$ and evaluate it at any $\mathbf{v} \in V$, noting that $T(\mathbf{v}) \in \mathscr{R}_T$. Then,

$$[T^*(f)](\mathbf{v}) = (f \circ T)(\mathbf{v}) = f(T(\mathbf{v})) = 0$$

Thus, $T^*(f)$ is identically 0 on all of V; that is, $T^*(f) = \bar{0}$. This means that $f \in \mathcal{N}_{T^*}$, and so, $(\mathcal{R}_T)^0 \subset \mathcal{N}_{T^*}$.

Combining this with the reverse inclusion, previously obtained, we get $\mathcal{N}_{T^*} = (\mathcal{R}_T)^0$. Q.E.D.

Corollary to Proposition 4.25

Let $T: V \to W$ be a linear transformation with adjoint $T^*: W^* \to V^*$. Then:

(1) *T is 1–1 if and only if T^* is onto.*
(2) *T is onto if and only if T^* is 1–1.*

Proof

(1) The following statements are equivalent, as the reader should verify:
(a) T is 1–1.
(b) $\mathcal{N}_T = \{\mathbf{0}\}$.
(c) $(\mathcal{N}_T)^0 = V^*$.
(d) $\mathcal{R}_{T^*} = V^*$.
(e) T^* is onto.

(2) The following statements are equivalent, as the reader should verify:
(a) T is onto.
(b) $\mathcal{R}_T = W$.
(c) $(\mathcal{R}_T)^0 = \{\cup\}$
(d) $\mathcal{N}_{T^*} = \{\bar{0}\}$
(e) T^* is 1–1. Q.E.D.

EXERCISES / 4.6

1.* Suppose that V is a finite-dimensional vector space over F, let $\mathcal{S}$ be the set of all vector subspaces of V, and let $\mathcal{S}^*$ be the set of all vector subspaces of V^*. In Corollary to Proposition 4.20, we proved that the association $U \to U^0$ determines a 1–1 function from $\mathcal{S}$ to $\mathcal{S}^*$. In this exercise, the goal is to show that when V is finite-dimensional, the function is also onto.

a. Choose any vector subspace W of V^*, and let W_0 be the subset of V consisting of all vectors $\mathbf{v} \in V$ such that $f(\mathbf{v}) = 0$ for every $f \in W$. *Prove that* $W_0 = \bigcap \{N_f \mid f \in W\}$. (The set on the right is the intersection of all null spaces of all $f \in W$.)

Since the intersection of a family of subspaces of V is a subspace of V, the above result implies that W_0 is a vector subspace of V.

b. Prove that $(W_0)^0 \supset W$. (cf. Exercise 4.5.**1**.**c**.)

c. For **a** and **b**, the finite-dimensionality of V was not needed. Now use the finite-dimensionality of V to show that $(W_0)^0 = W$. (cf. Exercises 4.5.**1**.**c**.)

Thus every $W \in \mathcal{S}^*$ is the annihilator of some U (namely, $U = W_0$).

2. Let the linear transformation $T:\mathbf{R}^3 \to \mathbf{R}^3$ be determined by the following specification of values on $\{\mathbf{e}_1^{(3)}, \mathbf{e}_2^{(3)}, \mathbf{e}_3^{(3)}\}$.

$$T(\mathbf{e}_1^{(3)}) = (2, -1, 1)$$

$$T(\mathbf{e}_2^{(3)}) = (0, 4, 8)$$

$$T(\mathbf{e}_3^{(3)}) = (7, -1, 0)$$

Compute the values $T^*((\mathbf{e}_1^{(3)})^*)$, $T^*((\mathbf{e}_2^{(3)})^*)$, and $T^*((\mathbf{e}_3^{(3)})^*)$.

3. Let $S:\mathbf{R}^3 \to \mathbf{R}^2$ be the linear transformation satisfying:

$$S(\mathbf{e}_1^{(3)}) = (2, 2)$$

$$S(\mathbf{e}_2^{(3)}) = (0, 1)$$

$$S(\mathbf{e}_3^{(3)}) = (-4, 1)$$

The adjoint of S, S^* takes $(\mathbf{R}^2)^*$ to $(\mathbf{R}^3)^*$. What are the values $S^*((\mathbf{e}_1^{(2)})^*)$ and $S^*((\mathbf{e}_2^{(2)})^*)$?

4. Let V be a vector space over F, and let V^* be its dual. V^*, of course, is a vector space over F, so that we can consider *its* dual, $(V^*)^*$. The members of $(V^*)^*$ are linear functionals whose arguments are linear functionals on V. The aim of this exercise is to show how, in some sense, V can be considered to be a vector subspace of $(V^*)^*$ and sometimes even equal to $(V^*)^*$.
   a. Choose any fixed $\mathbf{v} \in V$, and let $E_\mathbf{v}: V^* \to F$ be the evaluation at $\mathbf{v}$. That is, for any $f \in V^*$, let

$$E_\mathbf{v}(f) = f(\mathbf{v})$$

We have already shown (in Chapters 1 and 4) that $E_\mathbf{v}$ is a linear transformation from V^* to F. Thus, $E_\mathbf{v} \in (V^*)^*$. (The reader is advised to redo the proof that $E_\mathbf{v}$ is linear.)

Now, define a function $E: V \to (V^*)^*$ as follows:

$$E(\mathbf{v}) = E_\mathbf{v}$$

Prove that E is a 1–1 linear transformation.

Thus, $\mathscr{R}_E$ is a vector subspace of $(V^*)^*$ isomorphic to V.

   b. If V is finite-dimensional, prove that $\mathscr{R}_E = (V^*)^*$. [*Hint:* Compare $\dim \mathscr{R}_E$ and $\dim(V^*)^*$.]

Thus, if V is a finite-dimensional vector space, $E: V \to (V^*)^*$ is an isomorphism. Notice that the definition of E is completely independent of any arbitrary choice of basis of V. Contrast this with the way we defined isomorphisms from V to V^*. The isomorphism E depends only on the general defining properties of V and $(V^*)^*$.

Note that, in a certain sense, the passage from $\mathbf{v}$ to $E(\mathbf{v})$ involves only a slight conceptual change. The vector $\mathbf{v}$ is regarded as the "variable" or argument of fixed linear forms f. The vector $E(\mathbf{v})$ can be thought of as the form obtained by holding $\mathbf{v}$ fixed and letting f be the variable. The two points of view are, in a certain sense, two sides of the same coin, and they are related by the equation $(E(\mathbf{v}))(f) = f(\mathbf{v})$.

The preceding remarks are intended to convey the impression that the isomorphism E is "better" than most other isomorphisms from V to another vector space. It is beyond the scope of this text to make this idea precise, although this can be done. The technical term used to designate E's superiority is "natural." We say that E is a *natural isomorphism* from V to $(V^*)^*$.

We can give a rough description of naturality as follows.**

We introduced the notion of isomorphism from the viewpoint that certain distinctions among vector spaces were more superficial than others. In particular, the actual identity of this or that vector in a vector space was not considered as important as the structural role that it played, and, hence, it could be replaced (in an appropriate way) by other objects ("understudies," so to speak). The replacement process resulted in a 1–1 correspondence that preserved the vector-space operations, which we called an isomorphism.

Now the important point to note here is that the replacement procedure only involved one or two vector spaces: it was a very localized operation. Moreover, very few restrictions were placed on the procedure. Indeed, we only had to make sure that the operations were preserved.

The isomorphism E, described above, however, is an isomorphism that can be defined *in a uniform way for all vector spaces over F*, since the replacement of $\mathbf{v}$ by $E(\mathbf{v})$, far from haphazard, involves only slight change of conceptual outlook.

The next part of this exercise is designed to give more evidence of the uniformity of definition of E.

c. Given two vector spaces over F, V and W, let $E_V : V \to (V^*)^*$ and $E_W : W \to (W^*)^*$ be the 1–1 linear transformations defined in the same way as E, above.

Let $T : V \to W$ be any linear transformation, $T^* : W^* \to V^*$ its adjoint and $(T^*)^* : (V^*)^* \to (W^*)^*$ the adjoint of T^*.

Prove that $(T^*)^* \circ E_V = E_W \circ T$.

The above relation says, in intuitive terms, that $(T^*)^*$ does to $(V^*)^*$ what T does to V, the two being made comparable by E_V and E_W.

d. Let U be a vector subspace of V, and suppose that V is finite-dimensional [so that $E_V : V \to (V^*)^*$ is an isomorphism]. Then, of course, $E_V(U)$ is a vector subspace of $(V^*)^*$ isomorphic to U.

Prove that

$$E_V(U) = (U^0)^0,$$

where $(U^0)^0$ is the annihilator of U^0.

The above relation says, in intuitive terms, that U and $(U^0)^0$ are the "same," being made comparable by E_V.

e. Let V be as above with basis $\{\mathbf{x}_1, \ldots, \mathbf{x}_n\}$. Then V^* has as a basis $\{\mathbf{x}_1^*, \ldots, \mathbf{x}_n^*]$, and $(V^*)^*$ has as a basis $\{(\mathbf{x}_1^*)^*, \ldots, (\mathbf{x}_n^*)^*\}$.

** The interested reader might consult the considerably more advanced treatment in the first few pages of Peter Freyd's *Abelian Categories*, Harper & Row, 1964.

Let $V = \mathbf{R}^3$ and $x_i = \mathbf{e}_i^{(3)}$, $i = 1, 2, 3$. Suppose that the linear transformation $T: \mathbf{R}^3 \to \mathbf{R}^3$, is given by

$$T(\mathbf{e}_1^{(3)}) = 2\mathbf{e}_1^{(3)} - \mathbf{e}_2^{(3)} + \mathbf{e}_3^{(3)}$$

$$T(\mathbf{e}_2^{(3)}) = 3\mathbf{e}_2^{(3)} + \mathbf{e}_3^{(3)}$$

$$T(\mathbf{e}_3^{(3)}) = 4\mathbf{e}_1^{(3)} - \mathbf{e}_3^{(3)}$$

Evaluate $T^*((\mathbf{e}_1^{(3)})^*)$, $T^*((\mathbf{e}_2^{(3)})^*)$, $T^*((\mathbf{e}_3^{(3)})^*)$.
Evaluate $(T^*)^*(((\mathbf{e}_1^{(3)})^*)^*)$, $(T^*)^*(((\mathbf{e}_2^{(3)})^*)^*)$, $(T^*)^*(((\mathbf{e}_3^{(3)})^*)^*)$.

4 / LINEAR TRANSFORMATIONS AND MATRICES

4.1 Addition and Scalar Multiplication of Matrices

In this section, V will always be a vector space over F with basis $\{\mathbf{x}_1, \ldots, \mathbf{x}_m\} = X$, and W will always be a vector space over F with basis $\{\mathbf{y}_1, \ldots, \mathbf{y}_n\} = Y$. Moreover, we shall assume, henceforth in this section, when referring to X or Y, or to any other bases, that their members are arranged in a fixed order. That is, *all bases in this section will be ordered bases.* A change in the order of an ordered basis will result in a new ordered basis.

According to Proposition 4.17, every $T \in \text{Trans}(V, W)$ is completely and uniquely determined by its values $T(\mathbf{x}_1), \ldots, T(\mathbf{x}_m)$. These are vectors in W. Since Y is a basis of W, each of the vectors $T(\mathbf{x}_j)$, $j = 1, \ldots, m$, can be uniquely expressed as a linear combination of vectors of Y:

$$\begin{aligned} T(\mathbf{x}_1) &= a_{11}\mathbf{y}_1 + a_{21}\mathbf{y}_2 + \cdots + a_{n1}\mathbf{y}_n \\ T(\mathbf{x}_2) &= a_{12}\mathbf{y}_1 + a_{22}\mathbf{y}_2 + \cdots + a_{n2}\mathbf{y}_n \\ &\vdots \\ T(\mathbf{x}_m) &= a_{1m}\mathbf{y}_1 + a_{2m}\mathbf{y}_2 + \cdots + a_{nm}\mathbf{y}_n \end{aligned}$$

Thus, once the ordered bases $\{\mathbf{x}_1, \ldots, \mathbf{x}_m\}$ *of* V *and* $\{\mathbf{y}_1, \ldots, \mathbf{y}_n\}$ *of* W *are fixed, any linear transformation* $T: V \to W$ *is completely and uniquely determined by the mn bits of data* a_{ij}, $i = 1, \ldots, n$, $j = 1, \ldots, m$: these, of course, are any mn members of F, depending on T.

It is convenient to arrange this data in a rectangular array, which, as convention has it, is skew to the array exhibited above:

$$\begin{matrix} a_{11} & a_{12} & \cdots & a_{1m} \\ a_{21} & a_{22} & \cdots & a_{2m} \\ \vdots & \vdots & & \vdots \\ a_{n1} & a_{n2} & \cdots & a_{nm} \end{matrix}$$

Such a rectangular array of members of F is *called an* $n \times m$ *matrix over* F. Usually the array is enclosed in large parentheses:

$$\begin{pmatrix} a_{11} & a_{12} & \cdots & a_{1m} \\ a_{21} & a_{22} & \cdots & a_{2m} \\ \vdots & \vdots & & \vdots \\ a_{n1} & a_{n2} & \cdots & a_{nm} \end{pmatrix}$$

Sometimes we abbreviate the above array by writing ${}_n(a_{ij})_m$ or (a_{ij}). Even more briefly, we denote a $n \times m$ matrix over F by German letters ${}_n\mathfrak{a}_m$ or, simply, $\mathfrak{a}$(${}_n\mathfrak{b}_m$, or $\mathfrak{b}$, etc.). To indicate that a particular $n \times m$ matrix over F is obtained from a given linear transformation $T: V \rightarrow W$ (using the given bases X and Y), as above, we may denote the matrix by $\mathfrak{a}_T$ or $(a_{ij})_T$.

The set of all $n \times m$ matrixes over F will be denoted by $\mathfrak{M}(n, m)$.

Proposition 4.26

Let V, W, X, *and* Y *be as above. The association* $T \rightarrow \mathfrak{a}_T$ *is a* 1–1 *function from* Trans(V, W) *onto* $\mathfrak{M}(n, m)$.

Proof

The association is clearly a function, since given any $T \in \text{Trans}(V, W)$, the coefficients a_{ij} in the linear combination of vectors of $\{\mathbf{y}_1, \ldots, \mathbf{y}_n\}$ with value $T(\mathbf{x}_j)$, for all $j = 1, \ldots, m$, are uniquely determined.

The association is clearly 1–1, since, according to Proposition 4.17, the values $T(\mathbf{x}_1), \ldots, T(\mathbf{x}_m)$ completely determine T and, of course, the a_{ij} determine the $T(\mathbf{x}_j)$. Thus, distinct transformations cannot correspond to the same matrix.

Finally, the association is onto, again by Proposition 4.17. For, given any matrix ${}_n(a_{ij})_m$ over F, define a function $f: X \rightarrow W$ as follows:

$$f(\mathbf{x}_j) = a_{1j}\mathbf{y}_1 + \cdots + a_{nj}\mathbf{y}_n$$

Let T_f be the linear transformation determined by f, as in Proposition 4.17. Since $T_f | X = f | X$,

$$T_f(\mathbf{x}_j) = a_{1j}\mathbf{y}_1 + \cdots + a_{nj}\mathbf{y}_n,$$

so that, by definition of $\mathfrak{a}_T$,

$${}_n(a_{ij})_m = \mathfrak{a}_{T_f}$$

Since ${}_n(a_{ij})_m$ was chosen at random in $\mathfrak{M}(n, m)$, this implies that the function $T \rightarrow \mathfrak{a}_T$ is onto $\mathfrak{M}(n, m)$. Q.E.D.

Notice that, of course, the 1–1 correspondence $T \rightarrow \mathfrak{a}_T$ depends on the particular choice of X and Y. A different choice of X, or of Y, or both, even if it involves merely a change in their order, would lead to the same kind of 1–1 correspondence, but a given $T \in \text{Trans}(V, W)$ might correspond to one matrix under the first correspondence and a different one under the next. These two matrices are related in an interesting way, as we shall see in Chapter 7.

The correspondence $T \to \mathfrak{a}_T$ suggests a way of introducing operations on $\mathfrak{M}(n, m)$ in such a way that it becomes a vector space over F and so that the correspondence becomes an isomorphism from Trans(V, W) to $\mathfrak{M}(n, m)$. We now give a tentative definition of such operations.

Let V, W, X, and Y be as before. Choose any $\mathfrak{a}_1$ and $\mathfrak{a}_2$ in $\mathfrak{M}(n, m)$ and any $a \in F$. The 1–1 correspondence $\text{Trans}(V, W) \to \mathfrak{M}(n, m)$ will be given the name $\mathscr{A}_{X,Y}$. Thus,

$$\mathscr{A}_{X,Y}(T) = \mathfrak{a}_T \in \mathfrak{M}(n, m)$$

Since it is a 1–1 correspondence, there exists precisely one T_1 such that

$$\mathscr{A}_{X,Y}(T_1) = \mathfrak{a}_1 \tag{1}$$

and one T_2 such that

$$\mathscr{A}_{X,Y}(T_2) = \mathfrak{a}_2 \tag{2}$$

Now, since Trans(V, W) is a vector space over F, $T_1 + T_2$ and aT_1 are defined. Then, define $\mathfrak{a}_1 + \mathfrak{a}_2$ and $a \cdot \mathfrak{a}_1$ as follows:

$$\mathfrak{a}_1 + \mathfrak{a}_2 = \mathscr{A}_{X,Y}(T_1 + T_2) \tag{3}$$

and

$$a \cdot \mathfrak{a}_1 = \mathscr{A}_{X,Y}(aT_1) \tag{4}$$

Indeed, these definitions yield a binary operation $+$ on $\mathfrak{M}(n, m)$ and an operation $\cdot$ of F on $\mathfrak{M}(n, m)$.

Moreover, combining equations (1), (2), (3), (4), we get

$$\mathscr{A}_{X,Y}(T_1) + \mathscr{A}_{X,Y}(T_2) = \mathscr{A}_{X,Y}(T_1 + T_2) \tag{5}$$

and

$$a \cdot \mathscr{A}_{X,Y}(T_1) = \mathscr{A}_{X,Y}(aT_1), \tag{6}$$

where the operations on the left are the ones newly defined on $\mathfrak{M}(n, m)$ and the ones on the right are those of Trans(V, W). But, now we are in the situation covered by Proposition 4.12: namely, we have a vector space Trans(V, W), a set $\mathfrak{M}(n, m)$ with two appropriate operations, and a function $\mathscr{A}_{X,Y}\colon \text{Trans}(V, W) \to \mathfrak{M}(n, m)$ that respects the operations of both. We may therefore, conclude the following:

Proposition 4.27

With respect to operations introduced in (3) *and* (4), *above*, $\mathfrak{M}(n, m)$ *is a vector space over* F *and* $\mathscr{A}_{X,Y}\colon \text{Trans}(V, W) \to \mathfrak{M}(n, m)$ *is an isomorphism of vector spaces.*

This is a very nice result, and, indeed, it will lead to some useful consequences. The reader should, however, be somewhat disturbed by the arbitrariness with which we defined the operations on $\mathfrak{M}(n, m)$. For example, there are many m-dimensional vector spaces over F other than V, and many n-dimensional ones other than W. Choose any two such, say V' and W', respectively. Moreover, V' and W', unless trivial, and, hence, uninteresting, have a large number of distinct bases. Choose any basis X' of V' and any basis Y' of W'. Given such a selection V', W', X', Y', we can proceed exactly as above and get a 1–1 correspondence

$$\mathscr{A}_{X',Y'} : \text{Trans}\,(V', W') \to \mathfrak{M}(n, m),$$

with respect to which we can, as in (3) and (4) above, introduce operations $+'$ and $\cdot$ on $\mathfrak{M}(n, m)$. We have, as yet, no reason for believing that $+'$ bears a decent relationship to the $+$ introduced in (3), or that $\cdot'$ bears a decent relationship to $\cdot$ introduced in (4).

The next proposition shows that the relationship between these pairs of operations is as decent as can be: namely, it is equality.

Proposition 4.28

Let V, W, X, Y, and $\mathscr{A}_{X,Y}$ be as above. Suppose that $T_1, T_2 \in Trans(V, W)$ and that $a \in F$. Suppose, moreover, that $\mathscr{A}_{X,Y}(T_1) = (a_{ij})$ and $\mathscr{A}_{X,Y}(T_2) = (b_{ij})$.

Then:

(1) $\mathscr{A}_{X,Y}(T_1 + T_2) = (a_{ij} + b_{ij})$
(2) $\mathscr{A}_{X,Y}(aT_1) = (aa_{ij})$.

That is, the matrix corresponding to $T_1 + T_2$ under $\mathscr{A}_{X,Y}$ has, as its entry in the ith row and jth column, the field element $a_{ij} + b_{ij}$; the matrix corresponding to aT_1 under $\mathscr{A}_{X,Y}$ has, as its entry in the ith row and jth column, the field element aa_{ij}.

Proof

By assumption, for each $j = 1, \ldots, m$,

$$T_1(\mathbf{x}_j) = a_{1j}\mathbf{y}_1 + \cdots + a_{nj}\mathbf{y}_n,$$

$$T_2(\mathbf{x}_j) = b_{1j}\mathbf{y}_1 + \cdots + b_{nj}\mathbf{y}_n$$

Thus,

$$(T_1 + T_2)(\mathbf{x}_j) = (a_{1j} + b_{1j})\mathbf{y}_1 + \cdots + (a_{nj} + b_{nj})\mathbf{y}_n,$$

and

$$(aT_1)(\mathbf{x}_j) = (aa_{1j})\mathbf{y}_1 + \cdots + (aa_{nj})\mathbf{y}_n,$$

from which the result immediately follows. Q.E.D.

Now, we point out the following crucial fact to the reader. In the equations (1) and (2) of Proposition 4.28 above, no reference to V, W, X, or Y, appears on the right. Indeed, if V, W, X, and Y had been replaced by any (m-dimensional) V', (n-dimensional) W', (basis of V') X', and (basis of W') Y', respectively, the right-hand side of the equation would still be the same.**

But, by previous equations (3) and (4), the left-hand side of (1) and (2) in Proposition 4.28 above define the operations $+$ and $\cdot$ in $\mathfrak{M}(n, m)$. Thus, these operations satisfy.

$$(a_{ij}) + (b_{ij}) = (a_{ij} + b_{ij}) \tag{7}$$

$$a \cdot (a_{ij}) = (aa_{ij}) \tag{8}$$

If $+'$ and $\cdot'$ had been introduced similarly by means of V', W', X', Y' and $\mathscr{A}_{X',Y'}$, we could, likewise, conclude that

$$(a_{ij}) +' (b_{ij}) = (a_{ij} + b_{ij}) \tag{7$'$}$$

$$a \cdot' (a_{ij}) = (aa_{ij}) \tag{8$'$}$$

Since the right-hand sides in both cases are the same, we conclude that $+ = +'$ and $\cdot = \cdot'$, and, moreover, we may conclude that $+$ and $\cdot$ may be *defined* on $\mathfrak{M}(n, m)$ by (7) and (8). Thus, our tentative definition gives way to the following following formal definition and proposition.

Definition 4.6

Choose any (a_{ij}), $(b_{ij}) \in \mathfrak{M}(n, m)$ and any $a \in F$. Define $(a_{ij}) + (b_{ij})$ and $a \cdot (a_{ij})$ by equations (7) and (8) above. Henceforth, these will be referred to as the standard addition and scalar multiplication on $\mathfrak{M}(n, m)$.

Proposition 4.29

Let V be any m-dimensional vector space over F, X any ordered basis of V, W any n-dimensional vector space over F, and Y any ordered basis of W. Let $\mathscr{A}_{X,Y} : Trans(V, W) \to \mathfrak{M}(n, m)$ be the usual 1–1 correspondence. Then, with respect to the standard addition and scalar multiplication of matrices, $\mathfrak{M}(n, m)$ is a vector space over F, and $\mathscr{A}_{X,Y}$ is an isomorphism of vector spaces.

Notice that this proposition says something slightly different from what Proposition 4.27 says. In the earlier proposition, we used a particular V, W, X, Y, and $\mathscr{A}_{X,Y}$ to define operations on $\mathfrak{M}(n, m)$, which made $\mathfrak{M}(n, m)$ into a vector space over F and $\mathscr{A}_{X,Y}$ into an isomorphism of vector spaces. Now, in contrast, $\mathfrak{M}(n, m)$ is endowed with operations intrinsically defined [via (7) and (8), above], and we are claiming that, with respect to these operations, it is a vector space such that for *any* V, W (of the appropriate dimension), X, and Y, the corresponding function $\mathscr{A}_{X,Y}$ is, a linear transformation, indeed, an isomorphism.

** The left-hand side of the new equation would be $\mathscr{A}_{X',Y'}(T_1' + T_2')$, where $\mathscr{A}_{X',Y'}(T_1') = (a_{ij})$ and $\mathscr{A}_{X',Y'}(T_2') = (b_{ij})$.

The link between these two propositions is provided by the intervening one which tells us, essentially, that the two ways of defining the operations on $\mathfrak{M}(n, m)$ result in the same thing. Indeed, since the new operations coincide with the ones defined earlier [in (3) and (4)], the earlier proposition and the one above are proved to be equivalent.

EXERCISES / 4.7

1. Let $F=\mathbf{R}$, $V=\mathbf{R}^2$ and θ be any angle between 0 and $\pi/2$. Let $X = \{\mathbf{e}_1^{(2)}, \mathbf{e}_2^{(2)}\}$, the standard basis of $\mathbf{R}^2$. Recall that $R_\theta: \mathbf{R}^2 \to \mathbf{R}^2$ is a linear transformation, rotation by θ. Compute $\mathscr{A}_{X,X}(R_\theta)$.

2. Let

$$a_{11}x_2 + a_{12}x_2$$

and

$$a_{21}x_1 + a_{22}x_2$$

be any two linear expressions, where a_{11}, a_{12}, a_{21}, a_{22}, are say, real numbers. Let $A: \mathbf{R}^2 \to \mathbf{R}^2$ be the linear transformation determined by these expressions in the usual way. That is, for any $(x_1, x_2) \in \mathbf{R}^2$,

$$A(x_1, x_2) = (a_{11}x_1 + a_{12}x_2, a_{21}x_1 + a_{22}x_2)$$

Let $X = \{\mathbf{e}_1^{(2)}, \mathbf{e}_2^{(2)}\}$, the standard ordered basis, as in 1. Compute $\mathscr{A}_{X,X}(A)$.

3. Let $a_1x_1 + \cdots + a_kx_k$ be any linear expression with coefficients a_i in a field F, and let $f: F^k \to F$ be the linear form determined by it. That is, for any $(b_1, \ldots, b_k) \in F^k$,

$$f(b_1, \ldots, b_k) = a_1b_1 + \cdots + a_kb_k$$

Let $X = \{\mathbf{e}_1^{(k)}, \ldots, \mathbf{e}_k^{(k)}\}$, the standard ordered basis of F^k, and let $Y = \{1\}$, the standard basis of F. Compute $\mathscr{A}_{X,Y}(f)$.

4. Let V be any finite-dimensional vector space over F, let X be any ordered basis of V, and, for any $a \in F$, let $M_a: V \to V$ be the usual multiplication-by-a linear transformation. Compute $\mathscr{A}_{X,X}(M_a)$. What is $\mathscr{A}_{X,X}(M_0)$? $\mathscr{A}_{X,X}(M_1) = \mathscr{A}_{X,X}(I_V)$?

   Show that these matrices depend only on M_a and not on X.

5. Let $T: \mathbf{R}^3 \to \mathbf{R}^3$ be a linear transformation given by the following equation: For any $(x_1, x_2, x_3) \in \mathbf{R}^3$,

$$T(x_1, x_2, x_3) = (2x_1 + x_3, 3x_2 - x_3, x_1 - 4_{x_3})$$

Let $X = \{\mathbf{e}_1^{(3)}, \mathbf{e}_2^{(3)}, \mathbf{e}_3^{(3)}\}$, the standard basis of $\mathbf{R}^3$, and let $Y = \{\mathbf{e}_1^{(3)} - \mathbf{e}_2^{(3)}, \mathbf{e}_2^{(3)}, \mathbf{e}_3^{(3)} + 2\mathbf{e}_2^{(3)}\}$.

   a. Show that Y is a basis of $\mathbf{R}^3$.

   b. Compute $\mathscr{A}_{X,X}(T)$, $\mathscr{A}_{Y,Y}(T)$, $\mathscr{A}_{Y,X}(T)$ and $\mathscr{A}_{X,Y}(T)$.

6.* Let V and W be finite-dimensional vector spaces with bases $\{\mathbf{x}_1, \ldots, \mathbf{x}_m\}$ and $\{\mathbf{y}_1, \ldots, \mathbf{y}_n\}$, and let $T: V \to W$ be a linear transformation with matrix $\mathscr{A}_{X,Y}(T), = {}_n(a_{ij})_m$. Let X^* be the basis of V^* dual to X, Y^* the basis of W dual to Y, and let $T^*: W^* \to V^*$ be the adjoint of T. Let $\mathscr{A}_{Y^*,X^*}(T^*) = {}_m(b_{ij})_n$.

a. Prove that $b_{ij} = [T^*(\mathbf{y}_j^*)](\mathbf{x}_i)$. [Notice that this equation, at least, makes sense: for $T^*(\mathbf{y}_j^*) \in V^*$, so that it is a linear transformation from V to F; hence, we may evaluate it at $\mathbf{x}_i$; hopefully, the answer will be b_{ij}.]

b. Prove that $\mathbf{y}_j(T(\mathbf{x}_i)) = a_{ji}$.

Since $(T^*(\mathbf{y}_j^*))(\mathbf{x}_i) = \mathbf{y}_j(T(\mathbf{x}_i))$, we obtain the result that

$$b_{ij} = a_{ji}$$

This means that the entry in the ith row and jth column of $\mathscr{A}_{Y^*,X^*}(T^*)$ is the same as the entry in the ith column and jth row of $\mathscr{A}_{X,Y}(T)$. In other words, $\mathscr{A}_{Y^*,X^*}(T^*)$ is obtained from $\mathscr{A}_{X,Y}(T)$ by changing the rows of $\mathscr{A}_{X,Y}(T)$ into columns and columns into rows:

$$\underset{\mathscr{A}_{X,Y}(T)}{\begin{pmatrix} a_{11} & a_{12} & \cdots & a_{1m} \\ a_{21} & a_{22} & \cdots & a_{2m} \\ \vdots & \vdots & & \vdots \\ a_{n1} & a_{n2} & \cdots & a_{nm} \end{pmatrix}} \longrightarrow \underset{\mathscr{A}_{Y^*,X^*}(T^*)}{\begin{pmatrix} a_{11} & a_{21} & \cdots & a_{n1} \\ a_{12} & a_{22} & \cdots & a_{n2} \\ \vdots & \vdots & & \vdots \\ a_{1m} & a_{2m} & \cdots & a_{m} \end{pmatrix}}$$

7.* Choose any integers m, n, both greater than or equal to 1. Let $\mathfrak{M}(n, m)$ and $\mathfrak{M}(m, n)$ be the vector spaces of all $n \times m$ and $m \times n$ matrices over F, endowed with the standard operations of matrix addition and scalar multiplication. We define functions

$$t_{n,m}: \mathfrak{M}(n, m) \to \mathfrak{M}(m, n) \quad \text{and} \quad t_{m,n}: \mathfrak{M}(m, n) \to \mathfrak{M}(n, m)$$

as follows:

Given any matrix $\mathfrak{a} \in \mathfrak{M}(n, m)$, $t_{n,m}(\mathfrak{a})$ is the matrix obtained from $\mathfrak{a}$ by changing its rows to columns and columns to rows. More precisely, if $\mathfrak{a} = {}_n(a_{ij})_m$, we define $t_{n,m}(\mathfrak{a}) = {}_m(b_{ij})_n$, where $b_{ij} = a_{ji}$.

Similarly, we define $t_{m,n}: \mathfrak{M}(m, n) \to \mathfrak{M}(n, m)$ as follows: for any ${}_m(c_{ij})_n \in \mathfrak{M}(m, n)$, then $t_{m,n}({}_m(c_{ij})_n) = {}_n(d_{ij})_m$, where $d_{ij} = c_{ji}$.

a. Prove that $t_{m,n} \circ t_{n,m} = I_{\mathfrak{M}(n,m)}$ and $t_{n,m} \circ t_{m,n} = I_{\mathfrak{M}(m,n)}$.

Thus, $t_{n,m}$ and $t_{m,n}$ are 1–1 correspondences and $t_{n,m} = t_{m,n}^{-1}$.

b. Prove that $t_{n,m}$ is a linear transformation. (Hence, its inverse, $t_{m,n}$, is also a linear transformation.)

Thus, $\mathfrak{M}(n, m) \simeq \mathfrak{M}(m, n)$.

Notice that, using the notation of **6**, above,

$$\mathscr{A}_{X,Y}: \text{Trans}(V, W) \to \mathfrak{M}(n, m)$$

and

$$\mathscr{A}_{Y^*,X^*}: \text{Trans}(W^*, V^*) \to \mathfrak{M}(m, n)$$

are isomorphisms. The fact that $\mathfrak{M}(n, m) \simeq \mathfrak{M}(m, n)$, now implies that

Trans(V, W) $\simeq$ Trans(W^*, V^*). Note that this result holds only when both V and W are finite-dimensional.

The matrix $t_{n,m}[{}_n(a_{ij})_m]$ is called the *transpose* of ${}_n(a_{ij})_m$; the matrix $t_{m,n}[{}_m(b_{ij})_n]$ is called the *transpose* of ${}_m(b_{ij})_n$. (Rows and columns are transposed.)
The relations in **a** can be expressed as follows: the transpose of the transpose of a matrix equals the matrix.

8.* Let ${}_n(a_{ij})_m$ be any $n \times m$ matrix over F. Form the nm-tuple.

$$(a_{11}, \ldots, a_{1m}, a_{21}, \ldots, a_{2m}, \ldots, a_{n1}, \ldots, a_{nm}),$$

and call it $K({}_n(s_{ij})_m)$.

Let $(b_1, \ldots, b_{nm})$ be any nm-tuple in F^{nm}. Form the $n \times m$ matrix.

$$\begin{pmatrix} b_1 & \cdots & b_m \\ b_{m+1} & \cdots & b_{2m} \\ \vdots & & \vdots \\ b_{(n-1)m+1} & \cdots & b_{nm} \end{pmatrix}$$

and call it $L[(b_1, \ldots, b_{nm})]$.

Then, K is a function from $\mathfrak{M}(n, m) \to F^{nm}$, and L is a function from

$$F^{nm} \to \mathfrak{M}(n, m).$$

a. Prove that $L \circ K = I_{\mathfrak{M}(n,m)}$ and that $K \circ L = I_{F^{nm}}$.
Thus, L and K are 1–1 correspondences and $K = L^{-1}$ and $L = K^{-1}$.

b. Both $\mathfrak{M}(n, m)$ and F^{nm} are vector spaces over F with respect to standard operations. Prove that K is an isomorphism of vector spaces. (Hence, its inverse, L, is also an isomorphism of vector spaces.)

Thus, $\mathfrak{M}(n, m) \simeq F^{nm}$, so that dim $\mathfrak{M}(n, m) = nm$. Since, for any m-dimensional V and n-dimensional W, Trans(V, W) $\simeq \mathfrak{M}(n, m)$, we conclude that Trans(V, W) $\simeq F^{nm}$, so that dim Trans(V, W) $= nm$. (We proved this result, before, in Exercises 4.4.4.)

c. If V is m-dimensional and W n-dimensional, prove that Trans(V, W) $\simeq$ Trans(W, V).

d. Let Z be the standard basis of F^{nm}. Since $L: F^{nm} \to \mathfrak{M}(n, m)$ is an isomorphism, $L(Z)$ is a basis of $\mathfrak{M}(n, m)$. Describe the members of $L(Z)$. We call $L(Z)$ the standard basis of $\mathfrak{M}(n, m)$.

Let V and W be vector spaces over F, $X = \{\mathbf{x}_1, \ldots, \mathbf{x}_m\}$ an ordered basis of V and $Y = \{\mathbf{y}_1, \ldots, \mathbf{y}_n\}$ an ordered basis of W.

The linear transformation $\mathscr{A}_{X,Y}$ takes Trans(V, W) isomorphically to $\mathfrak{M}(n, m)$. Hence, $\mathscr{A}_{X,Y}{}^{-1}$ takes $\mathfrak{M}(n, m)$ isomorphically to Trans(V, W). Thus,

$$L: F^{nm} \to \mathfrak{M}(n, m) \text{ and } \mathscr{A}_{X,Y}{}^{-1}: \mathfrak{M}(n, m) \to \text{Trans}(V, W)$$

are isomorphisms, so that

$$\mathscr{A}_{X,Y}{}^{-1} \circ L: F^{nm} \to \text{Trans}(V, W)$$

is an isomorphism. This implies that $(\mathscr{A}_{X,Y}{}^{-1} \circ L)(Z)$ is a basis of Trans(V, W).

Describe the members of $(\mathscr{A}_{X,Y}{}^{-1} \circ L)(Z)$ in terms of their values on the basis $\{\mathbf{x}_1, \ldots, \mathbf{x}_m\}$. We call $(\mathscr{A}_{X,Y}{}^{-1} \circ L)(Z)$ the *standard basis of Trans(V, W) determined by X and Y.*

4.2 Multiplication of Matrices

Just as addition and scalar multiplication of linear transformations leads to corresponding operations on matrices, so does *composition* of linear transformations lead to an operation of *matrix multiplication*. We now make this precise.

Let V, W, X, Y, and $\mathscr{A}_{X,Y}$: Trans$(V, W) \to \mathfrak{M}(n, m)$ be as in the previous section. In addition, let U be a vector space over F with an ordered basis $Z = \{\mathbf{z}_1, \ldots, \mathbf{z}_k\}$.

There are, of course, defined, as before in 4.1, 1–1 correspondences

$$\mathscr{A}_{Z,X}: \text{Trans}(U, V) \to \mathfrak{M}(m, k)$$

and

$$\mathscr{A}_{Z,Y}: \text{Trans}(U, W) \to \mathfrak{M}(n, k)$$

If $\mathfrak{M}(n, k)$ and $\mathfrak{M}(m, k)$ are endowed with the standard operations of addition and scalar multiplication of matrices, they become vector spaces over F, and $\mathscr{A}_{Z,X}$ and $\mathscr{A}_{Z,Y}$ become isomorphisms of vector spaces, as in 4.1.

Now, given any $T_1 \in$ Trans(U, V) and any $T_2 \in$ Trans(V, W), their composition $T_2 \circ T_1$ is a member of Trans(U, W). This operation suggests that we should define an operation on matrices as follows: Let ${}_m\mathfrak{a}_k \in \mathfrak{M}(m, k)$ and ${}_n\mathfrak{b}_m \in \mathfrak{M}(n, m)$ be arbitrarily chosen matrices, and define $({}_n\mathfrak{b}_m) \cdot ({}_m\mathfrak{a}_k)$ (or, more briefly, $\mathfrak{b} \cdot \mathfrak{a}$) as follows: there is precisely one $T_1 \in$ Trans(U, V) such that

$$\mathscr{A}_{Z,X}(T_1) = {}_m\mathfrak{a}_k \tag{9}$$

and there is precisely one $T_2 \in$ Trans(V, W) such that

$$\mathscr{A}_{X,Y}(T_2) = {}_n\mathfrak{b}_m\,; \tag{10}$$

then let

$$({}_n\mathfrak{b}_m) \cdot ({}_m\mathfrak{a}_k) = \mathscr{A}_{Z,Y}(T_2 \circ T_1) \tag{11}$$

or, more briefly, $\mathfrak{b} \cdot \mathfrak{a} = \mathscr{A}_{Z,Y}(T_2 \circ T_1)$. This operation has certain nice properties, which we list and prove below. First, however, note that $\mathfrak{b} \cdot \mathfrak{a} \in \mathfrak{M}(n, k)$. That is, *the product of an $n \times m$ matrix and $m \times k$ matrix is an $n \times k$ matrix*. Note also *that, for the product* $\mathfrak{b} \cdot \mathfrak{a}$ *to be defined* $\mathfrak{b}$ *must have as many columns as* $\mathfrak{a}$ *has rows*. Finally, note that the above procedure can be extended to cover more than two matrices. For example, given ${}_n\mathfrak{b}_m \in \mathfrak{M}(n, m)$, ${}_m\mathfrak{a}_k \in \mathfrak{M}(m, k)$, and ${}_k\mathfrak{d}_\ell \in \mathfrak{M}(k, \ell)$, where ℓ is any integer $\geqq 1$, we may form $({}_n\mathfrak{b}_m) \cdot ({}_m\mathfrak{a}_k)$, an $n \times k$ matrix and $({}_m\mathfrak{a}_k) \cdot ({}_k\mathfrak{d}_\ell)$ an $m \times \ell$ matrix, and from these obtain

$$[({}_n\mathfrak{b}_m) \cdot ({}_m\mathfrak{a}_k)] \cdot ({}_k\mathfrak{d}_\ell)$$

and

$$({}_n\mathfrak{b}_m) \cdot [({}_m\mathfrak{a}_k) \cdot ({}_k\mathfrak{d}_\ell)]$$

or, more briefly, $(\mathfrak{b} \cdot \mathfrak{a}) \cdot \mathfrak{d}$ and $\mathfrak{b} \cdot (\mathfrak{a} \cdot \mathfrak{d})$. It would be nice to have an associative law that told us these two products were equal.

Proposition 4.30

Let $\mathfrak{a}_1, \mathfrak{a}_2 \in \mathfrak{M}(m, k)$, $\mathfrak{b}_1, \mathfrak{b}_2 \in \mathfrak{M}(n, m)$, *and* $\mathfrak{d} \in \mathfrak{M}(k, \ell)$ *be any matrices, and assume that* $\cdot$ *is as defined in* (11). *Let* $a \in F$ *be any scalar. Then*:

(1) $(\mathfrak{b}_1 \cdot \mathfrak{a}_1) \cdot \mathfrak{d} = \mathfrak{b}_1 \cdot (\mathfrak{a}_1 \cdot \mathfrak{d})$
(2) $a(\mathfrak{b}_1 \cdot \mathfrak{a}_1) = (a\mathfrak{b}_1) \cdot \mathfrak{a}_1 = \mathfrak{b}_1 \cdot (a\mathfrak{a}_1)$
(3) $\mathfrak{b}_1 \cdot (\mathfrak{a}_1 + \mathfrak{a}_2) = (\mathfrak{b}_1 \cdot \mathfrak{a}_1) + (\mathfrak{b}_1 \cdot \mathfrak{a}_2)$
(4) $(\mathfrak{b}_1 + \mathfrak{b}_2) \cdot \mathfrak{a}_1 = (\mathfrak{b}_1 \cdot \mathfrak{a}_1) + \mathfrak{b}_2 \cdot \mathfrak{a}_1$

Remarks: 1. (1) is an associative law for matrix multiplication; (2) is an associative law for scalar and matrix multiplication; (3) and (4) are (respectively, left and right) distributive for matrix multiplication over matrix addition.

Note that, so far, the definition of $\cdot$ for matrices depends on the choice of $U, V, W, X, Y, Z, \mathscr{A}_{X,Y}, \mathscr{A}_{Z,Y}, \mathscr{A}_{Z,X}$ [cf. (11)]. Technically, we have not really provided an explicit definition of multiplication by $\mathfrak{d} \in \mathfrak{M}(k, \ell)$. We now do this. Choose an ℓ-dimensional vector space U' and a basis Z' of U'. Define $\mathscr{A}'_{Z,Z}: \text{Trans}(U', U) \to \mathfrak{M}(k, \ell)$, $\mathscr{A}'_{Z,X}: \text{Trans}(U', V) \to \mathfrak{M}(m, \ell)$ and $\mathscr{A}'_{Z,Y}: \text{Trans}(U', W) \to \mathfrak{M}(n, \ell)$ as usual. Choose $\mathfrak{M}(k, \ell)$ and $R \in \text{Trans}(U', U)$ such that

$$\mathfrak{d} = \mathscr{A}_{Z'Z}(R)$$

Given any $\mathfrak{a} \in \mathfrak{M}(m, k)$ or $\mathfrak{g} \in \mathfrak{M}(n, k)$, choose $S \in \text{Trans}(U, V)$ and $T \in \text{Trans}(U, W)$ such that

$$\mathscr{A}_{Z,X}(S) = \mathfrak{a}$$

and

$$\mathscr{A}_{Z,Y}(T) = \mathfrak{g}$$

Then, let

$$\mathfrak{a} \cdot \mathfrak{d} = \mathscr{A}_{Z', X}(S \circ R) \tag{12}$$

and

$$\mathfrak{g} \cdot \mathfrak{d} = \mathscr{A}_{Z',Y}(T \circ R) \tag{12'}$$

This is obviously the same kind of definition as before.

Proof of Proposition 4.30

(1) Choose R, S, and T to be the counterparts of $\mathfrak{d}$, $\mathfrak{a}_1$ and $\mathfrak{b}_1$ respectively. $R \in \text{Trans}(U', U)$, $S \in \text{Trans}(U, V)$ and $T \in \text{Trans}(V, W)$. Thus (omitting subscripts from the $\mathscr{A}$'s, for simplicity) $\mathscr{A}(R) = \mathfrak{d}$, $\mathscr{A}(S) = \mathfrak{a}_1$, and $\mathscr{A}(T) = \mathfrak{b}_1$.

By definition (12), above, $\mathfrak{a}_1 \cdot \mathfrak{d} = \mathscr{A}(S \circ R)$ and, by (11), $\mathfrak{b}_1 \cdot \mathfrak{a}_1 = \mathscr{A}(T \circ S)$.

Thus, to obtain $\mathfrak{b}_1 \cdot (\mathfrak{a}_1 \cdot \mathfrak{d})$, we compose $T \circ (S \circ R)$ and apply $\mathscr{A}$. To obtain $(\mathfrak{b}_1 \cdot \mathfrak{a}_1) \cdot \mathfrak{d}$, we compose $(T \circ S) \circ R$ and apply the same $\mathscr{A}$.

That is, by definition

$$\mathfrak{b}_1 \cdot (\mathfrak{a}_1 \cdot \mathfrak{d}) = \mathscr{A}(T \circ (S \circ R))$$

and

$$(\mathfrak{b}_1 \cdot \mathfrak{a}_1) \cdot \mathfrak{d} = \mathscr{A}((T \circ S) \circ R),$$

where $\mathscr{A}: \text{Trans}(U', W) \to \mathfrak{M}(n, \ell)$ is the usual isomorphism.

But, composition of functions is associative. Therefore, $T \circ (S \circ R) = (T \circ S) \circ R$. Thus, their values under $\mathscr{A}$ must be the same. This completes the proof.

(2) Referring to the context of equation (11) [i.e., $\mathfrak{b} = \mathscr{A}_{X,Y}(T_2)$, $\mathfrak{a} = \mathscr{A}_{Z,X}(T_1)$, $\mathfrak{b} \cdot \mathfrak{a} = \mathscr{A}_{Z,Y}(T_2 \circ T_1)$], the reader can easily see that, by definition of $\cdot$ (omitting subscripts)

$$\mathscr{A}(T_2) \cdot \mathscr{A}(T_1) = \mathscr{A}(T_2 \circ T_1) \tag{13}$$

We use this to prove parts (2)–(4) Choose $S_1, S_2 \in \text{Trans}(U, V)$ and $T_1, T_2 \in \text{Trans}(V, W)$ such that $\mathscr{A}(S_1) = \mathfrak{a}_1$, $\mathscr{A}(S_2) = \mathfrak{a}_2$, $\mathscr{A}(T_1) = \mathfrak{b}_1$, $\mathscr{A}(T_2) = \mathfrak{b}_2$. Let $a \in F$ be any scalar, and *recall that all the $\mathscr{A}$'s are vector-space isomorphisms.* Then,

$$\begin{aligned} a(\mathfrak{b}_1 \cdot \mathfrak{a}_1) &= a\mathscr{A}(T_1 \circ S_1) \\ &= \mathscr{A}(a(T_1 \circ S_1)) \\ &= \mathscr{A}((aT_1) \circ S_1) \\ &= \mathscr{A}(a(T_1)) \cdot \mathscr{A}(S_1) = (a\mathscr{A}(T_1)) \cdot \mathscr{A}(S_1)) \\ &\qquad\qquad\qquad\qquad\quad = (a\mathfrak{b}_1) \cdot (\mathfrak{a}_1) \end{aligned}$$

The other equality in (2) is proved similarly. Note that in addition to the properties of $\mathscr{A}$ mentioned above, this proof used the relation

$$(aT_1) \circ S_1 = a(T_1 \circ S_1),$$

which the reader can easily verify by evaluating both sides at any $\mathbf{u} \in U$.

(3) We use (13) again

$$\begin{aligned} \mathfrak{b}_1 \cdot \mathfrak{a}_1 + \mathfrak{b}_1 \cdot \mathfrak{a}_2 &= \mathscr{A}(T_1 \circ S_1) + \mathscr{A}(T_1 \circ S_2) \\ &= \mathscr{A}(T_1 \circ S_1 + T_1 \circ S_2) \\ &= \mathscr{A}(T_1 \circ (S_1 + S_2)) \\ &= \mathscr{A}(T_1) \cdot \mathscr{A}(S_1 + S_2) \\ &= \mathscr{A}(T_1) \cdot (\mathscr{A}(S_1) + \mathscr{A}(S_2)) \\ &= \mathfrak{b}_1 \cdot (\mathfrak{a}_1 + \mathfrak{a}_2) \end{aligned}$$

Here, we use, in addition to (13) and the fact that the $\mathscr{A}$'s are linear transformations, the relation

$$T_1 \circ (S_1 + S_2) = T_1 \circ S_1 + T_1 \circ S_1$$

To verify it, we evaluate both sides at an arbitrary $\mathbf{u} \in U$

$$\begin{aligned}[T_1 \circ (S_1 + S_2)](\mathbf{u}) &= T_1((S_1 + S_2)(\mathbf{u}) \\ &= T_1(S_1(\mathbf{u}) + S_2(\mathbf{u})) \\ &= T_1(S_1(\mathbf{u}) + T_1(S_2(\mathbf{u})) \\ &= (T_1 \circ S_1)(\mathbf{u}) + (T_1 \circ S_2)(\mathbf{u}) \\ &= ((T_1 \circ S_1) + (T_1 \circ S_2))(\mathbf{u}),\end{aligned}$$

which concludes the verification.

(4) The proof is entirely analogous to that of (3) and so we omit it. Q.E.D.

These properties are very nice, and we shall have more to say about them later. First, however, we must clear up the same sort of difficulty that bothered us in 4.1. The operation of matrix multiplication is defined quite arbitrarily—in the sense that other vector spaces or bases could have been used, with *a priori* different results. The next proposition shows that all other choices of the same type would have led to the same operation.

Proposition 4.31

Let U, V, W, X, Y, Z be as before, and let $\mathfrak{a} \in \mathfrak{M}(m, k)$ and $\mathfrak{b} \in \mathfrak{M}(n, m)$ be as in (11). Suppose that $\mathfrak{a} = {}_m(a_{ij})_k$ and $\mathfrak{b} = {}_n(b_{ij})_m$. Finally, suppose that $T_1 \in$ Trans(U, V) and $T_2 \in$ Trans(V, W) such that $\mathscr{A}_{Z,X}(T_1) = \mathfrak{a}$ and $\mathscr{A}_{X,Y}(T_2) = \mathfrak{b}$. Then,

$$\mathscr{A}_{Z,Y}(T_2 \circ T_1) = {}_n(c_{ij})_k$$

where $c_{ij} = b_{i1}a_{1j} + b_{i2}a_{2j} + \cdots + b_{im}a_{mj}$.

Proof

By hypothesis, for any $\mathbf{z}_j \in Z$ and $\mathbf{x}_\ell \in X$,

$$T_1(\mathbf{z}_j) = a_{1j}\mathbf{x}_1 + a_{2j}\mathbf{x}_2 + \cdots + a_{mj}\mathbf{x}_m$$

and

$$T_2(\mathbf{x}_\ell) = b_{1\ell}\mathbf{y}_1 + b_{2\ell}\mathbf{y}_2 + \cdots + b_{m\ell}\mathbf{y}_m$$

Therefore,

$$\begin{aligned}(T_2 \circ T_1)(\mathbf{z}_j) &= T_2(a_{1j}\mathbf{x}_1 + a_{2j}\mathbf{x}_2 + \cdots + a_{m\,l}\mathbf{x}_m) \\ &= a_{1j}T(\mathbf{x}_1) + a_{2j}T(\mathbf{x}_2) + \cdots + a_{mj}T(\mathbf{x}_m) \\ &= a_{1j}(b_{11}\mathbf{y}_1 + b_{21}\mathbf{y}_2 + \cdots + b_{n1}\mathbf{y}_n) \\ &\quad + a_{2j}(b_{12}\mathbf{y}_1 + b_{22}\mathbf{y}_2 + \cdots + b_{n2}\mathbf{y}_2) \\ &\quad + \cdots + a_{mj}(b_{1m}\mathbf{y}_1 + b_{2m}\mathbf{y}_2 + \cdots + b_{nm}\mathbf{y}_n) \\ &= (b_{11}a_{1j} + b_{12}a_{2j} + \cdots + b_{1m}a_{mj})\mathbf{y}_1 \\ &\quad + (b_{21}a_{1j} + b_{22}a_{2j} + \cdots + b_{2m}a_{mj})\mathbf{y}_2 \\ &\quad + \cdots + (b_{n1}a_{1j} + b_{n2}a_{2j} + \cdots + b_{nm}a_{mj})\mathbf{y}_n\end{aligned}$$

By definition of $\mathscr{A}_{Z,Y}(T_2 \circ T_1)$, the c_{ij} are the coefficients of $(T_2 \circ T_1)(\mathbf{z}_j)$, when it is expressed as a linear combination of $\mathbf{y}_i$'s. These coefficients are, as just calculated, the desired ones. Q.E.D.

Now, again we point out the crucial fact about the above result. The matrix (c_{ij}) and the expression for (c_{ij}) in terms of (a_{ij}) and (b_{ij}) bears no reference whatsoever to $U, V, W, X, Y, Z, \mathscr{A}_{X,Y}, \mathscr{A}_{Z,X}$, or $\mathscr{A}_{Z,Y}$. If we had used different vector spaces and different ordered bases (of appropriate cardinalities, of course) and gone through the same procedure, we would have obtained the same (c_{ij}) on the right and the same expression of (c_{ij}) in terms of (a_{ij}) and (b_{ij}).

Now, recall that, by (11), the matrix $\mathscr{A}_{Z,Y}(T_2 \circ T_1)$ is $\mathfrak{b} \cdot \mathfrak{a}$. Thus, we have:

$$\mathfrak{b} \cdot \mathfrak{a} = {}_n(c_{ij})_k, \tag{14}$$

where, for each i between 1 and n and each j between 1 and k,

$$c_{ij} = b_{i1}a_{1j} + b_{i2}a_{2j} + \cdots + b_{im}a_{mj} \tag{15}$$

Definition 4.7

Choose any $\mathfrak{a} = (a_{ij}) \in \mathfrak{M}(m, K)$ *and* $\mathfrak{b} = (b_{ij}) \in \mathfrak{M}(n, m)$. *Define* $\mathfrak{b} \cdot \mathfrak{a}$ *by* (14) *and* (15) *above. Henceforth, this operation will be known as* (*standard*) *matrix multiplication.*

The following picture illustrates the method of forming a matrix product.

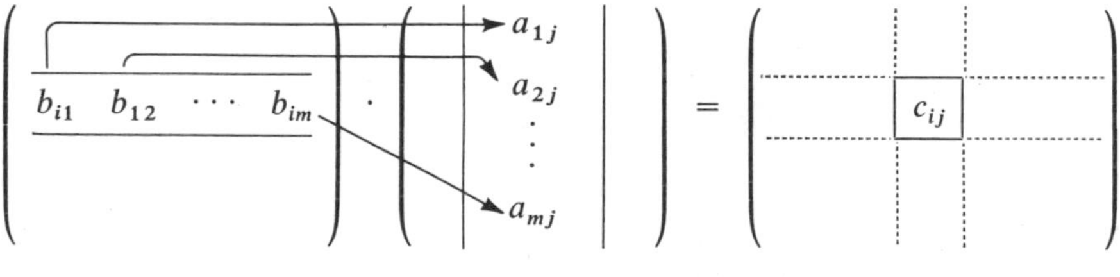

Corollary to Proposition 4.31

Standard matrix multiplication coincides with the multiplication previously defined. Thus, all of the properties of the previous multiplication (e.g. those in Proposition 4.30) *are properties of standard multiplication. In particular, the vector-space isomorphisms* $\mathscr{A}_{Z,X} : Trans(U, V) \to \mathfrak{M}(m, k)$, $\mathscr{A}_{X,Y} : Trans(V, W) \to \mathfrak{M}(n, m)$ *and* $\mathscr{A}_{Z,Y} : Trans(U, W) \to \mathfrak{M}(n, k)$, *satisfy, for any* $T_1 \in Trans(U, V)$, $T_2 \in Trans(V, W)$,

$$\mathscr{A}_{Z,Y}(T_2 \circ T_1) = \mathscr{A}_{X,Y}(T_2) \cdot \mathscr{A}_{Z,X}(T_1),$$

or (omitting subscripts),

$$\mathscr{A}(T_2 \circ T_1) = \mathscr{A}(T_2) \cdot \mathscr{A}(T_1) \tag{16}$$

Most of this needs no explanation or proof. We should, however, point out again that the last part of this corollary says something slightly different from what we observed in (13) above. For in (13) the operation $\cdot$ is the old multiplication, and, indeed (13) is just another form of the definition of the old multiplication: It was "rigged" to have that property. In the equation (16) above, the $\cdot$ is the (new) standard matrix multiplication, which can be defined independently of any knowledge of linear algebra! After all, (15) is a purely arithmetical statement. This purely arithmetical definition of $\cdot$ is, however, related to linear algebra via (16). Thus, (16) tells us that *the matrix of the composition of two linear transformations is the (standard, new, arithmetically defined) product of the matrices of the transformations.* Moreover, this is true for any U, V, W, X, Y, Z, $T_1: U \to V$ and $T_2: V \to W$ (provided the vector spaces are finite-dimensional).

Now, although the above statement is new, it needs no new proof. For, by Proposition 4.31, the old and new multiplications are the same.

EXERCISES / 4.8

1. Compute the following matrix products

a. $$\begin{pmatrix} 2 & 4 & -2 \\ -3 & 6 & 1 \\ 1 & 0 & 5 \end{pmatrix} \cdot \begin{pmatrix} 3 & -1 \\ 2 & 2 \\ 10 & 0 \end{pmatrix}$$

b. $$\begin{pmatrix} 2 & 0 & 1 \\ -1 & 4 & 4 \end{pmatrix} \cdot \begin{pmatrix} 8 & 0 \\ 0 & 1 \\ 0 & 1 \end{pmatrix}$$

c. $$\begin{pmatrix} 8 & 0 \\ 0 & 1 \\ 1 & 1 \end{pmatrix} \cdot \begin{pmatrix} 2 & 0 & 1 \\ -1 & 4 & 4 \end{pmatrix}$$

d. $$\begin{pmatrix} 1 & 0 & 0 \\ 0 & 1 & 0 \\ 0 & 0 & 1 \end{pmatrix} \cdot \begin{pmatrix} a & b & c \\ d & e & f \\ g & h & i \end{pmatrix},$$

where a, b, c, d, e, f, g, h, i, 1, 0 are members of a field F (1, 0 being the $\cdot$-identity and $+$-identity, respectively).

e. $\begin{pmatrix} a & b \\ c & d \end{pmatrix} \cdot \begin{pmatrix} e & f \\ g & h \end{pmatrix}$, a, b, c, d, e, f, g, h as in **d**

f. $\begin{pmatrix} a & b \\ 0 & c \end{pmatrix} \cdot \begin{pmatrix} e & f \\ 0 & h \end{pmatrix}$, a, b, c, e, f, h as above.

g. $\begin{pmatrix} 1 & 0 \\ 0 & 0 \end{pmatrix} \cdot \begin{pmatrix} 0 & 0 \\ 1 & 0 \end{pmatrix}$

i. $\begin{pmatrix} 3 & 0 & 0 \\ 0 & 3 & 0 \\ 0 & 0 & 3 \end{pmatrix} \cdot \begin{pmatrix} 1 & 1 & 1 \\ 1 & 1 & 1 \\ 1 & 1 & 1 \end{pmatrix}$

h. $\begin{pmatrix} 0 & 0 \\ 1 & 0 \end{pmatrix} \cdot \begin{pmatrix} 1 & 0 \\ 0 & 0 \end{pmatrix}$

j. $(a, b, c) \cdot \begin{pmatrix} x_1 \\ x_2 \\ x_3 \end{pmatrix}$

where a, b, c, x_1, x_2, x_3 are arbitrary members of a

k $\begin{pmatrix} a_{11} & a_{12} & a_{13} \\ a_{21} & a_{22} & a_{23} \\ a_{31} & a_{32} & a_{33} \end{pmatrix} \cdot \begin{pmatrix} x_1 \\ x_2 \\ x_3 \end{pmatrix}$

where a_{ij} and x_i are arbitrary members of a field F.

l. $\begin{pmatrix} 2 & 3 \\ -3 & -4 \end{pmatrix} \cdot \begin{pmatrix} -4 & -3 \\ 3 & 2 \end{pmatrix}$

m. $\begin{pmatrix} -4 & -3 \\ 3 & 2 \end{pmatrix} \cdot \begin{pmatrix} 2 & 3 \\ -3 & -4 \end{pmatrix}$

2.* Let n be any integer such that $n \geqq 1$, let V be any n-dimensional vector space over a field F, and let X be a basis of V. For any $a \notin F$, multiplication by a determines a linear transformation $M_a: V \to V$. In Exercises 4.7.**4**, the reader was asked to compute $\mathscr{A}_{X,X}(M_a)$. The answer should have been $\mathscr{A}_{X,X}(M_a) = (a_{ij})$, where a_{ij} if $i \neq j$, and $a_{ij} = a$, if $i = j$. Pictorially,

$$\mathscr{A}_{X,X}(M_a) = \underbrace{\begin{pmatrix} a & 0 & 0 & \cdot & \cdot & \cdot & 0 \\ 0 & a & 0 & \cdot & \cdot & \cdot & 0 \\ 0 & 0 & a & 0 & \cdot & \cdot & 0 \\ \cdot & \cdot & 0 & \ddots & \ddots & & \vdots \\ \cdot & \cdot & \cdot & & \ddots & \ddots & \vdots \\ \cdot & \cdot & \cdot & & & \ddots & 0 \\ 0 & 0 & 0 & \cdot & \cdot & 0 & a \end{pmatrix}}_{n \text{ columns}} \; n \text{ rows}$$

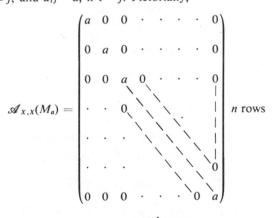

Henceforth, we denote this $n \times n$ matrix by $_n\mathfrak{d}(a)$, omitting the subscript n when there is no fear of ambiguity.

a. Prove that $M_a \circ M_b = M_{ab} = M_b \circ M_a$, for all a, b F.

b. Use Equation (16) and **a** to show that $\mathfrak{d}(a) \cdot \mathfrak{d}(b) = \mathfrak{d}(b) \cdot \mathfrak{d}(a) = \mathfrak{d}(ab)$.

c. Prove that $aM_b = M_{ab}$, for all a, b F.

d. Use Equation (16) and **c** to show that $a\mathfrak{d}(b) = \mathfrak{d}(ab)$, for all a, b F.

e. Let $\mathfrak{a}$ be any $n \times n$ matrix over F. Using Equation (16), and facts that you know about linear transformations, prove that

$$\textbf{i. } \mathfrak{a} \cdot \mathfrak{d}(0) = \mathfrak{d}(0) = \mathfrak{d}(0) \cdot \mathfrak{a}, \quad \text{and}$$

$$\textbf{ii. } \mathfrak{a} \cdot \mathfrak{d}(1) = \ \ (\mathfrak{a}) = \mathfrak{d}(1) \cdot \mathfrak{a}.$$

f. Prove the more general statement: $\mathfrak{d}(a) \cdot \mathfrak{a} = \mathfrak{a} \cdot \mathfrak{d}(a) = a\mathfrak{a}$.

g. Use **f** and Proposition 4.30(1) to prove Proposition 4.30(2).

The matrix $\mathfrak{d}(a)$ is known as the constant diagonal matrix with diagonal entry a. The places occupied by the a's, as pictured above, form one of the two diagonals of the rectangular array. This diagonal is known as the principal diagonal of the matrix. Formally, the principal diagonal of $_n(a_{ij})_n$ consists of all a_{ij} for which $i = j$. We usually refer to this diagonal in quasi-geometric terms. Thus, we talk about the matrix entries on the principal diagonal or off it. The matrix $\mathfrak{d}(a)$ can then be described as the $n \times n$ matrix over F with zero entries off the principal diagonal and constant entry a on it.

According to **e** above, the matrix $\mathfrak{d}(1)$ plays a special role with respect to matrix multiplication: It is an identity for matrix multiplication.** We give it the special symbol $(1)_n$, sometimes omitting the subscript when the number of columns (=number of rows $= n$) is clear. Thus, **e.ii** above becomes: $\mathfrak{a} \cdot (1) = (1) \cdot \mathfrak{a} = \mathfrak{a}$. The matrix $(1)_n$ always corresponds to the identity linear transformation under the correspondence $\mathscr{A}_{X,X}\colon \text{Trans}(V, V) \to \mathfrak{M}(n, n)$, no matter what the choice of X.

The matrix $\mathfrak{d}(0)$ will be given the special symbol $(0)_n$, sometimes omitting the subscript.

3. Let V and X be as in **2**, above. Consider any linear transformation $T\colon V \to V$ and its adjoint $T^*\colon V^* \to V^*$ and recall that in Exercises 4.7.**6**, it was shown that $\mathscr{A}_{X^*,X^*}(T^*)$ is obtained from $\mathscr{A}_{X,X}(T)$ by exchanging its columns and rows. That is, using the language introduced in Exercises 4.7.**7**,

$$\mathscr{A}_{X^*,X^*}(T^*) \text{ is the transpose of } \mathscr{A}_{X,X}(T)$$

Given any $n \times n$ matrix $\mathfrak{a}$ over F, its transpose is also an $n \times n$ matrix, which we denote by $\mathfrak{a}^t$. Using the language of Exercises 4.7.**7**, $\mathfrak{a}^t = t_{n,n}(\mathfrak{a})$. In **a** of this exercise, it was shown that $t_{n,n} \circ t_{n,n} = \text{I}_{\mathfrak{M}(n,n)}$. Thus, $(\mathfrak{a}^t)^t = \mathfrak{a}$.

a. If $T\colon V \to V$ and $S\colon V \to V$, then prove that for every $f \in V^*$,

$$(T \circ S)^*(f) = (S^* \circ T^*)(f)$$

Thus

$$(T \circ S)^* = S \circ T^*$$

** In precisely the same way that it was shown (Exercises 3.1.**5.a**, **b**) that there are only one $+$-identity and one $\cdot$-identity in a field F, it can be shown that there is only one $\cdot$ identity in $\mathfrak{M}(n, n)$. The reader is urged to verify this fact.

b. Use **a** and the discussion above it to prove that if $\mathfrak{a}$ and $\mathfrak{b}$ are matrices over F, then

$$(\mathfrak{a} \cdot \mathfrak{b})^t = \mathfrak{b}^t \cdot \mathfrak{a}^t$$

(*Hint:* You will probably want to use Equation (16), above.)

4.* Let V and X be as in Exercises **2** and **3**. Choose any 1–1, onto linear transformation $T: V \to V$, and let $\mathfrak{a} = \mathscr{A}_{X,X}(T)$ and $\mathfrak{b} = \mathscr{A}_{X,X}(T^{-1})$.

a. Use (16) and the definition of $(1)_n = {}_n\mathfrak{d}(1)$ given in 2, to prove that

$$\mathfrak{a} \cdot \mathfrak{b} = \mathfrak{b} \cdot \mathfrak{a} = (1)$$

Thus, $\mathfrak{b}$ is a $\cdot$-inverse of $\mathfrak{a}$. According to Exercises 4.9.**4.a**** then, $\mathfrak{b}$ is the *unique* $\cdot$-inverse of $\mathfrak{a}$. We denote it by $\mathfrak{a}^{-1}$, henceforth.
Thus

$$\mathscr{A}_{X,X}(T^{-1}) = [\mathscr{A}_{X,X}(T)]^{-1} \tag{17}$$

b. Prove that $(I_V)^*: V^* \to V^*$ equals I_{V^*}.

c. Use **b** and **4.a** to prove that

$$T^* \circ (T^{-1})^* = (T^{-1})^* \circ T^* = I_{V^*}$$

Thus, $(T^{-1})^*$ is a $\circ$-inverse of T^* (since, clearly, I_{V^*} is a o-identity), and, hence, it is the unique $\circ$-inverse of T^*.
Thus,

$$(T^{-1})^* = (T^*)^{-1}$$

d. Use **c** and **a** to prove that

$$(\mathfrak{a}^{-1})^t = (\mathfrak{a}^t)^{-1}$$

e. Let $S: V \to V$ be another isomorphism, and let $\mathfrak{g} = \mathscr{A}_{X,X}(S)$.
First, prove that $(T \circ S) \circ (S^{-1} \circ T^{-1}) = I_V = (S^{-1} \circ T^{-1}) \circ (T \circ S)$.
This means that $S^{-1} \circ T^{-1}$ is the unique inverse of $T \circ S$. Thus, $(T \circ S)^{-1} = S^{-1} \circ T^{-1}$.
Then, use this fact, (16), and (17) to prove that

$$(\mathfrak{a} \cdot \mathfrak{g})^{-1} = \mathfrak{g}^{-1} \cdot \mathfrak{a}^{-1}$$

Notice that this last equation describes a certain arithmetical relation between matrices. It is proved, however, without calculations.

Later, we develop methods for computing $\mathfrak{a}^{-1}$ in terms of $\mathfrak{a}$.

The results of this exercise are a semi-formal prologue to the next (and last) section.

4.3 Square Matrices and Polynomials

In this section V is a vector space over F with ordered basis $X = \{\mathbf{x}_1, \ldots, \mathbf{x}_n\}$. The function $\mathscr{A}_{X,X}$, as defined before, is an isomorphism from the vector space Trans(V, V) to the vector space $\mathfrak{M}(n, n)$. Both Trans(V, V) and $\mathfrak{M}(n, n)$ have,

** This is proved in precisely the same way as is the statement that each member of a field has a unique +-inverse (Exercises 3.1.**5.c**).

in addition to the usual vector-space operations, another operation, $\circ$ in the former case, and $\cdot$ in the latter case. Moreover, $\mathscr{A}_{X,X}$ respects all the operations of Trans(V, V) and $\mathfrak{M}(n, n)$. That is for any T_1, $T_2 \in$ Trans(V, V) and $a \in F$,

$$\mathscr{A}_{X,X}(aT_1) = a\mathscr{A}_{X,X}(T_1)$$
$$\mathscr{A}_{X,X}(T_1 + T_2) = \mathscr{A}_{X,X}(T_1) + \mathscr{A}_{X,X}(T_2)$$
$$\mathscr{A}_{X,X}(T_1 \circ T_2) = \mathscr{A}_{X,X}(T_1) \cdot \mathscr{A}_{X,X}(T_2)$$

We formalize the above situation by means of the following definitions.

Definition 4.8

Let A, $+$, $\cdot$, be a vector space space over a field F, $+$, $\cdot$. In addition, suppose that $*$ is an operation on A satisfying the following conditions:

(1) *$*$ is associative.*
(2) *For any $\mathbf{x}_1$, $\mathbf{x}_2 \in A$ and $a \in F$,*

$$a \cdot (\mathbf{x}_1 * \mathbf{x}_2) = (a \cdot \mathbf{x}_1) * \mathbf{x}_2 = \mathbf{x}_1 * (a \cdot \mathbf{x}_2)$$

(3) *A has a unique $*$-identity.*
(4) *For any $\mathbf{x}$, $\mathbf{y}$, $\mathbf{z}$ in A,*

$$\mathbf{x} * (\mathbf{y} + \mathbf{z}) = (\mathbf{x} * \mathbf{y}) + (\mathbf{x} * \mathbf{z}) \qquad \text{(left distributive law)}$$
$$(\mathbf{x} + \mathbf{y}) * \mathbf{z} = (\mathbf{x} * \mathbf{z}) + (\mathbf{y} * \mathbf{z}) \qquad \text{(right distributive law)}$$

We, then, call A an (associative) algebra over F. Note that we do not require, in general, that $\mathbf{x} * \mathbf{y} = \mathbf{y} * \mathbf{x}$. That is, $*$ need not be a commutative.

Sometimes to exhibit the operation $*$, we call the algebra A : A, $+$, $\cdot$, $*$. We refer to $*$ as the algebra multiplication (in contrast to $\cdot$, the scalar multiplication).

Definition 4.9

Let A, $+$, $\cdot$, $*$ and B, $+$, $\cdot$, $*$ be algebras over F. A linear transformation T from the vector space A, $+$, $\cdot$ to the vector space B, $+$, $\cdot$ is called a homomorphism of algebras if and only if, for all $\mathbf{x}_1$, $\mathbf{x}_2 \in A$,

$$T(\mathbf{x}_1 * \mathbf{x}_2) = T(\mathbf{x}_1) * T(\mathbf{x}_2)$$

and

$$T(\mathbf{1}) = \mathbf{1},$$

where the $\mathbf{1}$ on the left is the $*$-identity of A and the $\mathbf{1}$ on the right is the $*$-identity of B.

(Note that the operation on the left is the algebra multiplication of A, whereas the operation on the right is the algebra multiplication of B; these are not the same, of course, even though the same symbol is used.) If T is an isomorphism

of vector spaces and a homomorphism of algebras, then we say that T is an isomorphism of algebras.

Now we can state, more formally, the key facts about Trans(V, V) and $\mathfrak{M}(n, n)$.

Proposition 4.32

Trans(V, V) and $\mathfrak{M}(n, n)$ are algebras over F, and $\mathscr{A}_{X,X}$: Trans(V, V) $\to \mathfrak{M}(n, n)$ is an isomorphism of algebras. (The multiplication of Trans(V, V) is, of course, $\circ$, whereas the multiplication of $\mathfrak{M}(n, n)$ is matrix multiplication.)

Proof

The fact that $\circ$ satisfies requirements (1)–(4) follows from previous results, or it can easily be verified. The fact that $\cdot$ satisfies the requirements follows from Proposition 4.30 and Exercises 4.8.3. Formula (16) of the previous section implies that $\mathscr{A}_{X,X}$ is a homomorphism of algebras. We have already shown that it is an isomorphism of vector spaces. Q.E.D.

Next, we present an important example of an algebra over F, of which the multiplication is commutative.

Let $\mathscr{P}_F$ denote the set of all polynomial expressions in one variable x, with coefficients in F. A typical member of $\mathscr{P}_F$ is written as $a_nx^n + a_{n-1}x^{n-1} + \cdots + a_1x + a_0x^0$, where $a_n, a_{n-1}, \ldots, a_0$ are members of F, and n is any integer. We call the a's *coefficients* of the polynomial; the coefficient of x^i in the polynomial will be called the ith coefficient. We shall consider the polynomial expression unchanged if terms with zero coefficients are adjoined or deleted. Thus, given two polynomial expressions, we may, by adjoining or deleting terms with zero coefficients, if necessary, assume that both are of the form $a_nx^n + a_{n-1}x^{n-1} + \cdots + a_1x + a_0x^0$ and $b_nx^n + b_{n-1}x^{n-1} + \cdots + b_1x + b_0x^0$ (where some or all of the a_i's or b_i's may be zero). We may say that the two expressions are equal, if and only if $a_i = b_i$ for $i = 0, 1, \ldots, n$. Thus, if $F = R$,

$$0x^0 = 0x^0 + 0x + 0x^2 = 0x^0 + 0x^2 + 0x^5$$

and

$$1x^0 + 0x + 2x^2 + 3x^3 = 1x^0 + 2x^2 + 3x^3 + 0x^9,$$

but

$$1x^0 + x + x^2 \neq 1x^0 + x^2 + x^4, \text{ and so on}$$

In general, given any finite number of polynomial expressions in $\mathscr{P}_F$, we may, by adjoining or deleting terms with zero coefficients, always arrange things so that all the polynomials in question involve the same powers of x.

Define the sum and scalar product of polynomial expressions in $\mathscr{P}_F$ in the usual way: e.g., the sum of two such objects is the polynomial expression whose ith coefficient is the sum of the ith coefficients of the original polynomials.

We define the product of two polynomials $a_m x^m + \cdots + a_1 x + a_0 x^0$ and $b_n x^n + \cdots + b_1 x + b_0 x^0$ as follows:

$$(a_m x^m + \cdots + a_1 x + a_0 x^0) \cdot (b_n x^n + \cdots + b_1 x + b_0 x^0)$$
$$= (c_{m+n} x^{m+n} + \cdots + c_1 x + c_0 x^0),$$

where c_k is defined as follows: select all pairs a_i, b_j such that $i + j = k$ and form $a_i b_j$; c_k is defined to be their sum; symbolically, we write

$$c_k = \sum_{i+j=k} a_i b_j$$

This is just the usual notion of polynomial multiplication. To illustrate, let us suppose that $m = 2$ and $n = 3$. Then,

$$(a_2 x^2 + a_1 x + a_0 x^0) \cdot (b_3 x^3 + b_2 x^2 + b_1 x + b_0 x^0)$$
$$= [(a_2 b_3) x^5 + (a_2 b_2 + a_1 b_3) x^4 + (a_2 b_1 + a_1 b_2 + a_0 b_3) x^3$$
$$+ (a_2 b_0 + a_1 b_1 + a_0 b_2) x^2 + (a_1 b_0 + a_0 b_1) x + (a_0 b_0) x^0]$$

We assume, in this text that the reader is familiar with the usual notions of addition, scalar multiplication, and polynomial multiplication in the case $F = \mathbf{R}$. The above definitions are exact analogues of these usual notions, and, therefore, we give them somewhat hastily. For the same reason, we leave the verification of the following proposition to the reader.

Proposition 4.33

With respect to addition and scalar multiplication, as defined above, $\mathscr{P}_F$ is a vector space over F with basis $\{1x^0, 1x, 1x^2, 1x^3, \ldots\}$. With respect to these operations and polynomial multiplication, as defined above, $\mathscr{P}_F$ is an algebra over F. Polynomial multiplication is commutative.

Remarks: 1. The polynomial product

$$(ax^0) \cdot (a_n x^n + \cdots + a_1 x + a_0) = (aa_n) x^n + \cdots + (aa_1) x + (aa_0) x^0,$$

according to the definition of polynomial multiplication. Clearly, the right-hand side equals

$$a(a_n x^n + \cdots + a_1 x + a_0 x^0)$$

Thus, polynomial multiplication by the "constant" polynomial ax^0 is the same as scalar multiplication by a. Except when necessary to avoid confusion, we denote the polynomial ax^0 by a in all its appearances in the text.

2. By definition of polynomial multiplication,

$$(1x^m) \cdot (1x^n) = (1 \cdot 1) x^{m+n} = 1x^{m+n} = 1x^{n+m}$$
$$= (1x^n) \cdot (1x^m)$$

Henceforth, we denote the polynomial $1x^m$ by x^m, for all m. Thus,

$$(x^m) \cdot (x^n) = x^{m+n} = (x^n) \cdot (x^m)$$

Note that $1x^0 = x^0$ is the multiplicative identity of $\mathscr{P}_F$.

We urge the reader to verify that

$$(a_2x^2 + a_1x + a_0x^0) \cdot (b_3x^3 + b_2x^2 + b_1x + b_0x^0)$$
$$= (b_3x^3 + b_2x^2 + b_1x = b_0x^0) \cdot (a_2x^2 + a_1x + a_0x^0)$$

The fact about $\mathscr{P}_F$ that we will find very useful is given in the next proposition.

Proposition 4.34

Let A, $+$, $\cdot$, $*$ be any algebra over F, and choose any $\mathbf{t} \in A$. Then, there exists one and only one homomorphism of algebras $h: \mathscr{P}_F \to A$ satisfying $h(x) = \mathbf{t}$.

Remark: The purpose of this proposition is to formalize the notion of "substituting a 'value' for x." Suppose we have the simple polynomial expression $a_2x^2 + a_1x + a_0$, $a_2, a_1, a_0 \in F$, and suppose that $\mathbf{t} \in A$. Try to mimic the polynomial expression, using $\mathbf{t}$ instead of x. You will get $a_2\mathbf{t}^2 + a\mathbf{t} + a_0$. Now, this object is not defined. However, replace $\mathbf{t}^2$ by $\mathbf{t} * \mathbf{t}$, $+$ by $+$ and a_0 by $a_0 \cdot \mathbf{1}$ (where $\mathbf{1}$ is the $*$-identity of A). We, then, get

$$a_2(\mathbf{t} * \mathbf{t}) + a_1\mathbf{t} + a_0 \cdot \mathbf{1},$$

and this is a bona fide member of A. We may consider this to be the result of substituting $\mathbf{t}$ for x in the expression.

If a higher power of x, say x^4, is involved, then, we run into temporary trouble. Should we replace this by $(\mathbf{t} * \mathbf{t}) * (\mathbf{t} * \mathbf{t})$, or by $\mathbf{t} * (\mathbf{t} * (\mathbf{t} * \mathbf{t}))$, or by any of the other three possible meaningful ways in which the form $\mathbf{t}$'s can be paired? Upon reflection, however, we see that it doesn't matter which we choose, for $*$ is associative. Thus, all are the same.

Indeed, the preceding remarks suggest a change in notation when convenient: From now on, for any $\mathbf{t}$ in any algebra A over F, $\mathbf{t}^n$ will denote the n-fold product $\mathbf{t} * \mathbf{t} * \cdots * \mathbf{t}$, which is unambiguously determined because $*$ is associative. This makes sense for $n \geqq 1$. We will also find it convenient to define $\mathbf{t}^0 = \mathbf{1}$.

Proof

The preceding remarks should make the proof clear. Let A and $\mathbf{t}$ be as in the hypothesis. For any polynomial

$$a_nx^n + a_{n-1}x^{n-1} + \cdots + a_1x + a_0x^0 \in \mathscr{P}_F,$$

define

$$h(a_nx^n + a_{n-1}x^{n-1} + \cdots + a_1x + a_0x^0) = a_n\mathbf{t}^n + a_{n-1}\mathbf{t}^{n-1} + \cdots + a_1\mathbf{t} + a_0\mathbf{t}^0$$

The right-hand side is a well-defined member of A, so that h is a function from $\mathscr{P}_F$ to A. It is easily verified that h is a linear transformation. We show that h preserves the algebra multiplication.

Choose any other polynomial $b_m x^m + \cdots + b_1 x + b_0 x^0$ in $\mathscr{P}_F$. Then, by definition,

$$h(b_m x^m + \cdots + b_1 x + b_0 x^0) = b_m \mathbf{t}^m + b_{m-1}\mathbf{t}^{m-1} + \cdots + b_1 \mathbf{t} + b_0 \mathbf{t}^0.$$

Moreover,

$$(a_n x^n + \cdots + a_1 x + a_0 x^0) \cdot (b_m x^m + \cdots + b_1 x + b_0 x^0)$$
$$= c_{m+n} x^{m+n} + \cdots + c_1 x + c_0 x^0,$$

where

$$c_k = \sum_{i+j} a_i b_j$$

Now, using the properties satisfied by $*$, we compute

$$(a_n \mathbf{t}^n + \cdots + a_1 \mathbf{t} + a_0 \mathbf{t}^0) * (b_m \mathbf{t}^m + \cdots + b_1 \mathbf{t} + b_0 \mathbf{t}^0).$$

First, choose any monomial $a_i \mathbf{t}^i$ and compute as follows:

$$\begin{aligned}(a_i \mathbf{t}^i)*(b_m \mathbf{t}^m + \cdots + b_1 \mathbf{t} + b_0 \mathbf{t}^0) &= (a_i \mathbf{t}^i)*(b_m \mathbf{t}^m) + \cdots + (a_i \mathbf{t}^i)*(b_1 \mathbf{t}) \\ &\quad + (a_i \mathbf{t}^i)*(b_1 \mathbf{t}^0) \\ &= (a_i b_m)\mathbf{t}^{m+i} + \cdots + (a_i b_1)\mathbf{t}^{1+i} + (a_i b_0)\mathbf{t}^i\end{aligned}$$

Do this for all $i = 0, 1, \ldots, n$, and then add the results, collecting terms corresponding to the same power of $\mathbf{t}$. The coefficients of a particular power k of $\mathbf{t}$ will be, simply, the sum of the coefficients of $\mathbf{t}^k$ in each of the monomial multiples of $b_m \mathbf{t}^m + \cdots + b_1 \mathbf{t} + b_0 \mathbf{t}^0$ just computed. Each of these coefficients is a product of the form $a_i b_j$, where $i + j = k$. Thus, the coefficient of $\mathbf{t}^k$ is $\sum_{i+j=k} a_i b_j$, which we have called c_k. Thus,

$$\begin{aligned}h((a_n x^n + \cdots + a_1 x + a_0 x^0) \cdot (b_m x^m + \cdots + b_1 x + a_0 x^0))\\ &= h(c_{m+n} x^{m+n} + \cdots + c_1 x + c_0 x^0) \\ &= c_{m+n} \mathbf{t}^{m+n} + \cdots + c_1 \mathbf{t} + c_0 \mathbf{t}^0 \\ &= (a_n \mathbf{t}^n + \cdots + a_1 \mathbf{t} + a_0 \mathbf{t}^0)*(b_m \mathbf{t}^m + \cdots + b_1 \mathbf{t} + b_0 \mathbf{t}^0) \\ &= h(a_n x^n + \cdots + a_1 x + a_0 x^0)*h(b_m x^m + \cdots + b_1 x + b_0 x^0),\end{aligned}$$

so that h does, indeed, preserve the algebra multiplication.

Now, suppose that $g: \mathscr{P}_F \to A$ is any arbitrary algebra homomorphism satisfying $g(x) = \mathbf{t}$. Then, for any $n \geqq 1$.

$$g(x^n) = g(\underbrace{x \cdot x \cdot \ldots \cdot x}_{n \text{ fold}}) = \underbrace{g(x)*g(x)* \cdots *g(x)}_{n \text{ fold}} = \mathbf{t}^n,$$

and $g(x^0) = \mathbf{1} = \mathbf{t}^0$, since x^0 is the multiplicative identity for $\mathscr{P}_F$.

But, by definition of h,

$$h(x^n) = \mathbf{t}^n,$$

for all $n \geqq 0$. Therefore, $h(x^n) = g(x^n)$, for all $n \geqq 0$.

Now we use the fact that g and h are linear transformations and the fact that $\{x^0, x, x^2, x^3, \ldots\}$ is a basis of $\mathscr{P}_F$—we proved this for $F = \mathbf{R}$; the proof for general F is the same. Since linear transformations are completely determined by their values on a basis, and since g and h have the same values on x^0, x, $x^2, x^3, \ldots, g = h$.

This means that h is the only homomorphism of algebras from $\mathscr{P}_F$ to A sending x to $\mathbf{t}$. Q.E.D.

Henceforth, given an algebra A over F and an element $\mathbf{t} \in A$, we denote the homomorphism $h: \mathscr{P}_F \to A$ satisfying $h(x) = \mathbf{t}$ by $\mathscr{E}_\mathbf{t}$ (where $\mathscr{E}_\mathbf{t}$ can be thought of as *evaluation at* $\mathbf{t}$).

A very obvious and simple example of an algebra over F is provided by F itself. It is, of course, a vector space over itself, and we choose, as the algebra multiplication, the usual multiplication in F. That is, the algebra multiplication in F coincides with its scalar multiplication. To see that this operation satisfies the criteria of Definition 4.8, notice that (1) and (2) simply require it to be associative, (3) requires F to have a $\cdot$-identity, and (4) requires $\cdot$ and $+$ to satisfy the distributive laws. All these requirements are, of course, satisfied by F, since F is a field. Thus, F is an algebra over itself.

We may now apply the previous proposition in case $A = F$. Choose any $b \in F$. Then, $\mathscr{E}_b: \mathscr{P}_F \to F$ is the unique homomorphism of algebras sending x to b. For any polynomial $a_n x_n + \cdots + a_1 x + a_0 \in \mathscr{P}_F$

$$\mathscr{E}_b(a_n x^n + \cdots + a_1 x + a_0) = a_n b^n + \cdots + a_1 b + a_0 \in F$$

This is what we ordinarily mean when we say, "Evaluate $a_n x^n + \cdots + a_1 x + a$ at b," or "Substitute b for x in the polynomial." For example, if $F = \mathbf{R}$ and $b = 1$,

$$\mathscr{E}_1(7x^3 - 2x + 5) = 7.1 - 2.1 + 5 = 10 \in \mathbf{R}$$

Definition 4.10

Let A, $+$, $\cdot$, $*$ be any algebra over F (with $+$-identity denoted, as usual, by $\mathbf{0}$), let $\mathbf{t}$ be any member of A, and let $a_n x^n + \cdots + a_1 x + a_0$ be any polynomial in $\mathscr{P}_F$. Then, we say that $\mathbf{t}$ is a zero of $a_n x_n + \cdots + a_1 x + a_0$, if and only if

$$\mathscr{E}_\mathbf{t}(a_n x^n + \cdots + a_1 x + a_0) = \mathbf{0}$$

To put it another (equivalent) way $\mathbf{t}$ is a zero of $a_n x^n + \cdots + a_1 x + a_0$, if and only if

$$a_n x^n + \cdots + a_1 x + a_0 \in \mathscr{N}_{\mathscr{E}_\mathbf{t}}, \textit{ the null space of } \mathscr{E}_\mathbf{t}$$

The above definition merely formalizes the usual notion of a zero of a polynomial. In the usual situation, we say that a real number c is a zero of a polynomial $p(x)$, if and only if $p(c)$ (i.e., the result of evaluating p at c, or substituting c for x in p) $= 0$, the $+$-identity of $\mathbf{R}$. Thus, 2 is a zero of $x^2 - 5x + 6$ because

$$\mathscr{E}_2(x^2 - 5x + 6) = 2^2 - 5.2 + 6 = 0$$

We now apply the foregoing results to prove the following surprising result.

Proposition 4.35

(1) *Let T be any member of Trans(V, V), where V is as described at the outset. Then, T is a zero of some nontrivial polynomial in $\mathscr{P}_F$.*

(2) *Let $\mathfrak{a}$ be any member of $\mathfrak{M}(n, n)$. Then, $\mathfrak{a}$ is a zero of some nontrivial polynomial in $\mathscr{P}_F$.*

(3) *If $\mathscr{A}_{X,X}(T) = \mathfrak{a}$, then, every polynomial in $\mathscr{P}_F$ having T as a zero also has $\mathfrak{a}$ as a zero and vice versa.*

Proof

(1) Choose any $T \in \text{Trans}(V, V)$ and consider the homomorphism of algebras.

$$\mathscr{E}_T : \mathscr{P}_F \to \text{Trans}(V, V)$$

sending x to T. Suppose that $\mathscr{N}_{\mathscr{E}_T}$ consists only of the trivial polynomial $0x^0$. This is the $+$-identity of $\mathscr{P}_F$. Since $\mathscr{E}_T$, being a homomorphism of algebras, is *a fortiori* a linear transformation, the triviality of $\mathscr{N}_{\mathscr{E}_T}$ implies that $\mathscr{E}_T$ is 1–1. Thus, $\mathscr{R}_{\mathscr{E}_T}$ is a vector subspace of Trans(V, V) isomorphic to $\mathscr{P}_F$.

But $\mathscr{P}_F$ is infinite-dimensional, having the infinite basis $\{x^0, x, x^2, x^3, \ldots\}$, whereas Trans$(V, V)$ has dimension n^2, where $n = \dim V$. Thus, we obtain the impossible result that a finite-dimensional vector space has an infinite-dimensional subspace.

Therefore, $\mathscr{N}_{\mathscr{E}_T}$ is nontrivial, so that it contains a nonzero polynomial. This polynomial has T has a zero, by definition of zero of a polynomial.

(2) The proof of this result is an exact analogue of (1). Note that $\dim \mathfrak{M}(n, n) = n^2$, and consider $\mathscr{E}_{\mathfrak{a}} : \mathscr{P}_F \to \mathfrak{M}(n, n)$. Proceed as before.

(3) To prove this fact, we first note that the composition of two homomorphisms of algebras is a homomorphism of algebras. This fact is proved in exactly the same way that we proved the analogous statement for linear transformations. The proof is left to the reader (in Exercises 4.9.**1**).

Now, consider the three homomorphisms of algebras $\mathscr{E}_T : \mathscr{P}_F \to \text{Trans}(V, V)$, $\mathscr{E}_{\mathfrak{a}} : \mathscr{P}_F \to \mathfrak{M}(n, n)$ and $\mathscr{A}_{X,X} : \text{Trans}(V, V) \to \mathfrak{M}(n, n)$. Under the hypothesis of (3) that $\mathscr{A}_{X,X}(T) = \mathfrak{a}$, we show that

$$\mathscr{A}_{X,X} \circ \mathscr{E}_T = \mathscr{E}_{\mathfrak{a}} \qquad (1)$$

Note that the function on the left is a homomorphism of algebras, being the composition of two such. Note also that it takes $\mathscr{P}_F$ to $\mathfrak{M}(n, n)$ as does the homomorphism on the right. Next, evaluate the left side at x:

$$(\mathscr{A}_{X,X} \circ \mathscr{E}_T)(x) = \mathscr{A}_{X,X}(\mathscr{E}_T(x)) = \mathscr{A}_{X,X}(T) = \mathfrak{a}$$

Thus, $\mathscr{A}_{X,X} \circ \mathscr{E}_T : \mathscr{P}_F \to \mathfrak{M}(n, n)$ is a homomorphism of algebras taking x to $\mathfrak{a}$. According to Proposition 4.34, there is only one such homomorphism: namely, $\mathscr{E}_{\mathfrak{a}}$. Thus, the two are equal, as desired.

Finally, suppose that T is a zero of a polynomial $p(x) \in \mathscr{P}_F$. Then, $\mathscr{E}_T(p(x)) = \bar{\mathbf{0}}$, where $\bar{\mathbf{0}}$ is the constantly $\bar{\mathbf{0}}$ linear transformation from V to V. Thus,

$$\begin{aligned}\mathscr{E}_{\mathfrak{a}}(p(x)) &= \mathscr{A}_{X,X}(\mathscr{E}_T(p(x))) \\ &= \mathscr{A}_{X,X}(\bar{\mathbf{0}}) = (0),\end{aligned}$$

the +-identity of $\mathfrak{M}(n, n)$. Therefore, $p(x)$ has $\mathfrak{a}$ as a zero.

Notice that since $\mathscr{A}_{X,X}$ is an isomorphism, relation (1) can be altered to yield.

$$\mathscr{E}_T = \mathscr{A}_{X,X}{}^{-1} \circ \mathscr{E}_{\mathfrak{a}} \tag{2}$$

If, now, $\mathfrak{a}$ is a zero of a polynomial $g(x)$, then,

$$\begin{aligned}\mathscr{E}_T(g(x)) &= \mathscr{A}_{X,X}{}^{-1}(\mathscr{E}_{\mathfrak{a}}(g(x)) \\ &= \mathscr{A}_{X,X}{}^{-1}((0)) = \bar{\mathbf{0}},\end{aligned}$$

the +-identity of Trans(V, V). Thus, T is a zero of $g(x)$. Q.E.D.

This result is surprising because, given a linear transformation from V to V or a square matrix over F, it is not at all obvious that it is the zero of any polynomial; after all the multiplication of linear transformations and matrices is quite different from what we usually think of as multiplication.

For example, can the reader see immediately that the matrix

$$\begin{pmatrix} 2 & 9 \\ 1 & 3 \end{pmatrix} \quad \text{is a zero of} \quad x^2 - 5x - 3?$$

I would be surprised if he could. Nevertheless, he should verify that it is.

Note that the preceding proposition relies heavily on the fact that V is finite-dimensional.

The relationships between matrices, linear transformations and polynomials will be exploited to great advantage in Chapter 7.

EXERCISES / 4.9

1. Verify that the composition of two homomorphisms of algebras (over a field F) is a homomorphism of algebras. Verify that the inverse of an isomorphism of algebras is an isomorphism of algebras.

2. Evaluate the polynomial $x^3 + 4x^2 - 3$ at the following matrices:

a. $\begin{pmatrix} 1 & 0 \\ 0 & 1 \end{pmatrix}$

b. $\begin{pmatrix} 1 & 0 & 0 \\ 0 & 1 & 0 \\ 0 & 0 & 1 \end{pmatrix}$

c. $\begin{pmatrix} a & 0 & 0 \\ 0 & a & 0 \\ 0 & 0 & a \end{pmatrix}$, where a is any real number.

d. $\begin{pmatrix} 1 & 0 \\ 2 & 3 \end{pmatrix}$

e. $\begin{pmatrix} a & b \\ 0 & a \end{pmatrix}$, a, b real numbers

f. $\begin{pmatrix} 1 & 0 & -1 \\ 2 & 4 & 0 \\ 3 & 1 & 1 \end{pmatrix}$

3. Let A, $+$, $\cdot$, $*$ and B, $+$, $\cdot$, $*$ be any algebras over a field F, and let $h: A \to B$ be a homomorphism of algebras.

a. If $\mathbf{0} \in A$ is the $+$-identity, prove that $\mathbf{0} * \mathbf{0} = \mathbf{0}$.

b. A subalgebra of B is a vector subspace of B containing $\mathbf{1}$ (the $*$-identity of B) and closed with respect to the operation $*$. Prove that a subalgebra of B is an algebra over F in its own right, with respect to the operations of B.

c. Prove that $\mathscr{R}_h$ is a subalgebra of B.

d. An algebra is said to be *commutative* if its algebra multiplication is commutative. Suppose that A is commutative. Prove that the algebra $\mathscr{R}_h$ is commutative.

e. Let $A = \mathscr{P}_F$ and $B = \mathfrak{M}(n, n)$, n an integer $\geqq 1$. Choose any $\mathfrak{a} \in \mathfrak{M}(n, n)$ and consider the algebra homomorphism $\mathscr{E}_{\mathfrak{a}} : \mathscr{P}_F \to \mathfrak{M}(n, n)$. Apply the previous results to this situation to prove that if $a_m x^m + \cdots + a_1 x + a_0$ and $b_k x^k + \cdots + b_1 x + b_0$ are any polynomials in $\mathscr{P}_F$, then the matrix product

$$[a_m \mathfrak{a}^m + \cdots + a_1 \mathfrak{a} + a \cdot (1)_n] \cdot [b_k \mathfrak{a}^k + \cdots + b_1 \mathfrak{a} + b_0 (1)_n]$$

equals the matrix product

$$[b_k \mathfrak{a}^k + \cdots + b_1 \mathfrak{a} + b_0 (1)_n] \cdot [a_m \mathfrak{a}^m + \cdots + a_1 \mathfrak{a} + a_0 (1)_n],$$

where $(1)_n$ is the constant diagonal matrix ${}_n\mathfrak{d}(1)_n$.

4.* Let A, $+$, $\cdot$, $*$ be any algebra over F.

It is quite possible for A to contain nonzero members $\mathbf{x}_1$ and $\mathbf{x}_2$ such that $\mathbf{x}_1 * \mathbf{x}_2 = \mathbf{0}$. For example of this, see Exercises 4.8.1.**g**. In such a case $\mathbf{x}_1$ is called a *left zero divisor* and $\mathbf{x}_2$ is called a *right zero divisor*. It is also possible, for two nonzero members of A, $\mathbf{y}_1$ and $\mathbf{y}_2$, to satisfy $\mathbf{y}_1 * \mathbf{y}_2 = \mathbf{1}$, where $\mathbf{1}$ is the $*$-identity of A. For example, when $A = F$, any nonzero $y \in F$ has a multiplicative inverse, y^{-1}, such that $y \cdot y^{-1} = 1$. For a less obvious example, see Exercises 4.8.1.**l**. $\mathbf{y}_1$ is said to have a *right inverse* and to be a *left inverse*. Similarly, $\mathbf{y}_2$ is said to have a *left inverse* and to be a *right inverse*. *If* $\mathbf{y}$ *has a right inverse and a left inverse* (i.e., is a left inverse and a right inverse) *then we say that* y *is invertible*. We say that $\mathbf{y}_1$ is a left inverse of $\mathbf{y}_2$, and so on. [cf. Definition 3.2(5).]

a. Suppose $\mathbf{y}$ is invertible. That is, for some $\mathbf{y}_1, \mathbf{y}_2 \in A$, $\mathbf{y} * \mathbf{y}_1 = \mathbf{y}_2 * \mathbf{y} = \mathbf{1}$. Prove that $\mathbf{y}_1 = \mathbf{y}_2$. (cf. Exercises 3.1.**5.c**, Exercises 3.2.**3.b**.)

Thus, invertible members of A have a single, unique right and left inverse. If $\mathbf{y}$ is invertible we denote its $*$-inverse by $\mathbf{y}^{-1}$.

b. Prove that if $\mathbf{y}$ is a right inverse, then it is not a left zero divisor.

Prove that if $\mathbf{y}$ is a left inverse, then it is not a right zero divisor.

Thus, if $\mathbf{y}$ is invertible, it is neither a left nor a right zero divisor.

5. The degree of a polynomial in $\mathscr{P}_F$ is the highest power of x in the polynomial with nonzero coefficient. The degree of the constantly 0 polynomial is not defined.

a. Let X be any subset of $\mathscr{P}_F$ containing at least one nonzero polynomial. Prove the X contains a polynomial whose degree is $\leqq$ that of all the other polynomials in X. (*Hint:* See *Fact about* **N**, Chapter 2.)

We say that such a polynomial has *minimal degree* in X.

b. Choose any invertible $\mathfrak{a} \in \mathfrak{M}(n, n)$, $n \geqq 1$. Let X consist of all polynomials in $\mathscr{P}_F$ of which $\mathfrak{a}$ is a zero. According to Proposition 4.35.**b**, X contains at least one nonzero polynomial. Let $p(x) = a_k x^k + a_{k-1}x^{k-1} + \cdots + a_1 x + a_0$ be a polynomial of minimal degree in X. *Prove that if* $a_0 = 0$, *then* $\mathfrak{a}$ *is a right zero divisor in* $\mathfrak{M}(n,n)$. (*Hint:* Use the facts that $\mathfrak{a}$ is a zero of $p(x)$ and that $a_k x^k + a_{k-1}x^{k-1} + \cdots + a_1 x = (a_k x^{k-1} + a_{k-1}x^{k-2} + \cdots + a_1)x$, and show that $\mathfrak{a}$ cannot be a zero of $a_k x^{k-1} + a_{k-1}x^{k-2} + \cdots + a_1$.) See 4, above, for the definition of *right zero* divisor.

According to **4.b**, since $\mathfrak{a}$ is invertible, it cannot be a right zero divisor. Thus, $a_0 \neq 0$.

c. Using the terminology of **b**, above, prove that

$$\mathfrak{a}^{-1} = -\left[\frac{a_k}{a_0}\mathfrak{a}^{k-1} + \frac{a_{k-1}}{a_0}\mathfrak{a}^{k-2} + \cdots + \frac{a_2}{a_0}\mathfrak{a} + \frac{a_1}{a_0}(1)_n\right]$$

Thus, given an invertible $\mathfrak{a}$, if we can find a polynomial $p(x)$ of minimal degree such that $\mathfrak{a}$ is a zero of $p(x)$ we can then compute $\mathfrak{a}^{-1}$ in terms of $\mathfrak{a}$.

In general, given any $\mathfrak{b} \in \mathfrak{M}(n, n)$, a polynomial of minimal degree of which $\mathfrak{b}$ is a zero is called a *minimal polynomial belonging to* $\mathfrak{b}$.

6. Let V be an n-dimensional vector space over F.

a. Prove that every $T \in \text{Trans}(V, V)$ that has a right inverse is invertible. (See **4**, above.)

b. Prove that every $T \in \text{Trans}(V, V)$ that has a left inverse is invertible.

c. Prove the same for every $\mathfrak{a} \in \mathfrak{M}(n, n)$.

7. We define two members of Trans($\mathscr{P}_F, \mathscr{P}_F$), T_1 and T_2. Let

$$T_1(a_n x^n + \cdots + a_1 x + a_0 x_0) = a_n x^{n-1} + a_{n-1}x^{n-2} + \cdots + a_2 x + a_1 x_0$$

$$T_2(a_n x^n + \cdots + a_1 x + a_0 x^0) = a_n x^{n+1} + a_{n-1}x^n + \cdots + a_1 x^2 + a_0 x,$$

for all $a_n x^n + \cdots + a_1 x + a_0 \in \mathscr{P}_F$. *Prove that* $T_2 \circ T_1 \neq \mathrm{I}_{\mathscr{P}_F}$ *but that* $T_1 \circ T_2 = \mathrm{I}_{\mathscr{P}_F}$.

Thus, T_2 has a left inverse, T_1. According to **4.a**, if T_2 also had a right inverse, it would equal the left inverse T_1; thus if T_2 had a right inverse, $T_2 \circ T_1 = \mathrm{I}_{\mathscr{P}_F}$. Since this is not true, T_2 has no right inverse.

Thus, T_2 is an example of a noninvertible element of an algebra [namely, Trans($\mathscr{P}_F$, $\mathscr{P}_F$)] that has a left-inverse.

According to **4.b**, T_2 is not a left zero divisor.

Define $S:\mathscr{P}_F \to \mathscr{P}_F$ as follows:

$$S(a_nx^n + \cdots + a_1x + a_0) = a_0,$$

for all $a_nx^n + \cdots + a_1x + a_0$ in $\mathscr{P}_F$. It is easily verified that $S \in \text{Trans}(\mathscr{P}_F, \mathscr{P}_F)$ and that $S \neq \bar{0}$ the constantly 0 transformation.

Prove that $S \circ T_2 = \bar{0}$.

Thus, although T_2 is a right inverse, it is also a right zero divisor.

8. Let F be any field, a, b, c, d any members of F, and

$$\mathfrak{a} = \begin{pmatrix} a & b \\ c & d \end{pmatrix} \in \mathfrak{M}(2, 2)$$

Let $p(x) = (a - x)(d - x) - bc = x^2 - (a + d)x + (ad - bc) \in \mathscr{P}_F$.

Prove, by direct computation, that $\mathfrak{a}$ is a zero of $p(x)$.

9. Let F be as above. Consider the set Δ of all 2×2 matrices over F of the form

$$\begin{pmatrix} a & b \\ 0 & c \end{pmatrix},$$

where a, b, c are arbitrary members of F and 0 is the $+$-identity of F.

Prove that Δ is a subalgebra of $\mathfrak{M}(2, 2)$. (See **3.b**, above, for a definition of *subalgebra*.)

10. Let F be as above and let $GL(n, F)$ be the subset of $\mathfrak{M}(n, n)$, $n > 1$, consisting of all invertible matrices. (See Exercise **4** for a definition of *invertible*.) Prove that $GL(n, F)$ is closed with respect to *matrix multiplication*, taking the *transpose*, and taking the *inverse*.

That is, if $\mathfrak{a}_1$ and $\mathfrak{a}_2 \in GL(n, F)$, prove that $\mathfrak{a}_1 \cdot \mathfrak{a}_2 \in GL(n, F)$, $\mathfrak{a}_1{}^t \in GL(n, F)$ and $\mathfrak{a}_1{}^{-1} \in GL(n, F)$. Prove that $(\mathfrak{a}_1{}^{-1})^{-1} = \mathfrak{a}_1$. (See Exercises 4.8.**4d**, **e.**)

11. Let $T : F^n \to F^n$ be a linear transformation, and let X be the standard basis of F^n. Let $\mathscr{A}_{X,X}(T)$ be

$$\begin{pmatrix} a_{11} & a_{12} & \cdots & a_{1n} \\ a_{21} & 2_{22} & \cdots & a_{2n} \\ \vdots & \vdots & & \vdots \\ a_{nJ} & a_{n2} & & a_{nn} \end{pmatrix}$$

Choose any n-tuple $(b_1, \ldots, b_n) \in F^n$. Consider the corresponding $n \times 1$ matrix.

$$\begin{pmatrix} b_1 \\ \vdots \\ b_n \end{pmatrix}$$

The matrix product

$$\begin{pmatrix} a_{11} & a_{12} & \cdots & a_{1n} \\ a_{21} & a_{22} & \cdots & a_{2n} \\ \vdots & \vdots & & \vdots \\ a_{n1} & a_{n2} & & a_{nn} \end{pmatrix} \cdot \begin{pmatrix} b_1 \\ \vdots \\ b_n \end{pmatrix}$$

will be an $m \times 1$ matrix.
Define a function

$$\mathscr{A}_X : F^n \to \mathfrak{M}(n, 1)$$

as follows:

$$\mathscr{A}_X(b_1, \ldots, b_n) = \begin{pmatrix} b_1 \\ \vdots \\ b_n \end{pmatrix}$$

for every $(b_1, \ldots, b_n) \in F^n$.

a. Prove that $\mathscr{A}_X$ is an isomorphism of vector spaces.

b. Prove that

$$\mathscr{A}_{X,X}(T) \cdot \mathscr{A}_X(b_1, \ldots, b_n) = \mathscr{A}_X(T(b_1, \ldots, b_n))$$

That is, if $T(b_1, \ldots, b_n) = (c_1, \ldots, c_n)$, show that

$$\begin{pmatrix} a_{11} & a_{12} & \cdots & a_{1n} \\ a_{21} & a_{22} & \cdots & a_{2n} \\ \vdots & \vdots & & \vdots \\ a_{n1} & a_{n2} & \cdots & a_{nn} \end{pmatrix} \cdot \begin{pmatrix} b_1 \\ \vdots \\ b_n \end{pmatrix} = \begin{pmatrix} c_1 \\ \vdots \\ c_n \end{pmatrix}$$

12. The field **C** of complex numbers can be regarded as a vector space over **R**. We do so throughout this exercise. In addition to its operations as a vector space over **R**, **C** has the operation of multiplication of complex numbers.

a. Verify that **C**, together with the operations of addition, real (scalar) multiplication, and multiplication of complex numbers, is an algebra over **R**.

Since multiplication of complex numbers, when restricted to **R** becomes ordinary multiplication of real numbers, **R** is a subalgebra of **C**.

b. Let A be any algebra over **R** of which **R** itself is a subalgebra.** Suppose moreover that there is an element $\mathbf{y} \in A$ that is a zero of the polynomial $x^2 + 1$. That is, $x^2 + 1$ is in the null space of the evaluation map

$$\mathscr{P} = \mathscr{P}_{\mathbf{R}} \xrightarrow{\mathscr{E}_{\mathbf{y}}} A$$

Prove that every polynomial multiple of $x^2 + 1$ belongs to $\mathscr{N}_{\mathscr{E}_{\mathbf{y}}}$ (i.e., show that $(x^2 + 1)p(x) \in \mathscr{N}_{\mathscr{E}_{\mathbf{y}}}$ for all $p(x) \in \mathscr{P}_{\mathbf{R}}$).

** This implies, among other things, that the $*$-identity of A is $1 \in \mathbf{R}$, and that the $+$ identity of A is $0 \in \mathbf{R}$.

c. Suppose $g(x) \in \mathscr{P}_{\mathbf{R}}$ is not a multiple of $x^2 + 1$, then, upon dividing it by $g(x)$ one obtains a remainder of the form $ax + b$, where a and b are some real numbers. Use this fact to prove the following: *If $g(x) \in \mathscr{N}_{\mathscr{E}_{\mathbf{y}}}$ and $g(x)$ is not a multiple of $x^2 + 1$, then* **y** *belongs to* **R**.

Now, it is easy to show that no real number is a zero of $x^2 + 1$. Indeed, for all real x, $x^2 \geqq 0$, so that $x^2 + 1 \geqq 1$. Thus, by the above result, every $g(x) \in \mathscr{N}_{\mathscr{E}_{\mathbf{y}}}$ must be a multiple of $x^2 + 1$. Combining this with the conclusion of **a**, we obtain the result that

$$\mathscr{N}_{\mathscr{E}_{\mathbf{y}}} = \text{set of all polynomial multiples of } x^2 + 1$$

This vector subspace of $\mathscr{P} = \mathscr{P}_{\mathbf{R}}$ has been discussed before (cf. Exercises 3.10.**6**, and Exercises 4.3.**9**). In these exercises we called this subspace U, and we constructed an onto linear transformation

$$\mathscr{P}_{\mathbf{R}} \xrightarrow{t} \mathbf{C}$$

with null space U.

According to Exercises 4.4.**3**, there is determined a linear transformation (linear over **R**)

$$s: \mathbf{C} \to A$$

such that

$$s \circ t = \mathscr{E}_{\mathbf{y}}$$

Indeed, we can define s as follows: for every $ai + b \in \mathbf{C}$, a, b real numbers, let

$$s(ai + b) = a * \mathbf{y} \mathbin{\pmb{+}} b$$

where $*$ and $\pmb{+}$ are operations of A.

d. Prove that s is an algebra homomorphism. That is, prove that s is a linear transformation (over **R**) and that

$$s((ai + b) \cdot (ci + d)) = s(ai + b) * s(ci + d)$$

For this last step, you will have to make use of the fact that $\mathbf{y}^2 \mathbin{\pmb{+}} \mathbf{1} = \mathbf{0}$.

Therefore, $\mathscr{R}_s$ is a subalgebra of A.

e. Prove that if $s(ai + b) = \mathbf{0}$, then $\mathbf{y} \in \mathbf{R}$ or $a = b = 0$. Since the former is impossible, the latter must be true. Thus $\mathscr{N}_s = \{0\}$, so that s is 1–1.

Thus, $s: \mathbf{C} \to \mathscr{R}_s \subset A$ is an isomorphism of algebras.

It does not have to be pointed out that **C** itself is an example of an algebra A over **R** that contains **R** as a subalgebra and contains a zero of the equation $x^2 + 1$: Namely, i.

The above results show that, in a certain sense, **C** is the *smallest* such algebra over **R**. For the above results show that each such A contains a subalgebra $\mathscr{R}_s$ isomorphic (as an algebra over **R**) to **C**.

f. Prove that the linear transformation

$$t: P_{\mathbf{R}} \to \mathbf{C}$$

is a homomorphism of algebras.

CHAPTER 5

LINEAR EQUATIONS AND DETERMINANTS

1 / INTRODUCTION AND QUALITATIVE ANALYSIS

In this chapter, we shall study systems of linear equations, such as those described in the last part of Chapter 1, only we shall generalize our considerations to allow coefficients in an arbitrary field F.**

First, we remind the reader of the basic definitions. A *linear expression* in *indeterminates* $x_1, x_2, \ldots, x_n$ with *coefficients* $a_1, a_2, \ldots, a_n \in F$ is an expression

$$a_1x_1 + \cdots + a_nx_n \tag{1}$$

The indeterminates $x_1, \cdots, x_n$ can be thought of as variables ranging over F. The expression then can be thought of as a shorthand description of the linear transformation from F^n to F given by the rule: Every $(c_1, \ldots, c_n) \in F^n$ is taken to $a_1c_1 + \cdots + a_nc_n$. Thus, we shall think of the expression $a_1x_1 + \cdots + a_nx_n$ as a member of $(F^n)^*$.

If we are interested in determining those $c_1, c_2, \ldots, c_n$ for which the value of the linear expression is some particular $b \in F$, then we express this interest via the equation

$$a_1x_1 + \cdots + a_nx_n = b \tag{2}$$

** The reader who is uninterested in arbitrary fields F may safely pretend, throughout this chapter, that $F = \mathbf{R}$.

Those $(c_1, \ldots, c_n)$ actually taken to b by the function are called *solutions* to Equation (2). We may also say that $c_1, \ldots, c_n$ *satisfy* (2) (when substituted for $x_1, \ldots, x_n$, respectively).

Given k expressions of the type in (1) and k values in F (not necessarily distinct), we may be interested in those $c_1, \ldots, c_n$ that *simultaneously* satisfy the corresponding equations. We express our interest via the (simultaneous) system of linear equations

$$\begin{aligned} a_{11}x_1 + \cdots + a_{1n}x_n &= b_1 \\ \vdots \qquad\quad\ \ \vdots\quad & \quad\ \vdots \\ a_{k1}x_1 + \cdots + a_{kn}x_n &= b_k \end{aligned} \tag{3}$$

where a_{ij}, b_i, belong to F.

Closely related to Equation (3) is the homogeneous system of linear equations

$$\begin{aligned} a_{11}x_1 + \cdots + a_{1n}x_n &= 0 \\ \vdots \qquad\quad\ \ \vdots\quad & \quad\ \vdots \\ a_{k1}x_1 + \cdots + a_{kn}x_n &= 0 \end{aligned} \tag{4}$$

If (3) is given first, then (4) is called the homogeneous system associated with (3). A solution to (3) is an n-tuple $(c_1, \ldots, c_n) \in F^n$ taken to b_1 by the first expression, b_2 by the second, and so on.

There is another way of thinking of the system (3) that is closely related to the preceding. We may think of the k expressions in (3) as determining a linear transformation by the following rule: *every* $(c_1, \ldots, c_n)$ *is taken by the system of expressions* (*on the left side*) *of* (3), *to the k-tuple*

$$(a_{11}c_1 + \cdots + a_{1n}c_n, a_{21}c_1 + \cdots + a_{2n}c_n, \ldots, a_{k1}c_1 + \cdots + a_{kn}c_n). \tag{5}$$

The system (3), then, expresses our interest in determining those $(c_1, \ldots, c_n)$ sent by the above described transformation to $(b_1, \ldots, b_k)$.

Given any system, such as (3), above, we denote by $A: F^n \to F^k$ the linear transformation determined by the above rule, (5). Then, if $\mathbf{x} = (x_1, \ldots, x_n)$ and $\mathbf{b} = (b_1, \ldots, b_k)$, system (3) becomes

$$A(\mathbf{x}) = \mathbf{b} \tag{6}$$

or

$$A(x_1, \ldots, x_n) = (b_1, \ldots, b_k) \tag{6'}$$

If we denote the first expression in system (3) by $A_1: F^n \to F$, the second by $A_2: F \to F$, and so on, then, the individual equations in (3) become

$$A_i(\mathbf{x}) = b_i,\ i = 1, \ldots, k \tag{7}$$

and the defining rule for A becomes

$$A(\mathbf{x}) = (A_1(\mathbf{x}), A_2(\mathbf{x}), \ldots, A_k(\mathbf{x})) \tag{8}$$

Each $A_i \in \text{Trans}(F^n, F) = (F^n)^*$ and $A \in \text{Trans}(F^n, F^k)$.

We can now interpret questions about linear equations in terms of questions about vector spaces and linear transformations.

First of all, the *set of all* $(b_1, \ldots, b_k) = \mathbf{b}$ for which (3) (*or, equivalently*, (6)) *has a solution is just* $\mathscr{R}_A$, *the range of* A.

The set of all solutions $(c_1, \ldots, c_n) = \mathbf{c}$ *to* (4), *or, equivalently, to*

$$A(\mathbf{x}) = \mathbf{0}, \tag{9}$$

is just $\mathscr{N}_A$, *the null space of* A.

Proposition 5.1

The set of all solutions to (3) [*or to* (6)] *is either the empty set or a translate*

$$\mathbf{c} + \mathscr{N}_A,^{**}$$

where $\mathbf{c}$ *is any single solution to* (3) (*or* (6)).

Call the set of solutions to (3) $S_\mathbf{b}$ and suppose that $S_\mathbf{b}$ is not empty. Choose any $\mathbf{c} \in S_\mathbf{b}$. We show, first, that $\mathbf{c} + \mathscr{N}_A \subset S_\mathbf{b}$.

Choose any $\mathbf{v} \in \mathbf{c} + \mathscr{N}_A$. Then, $\mathbf{v} = \mathbf{c} + \mathbf{u}$, where $\mathbf{u} \in \mathscr{N}_A$. That is, $A(\mathbf{u}) = \mathbf{0}$. Therefore,

$$A(\mathbf{v}) = A(\mathbf{c} + \mathbf{u}) = A(\mathbf{c}) + A(\mathbf{u}) = A(\mathbf{c}) = \mathbf{b}$$

Thus, $\mathbf{v} \in S_\mathbf{b}$, which implies that $\mathbf{c} + \mathscr{N}_A \subset S_\mathbf{b}$.

Next, we prove the reverse inclusion. Choose any $\mathbf{w} \in S_\mathbf{b}$. Then,

$$A(\mathbf{w} - \mathbf{c}) = A(\mathbf{w}) - A(\mathbf{c}) = \mathbf{b} - \mathbf{b} = \mathbf{0}$$

Thus, $\mathbf{w} - \mathbf{c} \in \mathscr{N}_A$. But $\mathbf{w} = \mathbf{c} + (\mathbf{w} - \mathbf{c}) \in \mathbf{c} + \mathscr{N}_A$. Therefore, $S_\mathbf{b} \subset \mathbf{c} + \mathscr{N}_A$, and the desired result is proved. Q.E.D.

Thus, we have already shown that our linear equation setup has a good deal of structure. Sets of solutions are hyperplanes** in a vector space, the range of values for which solutions exist is a vector subspace of a vector space, the equation system itself can be thought of as a linear transformation. We next obtain even more structure by using the following result, proved in Chapter 4.

If V *is any finite-dimensional vector space over* F, *and if* $T : V \to W$ *is any linear transformation, then*

$$\dim V = \dim \mathscr{N}_T + \dim \mathscr{R}_T \tag{10}$$

From now on, *denote the set of solutions to* (4) [or equivalently, to (9)] *by* $S_\mathbf{0}$. This conforms to the notation used in the proof of Proposition 5.1. Of course, $S_\mathbf{0} = \mathscr{N}_A$. Thus, we may conclude the following:

Proposition 5.2

Any homogeneous system of k linear equations in n indeterminates [*i.e. system* (4)] *satisfies*

$$\dim S_\mathbf{0} \geqq n - k$$

** See Definition 3.9 for a definition of "translate." Also, see the discussion before and after this definition.

Proof

Use relation (10) to conclude that

$$\dim S_0 = \dim \mathcal{N}_A = \dim F^n - \dim \mathcal{R}_A = n - \dim \mathcal{R}_A$$

The result now follows by observing that $\mathcal{R}_A$ is a vector subspace of F^k, so that $\dim \mathcal{R}_A \leqq k$. Q.E.D.

Corollary to Proposition 5.2

Any homogeneous system of k linear equations in n indeterminates, where $k < n$, has at least one non-trivial solution. (The n-tuple $(0, 0, \ldots, 0)$ *is called the trivial solution to a homogeneous system in n indeterminates; every other solution is called nontrivial.)*

Indeed, such a system has at least $n - k$ linearly independent solutions.

Proof

If $k < n$, then $n - k > 0$, so that according to Proposition 5.2, $\dim S_0 > 0$. Thus, it contains a nonzero vector, which, by definition, is a nontrivial solution to the system.

The last statement is merely a restatement of Proposition 5.2. Q.E.D.

Proposition 5.3

If $n = k$, then: $S_0 = \{\mathbf{0}\}$ if and only if $\mathcal{R}_A = F^k$.

In other words, if $n = k$, then: the set of solutions to (4) *consists only of* $(0, 0, \ldots, 0)$ *if and only if* (3) *has a solution for every* $\mathbf{b} \in F^k$.

In this case (i.e., $n = k$, $\mathcal{R}_A = F^k$, $S_0 = \{\mathbf{0}\}$) *system* (3) *has a unique solution for every* $\mathbf{b} \in F^k$.

Proof

The last statement is easy to prove. If $\mathcal{R}_A = F^k$, this means that (3) has *at least one* solution for every $\mathbf{b} \in F^k$. Since $S_0 = \{\mathbf{0}\}$ and, by definition, $S_0 = \mathcal{N}_A$, A is 1–1, which means that (3) has *at most one* solution for each $\mathbf{b} \in F^k$. Thus, under the stated conditions (3) has exactly one solution for each $\mathbf{b} \in F^k$.

To prove the first statement, suppose first that $S_0 = \{\mathbf{0}\}$. Then, $\dim S_0 = 0$, so that by (10),

$$n = \dim F^n = \dim \mathcal{R}_A$$

Since $n = k$ and $\mathcal{R}_A$ is a vector subspace of F^k, this equation tells us that $\mathcal{R}_A = F^k$.

On the other hand, suppose that $\mathcal{R}_A = F^k$. Then,

$$\dim S_0 = \mathcal{N}_A = \dim F^n - \dim \mathcal{R}_A = n - k$$

Since $n = k$, $\dim S_0 = 0$, from which we conclude that $S_0 = \{\mathbf{0}\}$. Q.E.D.

If the number of indeterminates ($=n$) is less than the number of equations ($=k$) in (3), then (3) may not have a solution. Indeed, it is possible to state definitely that if $n < k$, then there are $\mathbf{b} \in F^k$ for which (3) has no solution.

To see this, note that if $n < k$, then

$$\dim \mathscr{R}_A = n - \dim \mathscr{N}_A \leqq n < k,$$

so that $\mathscr{R}_A \neq F^k$. Therefore, there are $\mathbf{b} \in F^k$ such that $\mathbf{b} \notin \mathscr{R}_A$.

Indeed, a previous result (Proposition 3.18) implies that $\mathscr{R}_A$ has a complementary subspace U: that is, $\mathscr{R}_A \oplus U = F^k$. Since, then,

$$\dim \mathscr{R}_A + \dim U = k,$$

and since we have just seen $\dim \mathscr{R}_A \leqq n$, it follows that

$$\dim U \geqq k - n$$

Thus, *there is a linearly independent set of at least* $k - n$ *vectors* $\mathbf{b} \in F^k$ *for which* (3) *has no solution.*

A few more general results of the above type are possible, but they require a slightly finer analysis of the situation. The following proposition is a first step in this analysis.

Proposition 5.4

Let a_{ij} *be the coefficients of the system of linear equations in* (3), $i = 1, \ldots, k$, $j = 1, \ldots, n$. *Let A be the linear transformation determined by system* (3) *and rule* (5), *as above. Finally, let X be the standard basis of* F^n *and Y the standard basis of* F^k, *both ordered in the usual way. Then,*

$$\mathscr{A}_{X,Y}(A) = {}_k(a_{ij})_n$$

In other words, the matrix (with respect to standard bases) *of the linear transformation determined by a linear equation system equals the matrix of coefficients of the system.*

Proof

The matrix $\mathscr{A}_{X,Y}(A)$, by its definition, is obtained by expressing the vectors $A(\mathbf{e}_j^{(n)})$, $j = 1, \ldots, n$, as linear combinations of the vectors $\mathbf{e}_1^{(k)}, \ldots, \mathbf{e}_k^{(k)}$ and writing the coefficients so obtained in columns of the matrix. (Recall that A takes F^n to F^k so that $A(\mathbf{e}_j^{(n)}) \in F^k$.)

Thus, if

$$A(\mathbf{e}_j^{(n)}) = b_{1j}\mathbf{e}_1^{(k)} + \cdots + b_{kj}\mathbf{e}_k^{(k)}, \tag{11}$$

$j = 1, \ldots, n$, then

$$\mathscr{A}_{X,Y}(A) = {}_k(b_{ij})_n$$

We must show, therefore, that the coefficients b_{ij}, $i = 1, \ldots, k$, in (11) are a_{ij}, $i = 1, \ldots, k$, respectively for every $j = 1, \ldots, n$.

Recall now that, by definition,

$$\mathbf{e}_j^{(n)} = \overbrace{(0, \ldots, 0, \underset{\substack{\uparrow \\ j\text{th place}}}{1}, 0, \ldots, 0)}^{n \text{ tuple}} \tag{12}$$

and that, by definition

$$A(c_1, \ldots, c_n) = (a_{11}c_1 + \cdots + a_{1n}c_n, a_{21}c_1 + \cdots + a_{2n}c_n, \ldots, a_{k1}c_1 + \cdots + a_{kn}c_n) \tag{13}$$

Now, if $(c_1, \ldots, c_n) = \mathbf{e}_j^{(n)}$, it is easy to verify that

$$a_{i1}c_1 + a_{i2}c_2 + \cdots + a_{in}c_n = a_{ij} \tag{14}$$

Combining (12), (13), and (14), therefore, we get

$$A(\mathbf{e}_j^{(n)}) = (a_{1j}, a_{2j}, \ldots, a_{kj}) \tag{15}$$

$$= a_{1j}\mathbf{e}_1^{(k)} + a_{2j}\mathbf{e}_2^{(k)} + \cdots + a_{kj}\mathbf{e}_k^{(k)} \tag{15'}$$

Compare (11) and (15′). Since $Y = \{\mathbf{e}_1^{(k)}, \ldots, \mathbf{e}_k^{(k)}\}$ is a basis of F^k, every vector in F^k is the value of exactly one linear combination of vectors of Y. Thus, the linear combinations in (11) and (15′) must be the same. That is, $a_{ij} = b_{ij}$ for all $i = 1, \ldots, k$. Since (11) and (15′) hold for all $j = 1, \ldots, n$, we have, indeed, proved that

$$\mathscr{A}_{X,Y}(A) = {}_k(a_{ij})_n \qquad \text{Q.E.D.}$$

Let us write the matrix ${}_k(a_{ij})_n$ more fully:

$$\begin{pmatrix} a_{11}a_{12} & \cdots & a_{ij} & \cdots & a_{1n} \\ a_{21}a_{22} & \cdots & a_{2j} & \cdots & a_{2n} \\ \vdots\ \ \vdots & & \vdots & & \vdots \\ a_{k1}a_{k2} & \cdots & a_{kj} & \cdots & a_{kn} \end{pmatrix} \tag{16}$$

Compare (15) and (16). Ignoring the fact that the jth column is written vertically, it is a member of F^k, and, by (15), we see that it is nothing but $A(\mathbf{e}_j^{(n)})$. Henceforth, we shall think of the columns of (16) in this way. Thus, we can immediately conclude the following.

Corollary to Proposition 5.4

Let ${}_k(a_{ij})_n$ be the matrix of coefficients of the system of linear equations (3). *Let $A: F^n \to F^k$ be the linear transformation determined by the system* (3), *as usual. Then, letting κ = the maximum number of linearly independent columns of (a_{ij}),*

$$\dim \mathscr{R}_A = \kappa$$

and

$$\dim S_0 = \dim \mathscr{N}_A = n - \kappa$$

Proof

Since $\dim \mathscr{N}_A + \dim \mathscr{R}_A = \dim F^n = n$, the second equation is an easy consequence of the first. To prove the first equality, note that, by the remarks following (16), above, the maximum number of linearly independent columns of (a_{ij}) is the same as the maximum number of linearly independent vectors among $A(\mathbf{e}_1^{(n)}), \ldots, A(\mathbf{e}_n^{(n)})$.

Next, note that

$$\begin{aligned}\operatorname{span}_{F^k}(\{A(\mathbf{e}_1^{(n)}), \ldots, A(\mathbf{e}_n^{(n)})\}) &= \operatorname{span}_{F^k}(A(\{\mathbf{e}_1^{(n)}, \ldots, \mathbf{e}_n^{(n)}\})) \\ &= A(\operatorname{span}_{F^n}(\{\mathbf{e}_1^{(n)}, \ldots, \mathbf{e}_n^{(n)}\}) \\ &= A(F^n) = \mathscr{R}_A\end{aligned}$$

Thus, $\dim \mathscr{R}_A = \dim(\operatorname{span}_{F^k}(\{A(\mathbf{e}_1^{(n)}), \ldots, A(\mathbf{e}_n^{(n)})\})$.

Therefore, $\kappa \leqq \dim \mathscr{R}_A$, because $\operatorname{span}_{F^k}(\{A(\mathbf{e}_1^{(n)}), \ldots, A(\mathbf{e}_n^{(n)})\})$ cannot contain a linearly independent subset with more members than its dimension (see Proposition 3.14). On the other hand, $\{A(\mathbf{e}_1^{(n)}), \ldots, A(\mathbf{e}_n^{(n)})\}$ generates

$$\operatorname{span}_{F^k}(\{A(\mathbf{e}_1^{(n)}), \ldots, A(\mathbf{e}_n^{(n)})\})$$

Thus, it contains a basis of this linear span. This basis is, by definition, linearly independent; since κ is the *maximal* number of linearly independent vectors among $A(\mathbf{e}_1^{(n)}), \ldots, A(\mathbf{e}_n^{(n)})$, the number of basis vectors must be $\leqq \kappa$. But, the number of basis vectors equals $\dim(\operatorname{span}_{F^k}(\{A(\mathbf{e}_1^{(n)}), \ldots, A(\mathbf{e}_n^{(n)})\})) = \dim \mathscr{R}_A$. Therefore, $\dim \mathscr{R}_A \leqq \kappa$.

Combining the two inequalities, we obtain the desired equality. Q.E.D.

Definition 5.1

Let ${}_k(a_{ij})_n$ be any $k \times n$ matrix over F. The maximum number of linearly independent columns of (a_{ij}) is called its column rank. We shall often denote this by κ. The maximum number of linearly independent rows of (a_{ij}), (these are members of F^n), is called its row rank and usually denoted by ρ.

The above corollary allows us to interpret the column rank, κ, of the matrix of coefficients of system (3) as the dimension of the subspace consisting of those vectors $\mathbf{b} \in F^k$ for which (3) [or, equivalently, (6)] has a solution. The number $n - \kappa$ is the dimension of S_0, the set of solutions to (4).

For a given matrix, however, it is sometimes easier to determine the row rank, ρ, than to determine the column rank, so that it is useful to determine the relationship between ρ and κ, if any.

Now, the rows of (a_{ij}) are just the columns of its transpose, $(a_{ij})^t$, so that the row rank of (a_{ij}) equals the column rank of $(a_{ij})^t$. Moreover, since

$$\mathscr{A}_{X,Y}(A) = (a_{ij})$$

we have, by Exercises 4.7.6,

$$\mathscr{A}_{Y^*,X^*}(A^*) = (a_{ij})^t$$

Clearly, as before, the column rank of $(a_{ij})^t$ equals the dimension of $\mathscr{R}_{A^*}$. But, by Proposition 4.25(1),

$$\mathscr{R}_{A^*} = (\mathscr{N}_A)^0,$$

the annihilator of $\mathscr{N}_A$.

Thus, using Corollary to Proposition 4.23,

$$\dim(\mathscr{R}_{A^*}) = \dim(\mathscr{N}_A)^0 = n - \dim \mathscr{N}_A = \dim \mathscr{R}_A = \kappa$$

We have, therefore, proved the following useful result.

Proposition 5.5

Let (a_{ij}) be any $k \times n$ matrix over F. Then, $\kappa = \rho$: that is, the column rank of (a_{ij}) equals its row rank.

The row or column rank of (a_{ij}) will be called, henceforth, its *rank*.

This is more or less as far as this kind of analysis can be pushed. After the following exercises, we present a computational method whereby solutions to linear equation systems can actually be determined.

EXERCISES / 5.1

1. What is the dimension of the subspace of solutions to the system

$$3x_1 + 2x_2 - 4x_3 = 0$$
$$x_1 - 2x_2 + x_3 = 0$$
$$10x_1 - 4x_2 - 4x_3 = 0?$$

Determine a basis for this subspace.

2. What is the dimension of the subspace of solutions to the system

$$2x_1 + x_2 = 0$$
$$x_2 - x_3 = 0$$
$$4x_1 - x_2 - x_3 = 0$$
$$x_1 + x_2 + 10x_3 = 0?$$

3. What is the dimension of the subspace of all $(b_1, b_2, b_3, b_4,) \in \mathbf{R}^4$ satisfying

$$-7x_1 - 3x_2 - x_3 = b_1$$
$$x_2 + 8x_3 = b_2$$
$$x_1 + 4x_2 - 2x_3 = b_3$$
$$5x_1 + 2x_2 = b_4?$$

Determine a basis of this subspace.

4. Compute the rank of the following matrices

a. $\begin{pmatrix} 1 & 0 & 0 \\ 0 & 1 & 0 \\ 0 & 0 & 1 \end{pmatrix}$

d. $\begin{pmatrix} -8 & 12 & \frac{1}{2} \\ 4 & 2 & 1 \\ 0 & 8 & 3 \end{pmatrix}$

b. $\begin{pmatrix} a & b & c \\ 0 & d & e \\ 0 & 0 & f \end{pmatrix}$, where $a, b, c, d, e, f, \in F$ and $a, d, f,$ are nonzero

c. $\begin{pmatrix} \cos\theta & -\sin\theta \\ \sin\theta & \cos\theta \end{pmatrix}$, for any real number θ

e. $\begin{pmatrix} 9 & 1 \\ 10 & 2 \\ 12 & 4 \end{pmatrix}$

5. Compute the row rank and column rank (separately) of each of the following matrices.

a. $\begin{pmatrix} 4 & 0 & 2 \\ 1 & 3 & 8 \\ 0 & -2 & 5 \end{pmatrix}$

c. $\begin{pmatrix} 1 & 0 & 2 & 3 \\ 0 & 1 & 1 & 4 \end{pmatrix}$

b. $\begin{pmatrix} -1 & 0 & 2 \\ 1 & 8 & 0 \\ 2 & 3 & 1 \\ 4 & 2 & 3 \end{pmatrix}$

d. $\begin{pmatrix} a & b \\ c & d \end{pmatrix}$, where $a, b, c, d \in F$ $ad - bc \neq 0$

6. In this exercise, we make precise the relationship between the linear transformation $A: F^n \to F^k$ and the linear transformations $A_i: F^n \to F$, $i = 1, \ldots, k$, discussed in the text above (cf. Equation 8).

Let $\Pi_i: F^k \to F$ be the ith coordinate projection. That is, for every $(c_1, \ldots, c^k) \in F^k$,

$$\Pi_i(c_1, \ldots, c_k) = c_i$$

Let $v_i: F \to F_i$ be the ith coordinate *injection*. That is, for each $c \in F$,

$$v_i(c) = \overbrace{(0, \ldots, 0, \underset{\substack{\uparrow \\ i\text{th place}}}{c}, 0, \ldots, 0)}^{k\text{-tuple}}$$

a. Prove that v_i is a linear transformation. (We know, of course, that Π_i is one; indeed, $\{\Pi_1, \Pi_2, \ldots, \Pi_k\}$ is the basis of $(F^k)^*$ dual to the standard basis of F^k (cf. Chapter 4, Section 3.2).)

b. Prove that $\Pi_i \circ v_i = I_F$ and $\Pi_j \circ v_i = \bar{0}$, if $j \neq i$.
The first equation implies that Π_i is onto and v_i is 1–1.

c. Prove that $v_i \circ \Pi_1 + v_2 \circ \Pi_2 + \cdots + v_k \circ \Pi_k = I_{F^k}$.

d. For any linear transformation $A: F^n \to F^k$, let $A_i = \Pi_i \circ A$, $i = 1, \ldots, k$. Clearly, A_i is linear; indeed $A_i \in (F^n)^*$, for

$$A_i = A^*(\Pi_i)$$

where $A^*: (F^k)^* \to (F^n)^*$ is the adjoint of A.

Use **c** to prove that

$$A = v_1 \circ A_1 + v_2 \circ A_2 + \cdots + v_k \circ A_k \tag{*}$$

For any $\mathbf{b} \in F^k$, $\Pi_i(\mathbf{b})$ is its ith component b_i. Use the definition of A_i above together with the equation (*) just derived to prove that

$$A(\mathbf{x}) = \mathbf{b}, \text{ if and only if } A_i(\mathbf{x}) = b_i, \text{ for } i = 1, \ldots, k$$

7.* Let $A: V \to W$ be any linear transformation, let $\{\mathbf{x}_1, \ldots, \mathbf{x}_n\} = X$ and $\{\mathbf{y}_1, \ldots, \mathbf{y}_k\} = Y$ be any bases of V and W respectively. Finally, let ${}_k(a_{ij})_n = \mathscr{A}_{X,Y}(A) \in \mathfrak{M}(k, n)$. Consider the system of linear expressions

$$\begin{gathered} a_{11}x_1 + \cdots + a_{1n}x_n \\ \vdots \\ a_{k1}x_1 + \cdots + a_{kn}x_n \end{gathered}$$

They determine a linear transformation $B: V \to W$ by the following rule:

$$B(c_1\mathbf{x}_1 + \cdots + c_n\mathbf{x}_n) = (a_{11}c_1 + \cdots + a_{1n}c_n)\mathbf{y}_1 + \cdots + (a_{k1}c_1 + \cdots + a_{kn}c_n)\mathbf{y}_k$$

This is the same rule by which we defined, in the text above, the linear transformation A (of the above text—not the A in this exercise) from the system (3).

Prove that $A = B$.

2† / ELIMINATION OF VARIABLES OR ROW REDUCTION

2.1 Introduction

We showed in Section 1 that if we start with a system of linear equations

$$\begin{aligned} a_{11}x_1 + \cdots + a_{1n}x_n &= b_1 \\ \vdots \qquad\quad & \quad \vdots \\ a_{k1}x_1 + \cdots + a_{kn}x_n &= b_k, \end{aligned} \tag{3}$$

it determines a linear transformation $A: F^n \to F^k$ by the rule

$$A(c_1\mathbf{e}_1^{(n)} + \cdots + c_n\mathbf{e}_n^{(n)}) = (a_{11}c_1 + \cdots + a_{1n}c_n)\mathbf{e}_1^{(k)} + \cdots + (a_{k1}c_1 + \cdots + a_{kn}c_n)\mathbf{e}_k^{(k)} \tag{5}$$

The system (3), then, is equivalent to the single equation

$$A(\mathbf{x}) = \mathbf{b}, \tag{6}$$

which is to say that, for every $\mathbf{b} = (b_1, \ldots, b_k)$, (3) and (6) have precisely the same solutions.

We may imagine the reverse situation. Suppose that we start with a linear transformation $A: F^n \to F^k$, form its matrix $(a_{ij}) = \mathscr{A}_{X,Y}(A)$, obtain the equation system (3) above, and from this, by (5) *obtain A again* (according to Exercises 5.1.7). Thus, in this reverse situation, equation (6) is still equivalent to equation system (3) (i.e., they have the same solutions).

Now, here is the key point. According to Exercises 5.1.7, we can use *any* bases of F^n and F^k to obtain an equation system from A. Of course, different choices of bases lead to different matrices and hence to different equation systems. Every one of these equation systems determines A again, by a rule analogous to (5) above, where the standard basis vectors are replaced by the newly chosen ones (cf. the rule in Exercises 5.1.7). As before, therefore, *every one* of these equation systems is equivalent to (6). Of course, some of these equation systems may be much simpler than others, from the point of view of obtaining solutions. This leads to the following idea.

Suppose that we are given system (3), which is perhaps very complicated. It determines $A: F^n \to F^k$ by rule (5), and it is equivalent to equation (6). Perhaps it will be possible to find bases of F^n and F^k, X' and Y', respectively, such that $\mathscr{A}_{X',Y'}(A)$ and the corresponding equation system are much simpler than (a_{ij}) and (3). Solving this simple system will be equivalent to solving (6), which, in turn, will be equivalent to solving (3).

This is one interpretation of the basic geometric idea underlying the algebra of elimination of variables, which we introduce below. The problem of solving (3), thus, becomes one of suitably altering the standard bases of F^n and F^k so as to change (3) into an easily solvable system. Now, there are certain standard, elementary ways of altering bases that turn out to fit our needs perfectly. It will also turn out that only the basis of F^k needs changing. Each elementary basis change will have the effect of producing a corresponding change in the equation system. These changes in the equation system can be described directly in terms of the system, without reference to bases, vector spaces and so on.

Now we can describe the main lines of this section. First, we shall describe how to change an equation system into another via elementary changes, as mentioned above. This technique is known as elimination of variables or row reduction. We show that the new systems obtained are equivalent to the original. This procedure will enable us to solve any given system of linear equations. Secondly, we describe how these system changes can be interpreted in terms of basis changes in F^k. Thus, the system changes can be thought of as leaving the linear transformation determined by the original system intact but changing its matrix representation. Alternatively, the system changes can also be thought of as simple changes of the transformation, while the bases are kept intact. We make this clear later. Subsequent exercises will fill out this part of the exposition.

2.2 The Procedure of Elimination of Variables

As always, we shall be working with an arbitrary but fixed field F.

Let $f_1 = a_1x_1 + \cdots + a_nx_n$ and $f_2 = b_1x_1 + \cdots + b_nx_n$ be any two linear expressions with coefficients in F. Suppose that $a_1 \neq 0$ and $b_1 \neq 0$, then

$$f_1 - \left(\frac{a_1}{b_1}\right) f_2 = \left(a_2 - \frac{a_1b_2}{b_1}\right)x_2 + \left(a_3 - \frac{a_1b_3}{b_1}\right)x_3 + \cdots + \left(a_n - \frac{a_1b_n}{b_1}\right)x_n$$

This is a linear expression involving only the variables $x_2, \ldots, x_n$; that is, x_1 has been eliminated. To describe this situation, we shall say that x_1 *has been eliminated from* f_1 *by subtracting multiple—namely,* (a_1/b_1)—of f_2. This simple elimination procedure can be extended to the case of an arbitrary (finite) number of given linear expressions to yield solutions to any equation systems.

These remarks motivate the following definitions.

Definition 5.2

Let $f_1, \ldots, f_k$ be any k linear expressions in indeterminates with coefficients in F. The ordered k-tuple $(f_1, \ldots, f_k)$ will be called the system of linear expressions determined by $f_1, \ldots, f_k$ (in the order given).

Given $(f_1, \ldots, f_k)$, consider the following three ways of altering it:

(1) *Exchange any two components of* $(f_1, \ldots, f_k)$.
(2) Multiply a component of $(f_1, \ldots, f_k)$ by a *nonzero scalar.*
(3) *Subtract a multiple of one component from another.*

These alteration procedures will be called elementary row operations of type 1, 2, 3, respectively.

Schematically, we can designate what happens as follows:

(1) *Exchange f_i and f_j, supposing $i < j$:*
$(f_1, \ldots, f_i, \ldots, f_j, \ldots f_k) \rightarrowtail (f_1, \ldots, f_j, \ldots, f_i, \ldots, f_k)$
(2) *Multiply f_i by a:*
$(f_1, \ldots, f_i, \ldots, f_k) \rightarrowtail (f_1, \ldots, af_i, \ldots, f_k)$
(3) *Subtract cf_j from f_i, supposing $i < j$.*
$(f_1, \ldots, f_i, \ldots, f_j, \ldots, f_k) \rightarrowtail (f_1, \ldots, f_i - cf_j, \ldots, f_j, \ldots, f_k)$.

If $i > j$ in (2) *or* (3), *the reader can readily supply the schematic representation of the operation.*

To indicate that the k-tuple $(g_1, \ldots, g_k)$ of linear expressions is obtained from $(f_1, \ldots, f_k)$ by one of the above operations, we may write "$(f_1, \ldots, f_k) \rightarrowtail (g_1, \ldots, g_k)$" or "$(f_1, \ldots, f_k) \rightarrowtail (g_1, \ldots, g_k)$ by an operation of type i," where $i = 1, 2, 3$, or "$(f_1, \ldots, f_k) \rightarrow (g_1, \ldots, g_k)$ by making such and such an exchange or multiplying f_i by such and such a scalar, etc."

Note that, given equation system (3), if we consider $f_1, \ldots, f_k$ to be the k *linear expressions* of the system, then the above operations can just be interpreted as the kind of operations one usually performs when trying to simplify equation systems. Of course, to maintain equality, the same operations must be performed on the b_i's on the other side of the equations. With this understood, operation (1) simply amounts to exchanging two of the equations in (3). Operation (2) amounts to multiplying (both sides of) an equation in (3) by some nonzero scalar. Operation (3) amounts to subtracting a multiple of one equation from another equation in (3).

Before we actually go into the process of using these operations to simplify equation systems, we shall prove certain useful facts about the operations. Notice that $f_1, \ldots, f_k$ are all members of $(F^n)^*$, so that the ordered k-tuple $(f_1, \ldots, f_k)$ belongs to $[(F^n)^*]^k$. Notice also that the symbol "$\rightarrowtail$" can be thought of as a relation on the set $[(F^n)^*]^k$: namely, $(f_1, \ldots, f_k) \rightarrowtail (g_1, \ldots, g_k)$ if and only if $(g_1, \ldots, g_k)$ is obtained from $(f_1, \ldots, f_k)$ by an elementary operation.

Proposition 5.6

$\rightarrowtail$ is a symmetric, reflexive relation on $[(F^n)^*]^k$. More precisely, for every $(f_1, \ldots, f_k) \in [(F^n)^*]^k$, $(f_1, \ldots, f_k) \rightarrowtail (f_1, \ldots, f_k)$, and if $(f_1, \ldots, f_k) \rightarrowtail (g_1, \ldots, g_k)$ by an operation of type ℓ, $\ell = 1$, 2, or 3, then $(g_1, \ldots, g_k) \rightarrowtail (f_1, \ldots, f_k)$ by an operation of the same type.

Remark: In its simplest form, the last statement of this proposition states that the operations (1), (2) and (3) are reversible. That is, if $(g_1, \ldots, g_k)$ is obtained from $(f_1, \ldots, f_k)$ by a certain operation, then this operation can be reversed (has an inverse) to yield $(f_1, \ldots, f_k)$ from $(g_1, \ldots, g_k)$.

Proof

(1) $\rightarrowtail$ *is reflexive*: Choose any $(f_1, \ldots, f_k)$ in $[(F^n)^*]^k$ and apply the following operation of type 2: multiply f_1 by 1. The result, clearly, is the same k-tuple $(f_1, \ldots, f_k)$. Thus, $(f_1, \ldots, f_k) \rightarrowtail (f_1, \ldots, f_k)$.

(2) $\rightarrowtail$ *is symmetric:* Suppose that $(f_1, \ldots, f_k) \rightarrowtail (g_1, \ldots, g_k)$ by exchanging f_i and f_j. Clearly, by exchanging g_j and g_i, we obtain $(f_1, \ldots, f_k)$ again. Thus, in this case $(g_1, \ldots, g_k) \rightarrowtail (f_1, \ldots, f_k)$.

Suppose, next, that $(f_1, \ldots, f_k) \rightarrowtail (g_1, \ldots, g_k)$ by multiplying f_i by a nonzero scalar $a \in F$. This means that $g_r = f_r$, if $j \neq i$, and $g_i = af_i$. But, then,

$$\frac{1}{a} g_i = \left(\frac{1}{a}\right)(a f_i) = f_i,$$

so that $(f_1, \ldots, f_k)$ can be obtained from $(g_1, \ldots, g_k)$ by multiplying g_i by the nonzero scalar $1/a \in F$. Thus, in this case, too, $(g_1, \ldots, g_k) \rightarrowtail (f_1, \ldots, f_k)$.

Finally, suppose that $(f_1, \ldots, f_k) \rightarrowtail (g_1, \ldots, g_k)$ by subtracting cf_j from f_i. This means that $g_r = f_r$, if $r \neq i$, and $g_i = f_i - cf_j$. But then, noting that $g_j = f_j$,

$$f_i = g_i + cf_j = g_i + cg_j = g_i - (-c)g_j$$

so that $(f_1, \ldots, f_k)$ is obtained from $(g_1, \ldots, g_k)$ by subtracting a multiple of g_j from g_i. Thus, in this case, too, $(g_1, \ldots, g_k) \rightarrowtail (f_1, \ldots, f_k)$. Q.E.D.

Now, we should point out that we are not really interested in the relation $\rightarrowtail$ itself. After all two k-tuples are $\rightarrowtail$-related, if and only if they are obtainable from one another by *one* elementary operation. We are interested in *repeatedly applying elementary operations* so as to simplify equation systems. Thus, we are interested in the relation determined by such repeated applications of elementary operations. We now make this precise.

Definition 5.3

Let $(f_1, \ldots, f_k)$ and $(g_1, \ldots, g_k)$ be any two ordered k-tuples of linear expressions, as above. We say that $(g_1, \ldots, g_k)$ is row-related to $(f_1, \ldots, f_k)$ if and only if there exists a finite sequence of k-tuples in $[(F^n)^*]^k$, $(f_1{}^0, \ldots, f_k{}^0)$, $(f_1{}^1, \ldots, f_k{}^1), \ldots, (f_1{}^m \ldots, f_k{}^m)$ such that $(f_1, \ldots, f_k) = (f_1{}^0, \ldots, f_k{}^0) \rightarrowtail (f_1{}^1, \ldots, f_k{}^1) \rightarrowtail \cdots \rightarrowtail (f_1{}^{m-1}, \ldots, f_k{}^{m-1})$

$$\downarrow$$

$$(f_1{}^m, \ldots, f_k{}^m) = (g_1, \ldots, g_k)$$

In other words, $(g_1, \ldots, g_k)$ is row-related to $(f_1, \ldots, f_k)$ if and only if it can be obtained from $(f_1, \ldots, f_k)$ by a finite sequence of elementary operations.

Proposition 5.7

Row-relatedness is an equivalence relation on $[(F^n)^*]^k$.

Proof

(1) *Reflexivity*: $(f_1, \ldots, f_k)$ is row-related to $(f_1, \ldots, f_k)$ because $(f_1, \ldots, f_k) \rightarrowtail (f_1, \ldots, f_k)$, by the preceding proposition.

(2) *Symmetry*: Suppose that $(g_1, \ldots, g_k)$ is row-related to $(f_1, \ldots, f_k)$. Then, there is a sequence, $(f_1, \ldots, f_k) = (f_1{}^0, \ldots, f_k{}^0) \rightarrowtail (f_1{}^1, \ldots, f_k{}^1) \rightarrowtail \cdots \rightarrowtail (f_1{}^{m-1}, \ldots, f_k{}^{m-1}) \rightarrowtail (f_1{}^m, \ldots, f_k{}^m) = (g_1, \ldots, g_k)$.

Since $\rightarrowtail$ is symmetric, all the arrows in the above sequence may be reversed. This means that $(f_1, \ldots, f_k)$ is row-related to $(g_1, \ldots, g_k)$.

(3) *Transitivity*: Suppose that $(g_1, \ldots, g_k)$ is row-related to $(f_1, \ldots, f_k)$, and suppose that $(h_1, \ldots, h_k)$ is row-related to $(g_1, \ldots, g_k)$. Then, we have the sequence above and another similar sequence, starting with $(g_1, \ldots, g_k)$ and ending with $(h_1, \ldots, h_k)$. Put the two sequences together, obtaining

$$(f_1, \ldots, f_k) \rightarrowtail \cdots \rightarrowtail (g_1, \ldots, g_k) \rightarrowtail \cdots \rightarrowtail (h_1, \ldots, h_k)$$

This is a finite sequence showing that $(h_1, \ldots, h_k)$ is row-related to $(f_1, \ldots, f_k)$. Q.E.D.

Henceforth, we shall call two row-related k-tuples of $[(F^n)^*]^k$ *row-equivalent*. We shall call two equation systems, such as (3), row equivalent if the k-tuple of *linear expressions* in one is row-equivalent to the k-tuple of *linear expressions* in the other, via some sequence of elementary operations, *and* if, when these same operations are successively applied to the right-hand sides of the k equations in the first system, the result is the right-hand sides of the k equations in the second system.

Now, there is another relation between systems of linear expressions that we mentioned in 2.1. Before we discuss it, note that if $(f_1, \ldots, f_n)$ is any system of linear expressions, and if $\mathbf{x}$ is any member of F^n, then $(f_1(\mathbf{x}), \ldots, f_k(\mathbf{x}))$ is a k-tuple belonging to F^k. The equation

$$(f_1(\mathbf{x}), \ldots, f_k(\mathbf{x})) = \mathbf{b} = (b_1, \ldots, b_k),$$

is then, precisely the same as equation system (3) of Section 1. Now, we shall say that $(f_1, \ldots, f_k)$ and $(g_1, \ldots, g_k)$ are *solution-equivalent* if and only if for every $\mathbf{b}_1 \in F^k$ there is a $\mathbf{b}_2 \in F^k$ such that the equations

$$(f_1(\mathbf{x}), \ldots, f_k(\mathbf{x})) = \mathbf{b}_1$$

and

$$(g_1(\mathbf{x}), \ldots, g_k(\mathbf{x})) - \mathbf{b}_2$$

have the same solutions, and vice versa, for every $\mathbf{b}_2 \in F^k$ there is a $\mathbf{b}_1 \in F^k$ such that the above equations have the same solutions. This is the notion of equivalence mentioned in 2.1, and it is not difficult to show that this is an equivalence relation.**

It will turn out that row-equivalence is the same as solution-equivalence! For the present, however, all we need is the following result.

Proposition 5.8

If $(f_1, \ldots, f_k)$ and $(g_1, \ldots, g_k)$ are row-equivalent, then they are solution-equivalent. More precisely, if $(g_1, \ldots, g_k)$ is obtained from $(f_1, \ldots, f_k)$ by a certain sequence of elementary operations, if $\mathbf{b}_1 \in F^k$, and if $\mathbf{b}_2$ is obtained from $\mathbf{b}_1$ by the same sequence of operations, then

$$(f_1(\mathbf{x}), \ldots, f_k(\mathbf{x})) = \mathbf{b}_1$$

and

$$(g_1(\mathbf{x}), \ldots, g_k(\mathbf{x})) = \mathbf{b}_2$$

have the same solutions, and vice versa, for any $\mathbf{b}_2 \in F^k$, if $\mathbf{b}_1$ is obtained from $\mathbf{b}_2$

** Actually, in 2.1, we intimated that both of the above equations had the same solutions as $A(\mathbf{x}) = \mathbf{b}$, where, say $(f_1, \ldots, f_k)$ and $\mathbf{b}_1 = \mathbf{b}$ correspond to the original equation system in 2.1. Where, then, does $\mathbf{b}_2$ come from? To answer this, we note that in the above equations, we are tacitly expressing everything in terms of the standard basis of F^k. This is all right for what we are doing here. But, in the context of 2.1, the second equation (involving the g's and $\mathbf{b}_2$) was thought of as being expressed in terms of a different basis. Thus, although the same vector was involved on the right in both cases, it had different coefficients with respect to the different bases. Above, we are using the same basis in both cases. Thus, since the coefficients are different, so are the vectors. Later, we elaborate on this point.

by the reverses of the above operations applied in the reverse order, then the above equations have the same solutions.

Proof

Choose any $\mathbf{b}_1 \in F^k$ and let $\mathbf{b}_2$ be obtained from it by applying the elementary operations that lead from $(f_1, \ldots, f_k)$ to $(g_1, \ldots, g_k)$. We show, first, that every solution to

$$(f_1(\mathbf{x}), \ldots, f_k(\mathbf{x})) = \mathbf{b}_1 \tag{4}$$

is a solution to

$$(g_1(\mathbf{x}), \ldots, g_k(\mathbf{x})) = \mathbf{b}_2 \tag{5}$$

The proof of this is easy. If (4) has no solutions, then there is nothing to prove. If (4) has some solutions, let $\mathbf{c} = (c_1, \ldots, c_k)$ be any such. Thus,

$$(f_1(\mathbf{c}), \ldots, f_k(\mathbf{c})) = \mathbf{b}_1$$

Now apply, to both sides of this equation, successively, the elementary operations leading from $(f_1, \ldots, f_k)$ to $(g_1, \ldots, g_k)$. Equality is maintained, and the result, obviously, is the equation

$$(g_1(\mathbf{c}), \ldots, g_k(\mathbf{c})) = \mathbf{b}_2$$

Thus, $\mathbf{c}$ is a solution to (2).

Now, note that by reversing the operations leading from $(f_1, \ldots, f_k)$ to $(g_1, \ldots, g_k)$, we get from $(g_1, \ldots, g_k)$ to $(f_1, \ldots, f_k)$. Similarly, applying the reverse operations to $\mathbf{b}_2$ above, we obtain $\mathbf{b}_1$.

Suppose, then, that $\mathbf{c}$ is a solution to (5). Substitute it for $\mathbf{x}$ in (5) and apply, to both sides of the equation, successively, the (reverse) operations leading back to $(f_1, \ldots, f_k)$ from $(g_1, \ldots, g_k)$. The result will be, of course,

$$(f_1(\mathbf{c}), \ldots, f_k(\mathbf{c})) = \mathbf{b}_1,$$

showing that $\mathbf{c}$ is a solution to (4).

Thus, for every $\mathbf{b}_1 \in F^k$ there is a $\mathbf{b}_2 \in F^k$ such that (4) and (5) have the same solutions.

The "vice-versa" statement is proved in precisely the same way, this time starting with operations that lead from $(g_1, \ldots, g_k)$ to $(f_1, \ldots, f_k)$. Q.E.D.

This result is important because it shows that the application of elementary operations to an equation system does not alter the set of solutions to the system. Thus, given a complicated linear equation system, if we succeed in simplifying it via elementary operations to the point where we can write down solutions to the simplified result, then we know that these solutions are also solutions to the original system and, indeed, that the set of all such solutions is the set of all solutions to the original system.

This result, however, leaves open the important question of how to simplify equation systems via elementary operations. For this we shall rely heavily on operation (3); this is the elementary operation that allows us to eliminate variables.

To proceed, consider again equation system (3):

$$\begin{matrix} a_{11}x_1 + \cdots + a_{1n}x_n = b_1 \\ \vdots \qquad\qquad \vdots \quad \vdots \\ a_{k1}x_1 + \cdots + a_{kn}x_n = b_k \end{matrix}$$

If all the a_{ij} are zero, then the system has a solution if and only if all the b_i are zero. In that case, every n-tuple $(c_1, \ldots, c_n) \in F^n$ is a solution to the system. This case, therefore, is trivial.

Suppose then that some $a_{ij} \neq 0$. Let R_1 be the set of all numbers j such that x_j has a nonzero coefficient in the system above. R_1 is not empty because some $a_{ij} \neq 0$. Let r_1 be the smallest member of R_1. Thus x_{r_1} has a nonzero coefficient in at least one of the rows of the above system, say the ith row: its coefficient, therefore, is a_{ir_1}. Moreover, for all j such that $1 \leqq j \leqq r_1 - 1$, x_j has only zero coefficients in the above system.

Now, subtract suitable multiples of the ith row from all the other rows, eliminating x_{r_1} from the other rows. Perhaps other x_j's have been thereby eliminated as well, or perhaps not; it does not matter. What does matter, however, is that in every row but the ith, all the x_j have zero coefficients, if $1 \leqq j \leqq r_1$!

Look at these remaining rows. Let R_2 be the set of all j such that, in these remaining rows, x_j has a nonzero coefficient. If R_2 is empty (i.e., if all x_j in these rows now have zero coefficients), then we are finished, as the reader will soon see. If R_2 is not empty, it has a smallest member, say r_2. Thus, x_{r_2} has a nonzero coefficient in the new system, not in the ith row, but in some other row. Subtract suitable multiples of this row from all the equations so as to eliminate x_{r_2} from the other rows.

Continue this procedure, each time eliminating from all but one row the x with lowest subscript not already eliminated. Since there are only n distinct subscripts of the x's, the procedure must end after no more than n steps.

Before going further, we illustrate the procedure so far by the following example.

Let the system be

$$\begin{aligned} x_1 + 4x_2 + x_3 &= 2 \\ 2x_1 + 3x_2 &= -1 \\ 8x_1 + 2x_3 &= 0 \end{aligned}$$

Let us denote the first row by ρ_1, the second by ρ_2, and the third by ρ_3.

TABLE 5.1

Step	Operation	Result
1	$\rho_2 - 2\rho_1$	$x_1 + 4x_2 + x_3 = 2$ $-5x_2 - 2x_3 = -5$ $8x_1 + 2x_3 = 0$
2	$\rho_3 - 8\rho_1$	$x_1 + 4x_2 + x_3 = 2$ $-5x_2 - 2x_3 = -5$ $-32x_2 - 6x_3 = -16$
3	$\rho_1 + \frac{4}{5}\rho_2$	$x_1 - \frac{3}{5}x_3 = -2$ $-5x_2 - 2x_3 = -5$ $-32x_2 - 6x_3 = -16$
4	$\rho_2 - \frac{5}{32}\rho_3$	$x_1 - \frac{3}{5}x_3 = -2$ $-\frac{17}{16}x_3 = -\frac{5}{2}$ $-32x_2 - 6x_3 = -16$
5	$\rho_3 - \frac{96}{17}\rho_2$	$x_1 - \frac{3}{5}x_3 = -2$ $-\frac{17}{16}x_3 = -\frac{5}{2}$ $-32x_2 = -\frac{32}{17}$
6	$\rho_1 - \frac{48}{85}\rho_3$	$x_1 = -\frac{10}{17}$ $-\frac{17}{16}x_3 = -\frac{5}{2}$ $-32x_2 = 16$

We should emphasize that the above procedure is by no means the only one compatible with the general procedure outlined. For example, in step 1, we might have chosen row three and subtracted suitable multiples of it from the others. We chose to use ρ_1 in this way.

Nevertheless, any choices would result in something like what we have above. We now attempt to describe the general case.

After completing the procedure outlined above, we end up with a linear equation system in which there are certain variables $x_{r_1}, x_{r_2}, \ldots, x_{r_p}$ which appear each in precisely one row (since their appearances in the other rows have been eliminated). Moreover, $r_1 < r_2 < \cdots < r_p$, where $1 \leqq p \leqq n$. Also, in the row in which x_{r_ℓ} appears, $\ell = 1, \ldots, p$, no x_j appears unless $j \geqq r_\ell$. This is because of the way that the x_{r_ℓ}'s were chosen.

To complete the procedure, we apply operations of type 1 and type 2. First, we multiply the row in which x_{r_ℓ} appears by the reciprocal of the coefficient of $x_{r_\ell}, \ell = 1, \ldots, p$. This has the effect of changing the coefficient of x_{r_ℓ} to 1. Finally, we exchange rows so that x_{r_1} goes to the first row, x_{r_2} to the second, x_{r_3} to the third and so on. To express the result in a convenient form, we introduce some new notation.

Let L be any nonempty finite set, and suppose that U is a subset of a vector space such that the members of U are indexed by L. That is, there is a function** from L to U, where each $\ell \in \mathrm{L}$ goes to $\mathbf{u}_\ell \in \mathrm{U}$. We denote by $\sum_{\ell \in \mathrm{U}} \mathbf{u}_\ell$ the sum of all the members of U, with repetitions, perhaps, occurring (if the indexing is not 1–1).

Now, let R be the set of natural numbers $r_1, r_2, \ldots, r_p$, where these are the subscripts of the x's as obtained above. Some of the x's, in general, will not be among these. The subscripts of this latter group comprise what is left of $\{1, 2, \ldots, n\} = \mathbf{N}_n$ when R is removed. That is, they comprise $\mathbf{N}_n \setminus R$.

We may now write the simplified system as follows:

$$\begin{aligned} x_{r_1} + \sum_{j \in \mathbf{N}_n \setminus R} \alpha_{1j} x_j &= \beta_1 \\ \vdots \qquad \vdots \qquad\quad & \ \ \vdots \\ x_{r_p} + \sum_{j \in \mathbf{N}_n \setminus R} \alpha_{pj} x_j &= \beta_p \\ 0 &= \beta_{p+1} \\ \vdots \quad & \ \ \vdots \\ 0 &= \beta_k \end{aligned} \tag{17}$$

where the coefficients α_{ij} and the values β_i are obtained from the original a_{ij} and b_i by applying the elementary row operations. Notice that p, in addition to being $\leqq n$, is also $\leqq k$. Notice, also, that although we have written the x_{r_ℓ} one underneath the other, they really occur in distinct columns.

Now system (17) is, indeed, in a particularly simple form. We can describe its solutions as follows.

Proposition 5.9

(1) *System* (17) *has a solution if and only if* $\beta_{p+1}, \ldots, \beta_k$ *are all zero.*

(2) *If* (17) *has a solution, then the set of all solutions to* (17) *is the set of all*

** We do not insist that the function be 1–1, only onto U.

n-tuples $(c_1, \ldots, c_n)$ *satisfying*:

(i) c_j *is arbitrary if* $j \in \mathbf{N}_n \setminus R$
(ii) $c_{r_i} = \beta_i - \sum_{j \in \mathbf{N}_n \setminus R} \alpha_{ij} c_j, \quad i = 1, \ldots, p$

Next suppose that, instead of system (3), we had started with the corresponding homogeneous system (4) (i.e., all the b_i's were zero). If we perform exactly the same operations that led to (17), we get a system which is identical with (17) on the left but has only zeros on the right (because the elementary operations applied to the original zeros leave them unchanged). That is, we obtain the homogeneous system corresponding to (17):

$$\begin{aligned} x_{r_1} + \sum_{j \in \mathbf{N}_n \setminus R} \alpha_{1j} x_j &= 0 \\ \vdots \qquad\qquad & \vdots \\ x_{r_p} + \sum_{j \in \mathbf{N}_n \setminus R} \alpha_{pj} x_j &= 0 \end{aligned} \tag{18}$$

(We may leave out the last $k - p$ equations since they are of the form $0 = 0$). According to statement (1) of the above proposition, equation (18) has solutions.

Corollary to Proposition 5.9

System (18) *always has a solution. The set of all solutions to* (18) *is the set of all n-tuples* $(c_1, \ldots, c_n)$ *satisfying:*

(i) c_j *is arbitrary if* $j \in \mathbf{N}_n \setminus R$
(ii) $c_{r_1} = - \sum_{j \in \mathbf{N}_n \setminus R} \alpha_{ij} c_j, \quad i = 1, \ldots, p$

Remarks:

(1) Note, first that according to Proposition 5.8 systems (3) and (17) have the same solutions, and systems (4) and (18) have the same solutions. Thus, the above proposition and corollary describe the set of solutions to (3) and (4), respectively—once these systems have been suitably simplified, of course.

(2) Let B be the linear transformation corresponding to system (17). Proposition 5.8 implies that $\mathscr{R}_B$ has dimension p. For $\mathscr{R}_B$ consists of all k-tuples $(\beta_1, \ldots, \beta_p, \beta_{p+1}, \ldots, \beta_k)$ for which (17) has a solution. According to Proposition 5.9(a), the set of such k-tuples is precisely the set of all $(\beta_1, \ldots, \beta_p, \beta_{p+1}, \ldots, \beta_k)$ for which $\beta_{p+1} = \cdots = \beta_k = 0$: that is, the set of all k-tuples of the form $(\beta_1, \ldots, \beta_p, 0, \ldots, 0)$. The reader should be able to show that this set is a vector subspace of F^k with basis $\{\mathbf{e}_1^{(k)}, \ldots, \mathbf{e}_p^{(k)}\}$. In the next section, we shall give this set a different interpretation.

In any case, the above implies that the subspace of solutions to equation (18) has dimension precisely equal to $n - p$. Since this is also the subspace of solutions to (4), this means that the dimension of that subspace is $n - p$ and that the dimension of $\mathscr{R}_A$, consequently, is p. In the next section, we show that, via a slight reinterpretation, $A = B$, so that $\mathscr{R}_A = \mathscr{R}_B$ as described above.

Another way to see that the subspace of solutions to equation (18) has dimension $n - p$ is to look at the above corollary. The solution set consists of all $(c_1, \ldots, c_n)$, where c_j is arbitrary for $j \in \mathbf{N}_n \setminus R$ and c_r is a linear combination of the $c_j, j \in \mathbf{N}_n \setminus R$, as given by (ii) of the corollary.

Now, let us list the members of $\mathbf{N}_n \setminus R$ in increasing order: $s_1 < s_2 < \cdots < s_{n-p}$. *Note that they may be intermingled with the r_i's.* Although the x_{r_i}'s are listed as appearing first in the above proposition and corollary this was only for notational convenience. In actuality it is possible that, say, $s_1 = 1$, $s_2 = 2$, $r_1 = 3$, $s_3 = 4$, $r_2 = 5, \ldots$ and so on.

Next, we define n-tuples $\mathbf{v}_1, \ldots, \mathbf{v}_{n-p} \in F^n$ as follows: For any $\ell = 1, \ldots, n - p$,

$$\mathbf{v}_\ell = (c_1, \ldots, c_n), \text{ where}$$

$$c_j = \begin{cases} 1, & \text{if } j = s_\ell \\ 0, & \text{if } j - s_i,\ i \neq \ell \\ -\alpha_{is_\ell}, & \text{if } j = r_i \end{cases}$$

To illustrate this definition, we take the case that $s_1 = 1, s_2 = 2, \ldots, s_{n-p} = n - p$, $r_1 = n - p + 1$, $r_2 = n - p + 2, \ldots, r_p = n$. In that case,

$$\begin{aligned} \mathbf{v}_1 &= (1, 0, \ldots, 0, -\alpha_{11}, -\alpha_{21}, \ldots, -\alpha_{p1}) \\ \mathbf{v}_2 &= (0, 1, 0, \ldots, 0, -\alpha_{12}, -\alpha_{22}, \ldots, -\alpha_{p2}) \\ &\ \ \vdots \\ \mathbf{v}_{n-p} &= (0, \ldots, 0, 1, -\alpha_{1,n-p}, -\alpha_{2,n-p}, \ldots, -\alpha_{p,n-p}) \end{aligned}$$

In general, the $\mathbf{v}$'s will each have the same components as those above, but the 0's and 1's may be intermingled with the α's, occurring in columns $s_1, s_2, \ldots, s_{n-p}$ instead of in columns $1, 2, \ldots, n - p$. Notice that the α components are precisely what one obtains when one substitutes the 0 and 1 components in (ii) of the corollary. That is, each of the n-tuples $\mathbf{v}_1, \ldots, \mathbf{v}_{n-p}$ is a solution to equation (18) [its components $c_j, j \in \mathbf{N}_n \setminus R$, being specified as 0 or 1, its other components being obtained as linear combinations of these via (ii)]. We leave to the reader the task of showing that they are linearly independent and generate the set of all solutions to equation (18).

A basis of the set of solutions to equation (18) [or to (4)] is known as a *fundamental set of solutions* to equation (18) [or to (4)].

(3) We remind the reader of our previous result that the set of all solutions to equation (17) is, if nonempty, a translate of the set of solutions to (18) by any n-tuple satisfying (18). Thus, if $\mathbf{c}$ is such an n-tuple, and if $\mathbf{v}_1, \ldots, \mathbf{v}_{n-p}$ is a fundamental set of solutions to (18), then every n-tuple of the form

$$\mathbf{c} + a_1\mathbf{v}_1 + \cdots + a_{n-p}\mathbf{v}_{n-p}$$

(where $a_1, \ldots, a_{n-p}$ are chosen arbitrarily in F) is a solution to (17), and, conversely, every solution to (17) is of the above form.

We conclude this section by working out several examples.

Examples

(1)

$$\begin{aligned} 4x_1 - 3x_2 + x_3 &= -1 \\ x_1 + 5x_2 - 2x_3 &= 2 \\ x_1 + 2x_2 &= 0 \end{aligned}$$

We avoid going into as much detail here as in the previous example.

Subtracting suitable multiples of row three from the others, we get:

$$\begin{aligned} -11x_2 + x_3 &= -1 \\ 3x_2 - 2x_3 &= 2 \\ x_1 + 2x_2 &= 0 \end{aligned}$$

Adding twice row one to row two, and then adding a suitable multiple of row two to rows one and three, we get,

$$\begin{aligned} x_3 &= -1 \\ -19x_1 &= 0 \\ x_1 &= 0 \end{aligned}$$

Thus, $x_1 = 0$, $x_2 = 0$, $x_3 = -1$, or $(0, 0, -1)$ is the unique solution to the system.

(2)

$$\begin{aligned} 2x_1 + 3x_2 + x_3 - 4x_4 &= 0 \\ x_1 - 5x_2 - 3x_3 + 2x_4 &= 0 \\ 5x_1 + 2x_2 - x_4 &= 0 \\ 2x_1 - 9x_2 - 5x_3 + 9x_4 &= 0 \end{aligned}$$

Subtract suitable multiples of row two from the others, obtaining:

$$\begin{aligned} 13x_2 + 7x_3 - 8x_4 &= 0 \\ x_1 - 5x_2 - 3x_3 + 2x_4 &= 0 \\ 27x_2 + 15x_3 - 11x_4 &= 0 \\ x_2 + x_3 + 5x_4 &= 0 \end{aligned}$$

Subtract suitable multiples of row four from the others:

$$\begin{aligned} - 6x_3 - 73x_4 &= 0 \\ x_1 + 2x_3 + 27x_4 &= 0 \\ - 12x_3 - 146x_4 &= 0 \\ x_2 + x_3 + 5x_4 &= 0 \end{aligned}$$

Subtract twice row one from row three, eliminating it. Then, eliminate x_3 from the other rows by subtracting suitable multiples of row one from them:

$$\begin{aligned} -6x_3 - 73x_4 &= 0 \\ x_1 \qquad + \frac{8}{3}x_4 &= 0 \\ x_2 \qquad - \frac{43}{6}x_4 &= 0 \end{aligned}$$

At this point the procedure stops, since each row has contributed to the elimination procedure. We may rearrange rows and multiply row one by $-(1/6)$ to obtain

$$\begin{aligned} x_1 \qquad + \frac{8}{3}x_4 &= 0 \\ x_2 \qquad - \frac{43}{6}x_4 &= 0 \\ x_3 + \frac{73}{6}x_4 &= 0 \end{aligned}$$

Thus, by the corollary to Proposition 5.9 (or, by immediate inspection) the set of solutions to this system consists of all quadruples of the form

$$\left(-\frac{8}{3}c_4, \frac{43}{6}c_4, -\frac{73}{6}c_4, c_4\right)$$

(3)

$$\begin{aligned} 8x_1 - 2x_2 + 4x_3 + 3x_4 + x_5 &= 2 \\ x_2 - 4x_3 + x_4 - 2x_5 &= -10 \\ 2x_1 + x_2 \qquad - 4x_4 \qquad &= 1 \end{aligned}$$

Subtract four times row three from row one:

$$\begin{aligned} -6x_2 + 4x_3 + 13x_4 + x_5 &= -2 \\ x_2 - 4x_3 + x_4 - 2x_5 &= -10 \\ 2x_1 + x_2 \qquad - 4x_4 \qquad &= 1 \end{aligned}$$

Subtract suitable multiples of row two from the others to eliminate x_2, and subtract suitable multiples of the resulting row one from the rest to eliminate x_3:

$$\begin{aligned} -20x_3 + 19x_4 - 11x_5 &= -62 \\ x_2 \qquad - \frac{14}{5}x_4 + \frac{1}{5}x_5 &= \frac{12}{5} \\ 2x_1 \qquad - \frac{6}{5}x_4 - \frac{1}{5}x_5 &= \frac{7}{5} \end{aligned}$$

Rearrange rows and multiply them by suitable constants:

$$
\begin{aligned}
x_1 \qquad\qquad - \frac{6}{10}x_4 - \frac{1}{10}x_5 &= \frac{7}{10}\\
x_2 \quad - \frac{14}{5}x_4 + \frac{1}{5}x_5 &= \frac{12}{5}\\
x_3 - \frac{19}{20}x_4 + \frac{11}{20}x_5 &= \frac{62}{20}
\end{aligned}
$$

Thus, the solutions to this system are all 5-tuples of the form

$$\left(\frac{7}{10} + \frac{6}{10}c_4 + \frac{1}{10}c_5, \frac{12}{5} + \frac{14}{5}c_4 - \frac{1}{5}c_5, \frac{62}{20} + \frac{19}{20}c_4 - \frac{11}{20}c_5, c_4, c_5\right),$$

where c_4 and c_5 are arbitrary. Alternatively, we may first determine a fundamental set of solutions to the corresponding homogeneous system:

$$\mathbf{v}_1 = \left(\frac{6}{10}, \frac{14}{5}, \frac{19}{20}, 1, 0\right) \quad \text{(we set } x_4 = 1, x_5 = 0\text{);}$$

$$\mathbf{v}_2 = \left(\frac{1}{10}, -\frac{1}{5}, -\frac{11}{20}, 0, 1\right) \quad \text{(we set } x_4 = 0, x_5 = 1\text{)}$$

Then, we obtain any single solution to the given (nonhomogeneous system):

$$\mathbf{c} = \left(\frac{7}{10}, \frac{12}{5}, \frac{62}{20}, 0, 0\right) \quad \text{(we set } x_4 = x_5 = 0$$

and solve for x_1, x_2. x_3 in the above nonhomogeneous system).

Then, the set of all solutions to the given system consists of all 5-tuples of the form

$$\mathbf{c} + c_4\mathbf{v}_1 + c_5\mathbf{v}_2,$$

where c_4 and c_5 range arbitrarily over F.

If the reader evaluates the above linear combination, he will see that it is precisely the 5-tuple originally *obtained above as a general solution to the system*.

EXERCISES / 5.2

1. Obtain *all* solutions to the following systems of equations:

a.
$$
\begin{aligned}
ax_1 + bx_2 &= e\\
cx_1 + dx_2 &= f
\end{aligned}
$$

b.
$$
\begin{aligned}
3x_1 - x_2 - x_3 &= 0\\
x_1 + 2x_2 - 5x_3 &= 0\\
4x_2 + x_3 &= 0
\end{aligned}
$$

c. $\begin{pmatrix} 2 & -1 & 0 \\ 1 & 4 & 2 \\ 3 & 5 & -6 \\ 0 & 1 & 2 \end{pmatrix} \cdot \begin{pmatrix} x_1 \\ x_2 \\ x_3 \end{pmatrix} = \begin{pmatrix} 4 \\ -1 \\ 3 \\ 0 \end{pmatrix}$

d. $2x_1 - x_2 + 5x_3 + 3x_4 = 0$

e. $\begin{aligned} 2x_1 + x_2 - 5x_3 &= -1 \\ 2x_2 + 5x_3 &= 2 \\ 2x_3 &= 6 \end{aligned}$

2. Every rational number is a real number. Thus, every system of linear equations with rational coefficients can be also considered to be a system of linear equations with real coefficients. Suppose that we are given such a system.

   Thinking of it as a system with rational coefficients (in, say, n indeterminates) we may attempt to determine whether or not it has a solution in $\mathbf{Q}^n$. Thinking of it as a system with real coefficients, we may attempt to find a solution in $\mathbf{R}^n$.

   Of course, since $\mathbf{Q}^n \subset \mathbf{R}^n$, every solution in $\mathbf{Q}^n$ will be in $\mathbf{R}^n$. Can there be a solution to the system in $\mathbf{R}^n$ that is not in $\mathbf{Q}^n$? Why?

3. You are given a system of m linear equations in n indeterminates with coefficients in F, $m \leqq n$, and you apply the reduction procedure outlined in the text to obtain solutions to the system. You are as efficient as possible. What is the maximum number of times that you might have to apply elementary operation (1)? Operation (2)? Operation (3)?

   What would your answers be if $m > n$?

   Justify your answers.

2.3 Changing a Basis: an Interpretation of Row Reduction

Let V be any n-dimensional vector space over a field F, and let $X = \{\mathbf{x}_1, \ldots, \mathbf{x}_n\}$ be an ordered basis of V. We introduce three elementary ways of changing X analogous to the elementary row operations of the previous section. Each change will result in an ordered basis X' of V. We may specify the change by describing what happens to each $\mathbf{x}_i \in X$; that is, by indicating what vector in X' $\mathbf{x}_i$ becomes. In short, we specify the change by presenting a function $X \to X'$. Of course, since V is a vector space with basis X, these functions determine uniquely certain linear transformations $V \to V$, which also describe the change of basis. These comments motivate the following definition.

Definition 5.4

Let F, V, and X be as above. Consider the following three types of functions from X to V:

(1) *Choose any i and j between 1 and n such that $i \neq j$. Define $\sigma_{ij} : X \to V$ as follows:*

$$\sigma_{ij}(\mathbf{x}_\ell) = \begin{cases} \mathbf{x}_\ell, & \text{if } \ell \neq i \text{ and } \ell \neq j \\ \mathbf{x}_j, & \text{if } \ell = i \\ \mathbf{x}_i, & \text{if } \ell = j \end{cases}$$

(2) *Choose any i between* 1 *and n and any $a \in F$, $a \neq 0$. Define $\mu_{i,a}$ $X \to V$ as follows:*

$$\mu_{i,a}(\mathbf{x}_\ell) = \begin{cases} \mathbf{x}_\ell, & \text{if } \ell \neq i \\ a\mathbf{x}_i, & \text{if } \ell = i \end{cases}$$

(3) *Choose any i and j between* 1 *and n, $i \neq j$, and any $c \in F$. Define $\tau_{ij,c}: X \to V$ as follows:*

$$\tau_{ij,c}(\mathbf{v}_\ell) = \begin{cases} \mathbf{v}_\ell, & \ell \neq j \\ \mathbf{v}_j + c\mathbf{v}_i, & \ell = j \end{cases}$$

Each of the above functions determines uniquely a linear transformation from V to V, which we denote by the same symbol. These linear transformations of V are called elementary transformations of V with respect to the basis X. We distinguish them by types in the usual way.

Note that the elementary transformation [of type (1)] σ_{ij} has the effect of switching the basis vectors $\mathbf{x}_i$ and $\mathbf{x}_j$ and of leaving the others unchanged. The elementary transformation [of type (2)] $\mu_{i,a}$ has the effect of multiplying $\mathbf{x}_i$ by a and of leaving the other basis vectors unchanged. The elementary transformation [of type (3)] $\tau_{ij,c}$ has the effect of adding $c\mathbf{v}_i$ to $\mathbf{v}_j$ and of leaving the other basis vectors unchanged.

Proposition 5.10

If $T: V \to V$ is an elementary transformation of V with respect to X, then T is an isomorphism and $T(X)$ is a basis of V. Moreover, T^{-1} is an elementary transformation of the same type as T (with respect to X).

Proof

To prove that T is an isomorphism, it suffices to show that $T \mid X$ is 1–1 and that $T(X)$ is a basis of V (Proposition 4.17).

If T is of type (1), then $T \mid X$ merely involves switching basis vectors. In this case, $T \mid X$ is clearly 1–1 and $T(X) = X$. Thus, in this case, T is clearly an isomorphism. Finally, it is not hard to see that T^{-1} merely involves switching the basis vectors back again and, thus, is an elementary transformation of type (1).

If T is of type (2), $T \mid X$ leaves all basis vectors fixed but, perhaps, one which it multiplies by a nonzero $a \in F$, obtaining, say, $a\mathbf{x}_i$. Now, $a\mathbf{x}_i$ is distinct from the other $\mathbf{x}$'s, since, if some other $\mathbf{x} \in X$ were a multiple of $\mathbf{x}_i$, X would not be linearly independent. Thus, $T \mid X$ is 1–1. Moreover, it is easy to show that $\{\mathbf{x}_1, \ldots, a\mathbf{x}_i, \ldots, \mathbf{x}_n\} = T(X)$ is linearly independent and, thus, is basis of V. Therefore, T is an isomorphism. T^{-1} is, clearly, the linear transformation that sends $\mathbf{x}_i$ to $(1/a)\mathbf{x}_i$ and leaves all the other $\mathbf{x}$'s in X fixed. Thus, T^{-1} is also an elementary transformation of type (2).

Finally, if T is of type (3), $T \mid X$ leaves all basis vectors fixed but, perhaps, one to which it adds an arbitrary multiple of another basis vector, obtaining, say $\mathbf{x}_j + c\mathbf{x}_i$. If this equaled any of the $\mathbf{x}_\ell \in X, \ell \neq j$, then X would be linearly dependent, which is impossible. Thus, $T \mid X$ is 1–1. Moreover, by a lemma in Chapter 4, $T(X) = \{\mathbf{x}_1, \ldots, \mathbf{x}_j + c\mathbf{x}_i, \ldots, \mathbf{x}_n\} = \{\mathbf{x}_1 + 0\mathbf{x}_i, \ldots, \mathbf{x}_j + c\mathbf{x}_i, \ldots, \mathbf{x}_n + 0\mathbf{x}_i\}$ is linearly independent. Thus, it is a basis of V, so that T is an isomorphism. The reader may verify that T^{-1} is the isomorphism that keeps all $\mathbf{x}$'s fixed, except $\mathbf{x}_j$ which it sends to $\mathbf{x}_j - c\mathbf{x}_i$. Therefore, T^{-1} is an elementary transformation of type (3). Q.E.D.

One consequence of the above proposition is that for every elementary transformation $T: V \to V$ with respect to the ordered basis X, $T(X)$ is a basis of V. This is the basis X' mentioned in the beginning.

Now, it will be important to distinguish between the different orders in which the basis X is presented. Thus, we formalize the notion of *an ordered basis of V. It is any basis of V together with a fixed ordering of the basis vectors: that is, it is an ordered n-tuple of linearly independent vectors of V.* Thus, the basis X, together with the ordering in which $\mathbf{x}_1$ is first, $\mathbf{x}_2$ is second, and so on, can be represented as $(\mathbf{x}_1, \mathbf{x}_2, \ldots, \mathbf{x}_n)$.

Definition 5.5

An ordered basis $(\mathbf{y}_1, \ldots, \mathbf{y}_n)$ of V is an elementary transform of an ordered basis $(\mathbf{x}_1, \ldots, \mathbf{x}_n)$ of V if and only if $(\mathbf{y}_1, \ldots, \mathbf{y}_n) = (T(\mathbf{x}_1), \ldots, T(\mathbf{x}_n))$, for some elementary transformation $T: V \to V$ with respect to the basis X.

Proposition 5.11

Let $T: V \to V$ be an elementary transformation with respect to $X = \{\mathbf{x}_1, \ldots, \mathbf{x}_n\}$, and let $(\mathbf{y}_1, \ldots, \mathbf{y}_n) = (T(\mathbf{x}_1), \ldots, T(\mathbf{x}_n))$. Then, T^{-1} is an elementary transformation (of the same type as T) with respect to $Y = \{\mathbf{y}_1, \ldots, \mathbf{y}_n\}$.

Proof

In Proposition 5.10, we showed that T^{-1} is an elementary transformation with respect to X. Here, we must show it is one with respect to Y. We divide the proof into cases, according to the type of T, using the notation of Definition 5.3.

(1) Suppose $T = \sigma_{ij}$. Then, $\mathbf{y}_\ell = \mathbf{x}_\ell$, if $\ell \neq i$ and $\ell \neq j$, $\mathbf{y}_i = \mathbf{x}_j$ and $\mathbf{y}_j = \mathbf{x}_i$. Since, $T(\mathbf{x}_\ell) = \mathbf{y}_\ell$, for all ℓ, by definition of $\mathbf{y}_\ell$, we have

$$T^{-1}(\mathbf{y}_\ell) = \mathbf{x}_\ell = \begin{cases} \mathbf{y}_\ell, & \text{if } \ell \neq i \text{ and } \ell \neq j \\ \mathbf{y}_j, & \text{if } \ell = i \\ \mathbf{y}_i, & \text{if } \ell = j \end{cases}$$

Thus, T^{-1} is of type (1) with respect to Y.

(2) Suppose $T = \mu_{i,a}$. Then, $\mathbf{y}_\ell = \mathbf{x}_\ell$, if $\ell \neq i$, and $\mathbf{y}_i = a\mathbf{x}_i$. Since $T(\mathbf{x}_\ell) = \mathbf{y}_\ell$, for all ℓ,

$$T^{-1}(\mathbf{y}_\ell) = \mathbf{x}_\ell = \begin{cases} \mathbf{y}_\ell, & \text{if } \ell \neq i \\ (1/a)\mathbf{y}_i, & \text{if } \ell = i, \end{cases}$$

so that T^{-1} is of type (2) with respect to Y.

(3) Suppose $T = \tau_{ij,c}$. Then, $\mathbf{y}_\ell = \mathbf{x}_\ell$, if $\ell \neq j$, and $\mathbf{y}_j = \mathbf{x}_j + c\mathbf{x}_i$. Thus,

$$T^{-1}(\mathbf{y}_\ell) = \mathbf{x}_\ell = \begin{cases} \mathbf{y}_\ell, & \text{if } \ell \neq j \\ \mathbf{y}_j - c\mathbf{x}_i = \mathbf{y}_j - c\mathbf{y}_i, & \text{if } \ell = j, \end{cases}$$

so that T^{-1} is of type (3) with respect to Y. Q.E.D.

Corollary to Proposition 5.11

"Being an elementary transform of" is a reflexive, symmetric relation on the set of all ordered bases of V.

We leave a proof to the reader, suggesting that he compare this corollary to Proposition 5.6.

As we comment after that proposition, we are not interested in the elementary steps *per se* but in their repeated application. Thus, we define a more inclusive relation as follows.

Definition 5.6

Let V be as before and let $(\mathbf{x}_1, \ldots, \mathbf{x}_n)$ and $(\mathbf{y}_1, \ldots, \mathbf{y}_n)$ be ordered bases of V. We say that $(\mathbf{y}_1, \ldots, \mathbf{y}_n)$ is a transform of $(\mathbf{x}_1, \ldots, \mathbf{x}_n)$ if and only if there exists a sequence of ordered bases of V,

$$(\mathbf{v}_1^{(i)}, \ldots, \mathbf{v}_n^{(i)}), \; i = 0, \ldots, k,$$

such that $(\mathbf{x}_1, \ldots, \mathbf{x}_n) = (\mathbf{v}_1^{(0)}, \ldots, \mathbf{v}_n^{(0)})$, $(\mathbf{y}_1, \ldots, \mathbf{y}_n) = (\mathbf{v}_1^{(k)}, \ldots, \mathbf{v}_n^{(k)})$, and each member of the sequence is an elementary transform of the preceding.

Compare this definition with Definition 5.3 and the following proposition with Proposition 5.7.

Proposition 5.12

"Being a transform of" is an equivalence relation on the set of all ordered bases of V.

The proof is an analog of that of Proposition 5.7 and is, therefore, left to the reader.

Henceforth, we say that two ordered bases are *equivalent* if one is a transform of the other.

Proposition 5.13

Any two ordered bases of V are equivalent.

Proof

We proceed by induction on the dimension of V.

If $\dim V = 1$, then any ordered basis of V is a 1-tuple and any other consists of one vector which must be a nonzero multiple of the first. Thus, the second is an elementary transform of the first [by an elementary transformation of type (2)], and so the two are equivalent.

Assume the result for all vector spaces of dimension $k - 1$, and suppose that $\dim V = k$. Let $(\mathbf{x}_1, \ldots, \mathbf{x}_k)$ and $(\mathbf{y}_1, \ldots, \mathbf{y}_k)$ be any ordered bases of V. To indicate when $(\mathbf{y}_1, \ldots, \mathbf{y}_k)$ is a transform of $(\mathbf{x}_1, \ldots, \mathbf{x}_k)$, we write $(\mathbf{x}_1, \ldots, \mathbf{x}_k) \rightarrowtail (\mathbf{y}_1, \ldots, \mathbf{y}_k)$. Of course, we do not yet know whether this is the case or not.

Since $\{\mathbf{x}_1, \ldots, \mathbf{x}_k\}$ is a basis of V, every $\mathbf{y}_j$ can be expressed as a linear combination of the $\mathbf{x}_i$'s:

$$\begin{aligned} \mathbf{y}_1 &= a_{11}\mathbf{x}_1 + \cdots + a_{1k}\mathbf{x}_k \\ &\ \vdots \qquad \vdots \\ \mathbf{y}_k &= a_{k1}\mathbf{x}_1 + \cdots + a_{kk}\mathbf{x}_k \end{aligned}$$

Choose any $\mathbf{x}_i$ that appears with nonzero coefficient in the above linear combination with value $\mathbf{y}_1$.** We may assume, without losing generality (for notational convenience), that the $\mathbf{x}_i$ is $\mathbf{x}_1$; that is, we may assume $a_{11} \neq 0$.

Now, we claim, first, that $(\mathbf{x}_1, \mathbf{x}_2, \ldots, \mathbf{x}_k) \rightarrowtail (\mathbf{y}_1, \mathbf{x}_2, \ldots, \mathbf{x}_k)$. To prove this, apply the following elementary transformations to $(\mathbf{x}_1, \mathbf{x}_2, \ldots, \mathbf{x}_k)$ successively:

Multiply $\mathbf{x}_1$ by a_{11} and add to the result successively $a_{12}\mathbf{x}_2$, $a_{13}\mathbf{x}_3, \ldots, a_{1k}\mathbf{x}_k$. These are all elementary transformations, and they change $(\mathbf{x}_1, \mathbf{x}_2, \ldots, \mathbf{x}_k)$ to $(\mathbf{y}_1, \mathbf{x}_2, \ldots, \mathbf{x}_k)$.

Next, subtract suitable multiples of $\mathbf{y}_1$ from $\mathbf{y}_2, \ldots, \mathbf{y}_k$ (say $c_2\mathbf{y}_1, c_3\mathbf{y}_1, \ldots, c_k\mathbf{y}_1$, respectively) to eliminate terms involving $\mathbf{x}_1$ on the right. Thus, the vectors $\mathbf{y}_2 - c_2\mathbf{y}_1, \mathbf{y}_3 - c_3\mathbf{y}_1, \ldots, \mathbf{y}_n - c_k\mathbf{y}_1$ are linear combinations of $\mathbf{x}_2, \ldots, \mathbf{x}_k$. Moreover, they are linearly independent (by a lemma in Chapter 4). Let $U = \operatorname{span}(\{\mathbf{x}_2, \ldots, \mathbf{x}_k\})$. Then, both $\{\mathbf{x}_2, \ldots, \mathbf{x}_k\}$ and $\{\mathbf{y}_2 - c_2\mathbf{y}_1, \ldots, \mathbf{y}_k - c_k\mathbf{y}_1\}$ are bases of U. By the inductive assumption

$$(\mathbf{x}_2, \ldots, \mathbf{x}_k) \rightarrowtail (\mathbf{y}_2 - c_2\mathbf{y}_1, \ldots, \mathbf{y}_k - c_k\mathbf{y}_1)$$

That is, the ordered basis on the right can be obtained from the one on the left by a sequence of elementary transformations. But, then, it must be true that

$$(\mathbf{y}_1, \mathbf{x}_2, \ldots, \mathbf{x}_k) \rightarrowtail (\mathbf{y}_1, \mathbf{y}_2 - c_2\mathbf{y}_1, \ldots, \mathbf{y}_k - c_k\mathbf{y}_1),$$

using the same sequence of operations as above on the last k-1 vectors and simply sending $\mathbf{y}_1$ to $\mathbf{y}_1$.

** There must be at least one such because $\mathbf{y}_1 \neq \mathbf{0}$.

Finally, we observe that

$$(\mathbf{y}_1, \mathbf{y}_2 - c_2\mathbf{y}_1, \ldots, \mathbf{y}_n - c_n\mathbf{y}_1) \rightarrowtail (\mathbf{y}_1, \mathbf{y}_2, \ldots, \mathbf{y}_n),$$

since the right-hand ordered basis can be obtained from the one on the left by the elementary transformations of adding $c_2\mathbf{y}_1, c_3\mathbf{y}_1, \ldots, c_n\mathbf{y}_1$, respectively, to the second, third, . . . , nth basis vectors on the left.

We now combine our results:

$$(\mathbf{x}_1, \mathbf{x}_2, \ldots, \mathbf{x}_n) \rightarrowtail (\mathbf{y}_1, \mathbf{x}_2, \ldots, \mathbf{x}_n) \rightarrowtail$$
$$(\mathbf{y}_1, \mathbf{y}_2 - c_2\mathbf{y}_1, \ldots, \mathbf{y}_n - c_n\mathbf{y}_1) \rightarrowtail (\mathbf{y}_1, \mathbf{y}_2, \ldots, \mathbf{y}_n)$$

Since $\rightarrowtail$ is transitive, we conclude that

$$(\mathbf{x}_1, \mathbf{x}_2, \ldots, \mathbf{x}_n) \rightarrowtail (\mathbf{y}_1, \mathbf{y}_2, \ldots, \mathbf{y}_n),$$

which is to say that they are equivalent. Q.E.D.

This proposition has many useful consequences. First, it states that we can go from any basis of V to any other via a sequence of elementary transforms of the original. This will be useful for our interpretation of row reduction. Another consequence will be stated in the form of a corollary.

Corollary to Proposition 5.14

Let V be an n-dimensional vector space, as above, let $T: V \to V$ be an isomorphism, and let X be any basis of V. Then,

$$T = T_k \circ T_{k-1} \circ \cdots \circ T_2 \circ T_1$$

where T_i is an elementary transformation of V with respect to the ordered basis $(T_{i-1} \circ \cdots \circ T_2 \circ T_1)(X)$, if $i > 1$, or *X, if $i = 1$.*

Proof

First note that for any $i > 1$, $(T_{i-1} \circ \cdots \circ T_2 \circ T_1)(X)$ is a basis of V because it is the image of X under successively applied isomorphisms $T_1, T_2, \ldots, T_{i-1}$. Therefore, the above corollary at least makes sense.

Next, define a basis $Y = \{\mathbf{y}_1, \ldots, \mathbf{y}_n\}$ of V as follows: Let $\mathbf{y}_j = T(\mathbf{x}_j)$, $j = 1, \ldots, n$. This is, indeed, a basis of V because T is an isomorphism.

Now, by the preceding proposition, the ordered basis $(\mathbf{y}_1, \ldots, \mathbf{y}_n)$ is equivalent to $(\mathbf{x}_1, \ldots, \mathbf{x}_n)$. That is, there is a sequence of ordered bases of V,

$$(\mathbf{v}_1^{(i)}, \ldots, \mathbf{v}_n^{(i)})$$

$i = 0, \ldots, k$ such that $(\mathbf{x}_1, \ldots, \mathbf{x}_n) = (\mathbf{v}_1^{(0)}, \ldots, \mathbf{v}_n^{(0)})$, $(\mathbf{y}_1, \ldots, \mathbf{y}_n) = (\mathbf{v}_1^{(k)}, \ldots, \mathbf{v}_n^{(k)})$ and such that each $(\mathbf{v}_1^{(i)}, \ldots, \mathbf{v}_n^{(i)})$ is an elementary transform of $(\mathbf{v}_1^{(i-1)}, \ldots, \mathbf{v}_n^{(i-1)})$, $i = 1, \ldots, k$. More explicitly, there exist isomorphisms $T_i: V \to V$, $i = 1, \ldots, k$ such that

$$(\mathbf{v}_1^{(i)}, \ldots, \mathbf{v}_n^{(i)}) = (T_i(\mathbf{v}_1^{(i-1)}), \ldots, T_i(\mathbf{v}_n^{(i-1)})),$$

$i = 1, \ldots, k$, and such that T_i is an elementary transformation of V with respect to $\{\mathbf{v}_1^{(i-1)}, \ldots, \mathbf{v}_n^{(i-1)}\}$.

Choose any $\mathbf{y}_j \in Y$ and note that

$$\mathbf{y}_j = \mathbf{v}_j^{(k)} = T_k(\mathbf{v}_j^{(k-1)}) = T_k(T_{k-1}(\mathbf{v}_j^{(k-2)})) = \cdots$$
$$= T_k(T_{k-1}(\ldots T_1(\mathbf{v}_j^{(0)}))\ldots) = (T_k \circ \cdots \circ T_1)(\mathbf{x}_j)$$

This is true for every $j = 1, \ldots, n$. On the other hand, by definition,

$$\mathbf{y}_j = T(\mathbf{x}_j)$$

for every $j = 1, \ldots, n$. Thus, the linear transformations T and $T_k \circ T_{k-1} \circ \cdots \circ T_2 \circ T_1$ have the same values on the basis X. By Proposition 4.17, this means that they must be equal.

It remains only to observe that T_1 is an elementary transformation of V with respect to the basis

$$\{\mathbf{v}_1^{(0)}, \ldots, v_n^{(0)}\} = \{\mathbf{x}_1, \ldots, \mathbf{x}_n\} = X$$

and that T_i is an elementary transformation of V with respect to

$$\{\mathbf{v}_1^{(i-1)}, \ldots, \mathbf{v}_n^{(i-1)}\} = (T_{i-1} \circ \cdots \circ T_1)(X),$$

for $i > 1$. Q.E.D.

Now we turn to our main purpose, that of interpreting the row operations described in 2.2.

Proposition 5.15

Let V be any vector space over F with basis $X = \{\mathbf{x}_1, \ldots, \mathbf{x}_n\}$, let $\mathbf{v}$ be any vector in V, and let $T: V \to V$ be an elementary transformation of V with respect to X. Suppose that T is of type r, where r is 1, 2, or 3.

Let $a_1, \ldots, a_n$ be the coefficients of $\mathbf{v}$ with respect to the basis X. That is, in the linear combination of vectors of X with value $\mathbf{v}$, let a_1 be the coefficient of $\mathbf{x}_1$, a_2 the coefficient of $\mathbf{x}_2$, and so on. Similarly, let $b_1, \ldots, b_n$ be the coefficients of $\mathbf{v}$ with respect to the basis $T(X)$.

Then, the n-tuple $(b_1, \ldots, b_n)$ is obtained from the n-tuple $(a_1, \ldots, a_n)$ by an elementary (row) operation of type r (where, by "elementary row operation" we mean, as before, the operations described in Definition 5.2, applied here to n-tuples of scalars rather than to n-tuples of linear expressions).

Proof

The proof is divided into cases, depending on the type of T. We use the notation of Definition 5.4. Throughout, let $\mathbf{y}_j = T(\mathbf{x}_j)$, $j = 1, \ldots, n$, and let $Y = \{\mathbf{y}_1, \ldots, \mathbf{y}_n\} = T(X)$.

(1) $T = \sigma_{ij}$. In this case, $\mathbf{y}_\ell = \mathbf{x}_\ell$, if $\ell \neq i$ and $\ell \neq j$, and $\mathbf{y}_i = \mathbf{x}_j$, $\mathbf{y}_j = \mathbf{x}_i$. Therefore,

$$b_1\mathbf{y}_1 + \cdots + b_n\mathbf{y}_n = \mathbf{v} = a_1\mathbf{x}_1 + \cdots + a_i\mathbf{x}_i + \cdots + a_j\mathbf{x}_j + \cdots + a_n\mathbf{x}_n$$
$$= a_1\mathbf{y}_1 + \cdots + a_i\mathbf{y}_j + \cdots + a_j\mathbf{y}_i + \cdots + a_n\mathbf{y}_n,$$

or

$$(b_1 - a_1)\mathbf{y}_1 + \cdots + (b_i - a_j)\mathbf{y}_i + \cdots + (b_j - a_i)\mathbf{y}_j + \cdots + (b_n - a_n)\mathbf{y}_n = \mathbf{0}$$

Since Y is linearly independent,

$$b_\ell = a_\ell, \text{ if } \ell \neq i \text{ and } \ell \neq j,$$
$$b_i = a_j \text{ and } b_j = a_i$$

Thus, $(b_1, \ldots, b_n)$ is obtained from $(a_1, \ldots, a_n)$ by switching a_i and a_j.

(2) $T = \mu_{i,a}$. In this case $\mathbf{y}_\ell = \mathbf{x}_\ell$, $\ell \neq i$, and $\mathbf{y}_i = a\mathbf{x}_i$. Thus,

$$b_1\mathbf{y}_1 + \cdots + b_i\mathbf{y}_i + \cdots b_n\mathbf{y}_n = \mathbf{v} = a_1\mathbf{x}_1 + \cdots +$$
$$a_i\mathbf{x}_i + \cdots + a_n\mathbf{x}_n = a_1\mathbf{y}_1 + \cdots + a_i((1/a)\mathbf{y}_i) + \cdots + a_n\mathbf{y}_n$$

Thus, $b_\ell = a_\ell, \ell \neq i$, and $b_i = (1/a)a_i$. Therefore, $(b_1, \ldots, b_n)$ is obtained from $(a_1, \ldots, a_n)$ by an operation of type (2).

(3) $T = \tau_{ij,c}$. We have $\mathbf{y}_\ell = \mathbf{x}_\ell, \ell \neq j$, and $\mathbf{y}_j = \mathbf{x}_j + c\mathbf{x}_i$. Thus,

$$b_1\mathbf{y}_1 + \cdots + b_i\mathbf{y}_i + \cdots + b_j\mathbf{y}_j + \cdots + b_n\mathbf{y}_n = \mathbf{v}$$
$$= a_1\mathbf{x}_1 + \cdots + a_i\mathbf{x}_i + \cdots + a_j\mathbf{x}_j + \cdots + a_n x_n$$
$$= a_1\mathbf{y}_1 + \cdots + (a_i - ca_j)\mathbf{x}_i + \cdots + a_j(\mathbf{x}_j + c\mathbf{x}_i) + \cdots + a_n\mathbf{x}_n$$

Here, we have added and subtracted the term $ca_j\mathbf{x}_i$. Thus,

$$b_1\mathbf{y}_1 + \cdots + b_i\mathbf{y}_i + \cdots + b_j\mathbf{y}_j + \cdots + b_n\mathbf{y}_n$$
$$= a_1\mathbf{y}_1 + \cdots + (a_i - ca_j)\mathbf{y}_i + \cdots + a_j\mathbf{y}_j + \cdots + a_n\mathbf{y}_n$$

Therefore, $b_\ell = a_\ell, \ell \neq i$, and $b_i = a_i - ca_j$, so that $(b_1, \ldots, b_n)$ is obtained from $(a_1, \ldots, a_n)$ by an operation of type (3). Q.E.D.

Note that although the operation determined by the elementary transformation is of the same *type* as that of the transformation, it is not exactly the same. For example, when the elementary transformation involves multiplying by a, the corresponding operation involves multiplying by $1/a$. When the transformation *adds* a multiple of the ith member of the n-tuple *to the* jth, the operation corresponding to it subtracts a multiple of the jth member of the coefficient n-tuple from the ith. Indeed, one can say that the row operation corresponding to an elementary basis transformation is, *informally*, of course, *inverse* to the basis transformation.

Corollary to Proposition 5.15

Let V, X, $\mathbf{v}$, and T be as above. Then, the n-tuple of coefficients of $T^{-1}(\mathbf{v})$ with respect to X is obtained from $(a_1, \ldots, a_n)$, the n-tuple of coefficients of $\mathbf{v}$ with respect to X, by an operation of the same type as T^{-1}.

Proof

Let $(b_1, \ldots, b_n)$ be, as in the proof of the above proposition, the n-tuple of coefficients of $\mathbf{v}$ with respect to $Y = T(X)$. That is,

$$\mathbf{v} = b_1T(\mathbf{x}_1) + \cdots + b_nT(\mathbf{x}_n)$$

Therefore,

$$\mathbf{v} = T(b_1\mathbf{x}_1 + \cdots + b_n\mathbf{x}_n),$$

so that

$$T^{-1}(\mathbf{v}) = b_1\mathbf{x}_1 + \cdots + b_n\mathbf{x}_n$$

This means that $(b_1, \ldots, b_n)$ is also the n-tuple of coefficients of $T^{-1}(\mathbf{v})$ with respect to X. We showed, in the above proposition, that $(b_1, \ldots, b_n)$ is obtained from $(a_1, \ldots, a_n)$ by an elementary operation of the same type as T, which has the same type as T^{-1}. Q.E.D.

The above proposition and corollary provide us with two ways of interpreting the work of row reduction in 2.2.

Consider the linear transformation.

$$A: F^n \to F^k$$

and the vector $\mathbf{b} = (b_1, \ldots, b_k) \in F^k$. The equation

$$A(\mathbf{x}) = \mathbf{b}$$

can be thought of as a system of linear equations, such as system (3) described in the beginning of this chapter. We may think of $\mathbf{x} = (x_1, \ldots, x_n)$ as a "variable" vector ranging over F^n, so that $A(\mathbf{x})$ and $\mathbf{b}$ can be regarded as vectors in F^k. When we write $\mathbf{b}$ as a k-tuple, as above, the components b_i are just the coefficients of $\mathbf{b}$ with respect to the standard basis of F^k. Similarly, when we write $A(\mathbf{x})$ as a k-tuple, its components are the coefficients of $A(\mathbf{x})$ with respect to the standard basis of F^k.

Now, apply any elementary basis transformation to F^k, with respect to the standard basis of F^k. The result will be a new basis of F^k; *the k-tuples of coefficients of $A(\mathbf{x})$ and $\mathbf{b}$, respectively, with respect to this new basis, will be precisely what one gets when applying the appropriate elementary row operation to the original k-tuples.* This follows directly from Proposition 5.15. By the way, it is not hard to see, from the proof of Proposition 5.15, that *every* elementary row operation can be so obtained from an elementary transformation of F^k.

Next, apply another elementary transformation of F^k, this time with respect to the new basis just obtained. Again, the k-tuples of coefficients change by the corresponding row operation.

Thus, according to this interpretation, the row operations applied to a system of linear equations reflect the coefficient changes resulting from successively applied elementary transformations of F^k. The linear transformation A is never changed; nor is $\mathbf{x}$ or $\mathbf{b}$. The equation,

$$A(\mathbf{x}) = \mathbf{b},$$

therefore, is unchanged. What does change is the basis of F^k and, hence, the coefficients of the above vectors $A(\mathbf{x})$ and $\mathbf{b}$. The idea is to alter the basis of

F^k wisely so that the coefficients of the above vectors are simple enough to make a solution to the equation easy. We showed that this could be done in 2.2.

Now for another interpretation, using the corollary to Proposition 5.15. Again, consider the transformation A, the vector $\mathbf{b}$, the equation $A(\mathbf{x}) = \mathbf{b}$ and apply to F^k the elementary transformation (with respect to the standard basis of F^k) T_1^{-1}. The above corollary tells us that the vectors $T_1(A(\mathbf{x}))$ and $T_1(\mathbf{b})$ have coefficients, *with respect to the standard basis*, that are obtained from those of $A(\mathbf{x})$ and $\mathbf{b}$ by means of a row operation of the type of T_1.

Now, consider the equation

$$T_1(A(\mathbf{x})) = T_1(\mathbf{b}),$$

and apply to F^k another elementary transformation (with respect to the standard basis of F^k) T_2^{-1}. Then, the coefficients of $T_2(T_1(A(\mathbf{x})))$ and $T_2(R_1(\mathbf{b}))$, respectively, are obtained from those of $T_1(A(\mathbf{x}))$ and $T_1(\mathbf{b})$ by an elementary row operation of the type of T_2. All coefficients, here, are taken with respect to the standard basis of F^k.

Thus, according to this interpretation, the row operations applied to the equation

$$A(\mathbf{x}) = \mathbf{b}$$

correspond to elementary transformations $T_1^{-1}, T_2^{-1}, \ldots$ of F^k, with respect to the standard basis of F^k, the inverses of which are applied successively to the above equation.

After a number of steps, the result is an equation of the form

$$T(A(\mathbf{x})) = T(\mathbf{b}),$$

where $T: F^k \to F^k$ is an isomorphism. Indeed, if $T_1^{-1}, T_2^{-1}, \ldots, T_r^{-1}$, are the successive elementary transformations, the inverses of which are applied to the equation, then $T = T_r \circ T_{r-1} \circ \cdots \circ T_2 \circ T_1$.

In any case, the equations

$$A(\mathbf{x}) = \mathbf{b}$$

and

$$T(A(\mathbf{x})) = T(\mathbf{b})$$

have precisely the same solutions. For if

$$A(\mathbf{c}) = \mathbf{b},$$

then, applying T to both sides,

$$T(A(\mathbf{c})) = T(\mathbf{b})$$

Conversely, if

$$T(A(\mathbf{c})) = T(\mathbf{b}),$$

then, applying T^{-1} to both sides

$$A(\mathbf{c}) = \mathbf{b}$$

The difference between the two equations is that they will, in general, have different coefficients with respect to the standard basis of F^k. The hope is to find an isomorphism $T: F^k \to F^k$ so that the coefficients of

$$T(A(\mathbf{x})) = T(\mathbf{b})$$

are much simpler than those of

$$A(\mathbf{x}) = \mathbf{b}$$

In 2.2, from the viewpoint of row operations, we showed that this can be done.

EXERCISES / 5.3

1. Let X be the standard basis of F^k, and let σ_{ij}, $\mu_{i,a}\tau_{ij,c}$ be the elementary transformations of F^k with respect to X described in Definition 5.4. Compute $\mathscr{A}_{X,X}(\sigma_{ij})$, $\mathscr{A}_{X,X}(\mu_{i,a})$, $\mathscr{A}_{X,X}(\tau_{ij,c})$.

These are called elementary matrices of types (1), (2), and (3), respectively.

2. Let $\mathfrak{a}$ be any $k \times n$ matrix over F, and consider the $k \times k$ matrices $\mathscr{A}_{X,X}(\sigma_{ij})$, $\mathscr{A}_{X,X}(\mu_{i,a})$, and $\mathscr{A}_{X,X}(\tau_{ij,c})$ of **1**, above.

a. Show that the product $\mathscr{A}_{X,X}(\sigma_{ij}) \cdot \mathfrak{a}$ is a matrix that can be obtained from $\mathfrak{a}$ by a row operation of type (1) (i.e., by exchanging rows i and j of $\mathfrak{a}$).

b. Show that the product $\mathscr{A}_{X,X}(\mu_{i,a}) \cdot \mathfrak{a}$ can be obtained from $\mathfrak{a}$ by a row operation of type (2) (i.e., by multiplying row i of $\mathfrak{a}$ by a).

c. Show that the product $\mathscr{A}_{X,X}(\tau_{ij,c}) \cdot \mathfrak{a}$ can be obtained from $\mathfrak{a}$ by a row operation of type (3) (i.e., by multiplying row j by c and adding it to row i).

3. Let $(f_1, \ldots, f_k)$ and $(g_1 \ldots, g_k)$ be k-tuples of linear expressions in n indeterminates $x_1, \ldots, x_n$ over F. Define linear transformations $f: F^n \to F^k$ and $g: F^n \to F^k$ by

$$f(\mathbf{x}) = (f_1(\mathbf{x}), \ldots, f_k(\mathbf{x}))$$

and

$$g(\mathbf{x}) = (g_1(\mathbf{x}), \ldots, g_k(\mathbf{x}))$$

Suppose that $(f_1, \ldots, f_k)$ and $(g_1, \ldots, g_k)$ are solution equivalent. Recall that this means the following: For every $\mathbf{b}_1 \in F^k$ there is a $\mathbf{b}_2 \in F^k$ such that the equations

$$f(\mathbf{x}) = \mathbf{b}_1 \text{ and } g(\mathbf{x}) = \mathbf{b}_2$$

have the same solutions, and vice versa, for every $\mathbf{b}_2 \in F^k$ there is a $\mathbf{b}_1 \in F^k$ so that the above equations have the same solutions

a. Prove that $\mathcal{N}_f = \mathcal{N}_g$. This implies that dim $\mathcal{R}_f =$ dim $\mathcal{R}_g$.
According to Exercises 4.4.3, this means that

$$f = R \circ g \quad \text{and} \quad g = S \circ f$$

for some linear transformations $R : F^k \to F^k$ and $S : F^k \to F^k$.

b. Review Exercises 4.4.3, and, using the fact that dim $\mathcal{R}_f =$ dim $\mathcal{R}_g$, show that R and S may be chosen to be 1–1 linear transformations. Since F^k is finite-dimensional, all 1–1 transformations from F^k to itself are isomorphisms.

Corollary to Proposition 5.14 implies that

$$R = R_m \circ R_{m-1} \circ \cdots \circ R_2 \circ R_1,$$

where R_i is an elementary transformation of F^k with respect to the basis $(R_{i-1} \circ \cdots \circ R_2 \circ R_1)(X)$, if $i > 1$, or X, if $i = 1$ (where X is the standard basis of F^k).

c. Let g be as above, let T be any linear transformation from F^k to F^k and let $\pi_i : F^k \to F$ be the ith coordinate projection, $i = 1, \ldots, k$. Define

$$h_i = \pi_i \circ T \circ g$$

It is a linear transformation $F^k \to F^k \to F^k \to F$; that is, it is a linear expression over F in n indeterminates. Show that, for any $\mathbf{x} \in F^n$,

$$T \circ g(\mathbf{x}) = (h_1(\mathbf{x}), \ldots, h_k(\mathbf{x}))$$

Show that if T is an elementary transformation (with respect to the standard basis of F^k), then the system of linear expressions $(h_1, \ldots, h_k)$ is obtained from $(g_1, \ldots, g_k)$ by a row operation of the same type as T.

d. Combine the above results to show that $(f_1, \ldots, f_k)$ and $(g_1, \ldots, g_k)$ are row equivalent.

Thus, solution-equivalent systems are row equivalent.

4. Fill the gaps in the proof of Proposition 5.10. In particular, show that $T(X)$ is linearly independent when T is of type (2) or type (3), and verify the description of T^{-1} when T is of type (2) or type (3).

5. Prove Corollary to Proposition 5.11. Your proof should reflect the fact that this result is indeed a corollary. That is, Proposition 5.11 is needed in the proof. Read Definition 5.5 carefully.

6. Consider the system of equations

$$ax_1 + bx_2 = e$$

$$cx_1 + dx_2 = f,$$

where, say, a, b, c, d are all nonzero real numbers, e and f being real but, possibly, zero. Suppose that, $ad - bc \neq 0$.

Using the method of elimination of variables solve the above system, recording the row operation used in each step.

For each row operation, describe the elementary transformation of $\mathbf{R}^2$, with respect to the standard basis, that corresponds to the row operation (cf. the second interpretation of the row operations). Write down the matrix (with respect to the standard basis) of each such elementary transformation.

Show that the product of the matrices of the elementary transformations (in order) and

$$\begin{pmatrix} a & b \\ c & d \end{pmatrix}$$

is

$$\begin{pmatrix} 1 & 0 \\ 0 & 1 \end{pmatrix}$$

That is,

$$\mathfrak{a}_r \cdot \mathfrak{a}_{r-1} \cdot \cdots \cdot \mathfrak{a}_2 \cdot \mathfrak{a}_1 \cdot \begin{pmatrix} a & b \\ c & d \end{pmatrix} = \begin{pmatrix} 1 & 0 \\ 0 & 1 \end{pmatrix}$$

where $\mathfrak{a}_i$ is the matrix of the ith elementary transformation.

3 / DETERMINANTS

3.1† *Introduction*

An alternate method for solving systems of linear equations has occupied an important place in linear algebra: namely the method of determinants. Because of its importance here and in other areas of mathematics we develop the notion of determinant in some detail. We restrict ourselves temporarily to the case where F is the field of real numbers **R**.

Consider two vectors in $\mathbf{R}^2$. If they are linearly dependent, then they lie on the same straight line through the origin. If not, they determine a parallelogram with nonzero area, as pictured below.

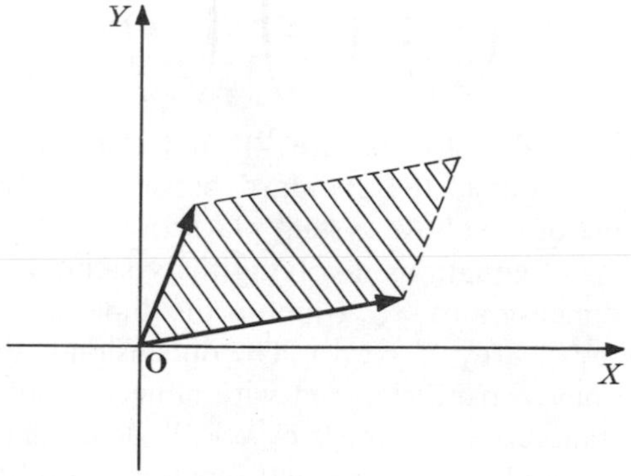

FIGURE 29

Similarly, consider three vectors in $\mathbf{R}^3$. If they are linearly dependent, then they all lie on some single plane through the origin. If not, they determine a parallelepiped with nonzero volume, as pictured below.

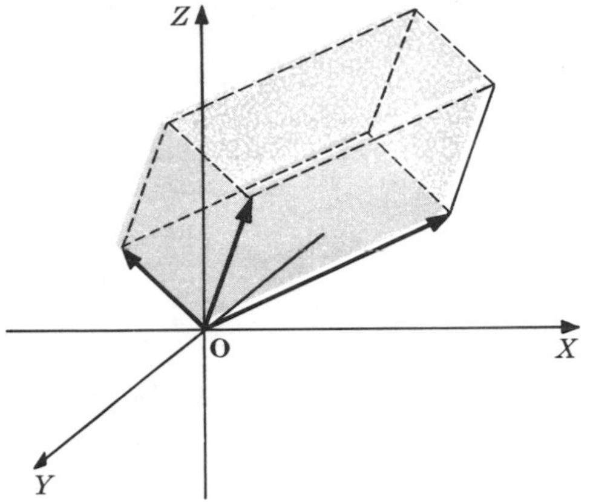

FIGURE 30

What does this have to do with systems of linear equations? For an answer, consider the system of three linear expressions in three indeterminates with real coefficients

$$a_{11}x_1 + a_{12}x_2 + a_{13}x_3$$

$$a_{21}x_1 + a_{22}x_2 + a_{23}x_3$$

$$a_{31}x_1 + a_{32}x_2 + a_{33}x_3$$

We have already seen that this system determines a linear transformation $A:\mathbf{R}^3 \to \mathbf{R}^3$ and that the columns of the coefficient matrix

$$\begin{pmatrix} a_{11} \\ a_{21} \\ a_{31} \end{pmatrix} \quad \begin{pmatrix} a_{12} \\ a_{22} \\ a_{32} \end{pmatrix} \quad \begin{pmatrix} a_{13} \\ a_{23} \\ a_{33} \end{pmatrix}$$

are just the triples in $\mathbf{R}^3$, $A(\mathbf{e}_1^{(3)})$, $A(\mathbf{e}_2^{(3)})$, and $A(\mathbf{e}_3^{(3)})$, respectively, where $\{\mathbf{e}_1^{(3)}, \mathbf{e}_2^{(3)}, \mathbf{e}_3^{(3)}\}$ is, of course, the standard basis of $\mathbf{R}^3$. We have also seen that the column rank of the above system plays an important role in questions concerning solutions of equations involving the system. The column rank, of course, is just the dimension of $\mathscr{R}_A$, which is the dimension of the subspace of $\mathbf{R}^3$ spanned by $A(\mathbf{e}_1^{(3)})$, $A(\mathbf{e}_2^{(3)})$, $A(\mathbf{e}_3^{(3)})$. The dimension is three if and only if these vectors determine a parallelepiped with nonzero volume.

Note that the standard basis $\{\mathbf{e}_1^{(3)}, \mathbf{e}_2^{(3)}, \mathbf{e}_3^{(3)}\}$ determines a parallelepiped with nonzero volume. Indeed, in the usual representation of $\mathbf{R}^3$ this parallelepiped is a cube with volume one. The application of A to these basis vectors yields another parallelepiped (perhaps one that is flattened into a planar or linear figure). We are interested in the extent to which A changes the volume of the original cube, particularly in whether or not it changes the volume to zero.

After this brief introduction, we now approach the notion of *determinant*. The determinant of a linear transformation is a scalar which "measures" the way in which the transformation changes the "volume" of "parallelepipeds." Quotes are placed around certain words in the preceding sentence because, in general, we shall be dealing with finite-dimensional vector spaces over an arbitrary field F, and, in that framework, quantitative language must be taken figuratively.

First, however, we shall deal with a special case: namely, we shall discuss two-dimensional volume (i.e., area) in $\mathbf{R}^2$ and determinants in this framework. Our procedure will be to start with some intuitive, geometric, working-definitions of area, to use these definitions to derive certain properties, and then to show that these properties completely characterize the notion of area in this setting. We then use these characterizations as the bases of more formal definitions, which, in contrast to our intuitive notions, can be easily generalized to more abstract situations. Exercises will sketch an analogous development in $\mathbf{R}^3$.

3.2† Oriented Area and Determinants in $\mathbf{R}^2$

Definition 5.7

Let $(\mathbf{v}, \mathbf{w})$ *be an ordered pair of vectors of* $\mathbf{R}^2$. *We denote by* $\text{par}(\mathbf{v}, \mathbf{w})$ *the oriented parallelogram determined by these vectors. The reader may think of an oriented parallelogram as an ordinary parallelogram together with a fixed sense of traversing the given vertices (from the first given,* $\mathbf{v}$, *to the second,* $\mathbf{w}$). *We make this more precise as follows:*

We assume that $\mathbf{R}^2$ is equipped with the standard basis $\{(1, 0), (0, 1)\}$. Let $\mathbf{v}$ and $\mathbf{w}$ be any two linearly independent vectors in $\mathbf{R}^2$. They determine $\text{par}(\mathbf{v}, \mathbf{w})$. Now, rotate $\text{par}(\mathbf{v}, \mathbf{w})$, keeping the vertex at $(0, 0)$ fixed so that $\mathbf{v}$ is rotated to a vector $\mathbf{v}'$ that points in the same direction as $(1, 0)$. The vector $\mathbf{w}$ is rotated to a vector $\mathbf{w}'$. It is easy to see, in this case, that $\mathbf{w}'$ can be written uniquely as $a(1, 0) + b(0, 1)$, where $b < 0$ (if $\mathbf{v}$, $\mathbf{w}$ are chosen as in the picture below). Figure 31 illustrates the situation.

In this case we say that $\text{par}(\mathbf{v}, \mathbf{w})$ has *negative* orientation. On the other hand, consider $\text{par}(\mathbf{w}, \mathbf{v})$. In this case $\mathbf{w}$ is first and $\mathbf{v}$ is second. If we now rotate $\text{par}(\mathbf{w}, \mathbf{v})$ (keeping the vertex at $(0, 0)$ fixed) so that $\mathbf{w}$ *is rotated to a vector pointing in the same direction as* $(1, 0)$, then $\mathbf{v}$ is rotated to a vector of the form $c(1, 0) + d(0, 1)$, where $d > 0$. In this case we say that $\text{par}(\mathbf{w}, \mathbf{v})$ has *positive orientation*.

Essentially, a pair $(\mathbf{v}, \mathbf{w})$ of linearly independent vectors determines a *negatively oriented parallelogram* if and only if the *sense of traversing* (*or rotating*)

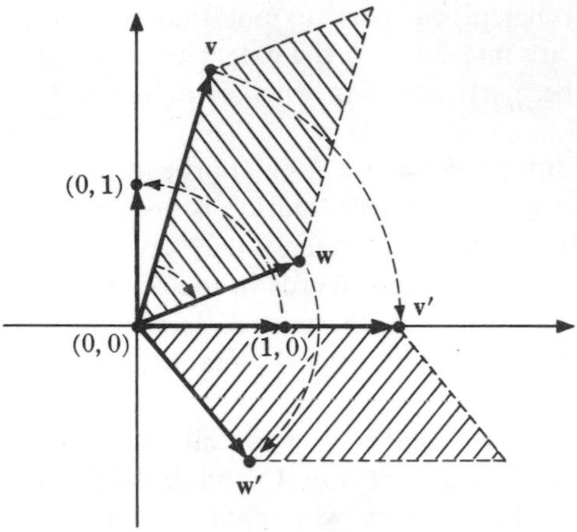

FIGURE 31

from **v** *to* **w** *is opposite to that of traversing (or rotating) from* (1, 0) *to* (0, 1); *it determines a positively oriented parallelogram if and only if the sense of traversing from* **v** *to* **w** *is the same as that of traversing from* (1, 0) *to* (0, 1).

If **v** *and* **w** *are linearly dependent, we say that they determine a degenerate parallelogram* par(**v**, **w**) *and omit considerations of orientation.*

Definition 5.8

We shall assume as known the ordinary definition of the area of a parallelogram (base × altitude). It is a nonnegative number.

We define the oriented area of an oriented parallelogram to be its area if the parallelogram has positive orientation and to be the negative of the area if the parallelogram has negative orientation. If the oriented parallelogram is degenerate, of course, the oriented area is zero. Given a particular oriented parallelogram par(**v**, **w**), *we denote its oriented area by* $\text{vol}_2[\text{par}(\mathbf{v}, \mathbf{w})]$.

Proposition 5.16

Oriented area has the following properties.

(1) *For all* $(\mathbf{v}, \mathbf{w}) \in \mathbf{R}^2 \times \mathbf{R}^2$,
$\text{vol}_2[\text{par}(\mathbf{v}, \mathbf{w})] = -\text{vol}_2[\text{par}(\mathbf{w}, \mathbf{v})]$

(2) *For all* $\mathbf{v}_1, \mathbf{v}_2, \mathbf{w} \in \mathbf{R}^2$ *and* $r, s \in \mathbf{R}$
$\text{vol}_2[\text{par}(r\mathbf{v}_1 + s\mathbf{v}_2, \mathbf{w})] = r\,\text{vol}_2[\text{par}(\mathbf{v}_1, \mathbf{w})] + s\,\text{vol}_2[\text{par}(\mathbf{v}_2, \mathbf{w})]$

(3) $\text{vol}_2[\text{par}((1, 0), (0, 1))] = 1$

Remarks: 1. Let Par be the set of all oriented parallelograms in $\mathbf{R}^2$ with one vertex equal to (0, 0). Then, the association $(\mathbf{v}, \mathbf{w}) \to \text{par}(\mathbf{v}, \mathbf{w})$ is a function

$$\text{par}: \mathbf{R}^2 \times \mathbf{R}^2 \to \text{Par}$$

and the association $\text{par}(\mathbf{v}, \mathbf{w}) \to \text{vol}_2[\text{par}(\mathbf{v}, \mathbf{w})]$ is a function

$$\text{vol}_2 : \text{Par} \to \mathbf{R}$$

Thus, the composite $\text{vol}_2 \circ \text{par}$, sending $(\mathbf{v}, \mathbf{w})$ to $\text{vol}_2[\text{par}(\mathbf{v}, \mathbf{w})]$, is a function

$$\mathbf{R}^2 \times \mathbf{R}^2 \to \mathbf{R}$$

Property (2) above states that $\text{vol}_2 \circ \text{par}$ is a linear function of its first variable. Applying (1) we can show that $\text{vol}_2 \circ \text{par}$ is a linear function of its second variable. Indeed, choose any $\mathbf{v}, \mathbf{w}_1, \mathbf{w}_2 \in \mathbf{R}^2$ and any $r, s \in \mathbf{R}$. Then,

$$\begin{aligned} \text{vol}_2 \circ \text{par}(\mathbf{v}, r\mathbf{w}_1 + s\mathbf{w}_2) &= -\text{vol}_2 \circ \text{par}(r\mathbf{w}_1 + s\mathbf{w}_2, \mathbf{v}) \\ &= -r \,\text{vol}_2 \circ \text{par}(\mathbf{w}_1, \mathbf{v}) - s \,\text{vol}_2 \circ \text{par}(\mathbf{w}_2, \mathbf{v}) \\ &= r \,\text{vol}_2 \circ \text{par}(\mathbf{v}, \mathbf{w}_1) + s \,\text{vol}_2 \circ \text{par}(\mathbf{v}, \mathbf{w}_2). \end{aligned}$$

(When we say that a function of several variables is *linear* in one of them, we are speaking informally about the situation in which we hold all other variables fixed and consider the function only as a function of the one remaining variable. To say it is linear in this variable means that for *any fixed configuration of the other variables*, the resulting function in the one remaining variable is linear.)

A vector-valued function of two vector variables (such as $\text{vol}_2 \circ \text{par}$) is called *bilinear* if it is linear in each variable. More generally, a vector-valued function of n vector variables is called *n-linear* (or *multilinear*) if it is linear in each of the n variables. If the values of the function are scalars, we say that the function is an *n-linear form* or *n-linear functional*. Thus, $\text{vol}_2 \circ \text{par}$ is a *bilinear form*.

2. Property (1) above says that if we exchange the two vector arguments of $\text{vol}_2 \circ \text{par}$, then we thereby change the sign of the function value. Any vector-valued function of more than one vector variable that has this property is called *skew-symmetric* ("skew" because the sign is changed when the variables are exchanged, "symmetric" because nothing more than the sign is changed).

Thus, properties (1) and (2), above, can be summarized by saying that $\text{vol}_2 \circ \text{par}$ is a skew-symmetric, bilinear functional over the field $\mathbf{R}$.

3. Property (3) amounts to a choice of scale or units of measurement. We could equally well have chosen any other positive number [since par((1, 0), (0, 1)) is positively oriented] as the value of $\text{vol}_2[\text{par}((1, 0), (0, 1))]$.

Proof

Since (1) and (3) are obvious, we restrict our attention to a proof of (2). We divide our proof into several cases.

Our viewpoint will be purely geometric. That is, although it is possible to obtain an algebraic expression for the oriented area of an oriented parallelogram and reduce the proof to a simple algebraic exercise, we shall avoid this approach here to give the reader a more vivid, geometric picture of why $\text{vol}_2 \circ \text{par}$ is bilinear. It is hoped that the gain in geometric insight will compensate for some loss in rigor. The conscientious reader will, no doubt, derive the above mentioned algebraic expression, and determine an algebraic proof.

Case 1: $\{\mathbf{v}_1, \mathbf{v}_2\}$ *linearly dependent.*

In this case, some nontrivial linear combination of $\mathbf{v}_1$ and $\mathbf{v}_2$ has value $\mathbf{0}$; say,

$$a\mathbf{v}_1 + b\mathbf{v}_2 = \mathbf{0}, \text{ where, say } a \neq 0$$

Thus, $\mathbf{v}_1 = -(b/a)\mathbf{v}_2$, and for any $r, s \in \mathbf{R}$,

$$r\mathbf{v}_1 + s\mathbf{v}_2 = r(-b/a)\mathbf{v}_2 + s\mathbf{v}_2 = (s - br/a)\mathbf{v}_2$$

Thus, to show that

$$\text{vol}_2[\text{par}(r\mathbf{v}_1 + s\mathbf{v}_2, \mathbf{w})] = r\,\text{vol}_2[\text{par}(\mathbf{v}_1, \mathbf{w})] + s\,\text{vol}_2[\text{par}(\mathbf{v}_2, \mathbf{w})]$$

it suffices to show that

$$\text{vol}_2\left[\text{par}\left(\left(s - \frac{br}{a}\right)\mathbf{v}_2, \mathbf{w}\right)\right] = r\,\text{vol}_2\left[\text{par}\left(-\frac{b}{a}\mathbf{v}_2, \mathbf{w}\right)\right] + s\,\text{vol}_2[\text{par}(\mathbf{v}_2, \mathbf{w})] \tag{1}$$

To prove this, it suffices to show that for any real t,

$$\text{vol}_2[\text{par}(t\mathbf{v}_2, \mathbf{w})] = t\,\text{vol}_2[\text{par}(\mathbf{v}_2, \mathbf{w})] \tag{2}$$

For, if this latter equation is true, then, letting $t = s - br/a$, we get

$$\begin{aligned}\text{vol}_2\left[\text{par}\left(\left(s - \frac{br}{a}\right)\mathbf{v}_2, \mathbf{w}\right)\right] &= \left(s - \frac{br}{a}\right)\text{vol}_2[\text{par}(\mathbf{v}_2, \mathbf{w})] \\ &= r\left(-\frac{b}{a}\right)\text{vol}_2[\text{par}(\mathbf{v}_2, \mathbf{w})] + s\,\text{vol}_2[\text{par}(\mathbf{v}_2, \mathbf{w})]\end{aligned}$$

Then, letting $t = -b/a$, we get

$$-\frac{b}{a}\,\text{vol}_2[\text{par}(\mathbf{v}_2, \mathbf{w})] = \text{vol}_2\left[\text{par}\left(-\frac{b}{a}\mathbf{v}_2, \mathbf{w}\right)\right]$$

Combining these two equations, we get equation (1). Thus, it suffices to prove (2), for all real t.

If $t = 0$, then the truth of (2) is not hard to see. The right-hand side is 0. The left-hand side is the area of a degenerate parallelogram (i.e., it has one side of length 0), and so its value is zero.

Suppose that $t \geqq 1$ and $\text{par}(\mathbf{v}_2, \mathbf{w})$ is positively oriented. We can represent this situation by Figure 32:

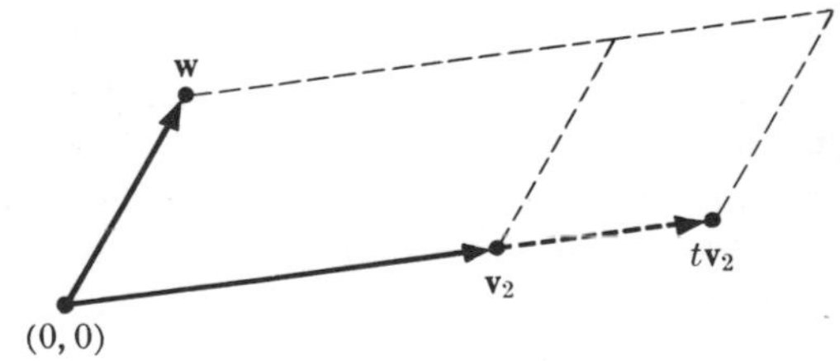

FIGURE 32

It is clear, in this case, that $\text{vol}_2[\text{par}(t\mathbf{v}_2, \mathbf{w})] = t\,\text{vol}_2[\text{par}(\mathbf{v}_2, \mathbf{w})]$.

Consider the same situation as above, except that $0 < t < 1$. In this case, let $s = 1/t > 1$. Then, $\text{par}(t\mathbf{v}_2, \mathbf{w})$ is positively oriented, and so, applying the preceding result to $\text{par}(t\mathbf{v}_2, \mathbf{w})$ and s,

$$\text{vol}_2[\text{par}(\mathbf{v}_2, \mathbf{w})] = \text{vol}_2[\text{par}(s(t\mathbf{v}_2), \mathbf{w})] = s\,\text{vol}_2[\text{par}(t\mathbf{v}_2, \mathbf{w})],$$

so that $t\,\text{vol}_2[\text{par}(\mathbf{v}_2, \mathbf{w})] = \text{vol}_2[\text{par}(t\mathbf{v}_2, \mathbf{w})]$, in this case, too.

Now suppose that $t = -1$. It is not hard to see that the parallelograms $\text{par}(\mathbf{v}_2, \mathbf{w})$ and $\text{par}(-\mathbf{v}_2, \mathbf{w})$ are congruent but have opposite orientation.

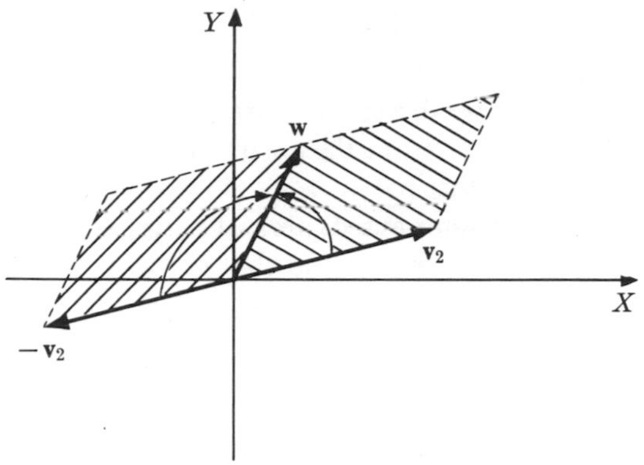

FIGURE 33

Thus,

$$\text{vol}_2[\text{par}(-\mathbf{v}_2, \mathbf{w})] = -\,\text{vol}_2[\text{par}(\mathbf{v}_2, \mathbf{w})]$$

Finally, let t be any negative number. Then, $s = -t > 0$. Therefore,

$$\begin{aligned}\text{vol}_2[\text{par}(t\mathbf{v}_2, \mathbf{w})] &= \text{vol}_2[\text{par}(s(-\mathbf{v}_2), \mathbf{w})] = s\,\text{vol}_2[\text{par}(-\mathbf{v}_2, \mathbf{w})]\\ &= -s\,\text{vol}_2[\text{par}(\mathbf{v}_2, \mathbf{w})] = t\,\text{vol}_2[\text{par}(\mathbf{v}_2, \mathbf{w})]\end{aligned}$$

Thus, $\text{vol}_2[\text{par}(t\mathbf{v}_2, \mathbf{w})] = t\,\text{vol}_2[\text{par}(\mathbf{v}_2, \mathbf{w})]$, for all real t. This concludes our proof in Case 1.

Case 2: $r = 1$, $\{\mathbf{v}_1, \mathbf{v}_2\}$ *is linearly independent, and* $\text{par}(\mathbf{v}_1, \mathbf{w})$ *and* $\text{par}(\mathbf{v}_2, \mathbf{w})$ *are positively oriented.*

We assume, temporarily, that $\text{par}(\mathbf{v}_1, \mathbf{v}_2)$ is positively oriented and that $\text{par}(\mathbf{v}_1, \mathbf{w})$ and $\text{par}(\mathbf{v}_2, \mathbf{w})$ are not degenerate. Then, our situation can be pictured as follows.

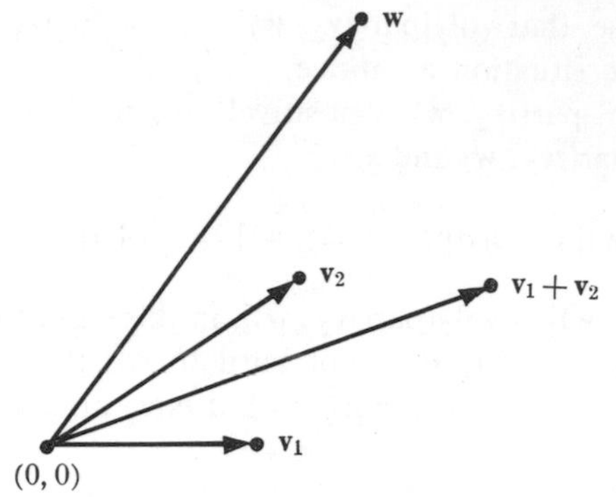

FIGURE 34

(Going in a counterclockwise direction, starting with $\mathbf{v}_1$, $\mathbf{v}_2$ must be reached first and then $\mathbf{w}$. This follows from the assumptions about orientation.) It is easy to see, in this situation that par($\mathbf{v}_1 + \mathbf{v}_2$, $\mathbf{w}$) has positive orientation. Thus, it suffices to check that the (unoriented) area of par($\mathbf{v}_1 + \mathbf{v}_2$, $\mathbf{w}$) equals the sum of the (unoriented) area of par($\mathbf{v}_1$, $\mathbf{w}$) and that of par($\mathbf{v}_2$, $\mathbf{w}$). Let us augment the figure above as follows.

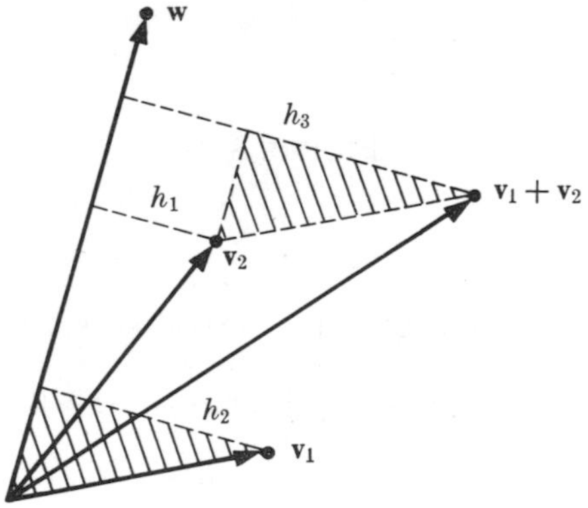

FIGURE 35

We have prolonged $\mathbf{w}$ and dropped perpendiculars from $\mathbf{v}_1$, $\mathbf{v}_2$ and $\mathbf{v}_1 + \mathbf{v}_2$ to $\mathbf{w}$. Since all the parallelograms in question have $\mathbf{w}$ as a base, it remains only to check that the altitudes h_1, h_2, and h_3 satisfy $h_1 + h_2 = h_3$. The figure immediately indicates that this is true.

If par($\mathbf{v}_1$, $\mathbf{v}_2$) is negatively oriented, we use the same argument as above with $\mathbf{v}_2$ and $\mathbf{v}_1$ exchanged (for, now, par($\mathbf{v}_2$, $\mathbf{v}_1$) is positively oriented). All that changes is the above picture: $\mathbf{v}_2$ becomes $\mathbf{v}_1$, $\mathbf{v}_1$ becomes $\mathbf{v}_2$, and $\mathbf{v}_1 + \mathbf{v}_2$ becomes $\mathbf{v}_2 + \mathbf{v}_1$ (which is, of course, the same as $\mathbf{v}_1 + \mathbf{v}_2$).

Suppose that $\text{par}(\mathbf{v}_2, \mathbf{w})$ is degenerate. Then, $\mathbf{w} = s\mathbf{v}_2$ for some real number s. We may picture the situation as follows (assuming $s > 1$):

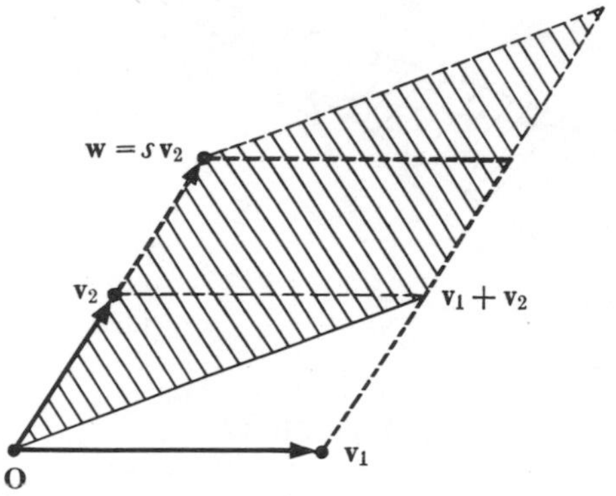

FIGURE 36

The heavily outlined parallelogram is $\text{par}(\mathbf{v}_1, \mathbf{w})$. The shaded-in parallelogram is $\text{par}(\mathbf{v}_1 + \mathbf{v}_2, \mathbf{w})$. Clearly, they have the same area and orientation. Thus,

$$\begin{aligned} \text{vol}_2[\text{par}(\mathbf{v}_1 + \mathbf{v}_2, \mathbf{w})] &= \text{vol}_2[\text{par}(\mathbf{v}_1, \mathbf{w})] \\ &= \text{vol}_2[\text{par}(\mathbf{v}_1, \mathbf{w})] + \text{vol}_2[\text{par}(\mathbf{v}_2, \mathbf{w})], \end{aligned}$$

the second summand being 0 (since $\text{par}(\mathbf{v}_2, \mathbf{w})$ is degenerate).

A similar argument applies when $\text{par}(\mathbf{v}_1, \mathbf{w})$ is degenerate.

The reader should draw the appropriate pictures when $s \leq 1$.

Case 3: $r = 1$; $\{\mathbf{v}_1, \mathbf{v}_2\}$ *is linearly independent, and* $\text{par}(\mathbf{v}_1, \mathbf{w})$ *and* $\text{par}(\mathbf{v}_2, \mathbf{w})$ *are negatively oriented.*

Apply Case 2 to prove that

$$\text{vol}_2[\text{par}(-\mathbf{v}_1 - \mathbf{v}_2, \mathbf{w})] = \text{vol}_2[\text{par}(-\mathbf{v}_1, \mathbf{w})] + \text{vol}_2[\text{par}(-\mathbf{v}_2, \mathbf{w})]$$

Case 2 is applicable because $\{-\mathbf{v}_1, -\mathbf{v}_2\}$ is linearly independent and $\text{par}(-\mathbf{v}_1, \mathbf{w})$ and $\text{par}(-\mathbf{v}_2, \mathbf{w})$ are positively oriented. (Recall that in Case 1 we indicated that $\text{par}(\mathbf{v}, \mathbf{w})$ and $\text{par}(-\mathbf{v}, \mathbf{w})$ have opposite orientation.)

Now use the fact, proved in Case 1, that $\text{vol}_2[\text{par}(-\mathbf{v}, \mathbf{w})] = -\text{vol}_2[\text{par}(\mathbf{v}, \mathbf{w})]$. Then, the above equation becomes,

$$-\text{vol}_2[\text{par}(\mathbf{v}_1 + \mathbf{v}_2, \mathbf{w})] = -\text{vol}_2[\text{par}(\mathbf{v}_1, \mathbf{w})] - \text{vol}_2[\text{par}(\mathbf{v}_2, \mathbf{w})]$$

or

$$\text{vol}_2[\text{par}(\mathbf{v}_1 + \mathbf{v}_2, \mathbf{w})] = \text{vol}_2[\text{par}(\mathbf{v}_1, \mathbf{w})] + \text{vol}_2[\text{par}(\mathbf{v}_2, \mathbf{w})],$$

as desired.

Case 4: $r = 1$, $\{\mathbf{v}_1, \mathbf{v}_2\}$ *is linearly independent,* $\text{par}(\mathbf{v}_1, \mathbf{w})$ *is positively oriented,* $\text{par}(\mathbf{v}_2, \mathbf{w})$ *is negatively oriented, and* $\text{par}(\mathbf{v}_1 + \mathbf{v}_2, \mathbf{w})$ *is degenerate.*

The following figure illustrates the situation.

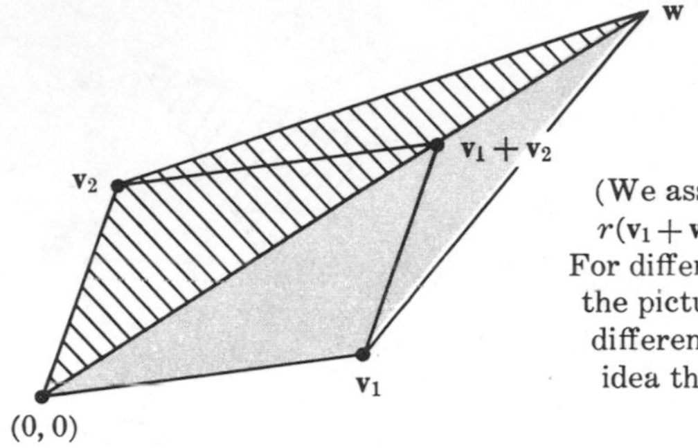

(We assume $\mathbf{w} = r(\mathbf{v}_1 + \mathbf{v}_2)$, $r > 1$. For different values, the picture will be different but the idea the same.)

FIGURE 37

The two shaded triangles, having the same base and altitude, have the same area. But, the bottom triangle is half of $\text{par}(\mathbf{v}_1, \mathbf{w})$ and the top triangle is half of $\text{par}(\mathbf{v}_2, \mathbf{w})$. Therefore, $\text{par}(\mathbf{v}_1, \mathbf{w})$ and $\text{par}(\mathbf{v}_2, \mathbf{w})$ have equal areas. Since they have opposite orientation

$$\text{vol}_2[\text{par}(\mathbf{v}_1, \mathbf{w})] + \text{vol}_2[\text{par}(\mathbf{v}_2, \mathbf{w})] = 0 = \text{vol}_2[\text{par}(\mathbf{v}_1 + \mathbf{v}_2, \mathbf{w})],$$

the second equality holding because $\text{par}(\mathbf{v}_1 + \mathbf{v}_2, \mathbf{w})$ is degenerate.

Case 5: *Same as Case* 4, *except that* $\text{par}(\mathbf{v}_1 + \mathbf{v}_2, \mathbf{w})$ *is nondegenerate.*

To fix ideas, suppose that $\text{par}(\mathbf{v}_1 + \mathbf{v}_2, \mathbf{w})$ is negatively oriented. The reader should take care of the other case. We obtain the following picture.

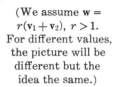

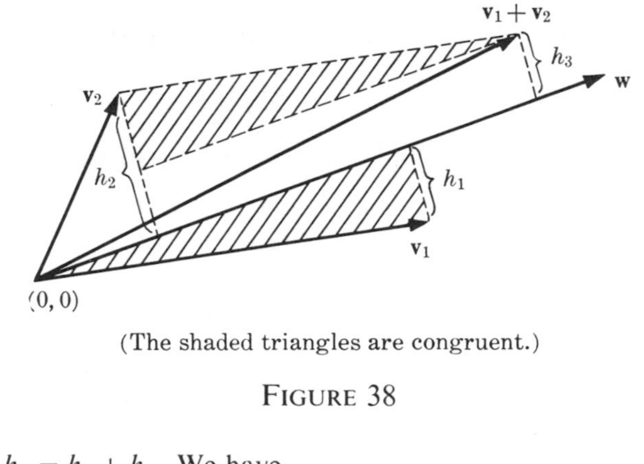

(The shaded triangles are congruent.)

FIGURE 38

Notice that $h_2 = h_1 + h_3$. We have

$$\text{area}\ [\text{par}(\mathbf{v}_1, \mathbf{w})] = h_1 \times \text{length}\ \mathbf{w}$$

$$\text{area}\ [\text{par}(\mathbf{v}_2, \mathbf{w})] = h_2 \times \text{length}\ \mathbf{w}$$

$$\text{area}\ [\text{par}(\mathbf{v}_1 + \mathbf{v}_2, \mathbf{w})] = h_3 \times \text{length}\ \mathbf{w}$$

Thus, using the fact that $-h_3 = -h_2 + h_1$, we get

$$-\text{area}[\text{par}(\mathbf{v}_1 + \mathbf{v}_2, \mathbf{w})] = \text{area}[\text{par}(\mathbf{v}_1, \mathbf{w})] - \text{area}[\text{par}(\mathbf{v}_2, \mathbf{w})],$$

or, taking orientation into account,

$$\text{vol}_2[\text{par}(\mathbf{v}_1 + \mathbf{v}_2, \mathbf{w})] = \text{vol}_2[\text{par}(\mathbf{v}_1, \mathbf{w})] + \text{vol}_2[\text{par}(\mathbf{v}_2, \mathbf{w})]$$

Case 6: $r = 1$, $\{\mathbf{v}_1, \mathbf{v}_2\}$ *linearly independent*, $\text{par}(\mathbf{v}_1, \mathbf{w})$ *negatively oriented*, $\text{par}(\mathbf{v}_2, \mathbf{w})$ *positively oriented.*

This case is the same as Case 4 and Case 5 above except that the roles of $\mathbf{v}_2$ and $\mathbf{v}_1$ are exchanged. Thus the proof of the result in this case is obtained from the preceding two proofs by exchanging $\mathbf{v}_1$ and $\mathbf{v}_2$.

Case 7: The general case: Choose any $\mathbf{v}_1, \mathbf{v}_2, \mathbf{w} \in \mathbf{R}^2$ and any $r, s \in \mathbf{R}$. Then the preceding arguments imply that

$$\text{vol}_2[\text{par}(r\mathbf{v}_1 + s\mathbf{v}_2, \mathbf{w})] = \text{vol}_2[\text{par}(r\mathbf{v}_1, \mathbf{w})] + \text{vol}_2[\text{par}(s\mathbf{v}_2, \mathbf{w})],$$

since Case 1–Case 6 exhaust all the possible cases. Then, using the argument of Case 1

$$\text{vol}_2[\text{par}(r\mathbf{v}_1, \mathbf{w})] = r\,\text{vol}_2[\text{par}(\mathbf{v}_1, \mathbf{w})],$$

and

$$\text{vol}_2[\text{par}(s\mathbf{v}_2, \mathbf{w})] = s\,\text{vol}_2[\text{par}(\mathbf{v}_2, \mathbf{w})]$$

Combining these equalities with the preceding, we get the desired result. Q.E.D.

We now prove that the properties described in the above proposition completely characterize $\text{vol}_2 \circ \text{par}$.

Proposition 5.17

Let f be any skew-symmetric bilinear form from $\mathbf{R}^2 \times \mathbf{R}^2$ to $\mathbf{R}$. Then there is a real number r, depending only on f, such that

$$f = r(\text{vol}_2 \circ \text{par})$$

That is, f is a constant multiple of $\text{vol}_2 \circ \text{par}$.

Proof

Let $\{\mathbf{e}_1^{(2)}, \mathbf{e}_2^{(2)}\}$ be the standard basis of $\mathbf{R}^2$, and let $r = f(\mathbf{e}_1^{(2)}, \mathbf{e}_2^{(2)})$. We shall show that $f = r(\text{vol}_2 \circ \text{par})$, or, what amounts to the same thing, we shall show that

$$f(\mathbf{v}, \mathbf{w}) - r\,\text{vol}_2[\text{par}(\mathbf{v}, \mathbf{w})] = 0$$

for all $(\mathbf{v}, \mathbf{w}) \in \mathbf{R}^2 \times \mathbf{R}^2$.

Define

$$h(\mathbf{v}, \mathbf{w}) = f(\mathbf{v}, \mathbf{w}) - r\,\text{vol}_2[\text{par}(\mathbf{v}, \mathbf{w})],$$

for all $(\mathbf{v}, \mathbf{w}) \in \mathbf{R}^2 \times \mathbf{R}^2$. It is not hard to show that, because f and $\text{vol}_2 \circ \text{par}$ are bilinear and skew-symmetric, so is h. We leave a proof of this fact to the reader. Note, moreover, that

$$h(\mathbf{e}_1^{(2)}, \mathbf{e}_2^{(2)}) = f(\mathbf{e}_1^{(2)}, \mathbf{e}_2^{(2)}) - r\,\text{vol}_2[\text{par}(\mathbf{e}_1^{(2)}, \mathbf{e}_2^{(2)})] = r - r \cdot 1 = 0$$

Finally, note that for any $\mathbf{v} \in \mathbf{R}^2$ and for any skew-symmetric bilinear form k on $\mathbf{R}^2 \times \mathbf{R}^2$,

$$k(\mathbf{v}, \mathbf{v}) = -k(\mathbf{v}, \mathbf{v})$$

This follows by simply exchanging $\mathbf{v}$ with $\mathbf{v}$. But, *the only real number that is its own negative is* 0. Thus,

$$k(\mathbf{v}, \mathbf{v}) = 0$$

Now, choose any $\mathbf{v} = v_1\mathbf{e}_1^{(2)} + v_2\mathbf{e}_2^{(2)}$ and $\mathbf{w} = w_1\mathbf{e}_1^{(2)} + w_2\mathbf{e}_2^{(2)}$ in $\mathbf{R}^2$. Then, using the bilinearity of h, we get

$$\begin{aligned} h(\mathbf{v}, \mathbf{w}) &= v_1 h(\mathbf{e}_1^{(2)}, w_1\mathbf{e}_1^{(2)} + w_2\mathbf{e}_2^{(2)}) + v_2 h(\mathbf{e}_2^{(2)}, w_1\mathbf{e}_1^{(2)} + w_2\mathbf{e}_2^{(2)}) \\ &= v_1 w_1 h(\mathbf{e}_1^{(2)}, \mathbf{e}_1^{(2)}) + v_1 w_2 h(\mathbf{e}_1^{(2)}, \mathbf{e}_2^{(2)}) \\ &\quad + v_2 w_1 h(\mathbf{e}_2^{(2)}, \mathbf{e}_1^{(2)}) + v_2 w_2 h(\mathbf{e}_2^{(2)}, \mathbf{e}_2^{(2)}) \\ &= v_1 w_1 \cdot 0 + v_1 w_2 \cdot 0 + v_2 w_1 \cdot 0 + v_2 w_2 \cdot 0 = 0 \qquad \text{Q.E.D.} \end{aligned}$$

Corollary 1 to Proposition 5.17

Let f be any skew-symmetric, bilinear form on $\mathbf{R}^2 \times \mathbf{R}^2$ such that

$$f((1, 0), (0, 1)) = 1$$

Then, $f = \text{vol}_2 \circ \text{par}$. *Thus, properties* (1)–(3) *completely characterize* $\text{vol}_2 \circ \text{par}$.

Proof

By the preceding proposition $f = r(\text{vol}_2 \circ \text{par})$, for some real number r. By the proof of the proposition,

$$r = f((1, 0), (0, 1)) = 1 \qquad \text{Q.E.D.}$$

Corollary 2 to Proposition 5.17

Let f be any nontrivial (*i.e., not constantly zero*) *skew-symmetric bilinear form on* $\mathbf{R}^2 \times \mathbf{R}^2$. *Then,* $f(\mathbf{v}, \mathbf{w}) = 0$ *if and only if* $\{\mathbf{v}, \mathbf{w}\}$ *is linearly dependent and* $\mathbf{v} \neq \mathbf{w}$.

Proof

According to Proposition 5.17,

$$f = r(\text{vol}_2 \circ \text{par}),$$

for some real r, which cannot be 0 (for then f would be trivial). Clearly, $(\text{vol}_2 \circ \text{par})(\mathbf{v}, \mathbf{w}) = 0$ if and only if $\{\mathbf{v}, \mathbf{w}\}$ is linearly dependent and $\mathbf{v} \neq \mathbf{w}$. Thus, using the above equation, it is easy to show that f has the same property. Q.E.D.

Remark on the proof of Proposition 5.17: One key step in the proof involved showing that $k(\mathbf{v}, \mathbf{v}) = 0$, for every bilinear, skew-symmetric form k on $\mathbf{R}^2 \times \mathbf{R}^2$ and every $\mathbf{v} \in \mathbf{R}$. We showed that this was true by observing that, by definition,

$$k(\mathbf{v}, \mathbf{v}) = -k(\mathbf{v}, \mathbf{v}),$$

and noting that the only real number that is its own negative is 0.

This last fact is false for arbitrary fields. In fact, in the field $\mathbf{Z}_2$ (congruence classes of integers modulo 2—see Exercises 3.1.**10**),

$$1 + 1 = 0,$$

so that $1 = -1$. Thus, in general, we shall not be able to deduce, from the skew-symmetry and bilinearity of a form over an arbitrary field, that it sends $(\mathbf{v}, \mathbf{v})$ to 0.

To remedy this situation, we introduce, in the later abstract development, a condition slightly stronger than skew-symmetry, in general, but equivalent to it in the case that the scalar field is $\mathbf{R}$.

We can now introduce the key proposition that leads to the notion of *determinant*.

Proposition 5.18

Let $T: \mathbf{R}^2 \to \mathbf{R}^2$ be a linear transformation. Then, there is a real number λ_T such that for any skew-symmetric, bilinear form f on $\mathbf{R}^2 \times \mathbf{R}^2$ and for any pair $(\mathbf{v}, \mathbf{w}) \in \mathbf{R}^2 \times \mathbf{R}^2$,

$$f(T(\mathbf{v}), T(\mathbf{w})) = \lambda_T f(\mathbf{v}, \mathbf{w})$$

Proof

Define $g: \mathbf{R}^2 \times \mathbf{R}^2 \to \mathbf{R}$ by the equation

$$g(\mathbf{v}, \mathbf{w}) = \text{vol}_2[\text{par}(T(\mathbf{v}), T(\mathbf{w}))]$$

for all $(\mathbf{v}, \mathbf{w}) \in \mathbf{R}^2 \times \mathbf{R}^2$. We show that g is skew-symmetric and bilinear. Choose any $\mathbf{v}_1, \mathbf{v}_2, \mathbf{w}$ in $\mathbf{R}^2$ and any r, s in $\mathbf{R}$. Then,

$$g(\mathbf{w}, \mathbf{v}_1) = \text{vol}_2[\text{par}(T(\mathbf{w}), T(\mathbf{v}_1))] = -\text{vol}_2[\text{par}(T(\mathbf{v}_1), T(\mathbf{w}))] = -g(\mathbf{v}_1, \mathbf{w})$$

Moreover,

$$\begin{aligned} g(r\mathbf{v}_1 + s\mathbf{v}_2, \mathbf{w}) &= \text{vol}_2[\text{par}(T(r\mathbf{v}_1 + s\mathbf{v}_2), T(\mathbf{w}))] \\ &= \text{vol}_2[\text{par}(rT(\mathbf{v}_1) + sT(\mathbf{v}_2), T(\mathbf{w}))] \\ &= r\,\text{vol}_2[\text{par}(T(\mathbf{v}_1), T(\mathbf{w}))] + s\,\text{vol}_2[\text{par}(T(\mathbf{v}_2), T(\mathbf{w}))] \\ &= rg(\mathbf{v}_1, \mathbf{w}) + sg(\mathbf{v}_2, \mathbf{w}), \end{aligned}$$

so that g is linear in its first variable. Linearity in the second variable follows from this and the skew-symmetry of g.

Since g is skew-symmetric and bilinear, there is a real number, which we call λ_T, such that

$$g = \lambda_T(\text{vol}_2 \circ \text{par})$$

Thus, for every $(\mathbf{v}, \mathbf{w}) \in \mathbf{R}^2 \times \mathbf{R}^2$,

$$\text{vol}_2[\text{par}(T(\mathbf{v}), T(\mathbf{w}))] = g(\mathbf{v}, \mathbf{w}) = \lambda_T \text{ vol}_2[\text{par}(\mathbf{v}, \mathbf{w})]$$

This means that the desired equation holds for the special skew-symmetric bilinear form $\text{vol}_2 \circ \text{par}$.

Now, let f be *any* skew-symmetric bilinear form on $\mathbf{R}^2 \times \mathbf{R}^2$. Then there is a real number r such that

$$f = r(\text{vol}_2 \circ \text{par})$$

Then, for any $(\mathbf{v}, \mathbf{w}) \in \mathbf{R}^2 \times \mathbf{R}^2$,

$$\begin{aligned} f[T(\mathbf{v}), T(\mathbf{w})] &= r \text{ vol}_2[\text{par}(T(\mathbf{v}), T(\mathbf{w}))] = r\lambda_T \text{ vol}_2[\text{par}(\mathbf{v}, \mathbf{w})] \\ &= \lambda_T(r \text{ vol}_2[\text{par}(\mathbf{v}, \mathbf{w})]) = \lambda_T f(\mathbf{v}, \mathbf{w}) \qquad \text{Q.E.D.} \end{aligned}$$

Remark: Note that λ_T depends only on T. Indeed, we have

$$\text{vol}_2[\text{par}(T(\mathbf{e}_1^{(2)}), T(\mathbf{e}_2^{(2)})] = \lambda_T \text{ vol}_2[\text{par}(\mathbf{e}_1^{(2)}, \mathbf{e}_2^{(2)})] = \lambda_T \cdot 1 = \lambda_T,$$

so that λ_T, indeed, does measure the extent to which T changes the area of the standard unit square determined by $\mathbf{e}_1^{(2)}$ and $\mathbf{e}_2^{(2)}$.

Note also that, for any nontrivial skew-symmetric bilinear form f on $\mathbf{R}^2 \times \mathbf{R}^2$,

$$\lambda_T = \frac{f(T(\mathbf{v}), T(\mathbf{w}))}{f(\mathbf{v}, \mathbf{w})},$$

for every linearly independent set $\{\mathbf{v}, \mathbf{w}\} \subset \mathbf{R}^2$.**

Thus, when $f = \text{vol}_2 \circ \text{par}$, this equation implies that T changes the area of every nondegenerate parallelogram by a factor that depends only on T and not on the parallelogram. This is another indication of the rigidity of behavior of linear transformations.

Definition 5.9

Let T be any linear transformation from $\mathbf{R}^2$ to $\mathbf{R}^2$. The determinant of T, written $\det_2 T$, or, more simply, $\det T$, is the number λ_T given by the preceding proposition.

More precisely, we have seen that $\det_2 T$ can be unambiguously obtained as follows:

** Note that by Corollary 2 to Proposition 5.17, $f(\mathbf{v}, \mathbf{w}) \neq 0$, so that we can divide by it.

Choose any basis $\{\mathbf{v}, \mathbf{w}\}$ *of* $\mathbf{R}^2$ *and any nontrivial, skew-symmetric, bilinear form* $f: \mathbf{R}^2 \times \mathbf{R}^2 \to \mathbf{R}$. *Then*

$$\det_2 T = \frac{f(T(\mathbf{v}), T(\mathbf{w}))}{f(\mathbf{v}, \mathbf{w})}$$

The preceding proposition assures us that this number is independent of the choice of f or $\{\mathbf{v}, \mathbf{w}\}$ (as long as f is nontrivial and $\{\mathbf{v}, \mathbf{w}\}$ is a basis of $\mathbf{R}^2$).

Proposition 5.19

Let S and T be any linear transformations from $\mathbf{R}^2$ to $\mathbf{R}^2$. Then:

(1) $\det_2(S \circ T) = (\det_2 S) \cdot (\det_2 T)$.
(2) *If* $S = I_{\mathbf{R}^2}$, *then* $\det_2 S = 1$.
(3) $\det_2 S \neq 0$ *if and only if S is an isomorphism.*

Proof

(1) Choose any basis $\{\mathbf{v}, \mathbf{w}\}$ of $\mathbf{R}^2$ and let $\lambda_T = \det_2 T$, $\lambda_S = \det_2 S$, $\lambda_{S \circ T} = \det_2(S \circ T)$. Then, by Proposition 5.18, for any nontrivial, skew-symmetric, bilinear form f,

$$\begin{aligned}\lambda_{S \circ T} f(\mathbf{v}, \mathbf{w}) &= f(S \circ T(\mathbf{v}), S \circ T(\mathbf{w})) = f(S(T(\mathbf{v})), S(T(\mathbf{w}))) \\ &= \lambda_S f(T(\mathbf{v}), T(\mathbf{w})) = \lambda_S \cdot \lambda_T f(\mathbf{v}, \mathbf{w})\end{aligned}$$

Since f is nontrivial and $\{\mathbf{v}, \mathbf{w}\}$ is linearly independent, $f(\mathbf{v}, \mathbf{w}) \neq 0$, and so we may divide both sides of the equation by $f(\mathbf{v}, \mathbf{w})$, obtaining the desired result.

(2) Let λ_S, f and $\{\mathbf{v}, \mathbf{w}\}$ be as in (1). Then,

$$\lambda_S f(\mathbf{v}, \mathbf{w}) = f(S(\mathbf{v}), S(\mathbf{w})) = f(\mathbf{v}, \mathbf{w}),$$

because $S = I_{\mathbf{R}^2}$. Thus, $\lambda_S = 1$, as desired.

(3) If S is 1–1 and onto, S has an inverse: $S \circ S^{-1} = I_{\mathbf{R}^2}$. Then, combining (1) and (2), we get,

$$(\det_2 S \cdot \det_2 S^{-1}) = \det_2(S \circ S^{-1}) = \det_2 I_{\mathbf{R}^2} = 1$$

Therefore, $\det_2 S$ cannot be zero.

Conversely, suppose that

$$\det_2 S \neq 0$$

Let $\{\mathbf{v}, \mathbf{w}\}$, λ_S, and f be as in (1) and (2), above. Then,

$$\lambda_S f(\mathbf{v}, \mathbf{w}) = f(S(\mathbf{v}), S(\mathbf{w}))$$

Since $\lambda_S \neq 0$ and $f(\mathbf{v}, \mathbf{w}) \neq 0$, it follows that $f(S(\mathbf{v}), S(\mathbf{w})) \neq 0$. Therefore, by Corollary 2 to Proposition 5.17,

$$\{S(\mathbf{v}), S(\mathbf{w})\}$$

is linearly independent and $S(\mathbf{v}) \neq S(\mathbf{w})$. Thus, $S \mid \{\mathbf{v}, \mathbf{w}\}$ is 1–1, and $S(\{\mathbf{v}, \mathbf{w}\})$ is a basis of $\mathbf{R}^2$. By Proposition 4.17, S is an isomorphism. Q.E.D.

EXERCISES / 5.4

1.* For any pair of pairs $((a, c), (b, d)) \in \mathbf{R}^2 \times \mathbf{R}^2$, let $f((a, c), (b, d)) = ad - bc$. Prove that f is skew-symmetric, bilinear, and that $f(\mathbf{e}_1^{(2)}, \mathbf{e}_2^{(2)}) = 1$. Thus, by Corollary 1 to Proposition 5.17,

$$f((a, c), (b, d)) = \text{vol}_2[\text{par}((a, c), (b, d))]$$

for all $((a, c), (b, d)) \in \mathbf{R}^2 \times \mathbf{R}^2$.

2.* Let $A : \mathbf{R}^2 \to \mathbf{R}^2$ be any linear transformation, let X be the standard basis of $\mathbf{R}^2$, and let

$$\mathscr{A}_{X,X}(A) = \begin{pmatrix} a & b \\ c & d \end{pmatrix}$$

Prove that $\det_2 A = ad - bc$.

(*Hint*: Use **1**, above, together with the fact, mentioned after the proof of Proposition 5.18, that

$$\det_2 A = \text{vol}_2[\text{par}(A(\mathbf{e}_1^{(2)}), A(\mathbf{e}_2^{(2)}))])$$

3. Let A be as in **2**, let X be *any* basis of $\mathbf{R}^2$, and let

$$\mathscr{A}_{X,X}(A) = \begin{pmatrix} e & f \\ g & h \end{pmatrix}$$

Prove that $\det_2 A = eh - gf$.

(*Hint*: Use the definitions of $\det_2 A, \mathscr{A}_{X,X}(A)$.)

4. Let $M_a : \mathbf{R}^2 \to \mathbf{R}^2$ be multiplication by the real number a. Prove that $\det_2 M_a = a^2$.

5. For any pair $((a, c), (b, d)) \in \mathbf{R}^2 \times \mathbf{R}^2$, define $f((a, c), (b, d)) = ab + cd$. Prove that f is bilinear. Prove that $f(\mathbf{v}, \mathbf{w}) = f(\mathbf{w}, \mathbf{v})$, for all $(\mathbf{v}, \mathbf{w}) \in \mathbf{R}^2 \times \mathbf{R}^2$. (We say, in this case, that f is symmetric.)

6.* Given any triple $(\mathbf{u}, \mathbf{v}, \mathbf{w}) \in \mathbf{R}^3 \times \mathbf{R}^3 \times \mathbf{R}^3$, let $\text{par}(\mathbf{u}, \mathbf{v}, \mathbf{w})$ be the parallelepiped determined by $(\mathbf{u}, \mathbf{v}, \mathbf{w})$, with orientation as specified below. If $\{\mathbf{u}, \mathbf{v}, \mathbf{w}\}$ is dependent, or if the vectors are not distinct, we say that $\text{par}(\mathbf{u}, \mathbf{v}, \mathbf{w})$ is degenerate and omit considerations of orientation. Suppose that $\{\mathbf{u}, \mathbf{v}, \mathbf{w}\}$ consists of three distinct linearly independent vectors.

We define the *orientation* of $\text{par}(\mathbf{u}, \mathbf{v}, \mathbf{w})$ as follows: rotate $\text{par}(\mathbf{u}, \mathbf{v}, \mathbf{w})$, with $(0, 0, 0)$ fixed, so that $\mathbf{u}$ and $\mathbf{v}$ are rotated into distinct vectors $\mathbf{u}'$ and $\mathbf{v}'$ in the plane determined by $\{\mathbf{e}_1^{(3)}, \mathbf{e}_2^{(3)}\}$. We consider this plane to be the same as $\mathbf{R}^2$ and the vectors $\mathbf{e}_1^{(3)}$ and $\mathbf{e}_2^{(3)}$ to be the standard basis vectors of $\mathbf{R}^2$. Then, $\text{par}(\mathbf{u}', \mathbf{v}')$ is an oriented parallelogram in $\mathbf{R}^2$. Suppose that the rotation takes $\mathbf{w}$ to

$$\mathbf{w}' = a\mathbf{e}_1^{(3)} + b\mathbf{e}_2^{(3)} + c\mathbf{e}_3^{(3)}$$

Then, if par($\mathbf{u}'$, $\mathbf{v}'$) has negative orientation and $c < 0$, or if par($\mathbf{u}'$, $\mathbf{v}'$) has positive orientation and $c > 0$, we say that par(**u**, **v**, **w**) has positive orientation. If par($\mathbf{u}'$, $\mathbf{v}'$) has negative orientation and $c > 0$, or if par($\mathbf{u}'$, $\mathbf{v}'$) has positive orientation and $c < 0$, then we say that par(**u**, **v**, **w**) has negative orientation.

Show, *informally*, that this definition of the orientation of par(**u**, **v**, **w**) is independent of the particular vectors $\mathbf{u}'$, $\mathbf{v}'$, $\mathbf{w}'$ to which **u**, **v**, **w** are rotated. That is, show that if $\mathbf{u}''$, $\mathbf{v}''$, $\mathbf{w}''$ are any other such vectors (where $\mathbf{u}''$, $\mathbf{v}''$ lie in $\mathbf{R}^2$), then the orientation of par (**u**, **v**, **w**) that they determine is the same as the orientation determined by $\mathbf{u}'$, $\mathbf{v}'$, $\mathbf{w}'$.

7.* Let **u**, **v**, **w** be any distinct, linearly independent vectors in $\mathbf{R}^3$. Suppose that par(**u**, **v**, **w**) is positively oriented. Show that par(**u**, **w**, **v**), par(**u**, **v**, **u**), and par(**v**, **u**, **w**) are negatively oriented and that par(**v**, **w**, **u**) and par(**w**, **u**, **v**) are positively oriented. Show that par(−**u**, **v**, **w**) is negatively oriented. Define vol_3(par(**u**, **v**, **w**)) to be zero if par(**u**, **v**, **w**) is degenerate, to be its volume if par(**u**, **v**, **w**) is positively oriented, and to be the negative of the volume if par(**u**, **v**, **w**) is negatively oriented.

a. $\text{vol}_3 \circ \text{par}$ is a function of three vector variables. Show that it is skew-symmetric (i.e., exchanging any two of the variables changes the sign of the function value).

b. If (**u**, **v**, **w**) is the standard basis of $\mathbf{R}^3$, in the usual order, show that $(\text{vol}_3 \circ \text{par})$ (**u**, **v**, **w**) $= 1$.

c. By going through some special cases, as in the proof of Proposition 5.16, indicate how one could prove that $\text{vol}_3 \circ \text{par}$ is linear in its first variable.

d. Deduce from the result of **c** and **a** that $\text{vol}_3 \circ \text{par}$ is trilinear.

e. Show that any skew-symmetric, real-valued function f on $\mathbf{R}^3 \times \mathbf{R}^3 \times \mathbf{R}^3$ has the property that if **u** and **v** are any vectors in $\mathbf{R}^3$, then

$$f(\mathbf{v}, \mathbf{v}, \mathbf{u}) = f(\mathbf{v}, \mathbf{u}, \mathbf{v}) = f(\mathbf{u}, \mathbf{v}, \mathbf{v}) = 0$$

f. Use **e** and an analog of the proof of Proposition 5.17 to prove that if f is any skew-symmetric trilinear form on $\mathbf{R}^3 \times \mathbf{R}^3 \times \mathbf{R}^3$, then there is a real number r such that

$$f = r(\text{vol}_3 \circ \text{par})$$

g. Use **f** to prove that if f is any skew-symmetric, trilinear form on $\mathbf{R}^3 \times \mathbf{R}^3 \times \mathbf{R}^3$ such that

$$f(1, 0, 0), (0, 1, 0), (0, 0, 1)) = 1$$

then $f = \text{vol}_3 \circ \text{par}$.

8.* For any triple of triple $((a_{11}, a_{21}, a_{31}), (a_{12}, a_{22}, a_{32}), (a_{13}, a_{23}, a_{13})) \in \mathbf{R}^3 \times \mathbf{R}^3 \times \mathbf{R}^3$, let

$$h((a_{11}, a_{12}, a_{13}), (a_{21}, a_{22}, a_{23}), (a_{13}, a_{23}, a_{33})) =$$
$$a_{11}a_{22}a_{33} + a_{21}a_{32}a_{13} + a_{31}a_{12}a_{23} - a_{11}a_{32}a_{23} - a_{21}a_{12}a_{33} - a_{31}a_{22}a_{13}$$

Prove that h is skew-symmetric, trilinear, and that

$$h((1, 0, 0), (0, 1, 0), (0, 0, 1)) = 1$$

Thus, by **7**, above, $h = \text{vol}_3 \circ \text{par}$.

9. Use **7** and **8** to prove that for any linear transformation $T: \mathbf{R}^3 \to \mathbf{R}^3$, there exists a number λ_T such that for any triple $(\mathbf{u}, \mathbf{v}, \mathbf{w}) \in \mathbf{R}^3 \times \mathbf{R} \times \mathbf{R}^3$ and any skew-symmetric, trilinear form f on $\mathbf{R}^3 \times \mathbf{R}^3 \times \mathbf{R}^3$, we have

$$f(T(\mathbf{u}), T(\mathbf{v}), T(\mathbf{w})) = \lambda_T f(\mathbf{u}, \mathbf{v}, \mathbf{w})$$

(*Hint*: Follow the proof of Proposition 5.18.)

The λ_T given by this result will be called $\det_3 T$.

10. Let $A : \mathbf{R}^3 \to \mathbf{R}^3$ be any linear transformation, and let X be the standard basis of $\mathbf{R}^3$. Use **8** above to calculate $\det_3 A$ in terms of the scalar entries in the matrix $\mathscr{A}_{X,X}(A)$.

11. Choose S, T in Trans($\mathbf{R}^3$, $\mathbf{R}^3$). Prove:
a. $\det_3(S \circ T) = (\det_3 S) \cdot (\det_3 T)$.
b. if $S = I_{\mathbf{R}^3}$, then $\det_3(S) = 1$.
c. $\det_3 S \neq 0$, if and only if S is an isomorphism.
(Compare the above to Proposition 5.19.)
Let A be as in **2**, and let $M_\lambda: \mathbf{R}^2 \to \mathbf{R}^2$ be a multiplication by the real number λ.

12. Let

$$\begin{pmatrix} a & b \\ c & d \end{pmatrix}$$

be the matrix of A with respect to the standard basis of $\mathbf{R}^2$. Calculate the matrix of

$$A - M_\lambda$$

with respect to this basis, and use **2** to compute

$$\det_2(A - M_\lambda)$$

Regard λ as a variable; then the above expression for $\det_2(A - M_\lambda)$ is a second degree polynomial in λ. It is called the *characteristic polynomial* of A.

Show (by direct computation) that A and its matrix are zeros of this polynomial.

(This result holds, in general, as the reader will see.)

*3.3 Determinants: General Definition***

There are three ways in which we can generalize the previous definition of $\det_2$ (and of $\det_3$, in the above exercises).

First, we can lift the dimensionality restrictions. That is, we shall define a $\det_n$, where n is an arbitrary positive integer.

Secondly, we need no longer restrict ourselves to the standard vector spaces over $\mathbf{R}$, $\mathbf{R}^n$. That is, we shall define $\det_n T$, for all linear transformations $T : V \to V$, where V is an n-dimensional vector space over $\mathbf{R}$.

Finally, we need not even restrict ourselves to real scalars: We shall extend

** The reader who is not interested in the abstract presentation of determinants should skip to 3.3a and from there to 3.4.

our definition to include linear transformations $T: V \to V$, where V is any finite-dimensional vector space over an arbitrary field F.

There are several obstacles to such generalizations.

First, there is, in dimensions higher than three, no intuitive notion of volume.

Secondly, there are no *standard bases* in abstract vector spaces V.

Thirdly, for general fields F, the notion of skew-symmetry adopted will not suffice to prove a key result (namely, the analog of Proposition 5.17), because it may happen in an arbitrary field that

$$1 + 1 = 0$$

To circumvent the first difficulty, we shall, as we predicted, make use of the characteristic properties of vol_2 and vol_3, as listed in Proposition 5.16 and Exercises 5.4.7, respectively.

But, here, the second difficulty comes into play. For property (3) of Proposition 5.16 and that described in **g** of Exercises 5.4.7 both say something about the values of vol_2 and vol_3 on the *standard bases* of $\mathbf{R}^2$ and $\mathbf{R}^2$, respectively.

To circumvent this second obstacle, we avoid these properties altogether by using *any nontrivial skew-symmetric n-linear functional.* We showed in 3.2 that it was possible to define $\det_2$ using any such functional and an arbitrary basis. Of course, we do not know, in general, whether such a functional exists. We shall have to prove that it does. This, indeed, will be the main project in this section.

Thirdly, the third difficulty will be resolved, as already mentioned, by introducing a new notion, slightly stronger than that of skew symmetry, in general (i.e., it implies skew-symmetry but is not implied by it unless $1 + 1 \neq 0$ in the scalar field) but equivalent to it in case $F = \mathbf{R}$.

A final, more practical obstacle confronts us. In higher dimensions, we shall be dealing with large numbers of variables. For example, a function of n variables belonging to $\mathbf{R}^n$ involves n^2 scalars. Even worse, when we concern ourselves with all the possible ordered n-tuples determined by n distinct vectors $\mathbf{v}_1, \ldots, \mathbf{v}_n$, we shall be dealing with $n(n-1)(n-2) \cdots 4 \cdot 3 \cdot 2$ different configurations. For n as small as 10, this number is already over 3.5 million. We need, therefore, in addition to obvious notational abbreviations, some way of conveniently identifying appropriate sign changes resulting from changes in the given order of given vectors. For these reasons, which become clearer later, we must temporarily abandon linear algebra altogether and take a minor excursion to the land of *permutations*. We shall return, however.

(a) *Permutations*

Definition 5.10

Let X be any finite set. A permutation of the members of X is, simply, a 1–1 *correspondence $f: X \to X$.*

For any permutation $f: X \to X$ and any $x \in X$, we say that x is a fixed-point of f if and only if $f(x) = x$. Alternatively, we may say that x is left fixed by f, or f leaves x fixed.

A permutation is a transposition if and only if it leaves all but two elements fixed. (It exchanges these two: hence, the name "transposition.")

Notice that the inverse of any permutation of X is a permutation of X. If a permutation leaves x fixed, so does its inverse. Thus, the inverse of a transposition is a transposition. Indeed, the inverse of a transposition is the *same* transposition: A transposition keeps all but two elements fixed, exchanging these two (i.e., sending one to the other). The same function applied again restores the exchanged pair. Thus, calling the transposition f, $f \circ f = I_X$, so that $f^{-1} = f$.

Notice also that the composition of any two permutations of X is a permutation of X. It is not, however, true that the composition of transpositions is a transposition. Indeed, we have the following result.

Proposition 5.20

Suppose X consists of n members, $n > 1$. Then, every permutation of X is the composition of transpositions.

Proof

We proceed inductively.

Suppose that X has two members. Then, there are only two permutations of X: Namely, I_X and the transposition that exchanges the two members of X, $f: X \to X$. Clearly, the latter is a composition of transpositions: the one-fold composition of itself. Moreover, by our remarks above, $I_X = f \circ f$.

Now, assume that the result is true for all sets consisting of k members, $k > 1$, and suppose that X consists of the $k + 1$ distinct objects $x_1, x_2, \ldots, x_k, x_{k+1}$.

Choose any permutation $f: X \to X$. Let $X' = \{x_1, \ldots, x_k\}$.

Suppose, first that $f(x_{k+1}) = x_{k+1}$. Then, f takes X' onto X'. That is $f \mid X'$ is a permutation of X'. Therefore, there exist transpositions of X', $g_1', \ldots, g_\ell'$ such that

$$f \mid X' = g_1' \circ \cdots \circ g_\ell',$$

by the inductive assumption.

Define $g_i: X \to X$, $i = 1, \ldots, \ell$, as follows:

$$g_i(x_{k+1}) = x_{k+1}$$

$$g_i(x_j) = g_i'(x_j), \qquad \text{if} \quad j \neq k + 1$$

The reader should be able to show that $g_1, \ldots, g_\ell$ are transpositions of X and that $f = g_1 \circ \cdots \circ g_\ell$.

Suppose next that $f(x_{k+1}) = x_r$, for some $r \neq k+1$. Let $g: X \to X$ be the transposition that exchanges x_{k+1} and x_r. That is,

$$g(x_j) = \begin{cases} x_j, & \text{if } j \neq r \text{ and } j \neq k+1 \\ x_{k+1}, & \text{if } j = r \\ x_r, & \text{if } j = k+1 \end{cases}$$

Let $h = g \circ f$. Then, h is a permutation of X and,

$$h(x_{k+1}) = (g \circ f)(x_{k+1}) = g(f(x_{k+1})) = g(x_r) = x_{k+1}$$

Thus, we may apply the argument of the preceding paragraph to conclude that

$$h = g_1 \circ \cdots \circ g_\ell,$$

where g_i is a transposition of X, $i = 1, \ldots, \ell$.

But,

$$g \circ h = g \circ (g \circ f) = (g \circ g) \circ f = I_X \circ f = f,$$

since g is a transposition. Therefore,

$$f = g \circ h = g \circ g_1 \circ \cdots \circ g_\ell,$$

a composition of transpositions, as desired.

Thus, assuming the result true for any set of k members, $k > 1$, we have proved it to be true for any set of $k+1$ members. The inductive principle allows us, then, to conclude the desired result. Q.E.D.

In general, a given permutation may be obtained in many different ways as a composition of transpositions. All these compositions, however, have something in common. We arrive at what this "something" is via the following two propositions. First, a definition.

We define a certain, useful function

$$\Phi_n : \mathbf{R}^n \to \mathbf{R}, \qquad n > 1,$$

as follows: For every n-tuple $(x_1, \ldots, x_n) \in \mathbf{R}^n$,

$$\Phi_n(x_1, \ldots, x_n) = (x_1 - x_2)(x_1 - x_3) \cdots (x_1 - x_n)(x_2 - x_3) \cdots \cdots (x_2 - x_n) \cdots (x_{n-1} - x_n)$$

In other words, form all differences $x_i - x_j$, where $i < j$, i, j ranging between 1 and n, and multiply them together. Thus, for example,

$$\Phi_2(x_1, x_2) = x_1 - x_2, \quad \Phi_3(x_1, x_2, x_3) = (x_1 - x_2)(x_1 - x_3)(x_2 - x_3)$$

Proposition 5.21

For every $n > 1$, Φ_n is skew-symmetric. That is, given any n-tuple $(x_1, \ldots, x_n) \in \mathbf{R}^n$, let $(y_1, \ldots, y_n)$ be obtained from it by exchanging precisely two of the x's (i.e., by a transposition of the x's). Then,

$$\Phi_n(x_1, \ldots, x_n) = -\Phi_n(y_1, \ldots, y_n)$$

Proof

Choose any n-tuple $(x_1, \ldots, x_n) \in \mathbf{R}^n$. If the entries are not distinct (that is, if $x_i = x_j$, for some $i, j, i < j$) then $\Phi_n(x_1, \ldots, x_n) = 0$ (since the factor $x_i - x_j = 0$), and, for any n-tuple $(y_1, \ldots, y_n)$ obtained by transposition from $(x_1, \ldots, x_n)$, $\Phi_n(y_1, \ldots, y_n) = 0$, for the same reason. Thus, in this case, the proposition holds. Assume, henceforth, that the n-tuple $(x_1, \ldots, x_n)$ consists of distinct real numbers $x_1, \ldots, x_n$. Choose any i, j, $1 \leqq i < j \leqq n$ and let $(y_1, \ldots, y_n)$ be obtained from $(x_1, \ldots, x_n)$ by exchanging x_i and x_j. That is, $y_\ell = x_\ell$, if $\ell \neq i$ and $\ell \neq j$, $y_i = x_j$, and $y_j = x_i$.

Suppose, first that $j = i + 1$. We list the factors of $\Phi_n(x_1, \ldots, x_n)$ in which x_i and x_{i+1} appear:

$$x_r - x_i (r < i),\ x_i - x_{i+1},\ x_i - x_s (s > i + 1),$$

$$x_r - x_{i+1} (r < i),\ x_i - x_{i+1},\ x_{i+1} - x_s (s > i + 1)$$

The corresponding factors of $\Phi_n(y_1, \ldots, y_n)$ are:

$$y_r - y_i (r < i),\ y_i - y_{i+1},\ y_i - y_s (s > i + 1),$$

$$y_r - y_{i+1} (r < i),\ y_i - y_{i+1},\ y_{i+1} - y_s (s > i + 1)$$

Substituting the values of the y's, we see that the total collection of y-factors coincides with the total collection of x-factors, *with one exception*: instead of $x_i - x_{i+1}$, the y-factor is $x_{i+1} - x_i = -(x_i - x_{i+1})$.**

Thus, the exchange of x_i and x_{i+1} affects only the sign of one factor of $\Phi_n(x_1, \ldots, x_n)$, the other factors having been left unchanged (as a bloc, although shifted among themselves—see the footnote below). That is, in this case

$$\Phi_n(x_1, \ldots, x_n) = -\Phi_n(y_1, \ldots, y_n)$$

Now we remove the restriction that $j = i + 1$. Instead of exchanging i and j directly, however, we do it indirectly, via a number of auxiliary exchanges. We exchange x_i with x_{i+1}, then with x_{i+2}, and so on until x_j is reached. We exchange x_i with it. At this point, we have made $j - i$ exchanges, which we may schematically represent as follows:

$$(\ldots, x_i, x_{i+1}, x_{i+2}, \ldots, x_j, \ldots) \to$$

$$(\ldots x_{i+1}, x_i, x_{i+2}, \ldots, x_j, \ldots) \to$$

$$(\ldots x_{i+1}, x_{i+2}, x_i, \ldots, x_j, \ldots) \to$$

$$(\ldots, x_{i+1}, x_{i+2}, \ldots, x_i, x_j, \ldots) \to$$

$$(\ldots, x_{i+1}, x_{i+2}, \ldots, x_j, x_i, \ldots)$$

** Note that the factor $y_r - y_i = x_r - x_{i+1}$ and $y_{i+1} - y_s = x_i - x_s$. Thus, the individual factors do not correspond each to each as their subscripts suggest. There is a switching. But the *total collections correspond*—with the exception noted.

We now make a sequence of exchanges in the opposite direction, bringing x_j back to where x_i was. The total number of these, as the reader may count, will be $(j-i)-1$. The result will be precisely the desired exchange of x_i and x_j, the other arguments having been left fixed.

But each such exchange involves adjacent x's, and, thus, by the result obtained above, results in a change of sign of $\Phi_n(x_1, \ldots, x_n)$. There are, in all, $(j-i)+(j-i)-1 = 2(j-i)-1$ such exchanges, hence, sign changes. Since, this is an odd number, the final consequence of the exchanges is a change in the sign of $\Phi_n(x_1, \ldots, x_n)$, as desired. Q.E.D.

We now restrict our attention to the set $X = \mathbf{N}_n = \{1, 2, \ldots, n\}$, $n > 1$. The same considerations apply to all finite sets, but it is notationally more convenient (and sufficient for our purposes) to restrict to $\mathbf{N}_n$ in this way. The simple transition to the more general case is presented in the exercises.

Note that a permutation $f: \mathbf{N}_n \to \mathbf{N}_n$ determines a switching in any ordered n-tuple $(x_1, \ldots, x_n) \in \mathbf{R}^n$. The real numbers $x_{f(1)}, \ldots, x_{f(n)}$ coincide, as a set, with the real numbers $x_1, \ldots, x_n$, but they appear, perhaps, in a different order. For example, if $f: \mathbf{N}_2 \to \mathbf{N}_2$ is defined by, $f(1) = 2, f(2) = 1$ (i.e., it is the transposition of 1 and 2), and if $(x_1, x_2) = (\sqrt{2}, 7)$, then $(x_{f(1)}, x_{f(2)}) = (7, \sqrt{2})$. Thus, a permutation $f: \mathbf{N}_n \to \mathbf{N}_n$, "shuffles" or reorders, ordered n-tuples.

Definition 5.11

We say that a permutation $f: \mathbf{N}_n \to \mathbf{N}_n$, $n > 1$, is even if and only if

$$\Phi_n(x_{f(1)}, x_{f(2)}, \ldots, x_{f(n)}) = \Phi_n(x_1, x_2, \ldots, x_n),$$

for all n-tuples $(x_1, \ldots, x_n) \in \mathbf{R}^n$. We say that it is odd if and only if

$$\Phi_n(x_{f(1)}, x_{f(2)}, \ldots, x_{f(n)}) = -\Phi_n(x_1, x_2, \ldots, x_n),$$

for all n-tuples $(x_1, \ldots, x_n) \in R^n$.

Note that since $(x_{f(1)}, x_{f(2)}, \ldots, x_{f(n)})$ is simply a reordering of $(x_1, \ldots, x_n)$, the function values $\Phi_n(x_{f(1)}, \ldots, x_{f(n)})$ and $\Phi(x_1, \ldots, x_n)$ differ only possibly, in sign. Moreover, that they differ or not depends only on f and not on the choice of $(x_1, \ldots, x_n)$. We leave the reader to satisfy himself on this score. A consequence of these remarks is that every permutation $f: \mathbf{N}_n \to \mathbf{N}_n$ is either odd or even. For either it changes the sign of (all) nonzero function values or it doesn't. Clearly, no permutation can be both even and odd.

Proposition 5.22

(1) *A permutation is odd if and only if it is the composition of an odd number of transpositions.*

(2) *A permutation is even if and only if it is the composition of an even number of transpositions.*

Thus, a permutation cannot be both the composition of an even number of transpositions and the composition of an odd number of transpositions.

Remark: This last statement follows from (1) and (2) and the comment above that a permutation cannot be both even and odd. Recall that although we have shown that every permutation is the composition of transpositions, we have also asserted that there may be many different ways to compose different transpositions to obtain the same permutation. The last statement of the above proposition tells us, however, that either all these different ways involve an even number of "factors" or they all involve an odd number.

Proof

If $f: \mathbf{N}_n \to \mathbf{N}_n$, $n > 1$, is the composition of any number of transpositions, apply them successively to $\Phi_n(x_1, \ldots, x_n)$ (for any $(x_1, \ldots, x_n) \in \mathbf{R}^n$). More precisely, successively shuffle $(x_1, \ldots, x_n)$ via the transpositions applied to the subscripts. The end result will be the shuffle performed by f. Each transposition changes the sign, since Φ_n is skew-symmetric. Thus, f will change the sign if there are an odd number of transpositions (and, hence, intermediate sign changes) and it will leave the sign unchanged if there are an even number of transpositions (and, hence, an even number of intermediate sign changes).

Thus, if f is the composition of an odd number of transpositions, then f is odd; if f is the composition of an even number of transpositions, then f is even.

The converses of these statements are now easily proved. We prove only the converse of the first, leaving the other to the reader.

If f is odd, we must show that it is the composition of an odd number of transpositions. Suppose not. Then, since it is a composition of transpositions, it is a composition of an even number. But, then, it is even, which is impossible. Thus, it cannot be the composition of an even number of transpositions, so the number must be odd. Q.E.D.

Now, suppose $f: \mathbf{N}_n \to \mathbf{N}_n$ is any permutation, and suppose that $g_1, \ldots, g_\ell$ are transpositions of $\mathbf{N}_n$ such that

$$f = g_1 \circ \cdots \circ g_\ell$$

Then,

$$f^{-1} = g_\ell \circ \cdots \circ g_1$$

To see this, recall that, for any transposition g of $\mathbf{N}_n$, $g^2 = I_{\mathbf{N}_n}$. Thus,

$$\begin{aligned}(g_\ell \circ \cdots \circ g_2 \circ g_1) \circ (g_1 \circ g_2 \circ \cdots \circ g_\ell) &= g_\ell \circ \cdots \circ g_2 \circ I_{\mathbf{N}_n} \circ g_2 \circ \cdots \circ g_\ell \\ &= g_\ell \circ \cdots \circ g_2 \circ g_2 \circ \cdots \circ g_\ell \\ &= g_\ell \circ \cdots \circ I_{\mathbf{N}_n} \circ \cdots \circ g_\ell \\ &= I_{\mathbf{N}_n},\end{aligned}$$

the innermost factors successively canceling each other. Similarly

$$(g_1 \circ \cdots \circ g_\ell) \circ (g_\ell \circ \cdots \circ g_1) = I_{\mathbf{N}_n}$$

Thus, f^{-1} is as described above. Thus, we have

Corollary to Proposition 5.22

A permutation is even if and only if its inverse is even. (*Equivalently, it is odd if and only if its inverse is odd.*)

EXERCISES / 5.5

1. A convenient way of representing a permutation $f:\mathbf{N}_n \to \mathbf{N}_n$ is via the symbol

$$\begin{pmatrix} 1 & 2 & \cdots & n \\ f(1) & f(2) & \cdots & f(n) \end{pmatrix}$$

Thus, for example, the transposition that exchanges 1 and 2 can be represented by:

$$\begin{pmatrix} 1 & 2 & 3 & \cdots & n \\ 2 & 1 & 3 & \cdots & n \end{pmatrix}$$

Compute the following compositions of permutations.

a. $\begin{pmatrix} 1 & 2 & 3 \\ 3 & 1 & 2 \end{pmatrix} \circ \begin{pmatrix} 1 & 2 & 3 \\ 1 & 3 & 2 \end{pmatrix}$

b. $\begin{pmatrix} 1 & 2 & 3 & 4 \\ 4 & 1 & 3 & 2 \end{pmatrix} \circ \begin{pmatrix} 1 & 2 & 3 & 4 \\ 2 & 1 & 4 & 3 \end{pmatrix}$

c. $\begin{pmatrix} 1 & 2 & 3 & 4 \\ 4 & 1 & 3 & 2 \end{pmatrix} \circ \begin{pmatrix} 1 & 2 & 3 & 4 \\ 2 & 4 & 3 & 1 \end{pmatrix}$

d. $\begin{pmatrix} 1 & 2 & 3 & \cdots & n \\ n & (n-1) & (n-2) & \cdots & 1 \end{pmatrix} \circ \begin{pmatrix} 1 & 2 & 3 & \cdots & n \\ n & (n-1) & (n-2) & \cdots & 1 \end{pmatrix}$

e. $\begin{pmatrix} 1 & 2 & 3 & 4 \\ 2 & 1 & 4 & 3 \end{pmatrix} \circ \begin{pmatrix} 1 & 2 & 3 & 4 \\ 4 & 1 & 3 & 2 \end{pmatrix}$ (cf. with **b**)

Express the following permutations as compositions of transpositions.

f. $\begin{pmatrix} 1 & 2 & 3 \\ 3 & 1 & 2 \end{pmatrix}$ **g.** $\begin{pmatrix} 1 & 2 & 3 \\ 2 & 3 & 1 \end{pmatrix}$ **h.** $\begin{pmatrix} 1 & 2 & 3 & 4 \\ 3 & 4 & 1 & 2 \end{pmatrix}$

Which of the following permutations are even and which are odd?

i. $\begin{pmatrix} 1 & 2 & 3 & \cdots & n \\ 1 & 2 & 3 & \cdots & n \end{pmatrix}$ **j.** $\begin{pmatrix} 1 & 2 & 3 & 4 \\ 4 & 3 & 2 & 1 \end{pmatrix}$

k. $\begin{pmatrix} 1 & 2 & 3 \\ 2 & 1 & 3 \end{pmatrix}$ **l.** $\begin{pmatrix} 1 & 2 & 3 & 4 & 5 \\ 2 & 1 & 4 & 5 & 3 \end{pmatrix}$

2. Let X be any set consisting of n members, $n \geqq 2$, and let $\sigma: \mathbf{N}_n \to X$ be any 1–1 correspondence. For any permutation $f: X \to X$, the function

$$\sigma^{-1} \circ f \circ \sigma : \mathbf{N}_n \to \mathbf{N}_n$$

is 1–1 and onto, and hence, a permutation of $\mathbf{N}_n$. Let $\pi(X)$ be the set of all permutations of X, and let $\pi(\mathbf{N}_n)$ be the set of all permutations of $\mathbf{N}_n$. Define a function $\hat{\sigma}: \pi(X) \to \pi(\mathbf{N}_n)$ as follows: For any $f \in \pi(X)$,

$$\hat{\sigma}(f) = \sigma^{-1} \circ f \circ \sigma$$

a. Prove that $\hat{\sigma}$ is a 1–1 correspondence.
b. Prove that, for any f, g in $\pi(X)$, $\hat{\sigma}(f \circ g) = \hat{\sigma}(f) \circ \hat{\sigma}(g)$.
c. Prove that $\hat{\sigma}(I_X) = I_{\mathbf{N}_n}$.
d. Prove that $\hat{\sigma}(f^{-1}) = [\hat{\sigma}(f)]^{-1}$, for any $f \in \pi(X)$.
e. Prove that $\hat{\sigma}(f)$ leaves $i \in \mathbf{N}_n$ fixed if and only if f leaves $\sigma(i) \in X$ fixed.
f. Use **e** to prove that $\hat{\sigma}(f)$ is a transposition if and only if f is a transposition. Say that $f \in \pi(X)$ is *even* or *odd* as $\hat{\sigma}(f) \in \pi(\mathbf{N}_n)$ is even or odd.
g. Use Proposition 5.22 and the above results **a–f** to prove the following: f is even if and only if f is a composition of an even number of transpositions; f is odd if and only if f is a composition of an odd number of transpositions.

Thus, the definition of *evenness* and *oddness* for members of $\pi(X)$, although framed in terms of $\hat{\sigma}$, is actually independent of $\hat{\sigma}$, in the sense that any choice of a σ would result in the same class of even permutations of X and class of odd permutations of X.

3. A nonempty set Y, together with an associative operation $*: Y \times Y \to Y$, is called a *group* if Y has a $*$-identity and if every $y \in Y$ has a $*$-inverse.
a. Let $V, +, \cdot$ be any vector space over a field F. Prove that $V, +$ is a group.
b. Let X be any finite set of more than one member, and let $\circ$ be the operation of composition of functions from X to X. Let $\pi(X)$ be as in **2**, above. Prove that $\pi(X), \circ$ is a group.
c. Let X be as in **b** and let $\mathscr{A}(X)$ be the set of all even permutations of X. Show first, that the composition of even permutations is an even parmutation, so that $\circ$ is a binary operation on $\mathscr{A}(X)$. Then show that $\mathscr{A}(X), \circ$ is a group.

Show by example, that the operation $\circ$ in $\pi(X)$ or in $\mathscr{A}(X)$ need not be commutative (unless X consists only of two members).

4. Let X be a finite set with n members, $n > 1$. How many members does $\pi(X)$ have? Define a function $i: \pi(X) \to \pi(X)$ as follows:

$$i(f) = f^{-1}, \text{ for all } f \in \pi(X)$$

Prove that i is a permutation of $\pi(X)$ and that $i^2 = I_{\pi(X)}$.

Note that Corollary to Proposition 5.22 can be rephrased to read: f is even if and only if $i(f)$ is even.

5.* Let X be as in **4** above. Choose any transposition $g \in \pi(X)$. Define a function $\bar{g}: \pi(X) \to \pi(X)$ as follows:

$$\bar{g}(f) = f \circ g, \text{ for all } f \in \pi(X)$$

a. Prove that $\bar{g} \circ \bar{g} = I_{\pi(X)}$, and, thus that g is a 1–1 correspondence.
b. Prove that $\bar{g}(f)$ is even if and only if f is odd (or, equivalently, that $\bar{g}(f)$ is odd if and only if f is even).
c. Let $\mathscr{A}(X) \subset \pi(X)$ be as in **3.c.**, above. Then, show that $\bar{g}(\mathscr{A}(X))$ consists of all odd permutations.

Thus, $\pi(X) = \mathscr{A}(X) \cup \bar{g}(\phi(X))$, and $\mathscr{A}(X) \cap \bar{g}(\mathscr{A}(X)) = \varnothing$ (for every permutation is either even or odd and none is both). Moreover, $\bar{g}\,|\mathscr{A}(X)$ is a 1–1 correspondence between $\mathscr{A}(X)$ and $\bar{g}(\mathscr{A}(X))$, so that there are as many odd permutations as even ones.

6.* Show that $\begin{pmatrix} 1 & 2 & 3 \\ 3 & 1 & 2 \end{pmatrix} = \begin{pmatrix} 1 & 2 & 3 \\ 1 & 3 & 2 \end{pmatrix} \circ \begin{pmatrix} 1 & 2 & 3 \\ 2 & 1 & 3 \end{pmatrix}$

and that $\begin{pmatrix} 1 & 2 & 3 \\ 3 & 1 & 2 \end{pmatrix} = \begin{pmatrix} 1 & 2 & 3 \\ 2 & 1 & 3 \end{pmatrix} \circ \begin{pmatrix} 1 & 2 & 3 \\ 3 & 2 & 1 \end{pmatrix}$

Thus, the permutation

$$\begin{pmatrix} 1 & 2 & 3 \\ 3 & 1 & 2 \end{pmatrix}$$

is expressed in two different ways as a composition of transpositions.

(b)† *Skew-symmetric versus alternating forms*

Let V be any n-dimensional vector space over a field F, and let $f: V^n \to F$ be an n-linear form. We assume $n \geqq 2$, the case $n = 1$ being of little interest.

Definition 5.12

f is alternating if and only if $f(\mathbf{v}_1, \ldots, \mathbf{v}_n) = 0$ for every n-tuple $(\mathbf{v}_1, \ldots, \mathbf{v}_n) \in V^n$ in which at least two of the $\mathbf{v}_i$'s are the same.

Proposition 5.23

Let V and F be as above, and let $f: V^n \to F$ be an n-linear form, $n \geqq 2$. Then:
(1) If f is alternating, then f is skew-symmetric.
(2) If f is skew-symmetric and if $1 + 1 \neq 0$ in F, then f is alternating.

Proof

(1) Choose any i and j between 1 and n and any n-tuple $(\ldots, \mathbf{v}_i, \ldots, \mathbf{v}_j, \ldots) \in V^n$. We must show that

$$f(\ldots, \mathbf{v}_i, \ldots, \mathbf{v}_j, \ldots) = -f(\ldots, \mathbf{v}_j, \ldots, \mathbf{v}_i, \ldots),$$

under the assumption that f is alternating and n-linear. We deduce that

$$\begin{aligned} 0 &= f(\ldots, \mathbf{v}_i + \mathbf{v}_j, \ldots, \mathbf{v}_i + \mathbf{v}_j \ldots) \\ &= f(\ldots, \mathbf{v}_i, \ldots, \mathbf{v}_i, \ldots) + f(\ldots, \mathbf{v}_j, \ldots, \mathbf{v}_i, \ldots) \\ &\quad + f(\ldots, \mathbf{v}_i, \ldots, \mathbf{v}_j, \ldots) + f(\ldots, \mathbf{v}_j, \ldots, \mathbf{v}_j, \ldots) \\ &= f(\ldots, \mathbf{v}_j, \ldots, \mathbf{v}_i, \ldots) + f(\ldots, \mathbf{v}_i, \ldots, \mathbf{v}_j, \ldots), \end{aligned}$$

so that $f(\ldots, \mathbf{v}_i, \ldots, \mathbf{v}_j, \ldots) = -f(\ldots, \mathbf{v}_j, \ldots, \mathbf{v}_i, \ldots)$, as desired.

(2) Choose any i and j between 1 and n and any n-tuple in which the ith and jth entries are the same: $(\ldots, \mathbf{v}, \ldots, \mathbf{v}, \ldots) \in V^n$. We must show that

$$f(\ldots, \mathbf{v}, \ldots, \mathbf{v}, \ldots) = 0,$$

under the assumptions that f is skew-symmetric and $1 + 1 \neq 0$ in F. Exchange the ith and jth entries of the n-tuple chosen. It remains unchanged, but the skew-symmetry of f requires a sign change. Thus,

$$f(\ldots, \mathbf{v}, \ldots, \mathbf{v}, \ldots) = -f(\ldots, \mathbf{v}, \ldots, \mathbf{v}, \ldots),$$

which implies that

$$\begin{aligned} 0 &= f(\ldots, \mathbf{v}, \ldots, \mathbf{v}, \ldots) + f(\ldots, \mathbf{v}, \ldots, \mathbf{v}, \ldots) \\ &= (1 + 1)f(\ldots, \mathbf{v}, \ldots, \mathbf{v}, \ldots) \end{aligned}$$

Since $1 + 1 \neq 0$, we may divide both sides of this equation by it to obtain the desired result. Q.E.D.

(c)† *The vector space of alternating n-linear forms*

Let V be any n-dimensional vector space over a field F, $n \geqq 2$. Let $A(V)$ be the set of all alternating, n-linear forms $V^n \to F$. It is a subset of the vector space F^{V^n} of functions V^n to F.

Proposition 5.24

$A(V)$ is a vector space with respect to the usual operations of addition and scalar multiplication of functions.

Proof

Note that $A(V)$ is nonempty since the trivial function $\bar{0}: V^n \to F$ (i.e., the constantly zero function) is alternating and n-linear.

Since $A(V)$ is a nonempty subset of a vector space with the said operations, it suffices to prove that $A(V)$ is closed with respect to the operations. That is, we must show that the sum of two alternating, n-linear forms is again an alternating, n-linear form, and that a scalar multiple of an alternating, n-linear form, is again one. The proofs of these facts are purely mechanical and are left to the reader. Q.E.D.

The key result that we are aiming at is that $A(V)$ is 1-dimensional. That is, every alternating, n-linear form on V^n is a multiple of any nontrivial, alternating, n-linear form on V^n. This is the abstract analogue of Proposition 5.18 which says that every skew-symmetric, bilinear form on $\mathbf{R}^2 \times \mathbf{R}^2$ is a multiple of $\text{vol}_2 \circ \text{par}$. We first prove a preliminary result.

Proposition 5.25

Let f be an alternating, n-linear form on V^n, where V is, as above, an n-dimensional vector space over F and $n \geqq 2$. Let $(\mathbf{v}_1, \mathbf{v}_2, \ldots, \mathbf{v}_n)$ be any ordered basis of V. Then, f is uniquely determined by the value $f(\mathbf{v}_1, \ldots, \mathbf{v}_n)$. In particular, f is nontrivial if and only if this value is not zero.

Proof

Let $(\mathbf{w}_1, \ldots, \mathbf{w}_n) \in V^n$ be any n-tuple. Then, we may write

$$\mathbf{w}_1 = a_{11}\mathbf{v}_1 + \cdots + a_{n1}\mathbf{v}_n$$
$$\vdots$$
$$\mathbf{w}_n = a_{1n}\mathbf{v}_1 + \cdots + a_{nn}\mathbf{v}_n,$$

where a_{ij}, $i = 1, \ldots, n, j = 1, \ldots, n$ are scalars in F.

Since f is alternating, it is linear in each variable, by Proposition 5.24. Now, consider $f(\mathbf{w}_1, \ldots, \mathbf{w}_n) = f(a_{11}\mathbf{v}_1 + \cdots + a_{n1}\mathbf{v}_n, \mathbf{w}_2, \ldots, \mathbf{w}_n)$. We expand this expression using the linearity of f in its first variable:

$$f(\mathbf{w}_1, \mathbf{w}_2, \ldots, \mathbf{w}_n) = a_{11}f(\mathbf{v}_1, \mathbf{w}_2, \ldots, \mathbf{w}_n) + \cdots + a_{n1}f(\mathbf{v}_n, \mathbf{w}_2, \ldots, \mathbf{w}_n)$$

We repeat this procedure, expanding each summand, using the linearity of f in its second, third variable, and so on. We obtain, after all possible expansions, a sum of terms of the form

$$kf(\mathbf{v}_1', \mathbf{v}_2', \cdots, \mathbf{v}_n'),$$

where k is some scalar (a product of the a_{ij}'s) and where $\mathbf{v}_1', \mathbf{v}_2', \ldots, \mathbf{v}_n'$ are some or all of the vectors $\mathbf{v}_1, \mathbf{v}_2, \ldots, \mathbf{v}_n$, perhaps in a different order and with repetitions allowed. Of course, if there are repetitions, then $f(\mathbf{v}_1', \mathbf{v}_2', \ldots, \mathbf{v}_n') = 0$, because f is alternating. Thus, the nonzero summands are of the form

$$a_\sigma f(\mathbf{v}_{\sigma(1)}, \mathbf{v}_{\sigma(2)}, \ldots, \mathbf{v}_{\sigma(n)}),$$

where $\sigma: \mathbf{N}_n \to \mathbf{N}_n$ is a permutation and where

$$a_\sigma = a_{\sigma(1),1}a_{\sigma(2),2} \cdots a_{\sigma(n),n}$$

Indeed, it is not hard to see that all possible permutations of the **v**'s do occur, so that

$$f(\mathbf{w}_1, \mathbf{w}_2, \ldots, \mathbf{w}_n) = \sum_{\sigma \in \pi(\mathbf{N}_n)} a_\sigma f(\mathbf{v}_{\sigma(1)}, \mathbf{v}_{\sigma(2)}, \ldots, \mathbf{v}_{\sigma(n)})$$

Recall that the above summation notation means that the sum is extended over all possible permutations σ in $\pi(\mathbf{N}_n)$. To abbreviate, we shall omit explicit reference to $\pi(\mathbf{N}_n)$ in subsequent summation notation of this type.

Now, we use the fact that f, being alternating, is skew-symmetric. In particular, we have

$$f(\mathbf{v}_{\sigma(1)}, \mathbf{v}_{\sigma(2)}, \ldots, \mathbf{v}_{\sigma(n)}) = \begin{cases} f(\mathbf{v}_1, \mathbf{v}_2, \ldots, \mathbf{v}_n), & \text{if } \sigma \text{ is even} \\ -f(\mathbf{v}_1, \mathbf{v}_2, \ldots, \mathbf{v}_n), & \text{if } \sigma \text{ is odd} \end{cases}$$

For, in the first case, an even number of transpositions of the **v**'s leads from $f(\mathbf{v}_1, \mathbf{v}_2, \ldots, \mathbf{v}_n)$ to $f(\mathbf{v}_{\sigma(1)}, \mathbf{v}_{\sigma(2)}, \ldots, \mathbf{v}_{\sigma(n)})$, each of the transpositions resulting in a sign change. Thus, there is no net sign change at the end. In the second case, an odd number of transpositions are needed and so there is a net sign change.

Define a function $\text{sgn}: \pi(\mathbf{N}_n) \to F$ as follows:

$$\text{sgn}(\sigma) = \begin{cases} 1, & \text{if } \sigma \text{ is even} \\ -1, & \text{if } \sigma \text{ is odd} \end{cases}$$

(sgn is known as the *sign* or *signum* function.)

Then we have,

$$f(\mathbf{w}_1, \mathbf{w}_2, \ldots, \mathbf{w}_n) = \sum_\sigma \text{sgn}(\sigma) a_\sigma f(\mathbf{v}_1, \mathbf{v}_2, \ldots, \mathbf{v}_n),$$

for $f(\mathbf{v}_{\sigma(1)}, \ldots, \mathbf{v}_{\sigma(n)}) = \text{sgn}(\sigma) f(\mathbf{v}_1, \ldots, \mathbf{v}_n)$. Since $f(\mathbf{v}_1, \ldots, \mathbf{v}_n)$ is common to all summands, we may factor it out. We obtain,

$$f(\mathbf{w}_1, \mathbf{w}_2, \ldots, \mathbf{w}_n) = \left(\sum_\sigma \text{sgn}(\sigma) a_\sigma\right) f(\mathbf{v}_1, \mathbf{v}_2, \ldots, \mathbf{v}_n) \tag{1}$$

(We remind the reader that σ ranges over all permutations in $\pi(\mathbf{N}_n)$.)

Notice that once the value $f(\mathbf{v}_1, \ldots, \mathbf{v}_n)$ is specified, $f(\mathbf{w}_1, \ldots, \mathbf{w}_n)$ is determined by (1), for every $(\mathbf{w}_1, \ldots, \mathbf{w}_n)$. Thus, f is determined by the value $f(\mathbf{v}_1, \ldots, \mathbf{v}_n)$.

If $f(\mathbf{v}_1, \ldots, \mathbf{v}_n) \neq 0$, then, by definition, f is nontrivial. On the other hand, if f is nontrivial, there must be some n-tuple $(\mathbf{w}_1, \ldots, \mathbf{w}_n) \in V^n$ such that $f(\mathbf{w}_1, \ldots, \mathbf{w}_n) \neq 0$. Referring to (1), above, the reader can see immediately that $f(\mathbf{v}_1, \ldots, \mathbf{v}_n)$ cannot, then, be zero.

Thus, f is nontrivial if and only if $f(\mathbf{v}_1, \ldots, \mathbf{v}_n) \neq 0$. Q.E.D.

Corollary to Proposition 5.25

Let V be an n-dimensional vector space over F, $n \geqq 2$, and let $A(V)$ be the vector space of alternating, n-linear forms on V^n. Then

$$dim(A(V)) \leqq 1$$

Proof

It suffices to prove that, given any alternating, n-linear forms f and g on V, either $f = g$, or $\{f, g\}$ is linearly dependent. For, if we can prove this, no basis of $A(V)$ can have more than one member, implying that $\dim A(V) \leqq 1$.

Choose any f, g and suppose that $f \neq g$. Let $(\mathbf{v}_1, \ldots, \mathbf{v}_n)$ be any ordered basis of V, and consider the scalars $f(\mathbf{v}_1, \ldots, \mathbf{v}_n)$ and $g(\mathbf{v}_1, \ldots, \mathbf{v}_n)$. Since F is 1-dimensional, either $f(\mathbf{v}_1, \ldots, \mathbf{v}_n) = g(\mathbf{v}_1, \ldots, \mathbf{v}_n)$ or $\{f(\mathbf{v}_1, \ldots, \mathbf{v}_n), g(\mathbf{v}_1, \ldots, \mathbf{v}_n)\}$ is linearly dependent. The former cannot be true, because, if so, since f and g are determined by their values $f(\mathbf{v}_1, \ldots, \mathbf{v}_n)$ and $g(\mathbf{v}_1, \ldots, \mathbf{v}_n)$, we would have $f = g$, a possibility that we have eliminated. Therefore, the two (distinct) scalars are linearly dependent. That is, there are scalars $c, d \in F$, not both zero, such that

$$cf(\mathbf{v}_1, \ldots, \mathbf{v}_n) + dg(\mathbf{v}_1, \ldots, \mathbf{v}_n) = 0$$

Now choose any $(\mathbf{w}_1, \ldots, \mathbf{w}_n) \in V^n$ and use equation (1) of the above proposition:

$$\begin{aligned} cf(\mathbf{w}_1, \ldots, \mathbf{w}_n) + dg(\mathbf{w}_1, \ldots, \mathbf{w}_n) &= c\left(\sum_\sigma \operatorname{sgn}(\sigma)a_\sigma\right)f(\mathbf{v}_1, \ldots, \mathbf{v}_n) \\ &\quad + d\left(\sum_\sigma \operatorname{sgn}(\sigma)a_\sigma\right)g(\mathbf{v}_1, \ldots, \mathbf{v}_n) \\ &= \left(\sum_\sigma \operatorname{sgn}(\sigma)a_\sigma\right)(cf(\mathbf{v}_1, \ldots, \mathbf{v}_n) \\ &\quad + dg(\mathbf{v}_1, \ldots, \mathbf{v}_n)) \\ &= \left(\sum_\sigma \operatorname{sgn}(\sigma)a_\sigma\right) \cdot 0 = 0 \end{aligned}$$

That is, $(cf + dg)(\mathbf{w}_1, \ldots, \mathbf{w}_n) = 0$, for all $(\mathbf{w}_1, \ldots, \mathbf{w}_n)$ in V^n. Therefore, $cf + dg = \bar{0}$, or $\{f, g\}$ is linearly dependent. Q.E.D.

Note that we do not yet exclude the possibility that $\dim A(V) = 0$. That is, there may be *no* nontrivial alternating n-linear form on V^n. We now prove that this is false.

Proposition 5.26

There is a nontrivial, alternating n-linear form on V^n, where V and n are as in Proposition 5.25. Combining this with Corollary to Proposition 5.25, we conclude that

$$\dim A(V) = 1$$

Proof

The second statement follows immediately from the first. For, Corollary to Proposition 5.25 tells us that either dim $A(V) = 0$ or dim $A(V) = 1$. The first statement of this proposition tells us that dim $A(V) \neq 0$.

Choose any ordered basis $(\mathbf{v}_1, \mathbf{v}_2, \ldots, \mathbf{v}_n) \in V^n$. We define a function of n vector variables $f: V^n \to F$ as follows:

Choose any n-tuple $(\mathbf{w}_1, \ldots, \mathbf{w}_n) \in V^n$. We may express the $\mathbf{w}$'s uniquely in terms of the $\mathbf{v}$'s.

$$\begin{aligned} \mathbf{w}_1 &= a_{11}\mathbf{v}_1 + \cdots + a_{n1}\mathbf{v}_n \\ &\vdots \\ \mathbf{w}_n &= a_{1n}\mathbf{v}_1 + \cdots + a_{nn}\mathbf{v}_n \end{aligned}$$

Then, we let

$$f(\mathbf{w}_1, \ldots, \mathbf{w}_n) = \sum_\sigma \operatorname{sgn}(\sigma) a_\sigma, \tag{2}$$

using the notation introduced in the proof of Proposition 5.25.

If we express the vectors $\mathbf{v}_1, \ldots, \mathbf{v}_n$ in terms of themselves, we get $\mathbf{v}_1 = \mathbf{v}_1$, $\mathbf{v}_2 = \mathbf{v}_2 \ldots, \mathbf{v}_n = \mathbf{v}_n$. The coefficients a_{ij} of this system of equations satisfy,

$$a_{ij} = \begin{cases} 0, & i \neq j \\ 1, & i = j \end{cases}$$

Now consider

$$a_\sigma = a_{\sigma(1),1} a_{\sigma(2),2} \cdots a_{\sigma(n),n}$$

Unless $\sigma(i) = i$, for all $i = 1, \ldots, n$, one of the factors on the right will be zero. Thus, unless $\sigma = I_{\mathbf{N}_n}$, $a_\sigma = 0$, when the a_{ij} are as above. Therefore, the sum

$$\sum_\sigma \operatorname{sgn}(\sigma) a_\sigma$$

reduces to $\operatorname{sgn}(I_{\mathbf{N}_n}) a_{I_{\mathbf{N}_n}}$, all the other terms having dropped out. Clearly, $I_{\mathbf{N}_n}$ is an even permutation, so that $\operatorname{sgn}(I_{\mathbf{N}_n}) = 1$, and

$$a_{I_{\mathbf{N}_n}} = a_{11} a_{22} \cdots a_{nn} = 1 \cdot 1 \cdot \cdots \cdot 1 = 1$$

Thus, $f(\mathbf{v}_1, \ldots, \mathbf{v}_n) = 1$, so that f is nontrivial. It remains to show that f is n-linear and alternating.

We show that f is linear in its first variable, the proofs for the other variables being similar. Choose any $\mathbf{w}_1' \in V$ and write

$$\mathbf{w}_1' = a_{11}'\mathbf{v}_1 + \cdots + a_{n1}'\mathbf{v}_n$$

Let $a_\sigma' = a_{\sigma(1),1}' \cdot a_{\sigma(2),2} \cdot \cdots \cdot a_{\sigma(n),n}$, where the $a_{\sigma(i),i}$, $i \geqq 2$, are those obtained for $\mathbf{w}_2, \ldots, \mathbf{w}_n$. Then, by definition,

$$f(\mathbf{w}_1', \mathbf{w}_2, \ldots, \mathbf{w}_n) = \sum_\sigma \operatorname{sgn}(\sigma) a_\sigma'$$

Of course, we have, for any $c \in F$,

$$c\mathbf{w}'_1 = ca'_{11}\mathbf{v}_1 + \cdots + ca'_{n1}\mathbf{v}_n$$

By definition, then,

$$f(c\mathbf{w}'_1, \mathbf{w}_2, \ldots, \mathbf{w}_n) = \sum_\sigma \operatorname{sgn}(\sigma)(ca'_{\sigma(1),1} \cdot a_{\sigma(2),2} \cdot \cdots \cdot a_{\sigma(n),n})$$
$$= c \sum_\sigma \operatorname{sgn}(\sigma)a'_\sigma = cf(\mathbf{w}'_1, \mathbf{w}_2, \ldots, \mathbf{w}_n)$$

Moreover, we have

$$\mathbf{w}_1 + \mathbf{w}'_1 = (a_{11} + a'_{11})\mathbf{v}_1 + \cdots + (a_{n1} + a'_{n1})\mathbf{v}_n,$$

so that, by definition,

$$f(\mathbf{w}_1 + \mathbf{w}'_1, \mathbf{w}_2, \ldots, \mathbf{w}_n) = \sum_\sigma \operatorname{sgn}(\sigma)[(a_{\sigma(1),1} + a'_{\sigma(1),1})a_{\sigma(2),2} \cdots a_{\sigma(n),n}]$$
$$= \sum_\sigma \operatorname{sgn}(\sigma)a_\sigma + \sum_\sigma \operatorname{sgn}(\sigma)a'_\sigma$$
$$= f(\mathbf{w}_1, \mathbf{w}_2, \ldots, \mathbf{w}_n) + f(\mathbf{w}'_1, \mathbf{w}_2, \ldots, \mathbf{w}_n)$$

Therefore, f is linear in its first variable.

Finally, *we show that f is alternating.* Again, for notational convenience, we prove a special case: that f has value zero at all n-tuples in which the first two entries are the same (i.e., $f(\mathbf{w}_1, \mathbf{w}_2, \ldots, \mathbf{w}_n) = 0$, if $\mathbf{w}_1 = \mathbf{w}_2$). The general case follows by an almost identical argument. Choose any such n-tuple, write the $\mathbf{w}$'s in terms of the $\mathbf{v}$'s, as above. Notice that $a_{i1} = a_{i2}$, for all $i = 1, 2, \ldots, n$, because $\mathbf{w}_1 = \mathbf{w}_2$.

Let $\tau: \mathbf{N}_n \to \mathbf{N}_n$ be the transposition that exchanges 1 and 2. According to Exercises 5.5.5, determines a 1–1 correspondence

$$\bar{\tau}: \pi(\mathbf{N}_n) \to \pi(\mathbf{N}_n),$$

defined by the formula $\bar{\tau}(\sigma) = \sigma \circ \tau$, for all $\sigma \in \pi(\mathbf{N}_n)$, and $\pi(\mathbf{N}_n) = \mathscr{A}(\mathbf{N}_n) \cup \bar{\tau}(\mathscr{A}(\mathbf{N}_n))$, where $\mathscr{A}(\mathbf{N}_n)$ is the set of even permutations of $\mathbf{N}_n$ and $\bar{\tau}(\mathscr{A}(\mathbf{N}_n))$ is the set of odd permutations of $\mathbf{N}_n$. We may break up the sum $\sum_\sigma \operatorname{sgn}(\sigma)a_\sigma$ into two sums

$$\sum_{\sigma \in \mathscr{A}(\mathbf{N}_n)} \operatorname{sgn}(\sigma)a_\sigma + \sum_{\sigma \in \bar{\tau}(\mathscr{A}(\mathbf{N}_n))} \operatorname{sgn}(\sigma)a_\sigma$$

When σ is even $\operatorname{sgn}(\sigma) = 1$, when σ is odd $\operatorname{sgn}(\sigma) = -1$. Thus,

$$\sum_\sigma \operatorname{sgn}(\sigma)a_\sigma = \sum_{\sigma \in \mathscr{A}(\mathbf{N}_n)} a_\sigma - \sum_{\sigma \in \bar{\tau}(\mathscr{A}(\mathbf{N}_n))} a_\sigma$$

Now, $\bar{\tau}: \mathscr{A}(\mathbf{N}_n) \to \bar{\tau}(\mathscr{A}(\mathbf{N}_n))$ is a 1–1 correspondence, so that as σ ranges over $\mathscr{A}(\mathbf{N}_n)$, $\bar{\tau}(\sigma) = \sigma \circ \tau$ ranges, in a 1–1 way, over $\bar{\tau}(\mathscr{A}(\mathbf{N}_n))$. Thus, we get

$$\sum_\sigma \operatorname{sgn}(\sigma)a_\sigma = \sum_{\sigma \in \mathscr{A}(\mathbf{N}_n)} a_\sigma - \sum_{\sigma \in \mathscr{A}(\mathbf{N}_n)} a_{\sigma \circ \tau} = \sum_{\sigma \in \mathscr{A}(\mathbf{N}_n)} (a_\sigma - a_{\sigma \circ \tau})$$

It remains to compare a_σ and $a_{\sigma\circ\tau}$, for all $\sigma \in \mathscr{A}(\mathbf{N}_n)$. Since τ merely exchanges 1 and 2, $a_{\sigma\circ\tau}$ is obtained from a_σ by replacing $a_{\sigma(1),1}$ by $a_{\sigma(\tau(1)),1} = a_{\sigma(2),1}$ and $a_{\sigma(2),2}$ by $a_{\sigma(\tau(2)),2} = a_{\sigma(1),2}$. Thus, $a_\sigma - a_{\sigma\circ\tau} = (a_{\sigma(1),1}a_{\sigma(2),2} - a_{\sigma(2),1}a_{\sigma(1),2}) \cdot a_{\sigma(3),3} \cdots a_{\sigma(n),n}$. But $a_{\sigma(1),1} = a_{\sigma(1),2}$ and $a_{\sigma(2),1} = a_{\sigma(2),2}$, because $a_{i1} = a_{i2}$ for all i, so that

$$a_{\sigma(1),1}a_{\sigma(2),2} - a_{\sigma(2),1}a_{\sigma(1),2} = 0$$

Thus, $a_\sigma - a_{\sigma\circ\tau} = 0$, for all $\sigma \in \mathscr{A}(\mathbf{N}_n)$, which implies that

$$f(\mathbf{w}_1, \mathbf{w}_2, \ldots, \mathbf{w}_n) = \sum_\sigma \operatorname{sgn}(\sigma)a_\sigma = \sum_{\sigma \in \mathscr{A}(\mathbf{N}_n)} (a_\sigma - a_{\sigma\circ\tau}) = 0$$

A similar argument clearly can be applied to prove that f has value zero when repetitions occur in other places. Thus, f is alternating. Q.E.D.

We can now state and easily prove the analog of Proposition 5.18.

Proposition 5.27

Let V be an n-dimensional vector space over F, $n \geqq 2$, and let $T: V \to V$ be any linear transformation. Then, there exists a number λ_T such that for any alternating n-linear form f on V^n and any n-tuple $(\mathbf{w}_1, \ldots, \mathbf{w}_n) \in V^n$,

$$f(T(\mathbf{w}_1), \ldots, T(\mathbf{w}_n)) = \lambda_T f(\mathbf{w}_1, \ldots, \mathbf{w}_n)$$

Proof

Choose any nontrivial $f_0 \in A(V)$. There is at least one because $\dim A(V) = 1$. Indeed, $\{f_0\}$ is a basis of $A(V)$. Define a function $h: V^n \to F$ by the rule

$$h(\mathbf{w}_1, \ldots, \mathbf{w}_n) = f_0(T(\mathbf{w}_1), \ldots, T(\mathbf{w}_n))$$

for any $(\mathbf{w}_1, \ldots, \mathbf{w}_n) \in V^n$. We leave to the reader the task of showing that h is alternating and n-linear. That is, $h \in A(V)$. Thus, h is a multiple of f_0. We call this multiple λ_T.

Now, choose any $f \in A(V)$. Since $\{f_0\}$ is a basis of $A(V)$,

$$f = rf_0$$

Then, for any $(\mathbf{w}_1, \ldots, \mathbf{w}_n) \in V^n$,

$$\begin{aligned} f(T(\mathbf{w}_1), \ldots, T(\mathbf{w}_n)) &= rf_0(T(\mathbf{w}_1), \ldots, T(\mathbf{w}_n)) = rh(\mathbf{w}_1, \ldots, \mathbf{w}_n) \\ &= r\lambda_T f_0(\mathbf{w}_1, \ldots, \mathbf{w}_n) = \lambda_T f(\mathbf{w}_1, \ldots, \mathbf{w}_n) \end{aligned}$$ Q.E.D.

Definition 5.13

Let V be an n-dimensional vector space over F, $n \geqq 2$, and let $T: V \to V$ be any transformation. The determinant of T, written $\det T$ or $\det_n T$, is the scalar λ_T given by the preceding proposition.

More precisely, $\det T$ can be defined by the following equation: choose any *nontrivial, alternating, n-linear from* $f: V^n \to F$ *and any ordered basis of* V, $(\mathbf{v}_1, \ldots, \mathbf{v}_n) \in V^n$; *since* f *is nontrivial,* $f(\mathbf{v}_1, \ldots, \mathbf{v}_n) \neq 0$. *Then,*

$$\det T = \frac{f(T(\mathbf{v}_1), \ldots, T(\mathbf{v}_n))}{f(\mathbf{v}_1, \ldots, \mathbf{v}_n)} \tag{3}$$

Proposition 5.27 *assures us that the quantity on the right-hand side of* (3) *depends only on* T *and not on the particular choice of nontrivial* $f \in A(V)$ *or ordered basis* $(\mathbf{v}_1, \ldots, \mathbf{v}_n) \in V^n$.

When $F = R$ and $n = 2$ or 3, the above definition coincides with our previous definitions of $\det_2$ and $\det_3$. The main role played by $\mathrm{vol}_2 \circ \mathrm{par}$ or $\mathrm{vol}_3 \circ \mathrm{par}$, aside from that of providing geometric insight into the nature of determinants (i.e., that determinants measure the constant area change or volume change effected by a linear transformation), is to provide us with a nontrivial, alternating 2-linear or 3-linear form. In low dimensions, we can define this geometrically, whereas, in high dimensions (i.e., higher than three) we must rely on an algebraic definition (i.e., (2), above, in the proof of Proposition 5.26)

Choose any ordered basis $(\mathbf{v}_1, \ldots, \mathbf{v}_n) \in V^n$ of V, as above, and define a nontrivial $f \in A(V)$ by (2), above. Then, $f(\mathbf{v}_1, \ldots, \mathbf{v}_n) = 1$ and we get

$$\det T = f(T(\mathbf{v}_1), \ldots, T(\mathbf{v}_n))$$

Next, express $T(\mathbf{v}_1), \ldots, T(\mathbf{v}_n)$ in terms of the basis $X = \{\mathbf{v}_1, \ldots, \mathbf{v}_n\}$:

$$\begin{aligned} T(\mathbf{v}_1) &= a_{11}\mathbf{v}_1 + \cdots + a_{n1}\mathbf{v}_n \\ &\vdots \\ T(\mathbf{v}_n) &= a_{1n}\mathbf{v}_1 + \cdots + a_{nn}\mathbf{v}_n \end{aligned} \tag{4}$$

Then, the matrix $\mathscr{A}_{X,X}(T)$ is given by:

$$\mathscr{A}_{X,X}(T) = \begin{pmatrix} a_{11}a_{12} & \cdots & a_{1n} \\ a_{21}a_{22} & \cdots & a_{2n} \\ \vdots & & \vdots \\ a_{n1}a_{n2} & \cdots & a_{nn} \end{pmatrix} \tag{5}$$

[That is, $\mathscr{A}_{X,X}(T)$ is the *transpose* of the matrix of coefficients in (4).]

Finally, by definition of f,

$$\det T = \sum_{\sigma} \mathrm{sgn}(\sigma) a_{\sigma}, \tag{6}$$

where $a_\sigma = a_{\sigma(1),1} a_{\sigma(2),2} \cdots a_{\sigma(n),n}$, ranging over all permutations in $\pi(\mathbf{N}_n)$.

The above formula shows that we may compute $\det T$ once we are given, as in (5), the matrix of T with respect to a basis (any basis) X of V. Of course, a different choice of basis will yield different a_{ij}'s, but since $\det T$ is defined independently of a choice of basis, the sum on the right of (6) will always have the same value. Formula (6) is often used as a definition of $\det T$. That approach has the advantage of concreteness and of enabling the student to get to the algebraic computations more quickly. It has the disadvantage of not revealing the geometric roots of the notion of determinant, thus obscuring a rather simple geometric idea by complicated algebra. Moreover, such a definition depends on a choice of basis (that is, on a particular matrix of T), so that *a priori*, it would not be clear that the determinant of T revealed something intrinsic to T.

As a prelude to proving the analog of Proposition 5.19, we prove the following simple lemma.

Lemma

Let $f \in A(V)$ be nontrivial, where V is as above. Choose any n-tuple $(\mathbf{v}_1, \ldots, \mathbf{v}_n) \in V^n$. Then $f(\mathbf{v}_1, \ldots, \mathbf{v}_n) \neq 0$, if and only if $(\mathbf{v}_1, \ldots, \mathbf{v}_n)$ is an ordered basis of V.

Proof

If $(\mathbf{v}_1, \ldots, \mathbf{v}_n)$ is an ordered basis of V, then, since f is nontrivial, $f(\mathbf{v}_1, \ldots, \mathbf{v}_n) \neq 0$, by Proposition 5.25.

Suppose now that $(\mathbf{v}_1, \ldots, \mathbf{v}_n)$ is *not* an ordered basis of V. If there are repetitions among the $\mathbf{v}$'s, then, since f is alternating, $f(\mathbf{v}_1, \ldots, \mathbf{v}_n) = 0$. If there are no repetitions, then $\{\mathbf{v}_1, \ldots, \mathbf{v}_n\}$ must be a set of n distinct linearly dependent vectors. Then, one of the vectors, say $\mathbf{v}_1$, for notational convenience, is a linear combination of the others:

$$\mathbf{v}_1 = a_2\mathbf{v}_2 + \cdots + a_n\mathbf{v}_n$$

Therefore,

$$\begin{aligned} f(\mathbf{v}_1, \mathbf{v}_2, \ldots, \mathbf{v}_n) &= f(a_2\mathbf{v}_2 + \cdots + a_n\mathbf{v}_n, \mathbf{v}_2, \ldots, \mathbf{v}_n) \\ &= a_2 f(\mathbf{v}_2, \mathbf{v}_2, \ldots, \mathbf{v}_n) + \cdots + a_n f(\mathbf{v}_n, \mathbf{v}_2, \ldots, \mathbf{v}_n) \end{aligned}$$

Every term in the sum on the right involves an n-tuple with repeated $\mathbf{v}$'s. Thus, each term, and hence, the sum, is zero. Therefore, $f(\mathbf{v}_1, \ldots, \mathbf{v}_n) = 0$. This means that $f(\mathbf{v}_1, \ldots, \mathbf{v}_n)$ is nonzero only if $(\mathbf{v}_1, \ldots, \mathbf{v}_n)$ is an ordered basis of V. Combined with the first paragraph, this yields the desired result. Q.E.D.

Proposition 5.28

Let V be as above, and let $S: V \to V$ and $T: V \to V$ be linear transformations. Then:

(1) *$\det S \neq 0$ if and only if S is an isomorphism.*
(2) *$\det(S \circ T) = (\det S) \cdot (\det T)$*
(3) *If S is an isomorphism $\det(S^{-1}) = (\det S)^{-1}$*
(4) *$\det I_V = 1$*
(5) *$\det(S^*) = \det S$. (Recall that $S^*: V^* \to V^*$ is the adjoint of S.)*

Proof

(2), (4), and (1) are proved in precisely the same way as are their analogs in Proposition 5.19. The preceding lemma is needed in the proof of part of (1). (In particular, if $\det S \neq 0$, we must be able to deduce that $S(X)$ is a basis of V, if X is; for this the lemma is needed.) We leave details to the reader.

To prove (3), note that $S \circ S^{-1} = I_V$. Thus, by (2) and (4),

$$(\det S) \cdot [\det(S^{-1})] = \det(S \circ S^{-1}) = \det I_V = 1$$

Therefore, $\det S \neq 0$, so that we may divide both sides of the equation by it to get the desired result.

It remains to prove (5). Let X be any ordered basis of V, X^* the corresponding dual basis of V^*, $(a_{ij}) = \mathscr{A}_{X,X}(S)$, and $(b_{ij}) = \mathscr{A}_{X^*,X^*}(S^*)$. Recall that (a_{ij}) is the transpose of (b_{ij}) and vice versa. That is, $b_{ij} = a_{ji}$, for all $i = 1, \ldots, n$, $j = 1, \ldots, n$.

By formula (6), above,

$$\det S = \sum_{\sigma} \operatorname{sgn}(\sigma) a_\sigma$$

and

$$\det S^* = \sum_{\sigma} \operatorname{sgn}(\sigma) b_\sigma,$$

where

$$a_\sigma = a_{\sigma(1),1} \cdot a_{\sigma(2),2} \cdot \cdots \cdot a_{\sigma(n),n} \quad \text{and} \quad b_\sigma = b_{\sigma(1),1} \cdot b_{\sigma(2),2} \cdot \cdots \cdot b_{\sigma(n),n},$$

for all $\sigma \in \pi(\mathbf{N}_n)$.

Now, note that $b_{\sigma(i),i} = a_{i,\sigma(i)}$, by definition. Also note that as i ranges between 1 and n, so does $\sigma(i)$ and $\sigma^{-1}(i)$. Let $\ell = \sigma(i)$. Then, $i = \sigma^{-1}(\ell)$, and $a_{i,\sigma(i)} = a_{\sigma^{-1}(\ell),\ell}$. Thus,

$$b_{\sigma(i),i} = a_{\sigma^{-1}(\ell),\ell}$$

As ℓ ranges between 1 and n, so does $i = \sigma^{-1}(\ell)$. Thus, the n-tuple of scalars

$$(b_{\sigma(1),1}, b_{\sigma(2),2}, \ldots, b_{\sigma(n),n})$$

differs from the n-tuple

$$(a_{\sigma^{-1}(1),1}, a_{\sigma^{-1}(2),2}, \ldots, a_{\sigma^{-1}(n),n})$$

only by a rearrangement of entries. Since multiplication in F is commutative,

$$b_{\sigma(1),1} \cdot b_{\sigma(2),2} \cdot \cdots \cdot b_{\sigma(n),n} = a_{\sigma^{-1}(1),1} a_{\sigma^{-1}(2),2} \cdot \cdots \cdot a_{\sigma^{-1}(n),n}$$

That is,

$$b_\sigma = a_{\sigma^{-1}},$$

and so,

$$\sum_{\sigma} \operatorname{sgn}(\sigma) b_\sigma = \sum_{\sigma} \operatorname{sgn}(\sigma) a_{\sigma^{-1}}$$

Next, note that σ is even if and only if σ^{-1} is even, so that $\text{sgn}(\sigma) = \text{sgn}(\sigma^{-1})$. And, finally, note that as σ ranges over $\pi(\mathbf{N}_n)$, so does σ^{-1} (in a 1–1 way) and vice versa. Thus,

$$\sum_{\sigma} \text{sgn}(\sigma)b_\sigma = \sum_{\sigma^{-1}} \text{sgn}(\sigma^{-1})a_{\sigma^{-1}}$$

But, by the reverse of the remark just made,

$$\sum_{\sigma^{-1}} \text{sgn}(\sigma^{-1})a_{\sigma^{-1}} = \sum_{\sigma} \text{sgn}(\sigma)a_\sigma,$$

because each summand on the left has its equal counterpart on the right and vice versa, sums being taken over all permutations in $\pi(\mathbf{N}_n)$. Therefore,

$$\det(S^*) = \sum_{\sigma} \text{sgn}(\sigma)b_\sigma = \sum_{\sigma^{-1}} \text{sgn}(\sigma^{-1})a_{\sigma^{-1}} = \sum_{\sigma} \text{sgn}(\sigma)a = \det S$$

(Note that in the second sum, the summands correspond to the summands above each to each; that is, $\text{sgn}(\sigma^{-1})a_{\sigma^{-1}} = \text{sgn}(\sigma)b$. In the third sum, however, this is not true; that is, in general, $\text{sgn}(\sigma^{-1})a_{\sigma^{-1}} \neq \text{sgn}(\sigma)a_\sigma$. However, the entire second sum is equal to the entire third sum because they involve the same terms, displayed, perhaps, in different ways.) Q.E.D.

EXERCISES / 5.6

1.* In the above text, we defined determinants for all linear transformations $T: V \to V$, where V is n-dimensional, $n > 1$. In this exercise, we develop the simple case in which $n = 1$.

a. Let V be any 1-dimensional vector space over F, and let $T: V \to V$ be any linear transformation. Prove that there is one and only one scalar $a \in F$ such that $T = M_a$ (multiplied by a).

Define the determinant of T by

$$\det T = a$$

b. Prove Proposition 5.28 in the case that dim $V = 1$ (using **a**, above, and the above definition of det T).

2. Let $T: \mathbf{R}^3 \to \mathbf{R}^3$ be a linear transformation, and let X be the standard basis of $\mathbf{R}^3$. Calculate det T if the matrix of T with respect to X, $\mathscr{A}_{X,X}(T)$, is the following:

a. $\begin{pmatrix} 1 & 3 & 4 \\ 0 & -9 & 1 \\ 2 & 2 & 2 \end{pmatrix}$ **c.** $\begin{pmatrix} 1 & 0 & 2 \\ 3 & -9 & 2 \\ 4 & 1 & 2 \end{pmatrix}$

b. $\begin{pmatrix} 8 & 0 & 3 \\ 1 & 0 & -5 \\ 2 & 0 & 1 \end{pmatrix}$ **d.** $\begin{pmatrix} a_{11} & 0 & 0 \\ 0 & a_{22} & a_{23} \\ 0 & a_{32} & a_{33} \end{pmatrix}$, for some real $a_{11}, a_{22}, a_{33}, a_{32}$, and a_{23}.

e. $\begin{pmatrix} 4 & 2 & -2 \\ 9 & -1 & 0 \\ 8 & -3 & 10 \end{pmatrix}$

Use formula (6) of the above text.
Compare **a** and **c**; notice that they are transposes of one another.

3. Let $T: V \to V$ be any linear transformation with matrix ${}_n(a_{ij})_n$ with respect to some basis X of V. For any $\lambda \in F$, let M_λ be multiplication by λ.
   a. Calculate the matrix of $T - M_\lambda$ with respect to X.
   b. Regarding λ as a variable, show that $\det(T - M_\lambda)$ is a polynomial of degree n in the variable λ. What is the coefficient of λ^n in this polynomial? Show that the constant term of the polynomial is det T. (*Hint:* Let $\lambda = 0$.)
   c. Use **b** to prove that T is an isomorphism if and only if the polynomial $\det(T - M_\lambda)$ does *not* have 0 as a zero.

   The polynomial $\det(T - M_\lambda)$ is called *the characteristic polynomial of T.* We shall later prove a special case of the rather surprising fact that T is always a zero of its characteristic polynomial.

3.4 Computation of Determinants

Let V be an n-dimensional vector space over F, $n \geqq 1$. In 3.3, we defined a determinant function

$$\det: \text{Trans}(V, V) \to F$$

It is often useful, however, to talk about the determinant of a matrix. Many text books refer almost entirely to determinants as determinants of matrices.

We define the *determinant of an* $n \times n$ *matrix* (a_{ij}) (where $a_{ij} \in F$, $i = 1, \ldots ; n$, $j = 1, \ldots, n$) as follows:

$$det(a_{ij}) = \sum_\sigma \text{sgn}(\sigma) a_\sigma \tag{7}$$

The sum on the left was introduced in 3.3. We repeat its definition here:

Let σ be any permutation of $\mathbf{N}_n$. Then, we define

$$a_\sigma = a_{\sigma(1),1} \cdot a_{\sigma(2),2} \cdot \cdots \cdot a_{\sigma(n),n},$$

and $\sum_\sigma \text{sgn}(\sigma) a_\sigma$ is the sum of all the terms $\text{sgn}(\sigma) a_\sigma$ as σ ranges over $\pi(\mathbf{N}_n)$, the set of all permutations of $\mathbf{N}_n$; $\text{sgn}(\sigma) = \pm 1$ according as σ is even or odd.

Now, choose any basis of V, say X. We have an isomorphism

$$\mathscr{A}_{X,X}: \text{Trans}(V\ V) \to \mathfrak{M}(n, n)$$

Formula (6) of 3.2 tells us that

$$det \circ \mathscr{A}_{X,X} = \det \tag{8}$$

That is, to find det T, first find the matrix $\mathscr{A}_{X,X}(T)$ and then the sum $det(\mathscr{A}_{X,X}(T))$ associated with it. Or, equivalently, to find *det* of a matrix, determine det of the transformation corresponding to it via the ordered basis X.

Note that *det* and det have nothing whatsoever to do with the choice of basis X. It is interesting, therefore, that the above equation holds no matter which X was chosen.

For computational purposes, we now focus our attention on determinants of matrices, referring to their relationship to determinants of linear transformations when useful.

Given the matrix

$$(a_{ij}) = \begin{pmatrix} a_{11} & \cdots & a_{1n} \\ \vdots & & \vdots \\ a_{n1} & \cdots & a_{nn} \end{pmatrix}, \tag{9}$$

we shall sometimes write its determinant as follows:

$$\begin{vmatrix} a_{11} & \cdots & a_{1n} \\ \vdots & & \\ a_{n1} & \cdots & a_{nn} \end{vmatrix} \tag{10}$$

We may think of *det* as a function of n vector variables: namely, the n columns of the matrix argument (a_{ij}). From this point of view, *det* has the following two properties:

1. *det* is *alternating*. That is, if (a_{ij}) contains two identical columns, then $det(a_{ij}) = 0$. This implies that if (b_{ij}) is a matrix obtained from (a_{ij}) by exchanging two of its columns, then

$$det(b_{ij}) = -\det(a_{ij})$$

For a proof of this fact, see Proposition 5.23(1).

2. *det* is *n-linear*. That is, for each column of the matrix argument, if all of the other columns are held fixed, then *det* is a linear function of the given column variable, which we consider to range over F^n.

These two properties are proved (with slightly different notation) in the proof of Proposition 5.26. In this proof, the role of the columns of (a_{ij}) is played by the vectors $\mathbf{w}_1, \ldots, \mathbf{w}_n$, and the role of *det* is played by f.

Next, consider the transpose $(a_{ij})^t$ of (a_{ij}). If $X = \{\mathbf{v}_1, \ldots, \mathbf{v}_n\}$ is any basis of V and T is any linear transformation from V to V satisfying

$$\mathscr{A}_{X,X}(T) = (a_{ij}),$$

then the adjoint $T^*: V^* \to V^*$ satisfies

$$\mathscr{A}_{X^*,X^*}(T^*) = (a_{ij})^t$$

Thus,

$$\begin{aligned} det(a_{ij})^t &= \det \mathscr{A}_{X^*,X^*}(T^*) = \det T^* \\ &= \det T \text{ (cf. proof of Proposition 5.28(5))} \\ &= det(a_{ij}) \end{aligned}$$

Now, $det(a_{ij})^t$ is alternating and n-linear in the columns of $(a_{ij})^t$. But, these are the rows of (a_{ij}). Thus, $det(a_{ij})(=det(a_{ij})^t)$ is also alternating and n-linear *as a function of its rows.*

These observations allow us to list certain column and row operations and their effect on the value of the determinant. These operations are related to, but not quite the same as, the elementary row operations of Section 2. The operations listed are usually used to simplify the evaluation of determinants.

1. *Exchange two columns (or rows) of* (10). Clearly, this merely changes the sign of the value of (10), since (10) being alternating in its columns, is skew-symmetric.

2. *Add a new column (or row) to one of the columns (or rows) of* (10).

If we add a column to the kth column of (10), the n-linearity of (10) in its columns implies that the resulting determinant will equal the sum of the original determinant and the determinant obtained by substituting the new column for the kth column. Similar remarks apply to the addition of rows.

3. *Multiply a column (or a row) of* (10) *by a constant c.*

The result will equal the value of the original multiplied by c, because (10) is n-linear.

4. *Add a multiple of a column (or a row) of* (10) *to* another *column (or row of* (10)).

By 2, the result is the original *plus* the determinant obtained by substituting the multiplied column for the one to which it is added. By 3, we can factor out of the second summand the constant multiple, obtaining a determinant in which the same column appears twice. Since (10) is alternating in columns, the value of this determinant is zero. Thus, since the second summand is zero, the net result is to leave the original value unchanged.

For example, suppose we add c times the second column to the first:

$$\begin{vmatrix} a_{11}+ca_{12} & a_{12} & \cdots & a_{1n} \\ \vdots & \vdots & & \vdots \\ a_{n1}+ca_{n2} & a_{n2} & \cdots & a_{nn} \end{vmatrix}$$

$$= \begin{vmatrix} a_{11} & a_{12} & \cdots & a_{1n} \\ \vdots & \vdots & & \vdots \\ a_{n1} & a_{n2} & \cdots & a_{nn} \end{vmatrix} + c \begin{vmatrix} a_{12} & a_{12} & \cdots & a_{1n} \\ \vdots & & & \\ a_{n2} & a_{n2} & \cdots & a_{nn} \end{vmatrix}$$

$$= \begin{vmatrix} a_{11} & a_{12} & \cdots & a_{1n} \\ \vdots & & & \\ a_{n1} & a_{n2} & \cdots & a_{nn} \end{vmatrix} + c \cdot 0 = \begin{vmatrix} a_{11} & \cdots & a_{1n} \\ \vdots & & \vdots \\ a_{n1} & \cdots & a_{nn} \end{vmatrix}$$

Similar comments apply for rows.

With the aid of these four operations, we can simplify the matrix (a_{ij}) so that $det(a_{ij})$ can be more easily computed. For example, let

$$D = \begin{vmatrix} 1 & -1 & 0 \\ 3 & 4 & 4 \\ 2 & 1 & 1 \end{vmatrix}$$

Add column two to column one:

$$D = \begin{vmatrix} 0 & -1 & 0 \\ 7 & 4 & 4 \\ 3 & 1 & 1 \end{vmatrix}$$

Subtract four times row three from row two:

$$D = \begin{vmatrix} 0 & -1 & 0 \\ -5 & 0 & 0 \\ 3 & 1 & 1 \end{vmatrix}$$

Finally, subtract column three from column two, and subtract three times column three from column one:

$$D = \begin{vmatrix} 0 & -1 & 0 \\ -5 & 0 & 0 \\ 0 & 0 & 1 \end{vmatrix} = \begin{vmatrix} a_{11} & a_{12} & a_{13} \\ a_{21} & a_{22} & a_{23} \\ a_{31} & a_{32} & a_{33} \end{vmatrix}$$

The only nonzero term in the sum

$$\sum_{\sigma} \operatorname{sgn}(\sigma) a_{\sigma}$$

is $5 = a_{21}a_{12}a_{33}$. The corresponding permutation, σ, satisfies

$$\sigma(1) = 2, \quad \sigma(2) = 1, \quad \sigma(3) = 3$$

Clearly, σ is a (single) transposition, and so, it is odd. Thus, $\operatorname{sgn}(\sigma) = -1$. Therefore,

$$D = -5$$

One more major tool is useful in the evaluation of determinants: the procedure of *expansion by minors*.

Definition 5.14

Consider the $n \times n$ matrix over F, (a_{ij}), and its determinant

$$\begin{vmatrix} a_{11} & \cdots & a_{1n} \\ \vdots & & \vdots \\ a_{n1} & & a_{nn} \end{vmatrix} = D, \quad n \geq 2 \qquad (10')$$

A minor of (10) *of order k is any* $k \times k$ *subdeterminant of* (10)*: that is, choose any k rows of* (a_{ij}), $i_1 < i_2 < \cdots < i_k$, *and any k columns,* $j_1, \ldots, j_k$. *Consider the* $k \times k$ *matrix*

$$\begin{pmatrix} a_{i_1j_1} & a_{i_1j_2} & \cdots & a_{i_1j_k} \\ a_{i_2j_1} & & & \cdot \\ \vdots & & & \vdots \\ a_{i_kj_1} & \cdots & & a_{i_kj_k} \end{pmatrix} \tag{11}$$

The determinant of (11) *is called a minor of order k of* (10). *The determinant of the above matrix is usually denoted by*

$$M\begin{matrix} i_1 \cdots i_k \\ j_1 \cdots j_k \end{matrix}$$

We confine our attention now to minors of order $(n - 1)$. Notice that such a minor consists of all but one of the rows of (10) and all but one of the columns of (10): say the ith row and the jth column. In contravention of the notation established above, we denote such a minor by

$$M_{ij}$$

Proposition 5.29

(1) *Consider any column of* (10), *above, say column j. Then:*

$$(-1)^{j-1}D = a_{1j}M_{1j} - a_{2j}M_{2j} + \cdots + (-1)^{n-1}a_{nj}M_{nj} \tag{1'}$$

$$0 = a_{1k}M_{1j} - a_{2k}M_{2j} + \cdots + (-1)^{n-1}a_{nk}N_{nj}, \qquad j \neq k \tag{2'}$$

(2) *Consider any row of* (10), *above, say row i.*

$$(-1)^{i-1}D = a_{i1}M_{i1} - a_{i2}M_{i2} + \cdots + (-1)^{n-1}a_{in}M_{in} \tag{1''}$$

$$0 = a_{k1}M_{i1} - a_{k2}M_{i2} + \cdots + (-1)^{n-1}a_{kn}M_{in}, \qquad i \neq k \tag{2''}$$

Proof

We prove Part (1), the proof for Part (2) being similar. First, let $j = 1$. By definition,

$$D = \sum_{\sigma} \text{sgn}(\sigma)a_{\sigma} \tag{3'}$$

To obtain (1′), inspect the sum (3′), collecting together all terms $\text{sgn}(\sigma)a_{\sigma}$ in which a_{11} appears, collecting together all terms in which a_{21} appears, collecting together all terms in which a_{31} appears, and so on, up through a_{n1}. Every term in (3′) contains precisely one of these factors, for

$$a_{\sigma} = a_{\sigma(1),1}(a_{\sigma(2),2} \cdots a_{\sigma(n),n})$$

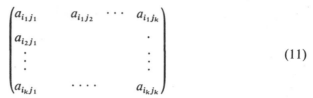

Now, a_{i1} appears in a_σ if and only if $\sigma(1) = i$. Thus, we may write

$$D = \sum_\sigma \operatorname{sgn}(\sigma)a_\sigma = \sum_{\sigma(1)=1} \operatorname{sgn}(\sigma)a_\sigma + \sum_{\sigma(1)=2} \operatorname{sgn}(\sigma)a_\sigma + \cdots + \sum_{\sigma(1)=n} \operatorname{sgn}(\sigma)a_\sigma,$$

where $\sum_{\sigma(1)=i}$ denotes the sum taken over all σ for which $\sigma(1) = i$. We shall show that

$$\sum_{\sigma(1)=i} \operatorname{sgn}(\sigma)a_\sigma = (-1)^{i-1}a_{i1}M_{i1}$$

This will prove (1′) for the case $j = 1$.

First, let $i = 1$. Then,

$$\sum_{\sigma(1)=1} \operatorname{sgn}(\sigma)a_\sigma = a_{11} \sum_{\sigma(1)=1} \operatorname{sgn}(\sigma)a_{\sigma(2),2} \cdots a_{\sigma(n),n}$$

Since $\sigma(1) = 1$, $\sigma \mid \{2, \ldots, n\}$ is a permutation of $\{2, \ldots, n\}$, which we call σ'. As σ ranges over all permutations of $\mathbf{N}_n$ that keep 1 fixed, σ' ranges over all permutations of $\{2, \ldots, n\}$. Let $a_{\sigma'} = a_{\sigma(2),2} \cdots a_{\sigma(n),n}$.

Then,

$$\sum_{\sigma(1)=1} \operatorname{sgn}(\sigma)a_\sigma = a_{11} \sum_{\sigma' \in \pi(\{2, \ldots, n\})} \operatorname{sgn}(\sigma)a_{\sigma'}$$

It is easily shown that σ is even if and only if σ' is, so that $\operatorname{sgn}(\sigma) = \operatorname{sgn}(\sigma')$. Therefore,

$$\sum_{\sigma(1)=1} \operatorname{sgn}(\sigma)a = a_{11} \sum_{\sigma' \in \pi(\{2, \ldots, n\})} \operatorname{sgn}(\sigma')a_{\sigma'} = a_{11}M_{11}$$

For the sum in the middle is precisely the definition of the determinant of the matrix that one gets from (a_{ij}) by striking out column one and row one: M_{11}.

Now, choose any i_0 between 1 and n. Let (a'_{ij}) be the matrix obtained from (a_{ij}) by exchanging row i_0 successively with rows $i_0 - 1, i_0 - 2, \ldots, 3, 2$, and 1. Thus, we can think of (a'_{ij}) as being obtained from (a_{ij}) by taking out the i_0th row of the latter, pushing the above rows down one, and placing the i_0th row in the first position. Let M'_{ij} be the minors of (a'_{ij}) of order $n - 1$. Clearly,

$$M'_{11} = M_{i_0 1},$$

since the former is obtained from (a'_{ij}) by deleting column one and row one, which are the same, respectively, as column one and row i_0 in (a_{ij}). Let $a'_\sigma = a'_{\sigma(1),1}a'_{\sigma(2),2} \cdots a'_{\sigma(n),n}$. Then, by the preceding,

$$\sum_\sigma \operatorname{sgn}(\sigma)a'_\sigma = a'_{11}M'_{11} = a_{i_0 1}M_{i_0 1}$$

It remains to show that

$$\sum_{\sigma(1)=i_0} \operatorname{sgn}(\sigma)a_\sigma = (-1)^{i_0-1} \sum_{\sigma(1)=1} \operatorname{sgn}(\sigma)a'_\sigma$$

Let $t \in \pi(\mathbf{N}_n)$ be the composition

$$t_1 \circ t_2 \circ \cdots \circ t_{i_0-1},$$

where t_i exchanges i and $i+1$ and leaves everything else fixed. This is precisely the sequence of switches used to bring row i_0 up to row 1. Therefore,

$$a_{ij} = a'_{t(i),j}$$

for all $i = 1, \ldots, n$, and, thus,

$$a_\sigma = a'_{t\circ\sigma}$$

for all permutations σ. In particular, if σ ranges over all permutations such that $\sigma(1) = i_0$, then $t \circ \sigma$ ranges (in a 1–1 way) over all permutations such that $(t\circ\sigma)(1) = t(i_0) = t_1 \circ \cdots \circ t_{i_0-1}(i_0) = 1$. Thus, the correspondence

$$a_\sigma \to a'_{t\circ\sigma}$$

is a 1–1 correspondence between the summands of the above two sums. Moreover, $\operatorname{sgn}(\sigma) = (-1)^{i_0-1}\operatorname{sgn}(t\circ\sigma)$, since t is the composition of $i_0 - 1$ transpositions. [That is $\operatorname{sgn}(\sigma) = \operatorname{sgn}(t\circ\sigma)$, if and only if $i_0 - 1$ is even, and $\operatorname{sgn}(\sigma) = -\operatorname{sgn}(t\circ\sigma)$ if and only if $i_0 - 1$ is odd.] Since the corresponding summands and their signs are equal, up to a factor of $(-1)^{i_0-1}$, the same is true of their sums. Thus, for every i,

$$\sum_{\substack{\sigma \\ \sigma(1)=i}} \operatorname{sgn}(\sigma)a_\sigma = (-1)^{i-1} \sum_{\substack{\sigma \\ \sigma(1)=1}} \operatorname{sgn}(\sigma)a'_\sigma = (-1)^{i-1}a'_{11}M'_{11} = (-1)^{i-1}a_{i1}M_{i1},$$

and so, $D = a_{11}M_{11} - a_{12}M_{12} + \cdots$, as desired.

This completes the proof of Part (1), equation (1′), for the case $j = 1$.

For arbitrary j_0, form the matrix (a''_{ij}) from (a_{ij}) by switching column j_0 with columns $j_0 - 1, j_0 - 2, \ldots 3, 2, 1$ successively. Let D'' be the determinant of (a''_{ij}), and let M''_{ij} be the minors of order $n - 1$. Clearly,

$$M''_{i1} = M_{i,j_0}, \qquad \text{for all} \quad i = 1, \ldots, n$$

Then, by the skew-symmetry of determinants, and by the result just proved for $j = 1$,

$$\begin{aligned}(-1)^{j_0-1}D = D'' &= a''_{11}M''_{11} - a''_{21}M''_{21} + \cdots \\ &= a_{1j_0}M_{1j_0} - a_{2j_0}M_{2j_0} + \cdots, \text{ as desired}\end{aligned}$$

This completes the proof of Part (1), equation (1′).

Part (1), equation (2′) is proved easily by, first choosing any j_0 and k between 1 and n, $j_0 \neq k$, and then replacing (a_{ij}) by the matrix (b_{ij}) which is the same as (a_{ij}) except in its j_0th column, in which appears the kth column of (a_{ij}). Let M'_{ij} denote the minors of (b_{ij}), and let M_{ij} denote the minors of (a_{ij}). Clearly,

$$M'_{ij_0} = M_{ij_0},$$

for, when their j_0th columns are deleted, (a_{ij}) and (b_{ij}) are identical.

Since (b_{ij}) has a repeated column and determinants are alternating in columns,

$$\begin{aligned} 0 = (-1)^{j_0-1} det(b_{ij}) &= b_{1j_0}M'_{1j_0} - b_{2j_0}M'_{2j_0} + \cdots \\ &= a_{1k}M_{1j_0} - a_{2k}M_{2j_0} + \cdots, \end{aligned}$$

which proves Part (1), equation (2′). Q.E.D.

Examples

(a) First, two general examples, in the cases $n = 2$ or 3.
Let

$$(a_{ij}) = \begin{pmatrix} a & b \\ c & d \end{pmatrix}, \qquad (b_{ij}) = \begin{pmatrix} b_{11} & b_{12} & b_{13} \\ b_{21} & b_{22} & b_{23} \\ b_{31} & b_{32} & b_{33} \end{pmatrix}$$

We expand both determinants by minors, using the first column:

$$\begin{vmatrix} a & b \\ c & d \end{vmatrix} = ad - cb$$

$$\begin{aligned} \begin{vmatrix} b_{11} & b_{12} & b_{13} \\ b_{21} & b_{22} & b_{23} \\ b_{31} & b_{32} & b_{33} \end{vmatrix} &= b_{11}\begin{vmatrix} b_{22} & b_{23} \\ b_{32} & b_{33} \end{vmatrix} - b_{21}\begin{vmatrix} b_{12} & b_{13} \\ b_{32} & b_{33} \end{vmatrix} \\ &\quad + b_{31}\begin{vmatrix} b_{12} & b_{13} \\ b_{22} & b_{23} \end{vmatrix} \\ &= b_{11}(b_{22}b_{33} - b_{32}b_{23}) - b_{21}(b_{12}b_{33} - b_{32}b_{13}) \\ &\quad + b_{31}(b_{12}b_{23} - b_{22}b_{13}) \end{aligned}$$

We expand both determinants by minors, using the second row:

$$(-1)^{2-1}\begin{vmatrix} a & b \\ c & d \end{vmatrix} = cb - da, \quad \text{or} \quad \begin{vmatrix} a & b \\ c & d \end{vmatrix} = -(cb - da)$$

$$\begin{aligned} (-1)^{2-1}\begin{vmatrix} b_{11} & b_{12} & b_{13} \\ b_{21} & b_{22} & b_{33} \\ b_{31} & b_{32} & b_{33} \end{vmatrix} & \\ = b_{21}\begin{vmatrix} b_{12} & b_{13} \\ b_{32} & b_{33} \end{vmatrix} - b_{22}\begin{vmatrix} b_{11} & b_{13} \\ b_{31} & b_{33} \end{vmatrix} + b_{23}\begin{vmatrix} b_{11} & b_{12} \\ b_{31} & b_{32} \end{vmatrix} & \\ = b_{21}(b_{12}b_{33} - b_{32}b_{13}) - b_{22}(b_{11}b_{33} - b_{31}b_{13}) & \\ + b_{23}(b_{11}b_{32} - b_{31}b_{12}) & \end{aligned}$$

Multiplying both sides of the last equation by $(-1)^{2-1} = -1$, we get the value of $\det(b_{ij})$. Clearly, this is the same as the first answer.

(b)

$$\begin{vmatrix} -5 & 0 & 2 \\ 6 & 1 & 2 \\ 2 & 3 & 1 \end{vmatrix} = -5\begin{vmatrix} 1 & 2 \\ 3 & 1 \end{vmatrix} - 6\begin{vmatrix} 0 & 2 \\ 3 & 1 \end{vmatrix} + 2\begin{vmatrix} 0 & 2 \\ 1 & 2 \end{vmatrix}$$

$$= -5(1-6) - 6(0-6) + 2(0-2)$$

$$= 25 + 36 - 4 = 57.$$

(c) Usually, one combines row and column operations with the method of expansion by minors.

$$\begin{vmatrix} 4 & 2 & 1 & 3 \\ -1 & 0 & 2 & 8 \\ 5 & -6 & 0 & -1 \\ 0 & 2 & 2 & 3 \end{vmatrix} = \begin{vmatrix} 0 & 0 & 1 & 0 \\ -9 & -4 & 2 & 2 \\ 5 & -6 & 0 & -1 \\ -8 & -2 & 2 & -3 \end{vmatrix}$$

(We subtracted suitable multiples of column three from the others.)

$$\begin{vmatrix} 0 & 0 & 1 & 0 \\ -9 & -4 & 2 & 2 \\ 5 & -6 & 0 & -1 \\ -8 & -2 & 2 & -3 \end{vmatrix} = 1 \cdot \begin{vmatrix} -9 & -4 & 2 \\ 5 & -6 & -1 \\ -8 & -2 & -3 \end{vmatrix}$$

(We expanded by minors, using row one.)

$$\begin{vmatrix} -9 & -4 & 2 \\ 5 & -6 & -1 \\ -8 & -2 & -3 \end{vmatrix} = \begin{vmatrix} 1 & -16 & 0 \\ 5 & -6 & -1 \\ -23 & 16 & 0 \end{vmatrix}$$

(We subtracted suitable multiples of row two from the others.)

$$\begin{vmatrix} 1 & -16 & 0 \\ 5 & -6 & -1 \\ -23 & 16 & 0 \end{vmatrix} = (-1)^2\left(-1\begin{vmatrix} 1 & -16 \\ -23 & 16 \end{vmatrix}\right) = -(16 - 23 \cdot 16)$$

$$= -(-352) = 352$$

[We expanded by minors, using column three. The factor $(-1)^{j-1}$ appears in Part (1), equation (1) on the left-hand side. Clearly, we can multiply both sides of Part (1), equation (1) by it, obtaining $(-1)^{j-1}$ on the right and $(-1)^{j-1} \cdot (-1)^{j-1} = 1$ on the left. Hence, the $(-1)^2$ on the right above. In this case, of course, this factor is irrelevant.]

EXERCISES / 5.7

1. Evaluate the following determinants by any of the techniques described in this section.

a. $\begin{vmatrix} 2 & 4 & -5 & 10 \\ -1 & 2 & 1 & 2 \\ 0 & -5 & 6 & -1 \\ 3 & 2 & 1 & 3 \end{vmatrix}$ **c.** $\begin{vmatrix} a_{11}-\lambda & a_{12} & a_{13} \\ a_{21} & a_{22}-\lambda & a_{23} \\ a_{31} & a_{32} & a_{33}-\lambda \end{vmatrix}$

b. $\begin{vmatrix} a_{11} & a_{12} & a_{13} & a_{14} \\ 0 & a_{22} & a_{23} & a_{24} \\ 0 & 0 & a_{33} & a_{34} \\ 0 & 0 & 0 & a_{44} \end{vmatrix}$ **d.** $\begin{vmatrix} 1 & 5 & -3 & 4 \\ 2 & 8 & 2 & -1 \\ -3 & -12 & 6 & 7 \\ 0 & 0 & 4 & 2 \end{vmatrix}$

2. Prove that

$$\begin{vmatrix} a_{11} & a_{12} & a_{13} & a_{14} \\ a_{21} & a_{22} & a_{23} & a_{24} \\ 0 & 0 & a_{33} & a_{34} \\ 0 & 0 & a_{43} & a_{44} \end{vmatrix} = \begin{vmatrix} a_{11} & a_{12} \\ a_{21} & a_{22} \end{vmatrix} \cdot \begin{vmatrix} a_{33} & a_{34} \\ a_{43} & a_{44} \end{vmatrix}$$

3. Let $\mathfrak{a}$ be an $n \times n$ matrix over F, $\mathfrak{b}$ an $n \times k$ matrix over F, and $\mathfrak{c}$ a $k \times k$ matrix over F. Let

$$\begin{pmatrix} \mathfrak{a} & \mathfrak{b} \\ 0 & \mathfrak{c} \end{pmatrix}$$

be the $(n+k) \times (n+k)$ matrix obtained by placing (the entries of) $\mathfrak{a}$ in the upper left-hand corner, $\mathfrak{b}$ in the upper right-hand corner, etc.

Use the definition of determinant of a matrix to prove that

$$det \begin{pmatrix} \mathfrak{a} & \mathfrak{b} \\ 0 & \mathfrak{c} \end{pmatrix} = (det\ \mathfrak{a}) \cdot (det\ \mathfrak{c})$$

4. Let $a_1, \ldots, a_n$ be any n distinct scalars in F. Consider the matrix

$$\begin{pmatrix} 1 & 1 & \cdots & 1 \\ a_1 & a_2 & \cdots & a_n \\ a_1^2 & a_2^2 & \cdots & a_n^2 \\ \vdots & \vdots & & \vdots \\ a_1^{n-1} & a_2^{n-1} & \cdots & a_n^{n-1} \end{pmatrix} = \mathfrak{a}$$

Replace a_1 by the indeterminate x and call the resulting matrix $\mathfrak{a}(x)$.

a. Show, by expanding by minors with respect to column one, that *det* $\mathfrak{a}(x)$ is a polynomial of degree $\leqq n-1$ in the indeterminate x.

b. Show that $a_2, \ldots, a_n$ are zeros of the polynomial det $\mathfrak{a}(x)$. (Thus, det $\mathfrak{a}(x)$ must have degree precisely $n-1$.)

This means, by standard results about polynomials, that $(x-a_2)(x-a_3)\cdots(x-a_n)$ is a factor of *det* $\mathfrak{a}(x)$. Since this polynomial is also of degree $(n-1)$, we must have

$$det\ \mathfrak{a}(x) = k(x-a_2)(x-a_3)\cdots(x-a_n),$$

where k is a constant depending on $a_2, \ldots, a_n$: $k = k(a_2, \ldots, a_n)$. Indeed, k is the coefficient of x^{n-1} in *det* $\mathfrak{a}(x)$.

c. Show that

$$(a_2 \cdot a_3 \cdots a_n) \cdot k(a_2, \ldots, a_n) = (-1)^{n-1} \begin{vmatrix} 1 & \cdots & 1 \\ a_2 & & a_n \\ a_2{}^2 & & a_n{}^2 \\ \vdots & & \vdots \\ a_2{}^{n-2} & & a_n{}^{n-2} \end{vmatrix}$$

d. Use **b** to show that

$$k(y, a_3, \ldots, a_n) = (-1)^{n-1}\ell(y-a_3)\cdots(y-a_n),$$

where ℓ is a constant, depending on $a_3, \ldots, a_n$.

e. Proceed inductively (informally), using **b**, **d** to show that

$$\begin{aligned} det\ \mathfrak{a} &= (-1)^r(a_1-a_2)\cdots(a_1-a_n)(a_2-a_3)\cdots(a_2-a_n)\cdots(a_{n-1}-a_n) \\ &= (-1)^r\Phi_n(a_1, \ldots, a_n), \end{aligned}$$

where $r = (n-1)+(n-2)+\cdots+3+2+1 = \frac{1}{2}n(n-1)$, and where Φ_n is as defined in 3.3(**a**).

In particular, the above shows that when $a_1, \ldots, a_n$ are distinct, *det* $\mathfrak{a} \neq 0$. This means that the n-tuples $(1, a_1, a_1^2, \ldots, a_n^{n-1})$, $(1, a_2, a_2^2, \ldots, a_1^{n-1})$, $\ldots, (1, a_n, a_n{}^2, \ldots, a_n{}^{n-1})$ are linearly independent.

5.* Let (a_{ij}) and (b_{ij}) be any two $n \times n$ matrices. Then $(a_{ij}) \cdot (b_{ij}) = (c_{ij})$, where

$$c_{ij} = a_{i1}b_{1j} + a_{i2}b_{2j} + \cdots + a_{in}b_{nj}$$

a. Prove that

$$det(c_{ij}) = b_{11}\begin{vmatrix} a_{11} & c_{12} & \cdots & c_{1n} \\ \vdots & \vdots & & \vdots \\ a_{n1} & c_{n2} & \cdots & c_{nn} \end{vmatrix} + b_{21}\begin{vmatrix} a_{12} & c_{12} & \cdots & c_{1n} \\ \vdots & \vdots & & \vdots \\ a_{n2} & c_{n2} & \cdots & c_{nn} \end{vmatrix}$$

$$+ \cdots + b_{n1}\begin{vmatrix} a_{1n} & c_{12} & \cdots & c_{1n} \\ \vdots & \vdots & & \vdots \\ a_{nn} & c_{n2} & \cdots & c_{nn} \end{vmatrix}$$

b. Prove that *det* (c_{ij}) is the sum of n^n terms of the form

$$b_{i_1 1} b_{i_2 2} \cdots b_{i_n n} \begin{vmatrix} a_{1i_1} & a_{1i_2} & \cdots & a_{1i_n} \\ \vdots & \vdots & & \vdots \\ a_{ni_1} & a_{ni_2} & \cdots & a_{ni_n} \end{vmatrix}$$

where $i_1, \ldots, i_n$ are (not necessarily distinct) integers between 1 and n.

c. Prove, directly from the definition of *det* that $det(1)_n = 1$, where $(1)_n$ is the matrix of the identity transformation.

d. Prove that the determinant on the right in **b** equals 0, if the i_r's are not all distinct and equals $\text{sgn}(\sigma) det(a_{ij})$, if the i_r's are distinct and σ is the permutation of $1, \ldots, n$ defined by $\sigma(r) = i_r$.

e. Use **b** and **d** to show that

$$det((a_{ij}) \cdot (b_{ij})) = (det(a_{ij})) \cdot (det(b_{ij}))$$

f. Use **c** and **e** to prove that if (a_{ij}) is invertible, then $det(a_{ij}) \neq 0$. Conclude that if (a_{ij}) has rank n, then $det(a_{ij}) \neq 0$.

6. Let (a_{ij}) be an $n \times n$ matrix.

a. Show that if (a_{ij}) is not invertible, then one of its columns is a linear combination of the others.

b. Show that if one of the columns of (a_{ij}), is a linear combination of the others, then

$$det(a_{ij}) = 0$$

(*Hint:* Use the facts that *det* is alternating and n-linear.)
Exercises **6.a** and **b**, together with Exercises **5.f**, yields:

$_n(a_{ij})_n$ is invertible (has rank n), if and only if $det(a_{ij}) \neq 0$

Using formula (8), this may be rephrased to yield:

$T \in Trans\,(V, V)$ is an isomorphism, if and only if $det\ T \neq 0$

We proved this result rather differently in Proposition 5.28.

3.5 Matrix Rank and Determinants

In this section we generalize Proposition 5.28(a) (or Exercises 5.7.6) which says that the determinant of a linear transformation is different from zero if and only if the transformation is an isomorphism. In terms of matrices, this result is that

$$\det(_n(a_{ij})_n) \neq 0,$$

if and only if ${}_n(a_{ij})_n$ has rank n. The generalization will allow us to extend this result, in a certain sense, to matrices that are not square (i.e., to $k \times n$ matrices for which $k \neq n$). First, we need to introduce some terminology.

Let ${}_k(a_{ij})_n$ be any $k \times n$ matrix over F. Choose any $h \leqq k$ and $m \leqq n$. An $h \times m$ *submatrix* of (a_{ij}) is an $h \times m$ matrix over F that can be obtained from (a_{ij}) by deleting all but h of its rows and m of its columns. To put it another way, select integers $i_1, i_2, \ldots, i_h$ and $j_1, j_2, \ldots, j_k$ such that

$$1 \leqq i_1 < i_2 < \cdots < i_h \leqq k \text{ and } 1 \leqq j_1 < j_2 < \cdots < j_m \leqq n$$

Then, the matrix

$$\begin{pmatrix} a_{i_1 j_1} & \cdots & a_{i_1 j_m} \\ \vdots & & \vdots \\ a_{i_h j_1} & \cdots & a_{i_h j_m} \end{pmatrix}$$

is an $h \times m$ submatrix of ${}_k(a_{ij})_n$. A minor of order p of ${}_k(a_{ij})_n$ is the determinant of some $p \times p$ submatrix of ${}_k(a_{ij})_n$. Clearly, this is the same as our use of the word "minor" above. Then, however, we were only considering matrices ${}_k(a_{ij})_n$ for which $k = n$. Now, we also allow $k \neq n$.

The following result provides the desired generalization.

Proposition 5.30

The rank of ${}_k(a_{ij})_n$ equals zero or the maximum order of all nonzero minors of ${}_k(a_{ij})_n$ the former occurring if and only if there are no nonzero minors.

Proof

Let $\rho = \text{rank}(a_{ij})$, and let $\mu =$ the maximum order of all nonzero minors. If $\rho = 0$, then (a_{ij}) has no linearly independent rows. This can only happen when all the entries are zero. In this case there are no nonzero minors. Conversely, if there are no nonzero minors, then (a_{ij}) can have no nonzero entries (for any such entry would determine a nonzero minor of order one). Thus, in this case, $\rho = 0$.

Henceforth, we assume that $\rho \geqq 1$ and $\mu \geqq 1$.

Now, (a_{ij}) has ρ linearly independent columns (since rank = column rank = row rank, by definition—see Proposition 5.5), say columns $j_1, \ldots, j_\rho$. Consider the submatrix

$$\begin{pmatrix} a_{1 j_1} & \cdots & a_{1 j_\rho} \\ \vdots & & \vdots \\ a_{k j_1} & & a_{k j_\rho} \end{pmatrix} \tag{11'}$$

It has rank $= \rho$, so that it has linearly independent rows, say rows $i_1, i_2, \ldots, i_\rho$. Therefore, the submatrix of (11′)

$$\begin{pmatrix} a_{i_1j_1} & \cdots & a_{i_1j_\rho} \\ \vdots & & \vdots \\ a_{i_\rho j_1} & & a_{i_\rho j_\rho} \end{pmatrix}$$

has rank ρ. Moreover, it is a square matrix. Thus, it is the matrix of an onto linear transformation $T: F^\rho \to F^\rho$, which is, being onto, also 1–1, and, hence, an isomorphism. Proposition 5.28(a) implies that $\det T \neq 0$; thus, the determinant of the above submatrix of (a_{ij}) is nonzero. Alternatively, this result is proved in Exercises 5.7.**5.f**, **6.a**, and **6.b**.

This means that (a_{ij}) has at least one nonzero minor of order ρ. Since μ is the maximum order of all nonzero minors, $\mu \geqq \rho$.

Next, consider any nonzero minor of order μ. That is consider any $\mu \times \mu$ submatrix of (a_{ij}) with nonzero determinant. There must be at least one such submatrix or else μ would not be the maximum order of all nonzero minors of (a_{ij}). For notational convenience only, we assume that the $\mu \times \mu$ submatrix in question is in the upper left-hand corner of (a_{ij}). That is, it is:

$$\begin{pmatrix} a_{11} & \cdots & a_{1\mu} \\ \vdots & & \vdots \\ a_{\mu 1} & \cdots & a_{\mu\mu} \end{pmatrix}$$

This is a square matrix with nonzero determinant. Thus, it corresponds to an isomorphism $T: F^\mu \to F^\mu$. The rank of the submatrix $= \dim \mathscr{R}_T = \mu$, since T is onto, so that the rows of the submatrix are linearly independent as μ-tuples in F^μ. (Again, this follows, alternatively, from Exercises 5.7.**5.f**, **6.a**, and **6.b**.)

Now, consider the submatrix of (a_{ij})

$$\begin{pmatrix} a_{11} & \cdots & a_{1\mu} \\ \vdots & & \vdots \\ a_{\mu 1} & & a_{\mu\mu} \\ \vdots & & \vdots \\ a_{k1} & \cdots & a_{k\mu} \end{pmatrix}$$

Its first μ rows are linearly independent, by the preceding remarks. Thus, its row rank is at least μ. Since column rank $=$ row rank, its column rank is $\geqq \mu$. That is, the columns of this submatrix are linearly independent. But, these are columns of (a_{ij}). Thus, (a_{ij}) has at least μ linearly independent columns. Since the maximum number of linearly independent columns of (a_{ij}) equals the rank of $(a_{ij}) = \rho$, we have $\rho \geqq \mu$.

The two inequalities, then, imply that $\rho = \mu$. Q.E.D.

EXERCISES / 5.8

1. Identify the nonzero minors of order two in the following matrices.

a. $\begin{pmatrix} 1 & 0 & 0 \\ 0 & 1 & 0 \\ 0 & 0 & 1 \end{pmatrix}$

c. $\begin{pmatrix} a_{11} & a_{12} & 0 & 0 \\ a_{21} & a_{22} & 0 & 0 \\ 0 & 0 & a_{33} & a_{34} \\ 0 & 0 & a_{43} & a_{44} \end{pmatrix}$

b. $\begin{pmatrix} 2 & -1 & 3 \\ -1 & 3 & 1 \\ 3 & -4 & 2 \end{pmatrix}$

d. $\begin{pmatrix} 2 & 1 \\ 3 & 4 \\ 4 & 2 \\ 6 & 8 \\ 5 & -1 \end{pmatrix}$

2. Determine the rank of the following matrices by computing minors.

a. $\begin{pmatrix} -1 & 5 & 7 \\ 2 & -2 & 2 \\ 0 & 8 & 16 \\ 3 & 0 & 9 \end{pmatrix}$

c. $\begin{pmatrix} 3 & 0 & 0 & 0 \\ 0 & 0 & 4 & 0 \\ 0 & 1 & 0 & 0 \\ 0 & 0 & 0 & 2 \end{pmatrix}$

b. $\begin{pmatrix} 8 & 0 & 1 \\ -1 & 7 & 4 \\ 2 & 3 & 1 \end{pmatrix}$

d. $\begin{pmatrix} 9 & 2 & 7 & -5 \\ 0 & 8 & 6 & 3 \\ 1 & 3 & 7 & 0 \end{pmatrix}$

3.6 Solution of Linear Equations via Determinants

(a) *A criterion for determining the solvability of a system of linear equations*

Let

$$\begin{aligned} a_{11}x_1 + \cdots + a_{1n}x_n &= b_1 \\ \vdots \qquad\qquad \vdots \quad & \quad \vdots \\ a_{k1}x_1 + \cdots + a_{kn}x_n &= b_k \end{aligned} \tag{12}$$

be the system of linear equations presented at the beginning of this chapter.

Let the rank of the matrix of coefficients (a_{ij}) be p. Consider the augmented matrix

$$\begin{pmatrix} a_{11} & \cdots & a_{1n} & b_1 \\ \vdots & & \vdots & \vdots \\ a_{k1} & & a_{kn} & b_k \end{pmatrix} \tag{13}$$

Proposition 5.31

Equation (12) *has a solution, if and only if the augmented matrix* (13) *has rank* p.

Proof

Let $A: F^n \to F^k$ be the linear transformation determined by (12), and recall that the columns of (a_{ij}), considered as k-tuples in F^k, are just the vectors $A(\mathbf{e}_1^{(k)}), \ldots, A(\mathbf{e}_k^{(k)})$, where $\{\mathbf{e}_1^{(k)}, \ldots, \mathbf{e}_k^{(k)}\}$ is the standard basis of F^k. Notice also that these vectors generate $\mathscr{R}_A$.

Now, (12) has a solution if and only if $(b_1, \ldots, b_k) \in \mathscr{R}_A = \text{span}_{F^k}(\{A(\mathbf{e}_1^{(k)}), \ldots, A(\mathbf{e}_k^{(k)})\})$. That is, (12) has a solution if and only if $(b_1, \ldots, b_k)$ is a linear combination of $A(\mathbf{e}_1^{(k)}), \ldots, A(\mathbf{e}_k^{(k)})$.

If $(b_1, \ldots, b_k)$ is a linear combination of $A(\mathbf{e}_1^{(k)}), \ldots, A(\mathbf{e}_k^{(k)})$, then the rank of the augmented matrix is p. For certainly, this rank is always $\geqq p$, since (a_{ij}), having rank p, has p linearly independent columns, and these columns are also columns of the augmented matrix. Moreover, the rank of the augmented matrix cannot be $>p$, since we do not increase the number of independent columns by adjoining $(b_1, \ldots, b_k)$.

Conversely, if the augmented matrix has rank p, then, we have not enlarged the linear span of the $A(\mathbf{e})$'s by adjoining $(b_1, \ldots, b_k)$. This can only happen when $(b_1, \ldots, b_k)$ is a linear combination of the $A(\mathbf{e})$'s.

Thus, (12) has a solution if and only if (13) has rank p. Q.E.D.

Proposition 5.31, together with Proposition 5.30 and the computational results of Subsections 3.3 and 3.4, provides a computational method of determining whether or not (12) has a solution: namely, by the techniques of Subsections 3.3 and 3.4, determine the maximal order of nonzero minors of (a_{ij}) and of the augmented matrix (13); these numbers, by Proposition 5.30, are the ranks of the corresponding matrices; Proposition 5.31 then tells us that (12) has a solution if and only if the two ranks are equal.

Proposition 5.31 does not, however, provide a method for determining solutions. We, now, turn to this task.

(b) *Cramer's Rule*

Consider system (12) above. We write it as

$$A(\mathbf{x}) = \mathbf{b} \tag{12'}$$

and we suppose that A is an isomorphism. That is, $k = n$ and det $A \neq 0$. Let $\{\mathbf{e}_1^{(n)}, \ldots, \mathbf{e}_n^{(n)}\}$ be the standard basis of F^n. Since A is an isomorphism, (12′) has a unique solution for every $\mathbf{b} \in F^n$: namely,

$$\mathbf{x} = A^{-1}(\mathbf{b})$$

We use determinants to compute this solution. The result is known as Cramer's Rule.

Let us suppose that $\mathbf{x} = (x_1, \ldots, x_n) = x_1\mathbf{e}_1^{(n)} + \cdots + x_n\mathbf{e}_n^{(n)}$ is a solution. Then,

$$x_1A(\mathbf{e}_1^{(n)}) + \cdots + x_nA(\mathbf{e}_n^{(n)}) = A(\mathbf{x}) = \mathbf{b} \tag{14}$$

We may think of $A(\mathbf{e}_1^{(n)}), \ldots A(\mathbf{e}_n^{(n)})$ as the columns of the matrix $\mathscr{A}_{X,X}(A) = (a_{ij})$, where $X = \{\mathbf{e}_1^{(n)}, \ldots, \mathbf{e}_n^{(n)}\}$. Let $f = det$, viewed as a function of columns, so that

$$f(A(\mathbf{e}_1^{(n)}), \ldots, A(\mathbf{e}_n^{(n)})) = det(a_{ij}) \tag{15}$$

Now, consider $f(\mathbf{b}, A(\mathbf{e}_2^{(n)}), \ldots, A(\mathbf{e}_n^{(n)}))$. By (14),

$$\begin{aligned} f(\mathbf{b}, A(\mathbf{e}_2^{(n)}), \ldots, A(\mathbf{e}_n^{(n)})) &= f\left(\sum_{i=1}^{n} x_iA(\mathbf{e}_i^{(n)}), A(\mathbf{e}_2^{(n)}), \ldots, A(\mathbf{e}_n^{(n)})\right) \\ &= \sum_{i=1}^{n} x_if(A(\mathbf{e}_i^{(n)}), A(\mathbf{e}_2^{(n)}), \ldots, A(\mathbf{e}_n^{(n)})), \end{aligned}$$

where we have used the linearity of f in its first variable. When $i \geqq 2$, $f(A(\mathbf{e}_i^{(n)}), A(\mathbf{e}_2^{(n)}), \ldots, A(\mathbf{e}_n^{(n)})) = 0$, since repeated terms occur in the argument of f. Therefore, we get,

$$\begin{aligned} f(\mathbf{b}, A(\mathbf{e}_2{}^{(n)}), \ldots, A_n(\mathbf{e}^{(n)})) &= x_1f(A(\mathbf{e}_1^{(n)}), \ldots, A(\mathbf{e}_n^{(n)})) \\ &= x_1det(a_{ij}) \end{aligned}$$

From this it follows that since $det(a_{ij}) \neq 0$,

$$x_1 = \frac{f(\mathbf{b}, A(\mathbf{e}_2^{(n)}), \ldots, A(\mathbf{e}_n^{(n)}))}{det(a_{ij})}$$

Now, let $B: F^n \to F^n$ be the linear transformation satisfying $B(\mathbf{e}_1^{(n)}) = \mathbf{b}$, and $B(\mathbf{e}_i^{(n)}) = A(\mathbf{e}_i^{(n)})$, $i \geqq 2$. Then, the matrices of B and A, with respect to the standard basis, are the same, except that in the first column of the matrix of B

$$\begin{pmatrix} b_1 \\ \vdots \\ b_n \end{pmatrix} \text{ has replaced } \begin{pmatrix} a_{11} \\ \vdots \\ a_{n1} \end{pmatrix}$$

Let $(a_{ij}) = \mathfrak{a}$, and let the matrix obtained from $\mathfrak{a}$ by replacing its jth column by $\mathbf{b}$ be called $\mathfrak{a}_j(\mathbf{b})$. Then,

$$\begin{aligned} f(\mathbf{b}, A(\mathbf{e}_2^{(n)}), \ldots, A(\mathbf{e}_n^{(n)})) &= f(B(\mathbf{e}_1^{(n)}), \ldots, B(\mathbf{e}_n^{(n)})) \\ &= det\ \mathfrak{a}_1(\mathbf{b}) \end{aligned}$$

Thus, we have

$$x_1 = \frac{det\ \mathfrak{a}_1(\mathbf{b})}{det\ \mathfrak{a}}$$

A similar proof yields

$$x_j = \frac{det\ \mathfrak{a}_j(\mathbf{b})}{det\ \mathfrak{a}} \tag{16}$$

for all $j = 1, \ldots, n$. Equation (16) is known as Cramer's Rule. Note that $\mathbf{x}$ is completely determined by the right-hand side of (16).

Thus, under the assumption that (12) or (12′) has a solution $\mathbf{x}$, equation (16), above, gives a computable expression for $\mathbf{x}$. This expression has one and only one value, once A and b are given, which implies that, if (12) or (12′) has a solution, then it is unique. Notice that the right-hand expression in (16) is meaningful if and only if $det\ \mathfrak{a} \neq 0$. Suppose that (12) or (12′) is given, and we are told only that $det\ \mathfrak{a} \neq 0$. Let $x = (x_1, \ldots, x_n)$ be given by (16), above. Substituting these x_j in (12), one can verify directly that $\mathbf{x}$ is a solution. This holds for any b, so that if $det\ \mathfrak{a} \neq 0$, A is onto (and, thus, an isomorphism—other proofs of this appear earlier).

We now apply Cramer's rule to compute the matrix of A^{-1}. That is, using the above notation, we compute $\mathfrak{a}^{-1}$ (the matrix of A^{-1}).**

The matrix of A^{-1}, that is $\mathfrak{a}^{-1}$, is obtained by writing out

$$A^{-1}(\mathbf{e}_1^{(n)}), \ldots, A^{-1}(\mathbf{e}_n^{(n)})$$

in terms of $\mathbf{e}_1^{(n)}, \ldots, \mathbf{e}_n^{(n)}$ and then placing the coefficients corresponding to $A^{-1}(\mathbf{e}_j^{(n)})$ in the jth column.

Choose any j between 1 and n, and let us suppose that

$$A^{-1}(\mathbf{e}_j^{(n)}) = x_1\mathbf{e}_1^{(n)} + \cdots + x_n\mathbf{e}_n^{(n)} = (x_1, \ldots, x_n) = \mathbf{x}$$

Then, $A(\mathbf{x}) = \mathbf{e}_j^{(n)}$, and we can determine $\mathbf{x}$ by Cramer's rule:

$$x_i = \frac{det\ \mathfrak{a}_i(\mathbf{e}_j^{(n)})}{det\ \mathfrak{a}}$$

Thus, $\mathfrak{a}^{-1}$ is the matrix whose i, jth entry is

$$\frac{det\ \mathfrak{a}_i(\mathbf{e}_j^{(n)})}{det\ \mathfrak{a}} \tag{17}$$

This gives a computational method of determining $\mathfrak{a}^{-1}$.

Let us look at the matrix $\mathfrak{a}_i(\mathbf{e}_j)$: All its columns coincide with those of $\mathfrak{a}$ except its ith column which equals $\mathbf{e}_j^{(n)}$. We expand $det\ \mathfrak{a}_i(\mathbf{e}_j^{(n)})$ with respect to its ith column:

$$det_n\ \mathfrak{a}_i(\mathbf{e}_j) = (-1)^{i-1} \sum_{\ell=1}^{n} (-1)^{\ell-1}\delta_{\ell j}M_{\ell i},$$

** "The matrix of A^{-1}" means $\mathscr{A}_{X,X}(A^{-1})$, where $X = \{\mathbf{e}_1^{(n)}, \ldots, \mathbf{e}_n^{(n)}\}$. Clearly, since $\mathfrak{a} = \mathscr{A}_{X,X}(A)$, we have $\mathscr{A}_{X,X}(A^{-1}) = \mathfrak{a}^{-1}$.

where $\delta_{\ell j} = 0$, if $\ell \neq j$, and $\delta_{jj} = 1$. Thus,

$$det\ \mathfrak{a}_i(\mathbf{e}_j) = (-1)^{i+j-2} M_{ji} = (-1)^{i+j} M_{ji},$$

where M_{ji} is the minor obtained from (a_{ij}) by deleting its jth row and ith column. Therefore, by (17),

$$\mathfrak{a}^{-1} = (det\ \mathfrak{a})^{-1}((-1)^{i+j} M_{ji}) \tag{18}$$

The first factor on the right is simply a scalar, the reciprocal of $det\ \mathfrak{a}$. The second is a matrix (c_{ij}), where

$$c_{ij} = (-1)^{i+j} M_{ji}$$

To illustrate this formula, we calculate the following simple example: Suppose that $ad\text{-}bc \neq 0$. Then

$$\begin{pmatrix} a & b \\ c & d \end{pmatrix}^{-1} = \begin{pmatrix} \dfrac{d}{ad-bc} & \dfrac{-b}{ad-bc} \\ \dfrac{-c}{ad-bc} & \dfrac{a}{ad-bc} \end{pmatrix}$$

$$= \left(det\begin{pmatrix} a & b \\ c & d \end{pmatrix}\right)^{-1} \begin{pmatrix} d & -b \\ -c & a \end{pmatrix},$$

for $M_{11} = d$, $M_{12} = c$, $M_{21} = b$, $M_{22} = a$.

(c) *General solution of linear equations*

Consider system (12) or equation (12′), and suppose that (a_{ij}) (the matrix of A) has rank p. Moreover, suppose that (12) [or (12′)] has at least one solution. Whether it does or not can be determined by the criterion of Proposition 5.13.

According to Proposition 5.30, (a_{ij}) has a nonzero minor of order p, which we assume, for simplicity of notation, to lie in the upper left-hand corner.

Consider, now, the system of equations

$$\begin{matrix} a_{11}x_1 + \cdots + a_{1p}x_p + a_{1p+1}x_{p+1} + \cdots + a_{1n}x_n = b_1 \\ \vdots \qquad\qquad \vdots \qquad\qquad \vdots \qquad\qquad\qquad \vdots \\ a_{p1}x_1 + \cdots + a_{pp}x_p + a_{pp+1}x_{p+1} + \cdots + a_{pn}x_n = b_p, \end{matrix} \tag{19}$$

obtained from (12) by ignoring the last $k - p$ equations of (12).

Note first that each of the last $k - p$ equations of (12) is a linear combination of the equations of (19). To see this, observe that since $\text{rank}(a_{ij}) = p$, (a_{ij}) has exactly p linearly independent rows. By our assumption as to the location of the nonzero minor, these rows are the first p. Any other row of (a_{ij}), then, when adjoined to the first p, forms a linearly dependent set with the first p. Thus, it is a combination of the first p.

Thus, calling row i, ρ_i, we have

$$\rho_i = c_{1i}\rho_i + \cdots + c_{pi}\rho_p,$$

for every ρ_i. But then

$$b_i = c_{1i}b_1 + \cdots + c_{pi}b_p,$$

since this is what the above equation becomes when we substitute the postulated solution for the x's. Therefore, both sides of each of the last $k - p$ equations are (the same) linear combinations of both sides of the first p. More briefly, the last $k - p$ equations are linear combinations of the first p.

Now, every solution of (12) is *a fortiori* a solution of (19). On the other hand, suppose that $\mathbf{c}$ is a solution of (19). Then, substituting $\mathbf{c}$ for $\mathbf{x}$ in $\rho_1, \ldots, \rho_p$, we get $b_1, \ldots, b_p$, respectively, by definition of "solution of (19)." The above equations then show that the result of substituting $\mathbf{c}$ for $\mathbf{x}$ in ρ_i is b_i for *every* i between 1 and k, so that $\mathbf{c}$ is a solution of (12). Thus, (12) and (19) have the same solutions.

Therefore, we may concentrate on solving (19). We rewrite it as follows:

$$\begin{aligned} a_{11}x_1 + \cdots + a_{1p}x_p &= b_1 - (a_{1,p+1}x_{p+1} + \cdots + a_{1n}x_n) \\ \vdots \qquad\qquad \vdots\ &\quad\ \vdots \qquad\qquad \vdots \\ a_{p1}x_1 + \cdots + a_{pp}x_p &= b_p - (a_{p,p+1}x_{p+1} + \cdots + a_{pn}x_n) \end{aligned} \tag{20}$$

Call the matrix of coefficients on the left $\tilde{\mathrm{a}}$. By assumption $\mathit{det}\ \tilde{\mathrm{a}} \neq 0$. We now may solve (20) by Cramer's rule, for every choice of $x_{p+1}, \ldots, x_n$.

First, some notation: let

$$\mathbf{a}_j = \begin{pmatrix} a_{1j} \\ a_{2j} \\ \vdots \\ a_{pj} \end{pmatrix}, \qquad j = 1, \ldots, n$$

Then, for any choice of $x_{p+1}, \ldots, x_n$, the column on the right-hand side of (20) is

$$\mathbf{b} - x_{p+1}\mathbf{a}_{p+1} - \cdots - x_n\mathbf{a}_n$$

Thus, applying Cramer's rule,

$$\begin{aligned} x_j &= (\mathit{det}\ \tilde{\mathrm{a}})^{-1} \cdot \mathit{det}\ \tilde{\mathrm{a}}_j(\mathbf{b} - x_{p+1}\mathbf{a}_{p+1} - \cdots - x_n\mathbf{a}_n), \\ &= (\mathit{det}\ \tilde{\mathrm{a}})^{-1}[\mathit{det}\ \tilde{\mathrm{a}}_j(\mathbf{b}) - x_{p+1}\mathit{det}\ \tilde{\mathrm{a}}_j(\mathbf{a}_{p+1}) - \cdots - x_n\ \mathit{det}\ \tilde{\mathrm{a}}_j(\mathbf{a}_n)], \end{aligned} \tag{21}$$

where we have used the fact that *det* is linear in the jth column (among others).

For all $j = 1, \ldots, p$ and $\ell = p + 1, \ldots, n$, let

$$c_{j\ell} = -(\mathit{det}\ \tilde{\mathrm{a}})^{-1} \cdot \mathit{det}\ \tilde{\mathrm{a}}_j(\mathbf{a}_\ell),$$

and let

$$\mathbf{c}_\ell = \underbrace{(c_{1\ell}, \ldots, c_{p\ell}, 0, \ldots, 0, 1, 0, \ldots, 0)}_{n\text{-tuple}} \qquad (22)$$

$\uparrow$ ℓth place;

Let

$$d_j = (det\ \tilde{\alpha})^{-1}\ det\ \tilde{\alpha}_j(\mathbf{b})),\ j = 1, \ldots, p$$

and let

$$\mathbf{d} = \underbrace{(d_1, \ldots, d_p, 0, \ldots, 0)}_{n\text{-tuple}} \qquad (23)$$

Equation (21) tells us that we obtain all solutions to (20) by letting $x_{p+1}, \ldots, x_n$ range freely, and by letting $x_1, \ldots, x_p$ be given by (21). Using (22) and (23), we may interpret this as follows:

The set of all solutions to (20) [*and, hence, to* (19) *and* (12)] *is the translate*

$$\mathbf{d} + \operatorname{span}_{F^n}(\{\mathbf{c}_{p+1}, \ldots, \mathbf{c}_n\}) \qquad (24)$$

In other words, the solution set consists of all $\mathbf{x} = (x_1, \ldots, x_p, x_{p+1}, \ldots, x_n)$ *such that*

$$\mathbf{x} = \mathbf{d} + x_{p+1}\mathbf{c}_{p+1} + \cdots + x_n\mathbf{c}_n \qquad (25)$$

To verify this, we suppose that $\mathbf{x}$ is a solution, $x_{p+1}, \ldots, x_n$ ranging freely and $x_1, \ldots, x_p$ given by (21). We then show that $\mathbf{x}$ satisfies (25) by comparing the ith components of each side of (25).

1. $i > p$: The ith component of $\mathbf{x}$ is x_i, that of $\mathbf{d}$ is 0, that of the remaining sum is $x_{p+1} \cdot 0 + \cdots + x_{i-1} \cdot 0 + x_i \cdot 1 + x_{i+1} \cdot 0 + \cdots + x_n \cdot 0 = x_i$. Thus, in this case the two are equal.
2. $i \leqq p$: The ith component of $\mathbf{x}$ is x_i, that of the right is $d_i + x_{p+1}c_{ip+1} + \cdots + x_n c_{in}$, which coincides with the right side of (21) and so equals x_i.

Using 1 and 2 it is easy to show that every $\mathbf{x} = (x_1, \ldots, x_n)$ satisfying (24) also has the property that its last n-p components are arbitrary and its first p, $x_1, \ldots, x_p$, satisfy (21). Thus, such an $\mathbf{x}$ is a solution to (19).

If $\mathbf{b} = \mathbf{0}$, then it is not hard to show that $\mathbf{d} = \mathbf{0}$, so that the set of solutions, then, is the subspace

$$\operatorname{span}_{F^n}(\{\mathbf{c}_{p+1}, \ldots, \mathbf{c}_n\})$$

It is not hard to show that $\{\mathbf{c}_{p+1}, \ldots, \mathbf{c}_n\}$ is a basis of this subspace, and so they comprise of fundamental set of solutions to the system.

The vector $\mathbf{d}$, of course, is itself a single solution to (19), and, hence, to (12). Thus, if only one solution is needed, compute $\mathbf{d}$ via (23).

We work out one example to illustrate the above result. Consider the system

$$2x_1 + 3x_2 = 1 - 5x_3 + 2x_4$$

$$3x_1 + 4x_2 = -6 + 10x_3 - 15x_4$$

Then,

$$\tilde{\mathfrak{a}} = \begin{pmatrix} 2 & 3 \\ 3 & 4 \end{pmatrix}, \mathbf{b} = \begin{pmatrix} 1 \\ -6 \end{pmatrix}, \mathbf{a}_3 = \begin{pmatrix} -5 \\ 10 \end{pmatrix}, \mathbf{a}_4 = \begin{pmatrix} 2 \\ -15 \end{pmatrix},$$

$$\tilde{\mathfrak{a}}_1(\mathbf{a}_3) = \begin{pmatrix} -5 & 3 \\ 10 & 4 \end{pmatrix},$$

$$\tilde{\mathfrak{a}}_2(\mathbf{a}_3) = \begin{pmatrix} 2 & -5 \\ 3 & 10 \end{pmatrix}, \tilde{\mathfrak{a}}_1(\mathbf{a}_4) = \begin{pmatrix} 2 & 3 \\ -15 & 4 \end{pmatrix}, \tilde{\mathfrak{a}}_2(\mathbf{a}_4) = \begin{pmatrix} 2 & 2 \\ 3 & -15 \end{pmatrix},$$

$$\tilde{\mathfrak{a}}_1(\mathbf{b}) = \begin{pmatrix} 1 & 3 \\ -6 & 4 \end{pmatrix}, \tilde{\mathfrak{a}}_2(\mathbf{b}) = \begin{pmatrix} 2 & 1 \\ 3 & -6 \end{pmatrix}.$$

The determinants of the matrices, starting with $\tilde{\mathfrak{a}}$, are: -1, -50, 35, 53, -36, 22, -15. Thus,

$$\mathbf{d} = (\det \tilde{\mathfrak{a}})^{-1}(22, -15, 0, 0) = -(22, -15, 0, 0)$$

$$\mathbf{c}_3 = -(\det \tilde{\mathfrak{a}})^{-1}(-50, 35, 1, 0) = (-50, 35, 1, 0)$$

$$\mathbf{c}_4 = -(\det \tilde{\mathfrak{a}})^{-1}(53, -36, 0, 1) = (53, -36, 0, 1)$$

Thus,

$$\mathbf{x} = \mathbf{d} + x_3\mathbf{c}_3 + x_4\mathbf{c}_4$$
$$= (-22, -50x_3 + 53x_4, -15 + 35x_3 - 36x_4, x_3, x_4)$$

is the general solution to the above system, x_3 and x_4 being arbitrary.

EXERCISES / 5.9

1. Which of the following systems of linear equations have a solution? (Use the criterion of 3.6a.)

a. $a_{11}x_1 + \cdots + a_{1n}x_n = 0$, a_{ij} in any field F.

$$\vdots \qquad \vdots \qquad \vdots$$

$$a_{k1}x_1 + \cdots + a_{kn}x_n = 0$$

b. $a_1x_1 + \cdots + a_nx_n = b$, a_i, b in any field F, $a_1 \neq 0$.

c.
$$\begin{aligned} x_1 - 3x_2 + 5x_3 &= -1 \\ 2x_1 + x_2 - 4x_3 &= 0 \\ x_1 + 2x_2 - 2x_3 &= 1 \\ -4x_1 + 3x_2 + x_3 &= 2 \end{aligned}$$

d.
$$\begin{aligned} 2x_1 + 7x_2 - 4x_4 &= 1 \\ x_2 + 3x_3 - x_4 &= 1 \\ x_1 - 5x_3 + x_4 &= 1 \\ 2x_1 + 16x_2 + 4x_3 - 8x_4 &= 1 \end{aligned}$$

e. $4x - 5y = 0$

$3y + 4x = 1$

f. $x_1 + x_2 = 1$

$x_2 + x_3 = 1$

$x_3 + x_4 = 1$

$x_4 + x_1 = 1$

2. Find all solutions to the systems in **1** (except for **1.a**). (Use the general method of 3.6c.)

3. Prove that the vectors $\mathbf{c}_{p+1}, \ldots, \mathbf{c}_n$, obtained above in 3.6(c) are linearly independent.

4. Compute the inverses of the following matrices.

a. $\begin{pmatrix} 1 & 1 \\ 1 & 0 \end{pmatrix}$ c. $\begin{pmatrix} 1 & 0 & 2 \\ 4 & -3 & 5 \\ 2 & 8 & 10 \end{pmatrix}$

b. $\begin{pmatrix} a_{11} & a_{12} & a_{13} \\ 0 & a_{22} & a_{23} \\ 0 & 0 & a_{33} \end{pmatrix}$, assuming that $a_{11}a_{22}a_{23} \neq 0$

5. Let A, B, C, D, W, X, Y, Z be $n \times n$ matrices over a field F. Form the $2n \times 2n$ matrices

$$\begin{pmatrix} A & B \\ C & D \end{pmatrix} \text{ and } \begin{pmatrix} W & X \\ Y & Z \end{pmatrix}$$

Prove that

$$\begin{pmatrix} A & B \\ C & D \end{pmatrix} \cdot \begin{pmatrix} W & X \\ Y & Z \end{pmatrix} = \begin{pmatrix} AW + BY & AX + BZ \\ CW + DY & CX + DZ \end{pmatrix}$$

where the entries on the right are all sums of matrix products.

6. Let A, B, D be as in **5** above. In addition, assume that A and D are invertible.

a. Prove that

$$\begin{pmatrix} A & B \\ 0 & D \end{pmatrix}$$ is invertible, by showing that its determinant is non-zero

Here "0" denotes the $n \times n$ zero matrix.

b. Verify that

$$\begin{pmatrix} A^{-1} & -A^{-1} \cdot B \cdot D^{-1} \\ 0 & D^{-1} \end{pmatrix}$$

is the inverse of the matrix in **a**.

7. Use the results of 3.6(**c**) to show that if A is the linear transformation from F^n to F^k in equation (12), then

$$\dim \mathcal{N}_A + \dim \mathcal{R}_A = n$$

8.* Let $\tilde{A}: F^p \to F^p$ be the linear transformation determined by the left-hand side of (20). (Its matrix, with respect to the standard basis of F^p, is $\tilde{\mathfrak{a}}$.) Let $\mathbf{x} = (x_1, \ldots, x_p)$. Then, (20) becomes

$$\tilde{A}(\mathbf{x}) = \mathbf{b} - x_{p+1}\mathbf{a}_{p+1} - \cdots - x_n\mathbf{a}_n$$

By assumption $\tilde{A}$ is invertible, so that,

$$\mathbf{x} = \tilde{A}^{-1}(\mathbf{b}) - x_{p+1}\tilde{A}^{-1}(\mathbf{a}_{p+1}) - \cdots - x_n\tilde{A}^{-1}(\mathbf{a}_n)$$

a. Show that every solution to (20) is of the form $(\mathbf{x}, x_{p+1}, \ldots, x_n) = (x_1, \ldots, x_p, x_{p+1}, \ldots, x_n)$, where $x_{p+1}, \ldots, x_n$ are arbitrary and $\mathbf{x}$ is given by the above equation.

b. Let $\tilde{\mathbf{c}}_\ell = \tilde{A}^{-1}(\mathbf{a}_\ell)$, $\ell = p + 1, \ldots, n$, and define a linear transformation

$$T: \operatorname{span}_{F^p}(\{\tilde{\mathbf{c}}_{p+1}, \ldots, \tilde{\mathbf{c}}_n\}) \to F^n$$

as follows:

$$T(\tilde{\mathbf{c}}_\ell) = \overbrace{(\tilde{\mathbf{c}}_\ell, 0, \ldots, 0, \underset{\substack{\uparrow \\ \ell\text{th place}}}{1}, 0, \ldots, 0)}^{n\text{-tuple}} = \tilde{\mathbf{c}}_\ell$$

Prove that T is an isomorphism from $\operatorname{span}_{F^p}(\{\tilde{\mathbf{c}}_{p+1}, \ldots, \tilde{\mathbf{c}}_n\})$ onto the subspace of F^n consisting of all solutions to the homogeneous system associated with (19) [or (12)].

c. Let $\mathbf{d} = \tilde{A}^{-1}(\mathbf{b})$, and let

$$\mathbf{d} = (\mathbf{d}, 0, \ldots, 0) \in F^n$$

Prove that $\mathbf{d} + \mathcal{R}_T$ is the set of solutions to (19).

CHAPTER 6

INNER PRODUCT SPACES

In Chapter 3, we introduced the notion of a vector-space basis as a means of quantifying, in some sense, our qualitative concept of a vector space. And, indeed, we saw how bases can be used for this purpose: that they serve as coordinate systems in a vector space.

To complete the analogy with the usual coordinate systems, we introduce, in this chapter, the notions of angle and distance measurement in a vector space. Again bases play a central role. Given any basis, we can introduce a method of angle and distance measurement with respect to which the given basis vectors are mutually perpendicular and of unit length. The basis, thus, has the properties which we usually associate with the standard bases of $\mathbf{R}^2$ and $\mathbf{R}^3$. Conversely, given any method of angle and distance measurement (in a vector space of at most countable dimension) we can find a basis consisting of mutually perpendicular vectors of unit length.

Of course, we must restrict our scalar fields somewhat: We must restrict our attention to fields in which we can meaningfully talk about "magnitude" of scalars. The usual fields employed in this context are the fields $\mathbf{R}$ and $\mathbf{C}$. We discuss these details later, in the more general treatment.

The interdependence of bases and measurement should not be too surprising. For individual vectors in a basis are, as it were, "measuring rods." The designation of a certain vector as having unit length amounts to a choice of scale on the measuring rod. The designation of a certain angle between basis vectors as a right angle amounts to a choice of scale in angle-measurement in the plane determined by the two vectors.

We now illustrate and motivate the general procedure by the special cases of $\mathbf{R}^2$ and $\mathbf{C}$.

1 / ANGLES AND DISTANCES IN $\mathbf{R}^2$ AND IN C

1.1 $\mathbf{R}^2$

(a) *The distance formula*

Given any vector $(x_1, x_2) \in \mathbf{R}^2$, the reader will recall that, using the usual geometric interpretation of $\mathbf{R}^2$, the distance d of (x_1, x_2) from $(0, 0)$ is given by

$$d(x_1, x_2) = (x_1{}^2 + x_2{}^2)^{\frac{1}{2}} \tag{1}$$

This is, of course, merely the algebraic form of the *Pythagorean Theorem.*

Given any two vectors (x_1, x_2) and (y_1, y_2), geometric considerations immediately indicate that the distance between them is equal to the distance from $(0, 0)$ of their difference $(x_1, x_2) - (y_1, y_2) = (x_1 - y_1, x_2 - y_2)$. Thus, the distance between (x_1, x_2) and (y_1, y_2) is

$$d(x_1 - y_1, x_2 - y_2) = ((x_1 - y_1)^2 + (x_2 - y_2)^2)^{\frac{1}{2}}$$

The function d, therefore, can be used in all questions of distance measurement.

(b) *The law of cosines*

Let (x_1, x_2) and (y_1, y_2) be any two vectors in $\mathbf{R}^2$ with an angle θ between them, as indicated in Figure 39.

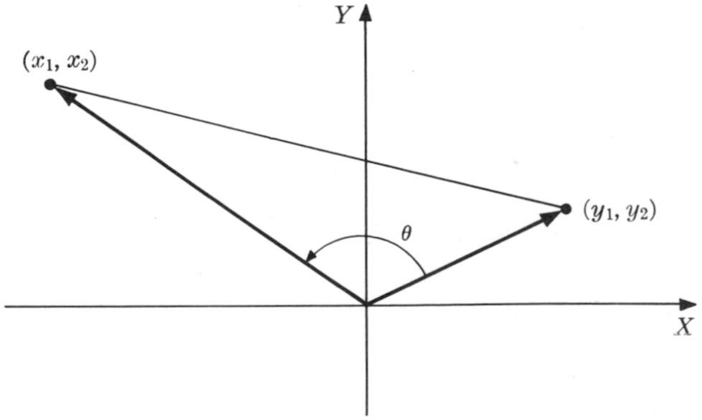

FIGURE 39

Let $a = d(x_1, x_2)$, $b = d(y_1, y_2)$, $c = d(x_1 - y_1, x_2 - y_2)$. Then, the Law of Cosines states that

$$\cos \theta = \frac{a^2 + b^2 - c^2}{2ab} \tag{2}$$

Since

$$\begin{aligned} a^2 + b^2 - c^2 &= {x_1}^2 + {x_2}^2 + {y_1}^2 + {y_2}^2 - (x_1 - y_1)^2 - (x_2 - y_2)^2 \\ &= 2(x_1 y_1 + x_2 y_2), \end{aligned}$$

we may rewrite (2) as

$$\cos \theta = \frac{x_1 y_1 + x_2 y_2}{d(x_1, x_2) d(y_1, y_2)} \tag{3}$$

Let us set

$$\alpha((x_1, x_2), (y_1, y_2)) = x_1 y_1 + x_2 y_2$$

Then, notice that

$$d(x_1, x_2) = \alpha((x_1, x_2), (x_1, x_2))^{1/2} \tag{4}$$

Thus, if we let $\mathbf{v} = (x_1, x_2)$ and $\mathbf{w} = (y_1, y_2)$, we get, finally,

$$\cos \theta = \frac{\alpha(\mathbf{v}, \mathbf{w})}{\alpha(\mathbf{v}, \mathbf{v})^{1/2} \alpha(\mathbf{w}, \mathbf{w})^{1/2}} \tag{5}$$

It should be clear, then, by (4) and (5), that for the purpose of studying angle and distance measurement in $\mathbf{R}^2$, it suffices to study the function α.

Notice that α can be obtained in terms of d as follows: let $\mathbf{v} = (x_1, x_2)$ and $\mathbf{w} = (y_1, y_2)$; then

$$\begin{aligned} (1/2)(d(\mathbf{v} + \mathbf{w})^2 - d(\mathbf{v})^2 - d(\mathbf{w})^2) &= (1/2)((x_1 + y_1)^2 + (x_2 + y_2)^2 \\ &\quad - {x_1}^2 - {x_2}^2 - {y_1}^2 - {y_2}^2) = (1/2)(2x_1 y_1 + 2x_2 y_2), \end{aligned}$$

so that

$$(1/2)(d(\mathbf{v} + \mathbf{w})^2 - d(\mathbf{v})^2 - d(\mathbf{w})^2) = \alpha(\mathbf{v}, \mathbf{w}) \tag{6}$$

Thus, knowledge of d implies knowledge of α, and, by (4), vice versa.

(c) *The function* α

We list and prove certain properties of α.

(i) α *is symmetric*. That is, for all $(\mathbf{v}, \mathbf{w}) \in \mathbf{R}^2 \times \mathbf{R}^2$, $\alpha(\mathbf{v}, \mathbf{w}) = \alpha(\mathbf{w}, \mathbf{v})$.

Proof

Let $\mathbf{v} = (x_1, x_2)$, $\mathbf{w} = (y_1, y_2)$. Then,

$$\alpha(\mathbf{v}, \mathbf{w}) = x_1 y_1 + x_2 y_2 = y_1 x_1 + y_2 x_2 = \alpha(\mathbf{w}, \mathbf{v}) \qquad \text{Q.E.D.}$$

(ii) α *is bilinear*.

Proof

Let $\mathbf{v}$, $\mathbf{w}$ be as above, let r be any real number, and let $\mathbf{u} = (z_1, z_2)$. Then,

$$\alpha(\mathbf{u} + \mathbf{v}, \mathbf{w}) = (x_1 + z_1)y_1 + (x_2 + z_2)y_2 = x_1y_1 + z_1y_1 + x_2y_2 + z_2y_2$$
$$= (x_1y_1 + x_2y_2) + (z_1y_1 + z_2y_2) = \alpha(\mathbf{u}, \mathbf{w}) + \alpha(\mathbf{v}, \mathbf{w}),$$

and

$$\alpha(r\mathbf{v}, \mathbf{w}) = (rx_1)y_1 + (rx_2)y_2 = r(x_1y_1 + x_2y_2) = r\alpha(\mathbf{v}, \mathbf{w}),$$

so that α is linear in its first variable. Using the symmetry of α, we get, for any $\mathbf{w}' = (y_1', y_2')$,

$$\alpha(\mathbf{v}, \mathbf{w} + \mathbf{w}') = \alpha(\mathbf{w} + \mathbf{w}', \mathbf{v}) = \alpha(\mathbf{w}, \mathbf{v}) + \alpha(\mathbf{w}', \mathbf{v}) = \alpha(\mathbf{v}, \mathbf{w}) + \alpha(\mathbf{v}, \mathbf{w}'),$$

and

$$\alpha(\mathbf{v}, r\mathbf{w}) = \alpha(r\mathbf{w}, \mathbf{v}) = r\alpha(\mathbf{w}, \mathbf{v}) = r\alpha(\mathbf{v}, \mathbf{w})$$

Therefore, α is linear in its second variable. Q.E.D.

(iii) *For any* $\mathbf{v} \in \mathbf{R}^2$, $\alpha(\mathbf{v}, \mathbf{v}) \geqq 0$. *Moreover,* $\alpha(\mathbf{v}, \mathbf{v}) = 0$ *if and only if* $\mathbf{v} = \mathbf{0}$.

Proof

Let $\mathbf{v} = (x_1, x_2)$. Then, $\alpha(\mathbf{v}, \mathbf{v}) = x_1{}^2 + x_2{}^2 \geqq 0$, which proves the first statement. Since $x_1{}^2 + x_2{}^2 = 0$ if and only if $x_1 = 0 = x_2$, $\alpha(\mathbf{v}, \mathbf{v}) = 0$ if and only if $\mathbf{v} = \mathbf{0}$. Q.E.D.

Given any vector space V *over* $\mathbf{R}$, *we say that a bilinear form from* $V \times V$ *to* $\mathbf{R}$ *is positive definite if and only if it satisfies the property described in* (*iii*).

Notice that if nonzero vectors $\mathbf{v}$ and $\mathbf{w}$ are perpendicular, then the angle θ between them equals $\pi/2$. In that case, $\cos\theta = 0$, so that $\alpha(\mathbf{v}, \mathbf{w}) = k\cos\theta = 0$, where $k = \alpha(\mathbf{v}, \mathbf{v})^{1/2}\alpha(\mathbf{w}, \mathbf{w})^{1/2}$ [cf. (5), above].

(iv) *Nonzero vectors* $\mathbf{v}, \mathbf{w} \in \mathbf{R}^2$ *are perpendicular if and only if* $\alpha(\mathbf{v}, \mathbf{w}) = 0$.

Proof

We have already proved the "only if" part of the proposition. We prove the "if" part equally easily.

If $\mathbf{v}$ and $\mathbf{w}$ are non-zero vectors, then, by (iii), $\alpha(\mathbf{v}, \mathbf{v})^{1/2}\alpha(\mathbf{w}, \mathbf{w})^{1/2}$ is a nonzero real number. Thus, letting θ denote the angle between $\mathbf{v}$ and $\mathbf{w}$, we get, using (5), above,

$$\cos\theta = \frac{\alpha(\mathbf{v}, \mathbf{w})}{\alpha(\mathbf{v}, \mathbf{v})^{1/2}\alpha(\mathbf{w}, \mathbf{w})^{1/2}} = 0,$$

so that $\theta = (\pi/2) + n\pi$, for some integer n. This means that the vectors are perpendicular, since, in geometric terms, $n\pi$ is a straight angle, for all n.

Let $\mathbf{e}_1$ and $\mathbf{e}_2$ denote the usual standard basis vectors of $\mathbf{R}^2$.

(v) *α is the only bilinear functional on* $\mathbf{R}^2 \times \mathbf{R}^2$ *satisfying*

$$\alpha(\mathbf{e}_1, \mathbf{e}_2) = 0 = \alpha(\mathbf{e}_2, \mathbf{e}_1)$$

$$\alpha(\mathbf{e}_1, \mathbf{e}_1) = 1 = \alpha(\mathbf{e}_2, \mathbf{e}_2)$$

Proof

That α satisfies the above equations is easily verified. That α is the *only* bilinear functional satisfying the equations is a consequence of the following result.

(vi) *A bilinear functional on* $\mathbf{R}^2 \times \mathbf{R}^2$ *is completely determined by its values on a (any) basis of* $\mathbf{R}^2$.

Proof

Let β be any bilinear functional on $\mathbf{R}^2 \times \mathbf{R}^2$, and let $\{\mathbf{v}_1, \mathbf{v}_2\}$ be any basis of $\mathbf{R}^2$. Then, for any vectors $\mathbf{v} = x_1\mathbf{v}_2 + x_2\mathbf{v}_2$ and $\mathbf{w} = y_1\mathbf{v}_1 + y_2\mathbf{v}_2$

$$\begin{aligned}\beta(\mathbf{v}, \mathbf{w}) &= \beta(x_1\mathbf{v}_1 + x_2\mathbf{v}_2, y_1\mathbf{v}_1 + y_2\mathbf{v}_2)\\ &= x_1y_1\beta(\mathbf{v}_1, \mathbf{v}_1) + x_1y_2\beta(\mathbf{v}_1, \mathbf{v}_2) + x_2y_1\beta(\mathbf{v}_2, \mathbf{v}_1) + x_2y_2\beta(\mathbf{v}_2, \mathbf{v}_2)\end{aligned}$$

Thus, once $\beta(\mathbf{v}_i, \mathbf{v}_j)$ is known, $i = 1, 2, j = 1, 2$, β is completely determined. Q.E.D.

We conclude with a trivial consequence of our definition of α, which will play a useful role in our later abstract development.

(vii) *For any vectors* $\mathbf{v}$ *and* $\mathbf{w}$ *in* $\mathbf{R}^2$,

$$\alpha(\mathbf{v}, \mathbf{w})^2 \leqq \alpha(\mathbf{v}, \mathbf{v})\alpha(\mathbf{w}, \mathbf{w}),$$

equality holding if and only if $\{\mathbf{v}, \mathbf{w}\}$ *is dependent or* $\mathbf{v} = \mathbf{w}$.

Proof

The inequality follows from (5) above:

$$\frac{\alpha(\mathbf{v}, \mathbf{w})^2}{\alpha(\mathbf{v}, \mathbf{v})\alpha(\mathbf{w}, \mathbf{w})} = \cos^2\theta,$$

where θ is the angle between $\mathbf{v}$ and $\mathbf{w}$. Since $\cos^2\theta \leqq 1$, we get the desired inequality.

Moreover, equality occurs if and only if $\cos^2\theta = 1$, that is, if and only if $\theta = n\pi$, for some integer n. In these cases, $\mathbf{v}$ and $\mathbf{w}$ lie on the same line through the origin and are, therefore, dependent or equal.

The above proof is valid when neither $\mathbf{v}$ nor $\mathbf{w}$ is the zero vector. If $\mathbf{v} = \mathbf{0}$ or $\mathbf{w} = \mathbf{0}$, equality holds in the stated relation; moreover, in this case also, $\{\mathbf{v}, \mathbf{w}\}$ is dependent or $\mathbf{v} = \mathbf{w}$. Q.E.D.

The above inequality is known as the *Cauchy-Schwarz inequality*, or, more commonly, as the *Schwarz inequality*.

1.2 C

We showed, in Chapter 3, that the linear transformation $T:\mathbf{R}^2 \to \mathbf{C}$ defined by

$$T(x_1, x_2) = x_1 + x_2 i,$$

for all $(x_1, x_2) \in \mathbf{R}^2$, is an isomorphism of real vector spaces. Thus, $\mathbf{C}$ may be given the same geometric interpretation as $\mathbf{R}^2$. In particular $\mathbf{C}$ is a plane in which there are two mutually perpendicular axes, an X-axis and a Y-axis. The former consists of all real multiples of $T(\mathbf{e}_1) = T(1, 0) = 1$ (in other words, all real numbers), the latter consists of all real multiples of $T(\mathbf{e}_2) = T(0, 1) = i$ (in other words, all imaginary numbers). The standard basis of $\mathbf{C}$, corresponding to the standard basis of $\mathbf{R}^2$, is $\{1, i\}$. A typical complex number $x_1 + x_2 i$ is located on the plane described just as is the typical ordered pair (x_1, x_2).

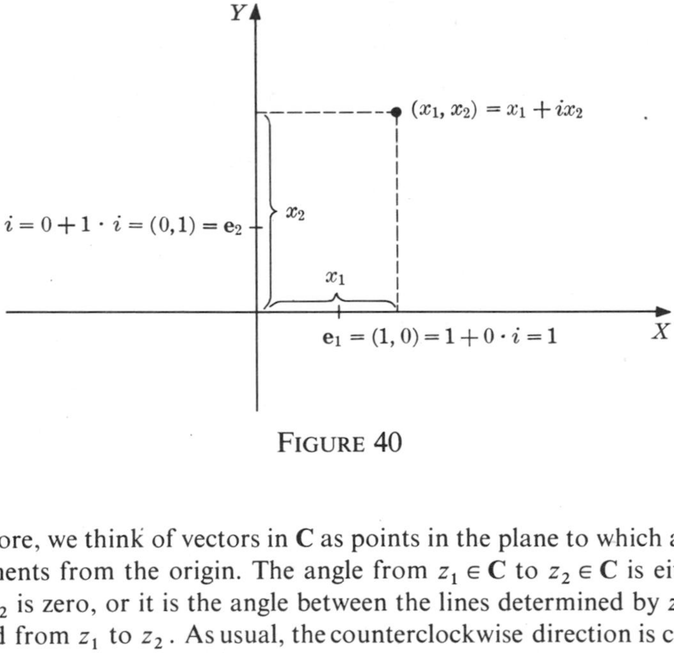

FIGURE 40

As before, we think of vectors in $\mathbf{C}$ as points in the plane to which are drawn line segments from the origin. The angle from $z_1 \in \mathbf{C}$ to $z_2 \in \mathbf{C}$ is either zero, if z_1 or z_2 is zero, or it is the angle between the lines determined by z_1 and z_2, measured from z_1 to z_2. As usual, the counterclockwise direction is considered to be positive for the purpose of angle measurement.

Thus, we have the same geometric setup as in 1.1. Here, however, we shall consider $\mathbf{C}$ as a vector space over itself. Whereas in 1.1 we showed that angle and distance measurement can be effected by a certain function, α, that is bilinear over $\mathbf{R}$, here we attempt to define an analog for the complex case. The formal structure of this section will be closely analogous to that of 1.1.

First, however, we must discuss a special aspect of $\mathbf{C}$.

(a) *Complex conjugation*

To every complex number $z = x_1 + x_2 i$, there corresponds a unique complex number $\bar{z} = x_1 - x_2 i$ called the *conjugate* of z. There is, therefore, defined a function $c : \mathbf{C} \to \mathbf{C}$, given by

$$c(z) = \bar{z}$$

for all $z \in C$.

Proposition 6.1

Consider $\mathbf{C}$ *as an algebra over* $\mathbf{R}$ *(see Chapter 4). Then,* $c : \mathbf{C} \to \mathbf{C}$ *is an isomorphism of algebras. Moreover:*

(1) $c(z) = z$, *if and only if* $z \in \mathbf{R}$
(2) $c(z) = -z$, *if and only if* $z = xi$, *where* $x \in \mathbf{R}$
(3) $c \circ c = I_{\mathbf{C}}$

Proof

We prove (3) first. Choose any $z = x_1 + x_2 i$ in $\mathbf{C}$. Then,

$$\begin{aligned}(c \circ c)(z) = c(c(z)) = c(x_1 - x_2 i) &= x_1 - (-x_2)i \\ &= x_1 + x_2 i \\ &= I_{\mathbf{C}}(z)\end{aligned}$$

This proves (3) and has, as a consequence, the fact that c is a 1–1 correspondence (and $c = c^{-1}$).

It remains to prove that c is a linear transformation (over $\mathbf{R}$) and that it preserves complex multiplication, and (1) and (2).

Choose any $z' = x_1' + x_2' i \in C$. Then

$$\begin{aligned}c(z + z') = c(x_1 + x_1' + (x_2 + x_2')i) &= x_1 + x_1' - (x_2 + x_2')i \\ &= (x_1 - x_2 i) + (x_1' - x_2' i) \\ &= c(z) + c(z')\end{aligned}$$

Moreover, for any real r,

$$c(rz) = c(rx_1 + rx_2 i) = rx_1 - rx_2 i = r(x_1 - x_2 i) = rc(z)$$

Therefore, c is a linear transformation. Moreover,

$$\begin{aligned}c(zz') &= c((x_1 + x_2 i)(x_1' + x_2' i)) \\ &= (x_1 x_1' - x_2 x_2') - (x_1 x_2' + x_2 x_1')i \\ &= (x_1 - x_2 i)(x_1' - x_2' i) = c(z)c(z')\end{aligned}$$

Thus, c preserves complex multiplication.

To prove (1) choose any $x \in \mathbf{R}$. Clearly, $x = x + 0i$, so that $c(x) = x - 0i = x$. On the other hand, suppose, for some $z = x_1 + x_2 i$, $c(z) = z$. Then $x_1 - x_2 i = x_1 + x_2 i$, so that $2x_2 i = 0$. Since $2i \neq 0$, x_2 must be 0, so that $z = x_1 + 0i = x_1 \in \mathbf{R}$. This proves (1).

To prove (2), choose any $x \in \mathbf{R}$. Clearly, $xi = 0 + xi$, so that $c(xi) = 0 - xi = -xi$. On the other hand, if, for some $z = x_1 + x_2 i$, we have $c(z) = -z$, then $x_1 + x_2 i = -(x_1 - x_2 i)$. From this it follows that $2x_1 = 0$, and hence, that $x_1 = 0$, so that $z = 0 + x_2 i = x_2 i$, as desired. Q.E.D.

Note that the equations

$$c(zz') = c(z)c(z')$$

$$c(z + z') = c(z) + c(z')$$

and

$$c(rz) = rc(z)$$

become

$$\overline{zz'} = \bar{z}\bar{z}'$$

$$\overline{z + z'} = \bar{z} + \bar{z}' \tag{7}$$

and

$$\overline{rz} = r\bar{z},$$

for all $z, z' \in \mathbf{C}$ and $r \in \mathbf{R}$.

Note also that although c preserves addition and real multiplication [in the sense that real factors "factor out"—$c(rz) = rc(z)$], and although it preserves complex multiplication [i.e., $c(zz') = c(z)c(z')$], it is *not* a linear transformation of $\mathbf{C}$ over $\mathbf{C}$. This is because, in general, $c(zz') \neq zc(z')$. Indeed, $c(zz') = c(z)c(z') = \bar{z}c(z')$, so that unless $z' = 0$, $c(zz') = zc(z')$ only if $z = \bar{z}$, that is only if z is real.

Later we shall deal with functions from one complex vector space to another that are linear transformations if we ignore all but real multiplication (i.e., if we consider the vector spaces to be vector spaces over $\mathbf{R}$ by ignoring all but real multiplication), yet fail to be linear transformations over $\mathbf{C}$ in precisely the way that c fails.

(b) *A distance formula*

For any complex number $z = x_1 + x_2 i$, the distance of z from 0 is, by the geometric interpretation of $\mathbf{C}$ described above, equal to $d(x_1, x_2) = x_1{}^2 + x_2{}^2$.

Now, it so happens that

$$z\bar{z} = (x_1 + x_2 i)(x_1 - x_2 i) = x_1{}^2 - (x_2 i)^2 = x_1{}^2 + x_2{}^2,$$

so that the distance $d(z)$ from 0 to z is given by

$$d(z)^2 = z\bar{z} \tag{8}$$

Given two complex numbers z and z', the distance between them equals the distance from 0 of their difference, $z - z'$. Thus, this distance is given by

$$d(z - z')^2 = (z - z')\overline{(z - z')} \tag{9}$$

(c) *Cosines and sines*

Let $w = x_1 + x_2 i$ and $z = y_1 + y_2 i$, both nonzero, and let θ be the angle from w to z. Then, as in Example 1.1(b),

$$\cos\theta = \frac{x_1 y_1 + x_2 y_2}{d(w)d(z)} \tag{10}$$

Therefore

$$\sin^2\theta = 1 - \cos^2\theta = \frac{({x_1}^2 + {x_2}^2)({x_1}^2 + {y_2}^2) - (x_1 y_1 + x_2 y_2)^2}{({x_1}^2 + {x_2}^2)(y_1^2 + y_2^2)}$$

$$= \left(\frac{x_1 y_2 - x_2 y_1}{d(w)d(z)}\right)^2,$$

so that

$$\sin\theta = \pm\frac{x_1 y_2 - x_2 y_1}{d(w)d(z)}$$

When $w = 1$ and $z = i$, then $x_1 = 1$, $x_2 = 0$, $y_1 = 0$, $y_2 = 1$, and $\theta = \pi/2$. Therefore, $\sin\theta = 1 = x_1 y_2 - x_2 y_1/d(w)\,d(z)$. This suggests that the sign of the expression on the right should be $+$, in the equation for $\sin\theta$. This, indeed, is a correct choice but we do not justify it any further here.

Therefore,

$$\sin\theta = \frac{x_1 y_2 - x_2 y_1}{d(w)d(z)} \tag{11}$$

Now, define a function

$$\gamma : \mathbf{C} \times \mathbf{C} \to \mathbf{C}$$

by the equation

$$\gamma(w, z) = w\bar{z} \tag{12}$$

In more detail, if w and z are as above,

$$\gamma(w, z) = w\bar{z} = (x_1 + x_2 i)(y_1 - y_2 i) = (x_1 y_1 + x_2 y_2) - (x_1 y_2 - x_2 y_1)i$$

$$= d(w)d(z)(\cos\theta - i\sin\theta)$$

Thus, for nonzero w and z

$$\cos\theta - i\sin\theta = \frac{\gamma(w, z)}{d(w)d(z)} \tag{13}$$

Notice that

$$\gamma(z, z) = z\bar{z} = d(z)^2 \tag{14}$$

Therefore (13) becomes

$$\cos\theta - i\sin\theta = \frac{\gamma(w, z)}{\gamma(w, w)^{1/2}\gamma(z, z)^{1/2}} \tag{15}$$

Finally, γ can be recovered from d, as was α from the function d in (6) of 1.1. The formula in this case is more complicated, and so we reserve its derivation for the exercises. Clearly, then, the function γ can be used for all questions of angle and distance measurement in **C**.

(d) *The function* γ

(i) γ *is conjugate-symmetric.* That is, for all $(w, z) \in \mathbf{C} \times \mathbf{C}$, $\gamma(w, z) = \overline{\gamma(z, w)}$.

Proof

For any $(w, z) \in \mathbf{C} \times \mathbf{C}$,

$$\gamma(w, z) = w\bar{z} = \bar{z}w = \overline{z\bar{w}} = \overline{\gamma(z, w)}$$

The third equality, $\bar{z}w = \overline{z\bar{w}}$, follows from property (3) of the function c (Proposition 5.1). For,

$$\bar{z}w = c(z) \cdot (c \circ c)(w) = c[z \cdot c(w)] = \overline{z\bar{w}} \qquad \text{Q.E.D.}$$

(ii) γ *is conjugate-bilinear* (as a complex-valued function of two vector variables). *That is,* γ *is linear in its first variable and, for any* u, v, w, z *in* **C** *satisfies* $\gamma(u, v + w) = \gamma(u, v) + \gamma(u, w)$ *and* $\gamma(u, zv) = \bar{z}\gamma(u, v)$.

Proof

For any u, v, w, z in **C**,

$$\gamma(u + v, w) = (u + v)\bar{w} = u\bar{w} + v\bar{w} = \gamma(u, w) + \gamma(v, w)$$

and $\gamma(zu, w) = (zu)\bar{w} = z(u\bar{w}) = z\gamma(u, w)$. Thus, γ is linear (over **C**) in its first variable.

Moreover,

$$\gamma(u, v + w) = u(\overline{v + w}) = u(\bar{v} + \bar{w}) = u\bar{v} + u\bar{w} = \gamma(u, v) + \gamma(u, w)$$

and

$$\gamma(v, zv) = u(\overline{zv}) = u(\bar{z}\bar{v}) = \bar{z}(u\bar{v}) = \bar{z}\gamma(u, v) \qquad \text{Q.E.D.}$$

(iii) $\gamma(z, z) \geqq 0$ *for all* $z \in Z$. *Moreover* $\gamma(z, z) = 0$ *if and only if* $z = 0$.

Let $z = x_1 + x_2 i$. Then, $\gamma(z, z) = z\bar{z} = {x_1}^2 + {x_2}^2 \geqq 0$. Moreover, equality occurs if and only if $x_1 = x_2 = 0$, which is true if and only if $z = 0$. Q.E.D.

Given any vector space V over $\mathbf{C}$, then we say that a conjugate bilinear function β from $V \times V$ to $\mathbf{C}$ is positive definite if and only if, for all $\mathbf{v} \in V$, $\beta(\mathbf{v}, \mathbf{v})$ is real and nonnegative, equaling 0 if and only if $\mathbf{v} = \mathbf{0}$.

The analog of property (iv) of α does not hold for γ. For $\gamma(w, z) = 0$ if and only if $w = 0$ or $z = 0$, as the reader may verify.

The next two properties are verified exactly as are their counterparts in 1.1(c).

(iv) *γ is the only conjugate bilinear functional on $\mathbf{C} \times \mathbf{C}$ satisfying $\gamma(1, i) = i$, $\gamma(i, 1) = \bar{\imath} = -i$, $\gamma(1, 1) = \gamma(i, i) = 1$.*

(v) *A conjugate bilinear functional on $\mathbf{C} \times \mathbf{C}$ is completely determined by its values on a (any) basis of $\mathbf{R}^2$.*

(vi) *For any $(w, z) \in \mathbf{C} \times \mathbf{C}$,*

$$\gamma(w, z)\overline{\gamma(w, z)} \leqq \gamma(w, w)\gamma(zz)$$

Proof

Indeed,

$$\gamma(w, z)\overline{\gamma(w, z)} = w\bar{z}\overline{w\bar{z}} = w\bar{w}z\bar{z} = \gamma(w, w)\gamma(zz)$$

(Note that the quantities on each side of the equation are real numbers. On the left is a complex number multiplied by its conjugate: This is a nonnegative real number, representing the square of the distance of the complex number from 0. On the right is the product of two nonnegative real numbers: respectively, the squares of the distances of w and z from 0.)

Although equality actually holds in this case, we prefer to state the result as an inequality, because this is the form taken by the later generalization. Q.E.D.

EXERCISES / 6.1

1. Let $T : \mathbf{R}^2 \to \mathbf{C}$ be the isomorphism described at the beginning of 1.2. Prove that for all $\mathbf{v}, \mathbf{w} \in \mathbf{R}^2$,

$$\alpha(\mathbf{v}, \mathbf{w}) = 1/2(\gamma(T(\mathbf{v}), T(\mathbf{w})) + \gamma(T(\mathbf{w}), T(\mathbf{v})))$$

2. Let $\beta : \mathbf{R}^2 \to \mathbf{R}$ be the bilinear form with the following values on the standard basis $\mathbf{e}_1, \mathbf{e}_2$ of $\mathbf{R}^2$.

$$\beta(\mathbf{e}_1, \mathbf{e}_1) = 0,\ \beta(\mathbf{e}_2, \mathbf{e}_2) = 2,\ \beta(\mathbf{e}_2, \mathbf{e}_1) = 1,\ \beta(\mathbf{e}_1, \mathbf{e}_2) = -3$$

Compute $\beta(\mathbf{v}, \mathbf{w})$ for $\mathbf{v}$ and $\mathbf{w}$ given as follows:

a. $\mathbf{v} = (1, 1), \mathbf{w} = (3, -4)$

b. $\mathbf{v} = (-2, 0), \mathbf{w} = (2, -5)$

c. $\mathbf{v} = (1, 1), \mathbf{w} = (1, 1)$

d. $\mathbf{v} = (x_1, y_1), \mathbf{w} = (y_1, y_2)$

3.* **a.** Choose any two independent vectors **v** and **w** in $\mathbf{R}^2$. Prove that

$$[d(\mathbf{v}+\mathbf{w})]^2 + [d(\mathbf{v}-\mathbf{w})]^2 = 2([d(\mathbf{v})]^2 + [d(\mathbf{w})]^2)$$

b. Given any parallelogram in $\mathbf{R}^2$ (nondegenerate), prove that the sum of the squares of the lengths of the diagonals of the parallelogram equals the sum of the squares of the lengths of (all four of) the sides of the parallelogram. Use **a.** It is known as the *parallelogram identity*.

4.* Choose any nonzero, perpendicular vectors **v**, **w** in $\mathbf{R}^2$. Prove that

$$[d(\mathbf{v}+\mathbf{w})]^2 = [d(\mathbf{v})]^2 + [d(\mathbf{w})]^2$$

5.* Let $\beta:\mathbf{R}^2 \times \mathbf{R}^2 \to \mathbf{R}$ be any bilinear form.

a. Prove that there are unique real numbers $b_{11}, b_{12}, b_{21}, b_{22}$ such that, for all (x_1, x_2) and (y_1, y_2) in $\mathbf{R}^2$,

$$\beta((x_1, x_2), (y_1, y_2)) = b_{11}x_1y_1 + b_{12}x_2y_2 + b_{21}x_2y_1 + b_{12}x_1y_2$$

b. Prove that β is symmetric if and only if $b_{12} = b_{21}$.

c. Suppose that β is symmetric and that $b_{11} \geqq 0$, $b_{22} \geqq 0$, and $b_{12}{}^2 < b_{11}b_{12}$. Prove that β is positive-definite. (*Hint*: If $x_1x_2 \geqq 0$, then prove that

$$b_{11}x_1{}^2 + 2b_{12}x_1x_2 + b_{22}x_2{}^2 \geqq (\sqrt{b_{11}}x_1 - \sqrt{b_{22}}x_{22})^2 \geqq 0$$

Prove a similar inequality to be true if $x_1x_2 \leqq 0$.)

d. Suppose, now, that β is given as a symmetric positive-definite bilinear form on $\mathbf{R}^2 \times \mathbf{R}^2$ and that $b_{11}, b_{12}, b_{21}, b_{22}$ are obtained as in **a**. Prove that $b_{11} \geqq 0$, $b_{22} \geqq 0$, and $b_{12}{}^2 < b_{11}b_{12}$. (*Hint:* Use the definitions of the b's, the definition of positive-definite, and Schwarz's inequality.)

This exercise, therefore, shows that all bilinear forms on $\mathbf{R}^2 \times \mathbf{R}^2$ are of the form described in **a**, that they are symmetric if and only if the criterion in **b** is satisfied, and that, if symmetric, they are positive-definite if and only if the criterion in **c** or in **d** is satisfied.

6. Which of the following formulas determine bilinear functions $\beta:\mathbf{R}^2 \times \mathbf{R}^2 \to \mathbf{R}$? [Let $\mathbf{x} = (x_1, x_2)$, $\mathbf{y} = (y_1, y_2)$.]

a. $\beta(\mathbf{x}, \mathbf{y}) = x_1x_2 + y_1y_2$

b. $\beta(\mathbf{x}, \mathbf{y}) = x_1y_1$

c. $\beta(\mathbf{x}, \mathbf{y}) = x_1y_2$

d. $\beta(\mathbf{x}, \mathbf{y}) = x_1y_2 - x_2y_2 - x_2y_1$

e. $\beta(\mathbf{x}, \mathbf{y}) = 2x_1 + 3y_1$

f. $\beta(\mathbf{x}, \mathbf{y}) = 2x_1y_1 + 3x_2y_2$

g. $\beta(\mathbf{x}, \mathbf{y}) = 0$

h. $\beta(\mathbf{x}, \mathbf{y}) = (x_1 + x_2)(3y_1 - 2y_2)$

Of the above bilinear functions, which are symmetric? Of the above symmetric, bilinear functions, which are positive-definite? Justify your answers, of course.

7. Let $\beta:\mathbf{R}^2 \times \mathbf{R}^2 \to \mathbf{R}$ be any bilinear form, and let $T:\mathbf{R}^2 \to \mathbf{R}^2$ be any linear transformation. Define $\nu:\mathbf{R}^2 \times \mathbf{R}^2 \to \mathbf{R}$ as follows:

$$\nu(x, y) = \beta[T(x), T(y)]$$

for all $(x, y) \in \mathbf{R}^2 \times \mathbf{R}^2$. Prove that ν is bilinear. Assume that T is an isomorphism. Prove that ν is positive-definite if and only if β is. Under the same assumption, show that ν is symmetric if and only if β is.

Give examples to show that these last two statements may be false if T is not an isomorphism.

Prove that for any T the symmetry of β implies that of ν.

8. Let $\beta : \mathbf{C} \times \mathbf{C} \to \mathbf{C}$ be any conjugate bilinear form.

a. Prove that there exists a unique constant $b \in \mathbf{C}$ such that for all $(w, z) \in \mathbf{C} \times \mathbf{C}$,

$$\beta(w, z) = bw\bar{z}$$

b. Prove that β is conjugate-symmetric.

c. Prove that β is positive-definite if and only if $b > 0$.

9. Let $\beta : \mathbf{R} \times \mathbf{R} \to \mathbf{R}$ be any bilinear form.

a. Prove that there exists a unique constant $a \in \mathbf{R}$ such that for all $(x, y) \in \mathbf{R} \times \mathbf{R}$

$$\beta(x, y) = axy$$

b. Prove that β is symmetric.

c. Prove that β is positive-definite if and only if $a > 0$.

10. Let $\mathbf{v}$ be any nonzero vector in $\mathbf{R}^2$ and let ℓ be the line through $(0, 0)$ consisting of all real multiples of $\mathbf{v}$. Let $\mathbf{w}$ be any vector in $\mathbf{R}^2$ not on ℓ.

a. Determine a real number t such that $\mathbf{w} - t\mathbf{v}$ is perpendicular to $\mathbf{v}$. (Express t in terms of $\mathbf{w}$, $\mathbf{v}$ and the bilinear function α discussed in 1.1.)

b. Prove that for any $s \in \mathbf{R}$,

$$d(\mathbf{w} - s\mathbf{v})^2 = d(\mathbf{w})^2 - \left[\frac{\alpha(\mathbf{v}, \mathbf{w})}{d(\mathbf{v})^2}\right]^2 + d(\mathbf{v})^2\left[s - \frac{\alpha(\mathbf{v}, \mathbf{w})}{d(\mathbf{v})^2}\right]^2$$

c. Use **b** to show that the t determined in **a** is the value of s for which $\mathbf{w} - s\mathbf{v}$ has minimal length. In other words, show that for all $s \neq t$, $d(\mathbf{w} - s\mathbf{v}) > d(\mathbf{w} - t\mathbf{v})$.

The following picture illustrates the situation.

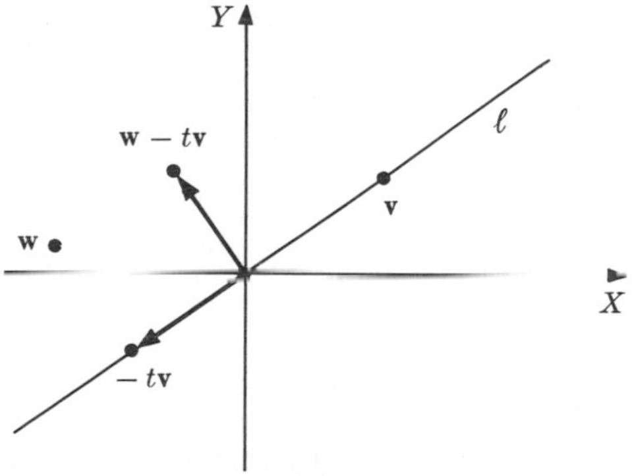

FIGURE 41

The above Exercise **c** proves that the shortest distance from a point to a line not passing through the point is the length of the perpendicular line segment dropped from the point to the line.

d. What is $d(\mathbf{w} - t\mathbf{v})^2$, in terms of $\mathbf{v}$, $\mathbf{w}$, d, and α?

11.* Prove that the following ("polarization") equality holds for $\gamma : \mathbf{C} \times \mathbf{C} \to \mathbf{C}$ defined as in 1.2, and $d : \mathbf{C} \times \mathbf{C} \to \mathbf{R}$ the distance function defined in 1.2: For all $(w, z) \in \mathbf{C} \times \mathbf{C}$

$$\gamma(\mathbf{w}, z) = (1/4)(d(w+z)^2 - d(w-z)^2 + id(w+iz)^2 - id(w-iz)^2)$$

This formula shows that γ can be "recovered" from d. That is, if d is given and we are told that

$$d(z) = \gamma(z, z),$$

for some conjugate-symmetric, conjugate-bilinear $\gamma : \mathbf{C} \times \mathbf{C} \to \mathbf{C}$, then γ is given by the above equation. (Your derivation of the equation should depend only on these two properties of γ.)

2 / BILINEAR FORMS, CONJUGATE-BILINEAR FORMS, AND INNER PRODUCTS

2.1 *Introductory Remarks and Definitions*

We generalize the special examples of 1.1 and 1.2 to general vector spaces over $\mathbf{R}$ or $\mathbf{C}$.

In 1.2, we saw how the notions of *bilinear form* and *symmetric form* had to be replaced by the notions of *conjugate-bilinear form* and *conjugate-symmetric form*. Much of the elementary theory of inner produce spaces can be developed for the complex case in a way entirely parallel to the development for the real case, using the replacement indicated above.

However, a very simple observation allows us to develop both cases at once. We use the fact that a number $z \in \mathbf{C}$ is real if and only if $z = \bar{z}$. Since $\mathbf{R} \subset \mathbf{C}$, the notion of the conjugate of a real number *makes sense, but it is trivial*, since every real number is self-conjugate. We, then, make the following definitions.

Definition 6.1

Let $F = \mathbf{R}$ or $\mathbf{C}$, and let V and W be any vector spaces over F.

(1) *A function $T : V \to W$ is said to be a conjugate-linear transformation (over F) if and only if for all $\mathbf{v}_1, \mathbf{v}_2 \in V$ and $a \in F$,*

$$T(\mathbf{v}_1 + \mathbf{v}_2) = T(\mathbf{v}_1) + T(\mathbf{v}_2) \text{ and } T(a\mathbf{v}_1) = \bar{a}T(\mathbf{v}_1)$$

(2) *A function $\beta : V \times V \to F$ is said to be a conjugate-bilinear form, if and only if it is linear in its first variable and conjugate-linear in its second.*

(3) *A conjugate-bilinear form $\beta : V \times V \to F$ is said to be conjugate-symmetric if and only if, for all $(\mathbf{v}_1, \mathbf{v}_2) \in V \times V$,*

$$\beta(\mathbf{v}_1, \mathbf{v}_2) = \overline{\beta(\mathbf{v}_2, \mathbf{v}_1)}$$

(4) *A conjugate-bilinear form* $\beta: V \times V \to F$ *is said to be positive-definite if and only if for every nonzero* $\mathbf{v} \in V$, $\beta(\mathbf{v}, \mathbf{v})$ *is real and strictly greater than* 0.

(5) *A conjugate-bilinear, conjugate-symmetric, positive-definite form on* $V \times V$ *is called an inner product on* V. *Inner products will play the role of the functions* α *and* γ *of* 1.1 *and* 1.2, *respectively.*

Remark: In the above definition, if we let $F = \mathbf{R}$, then, since real numbers are self-conjugate, we may conclude that: (1) A conjugate-linear transformation (over $\mathbf{R}$) is the same as a linear transformation (over $\mathbf{R}$). (2) A conjugate-bilinear form (over $\mathbf{R}$) is the same as a bilinear form (over $\mathbf{R}$). (3) A conjugate-symmetric form (over $\mathbf{R}$) is the same as a symmetric form (over $\mathbf{R}$).

We verify statement (1), leaving the rest to the reader. Let V and W be vector spaces *over* $\mathbf{R}$ and $T: V \to W$ a function. Then, T is *conjugate-linear*, if and only if, for all $\mathbf{v}_1, \mathbf{v}_2 \in V$ and $a \in \mathbf{R}$,

$$T(\mathbf{v}_1 + \mathbf{v}_2) = T(\mathbf{v}_1) + T(\mathbf{v}_2) \quad \text{and} \quad T(a\mathbf{v}_1) = \bar{a}T(\mathbf{v}_1) = aT(\mathbf{v}_1)$$

But these are precisely the defining conditions for a function to be a *linear* transformation over $\mathbf{R}$. Thus, T is conjugate-linear if and only if T is linear.

Thus, we may develop most of our results over a field F (which is either $\mathbf{R}$ or $\mathbf{C}$) using the notions of conjugate, conjugate-linear, and so on, recognizing that when $F = \mathbf{R}$, all conjugation disappears.

Let V and W be vector spaces over $\mathbf{C}$. Since $\mathbf{R} \subset \mathbf{C}$, we may consider V and W to be vector spaces over $\mathbf{R}$ by restricting scalar multiplication to real multiplication.

Proposition 6.2

Let V *and* W *be vector spaces over* $\mathbf{C}$, *and let* $T: V \to W$ *be a conjugate-linear transformation. Then, considering* V *and* W *to be vector spaces over* $\mathbf{R}$, *by allowing only real multiplication, as described above,* $T: V \to W$ *is a linear transformation of vector spaces over* $\mathbf{R}$.

Proof

Choose any $\mathbf{v}_1, \mathbf{v}_2 \in V$ and any $r \in R$. Then,

$$T(\mathbf{v}_1 + \mathbf{v}_2) = T(\mathbf{v}_1) + T(\mathbf{v}_2) \quad \text{and} \quad T(r\mathbf{v}_1) = \bar{r}T(\mathbf{v}_1) = rT(\mathbf{v}_1),$$

so that T is a linear transformation over $\mathbf{R}$. Q.E.D.

Note that this proposition says something different from what we said in our remarks above. There, we noted that a conjugate-linear transformation of vector spaces over F is the same as a linear transformation of these same vector spaces over F, *if F happens to be* $\mathbf{R}$. Here, we have vector spaces *over* $\mathbf{C}$ and a conjugate-linear transformation from one to the other. We then *alter the given vector spaces* by allowing only real multiplication (and vector addition), and we assert that the given function is a linear transformation of these new spaces (now vector spaces over $\mathbf{R}$).

This result and known facts about conjugation allow us to obtain results about conjugate linear transformations that are closely analogous to results obtained for ordinary linear transformations. These are developed in later exercises.

2.2 Examples of Conjugate-Bilinear Forms and Inner Products

The first four conjugate-bilinear forms will be inner products. The rest will not:

(a) The functions α and γ of 1.1 and 1.2 are inner products on $\mathbf{R}^2$ and $\mathbf{C}$, respectively.

(b) Let $F = \mathbf{R}$ or $\mathbf{C}$. For any vectors $\mathbf{v} = (x_1, \ldots, x_n) \in F^n$ and $\mathbf{w} = (y_1, \ldots, y_n) \in F^n$, let

$$\beta(\mathbf{v}, \mathbf{w}) = x_1\bar{y}_1 + x_2\bar{y}_2 + \cdots + x_n\bar{y}_n$$

Then, β is a positive-definite, conjugate-symmetric, conjugate bilinear form on F^n. The proof of this fact is analogous to the proofs of the corresponding facts for α and γ in 1.1 and 1.2. This example will be important in the next section. *β is called the standard inner product on F^n.*

(c) Let F be $\mathbf{R}$ or $\mathbf{C}$, and let V be the vector space of all F-valued, continuous functions defined on the interval (a, b), where $a, b \in \mathbf{R}$, $a < b$. Choose any $s \in V$ such that $s(x) > 0$, for all $x \in (a, b)$. Define $\gamma : V \times V \to F$ as follows: for any $f, g \in V$,

$$\gamma(f, g) = \int_a^b f(x)\overline{g(x)}s(x)\,dx$$

We leave to the reader the task of verifying that γ is conjugate-bilinear and that $\gamma(f, f) \geqq 0$ for all $f \in V$.

It is also true that $\gamma(f, f) = 0$ if and only if $f = \bar{0}$ and that γ is conjugate-symmetric. We do not verify these facts, however.

(d) Any bilinear form $\beta : \mathbf{R}^2 \times \mathbf{R}^2 \to \mathbf{R}$ given by

$$\beta(x, y) = b_{11}x_1y_1 + 2b_{12}x_1y_2 + b_{22}x_2y_2,$$

such that $b_{11} \geqq 0$, $b_{22} \geqq 0$, and ${b_{12}}^2 < b_{11}b_{22}$, is symmetric and positive definite (see Exercises 6.1.5).

(e) $\mathrm{vol}_2 \circ \mathrm{par}$ is a bilinear form on $\mathbf{R}^2 \times \mathbf{R}^2$. It is, of course, not symmetric but *skew-symmetric*. Moreover, for every $\mathbf{v} \in \mathbf{R}^2$, $\mathrm{vol}_2 \circ \mathrm{par}(\mathbf{v}, \mathbf{v}) = 0$, so that $\mathrm{vol}_2 \circ \mathrm{par}$ is far from being positive-definite.

(f) Let A be any nonempty set of real numbers, let a be any member of A and let $F = \mathbf{R}$ or $\mathbf{C}$. We consider the vector space F^A of all F-valued functions defined on A. Given any two such functions f and g, let

$$\delta(f, g) = f(a)\overline{g(a)}$$

Clearly, δ is conjugate-symmetric. We leave to the reader the task of showing that δ is conjugate-bilinear; we demonstrate only one part of this statement: Choose any $f, g, h \in F^A$, then

$$\delta(f, g + h) = f(a)\overline{(g + h)(a)} = f(a)(\bar{g}(a) + \bar{h}(a)) = f(a)\bar{g}(a) + f(a)\bar{h}(a)$$
$$= \delta(f, g) + \delta(f, h)$$

Finally, for any $f \in F^A$,

$$\delta(f, f) = f(a)\bar{f}(a) \geqq 0$$

If $\delta(f, f) = 0$, then we may conclude that $f(a) = 0$. This does not mean, however, that $f(x) = 0$, for *all* $x \in A$, unless A consists only of the member a. Thus, δ is *not* positive-definite, unless $A = \{a\}$.

(g) Let a_{ij} be any collection of scalars in F, $i = 1, \ldots, n$, $j = 1, \ldots, n$. F, here, is again either **R** or **C**. For any $(x, y) \in F^n \times F^n$, let

$$\mu(x, y) = \sum_{i=1}^{n} \sum_{j=1}^{n} a_{ij} x_i \bar{y}_j$$

(That is, $\mu(x, y)$ is simply the sum of *all possible* summands of the form $a_{ij} x_i \bar{y}_j$, where i and j range between 1 and n.)

Proposition 6.3

(1) *μ is conjugate-bilinear.* (2) *μ is conjugate-symmetric if and only if $a_{ij} = \bar{a}_{ji}$, for all $i = 1, \ldots, n$ and $j = 1, \ldots, n$.*

Proof

(1) We prove only part of this assertion, leaving the rest to the reader. Let **x**, **y** be as above, and let $\mathbf{y}' = (y_1', \ldots, y_n') \in F^n$. Then, $\mathbf{y} + \mathbf{y}' = (y_1 + y_1', \ldots, y_n + y_n')$, so that

$$\mu(\mathbf{x}, \mathbf{y} + \mathbf{y}') = \sum_{i=1}^{n} \sum_{j=1}^{n} a_{ij} x_i \overline{(y_j + y_j')} = \sum_{i=1}^{n} \sum_{j=1}^{n} a_{ij} x_i (\bar{y}_j + \bar{y}_j')$$
$$= \sum_{i=1}^{n} \sum_{j=1}^{n} a_{ij} x_i \bar{y}_j + \sum_{i=1}^{n} \sum_{j=1}^{n} a_{ij} x_i \bar{y}_j' = \mu(\mathbf{x}, \mathbf{y}) + \mu(\mathbf{x}, \mathbf{y}')$$

(2) Suppose that $a_{ij} = \bar{a}_{ji}$. Since

$$\mu(x, y) = \sum_{i=1}^{n} \sum_{j=1}^{n} a_{ij} x_i \bar{y}_j,$$

we have

$$\overline{\mu(y, x)} = \sum_{i=1}^{n} \sum_{j=1}^{n} \overline{a_{ij} y_i \bar{x}_j} = \sum_{i=1}^{n} \sum_{j=1}^{n} \bar{a}_{ij} \bar{y}_i x_j,$$

which, upon rearranging, becomes

$$\sum_{i=1}^{n} \sum_{j=1}^{n} \bar{a}_{ji} x_i \bar{y}_j$$

Thus,

$$\mu(x, y) - \overline{\mu(y, x)} = \sum_{i=1}^{n} \sum_{j=1}^{n} (a_{ij} - \bar{a}_{ji}) x_i \bar{y}_j = 0$$

Therefore, μ is conjugate-symmetric.

On the other hand, start by assuming μ to be conjugate-symmetric. Then, if $\mathbf{e}_1, \ldots, \mathbf{e}_n$ denotes the standard basis of F^n,

$$\mu(\mathbf{e}_r, \mathbf{e}_s) = \overline{\mu(\mathbf{e}_s, \mathbf{e}_r)}, \ r, s = 1, \ldots, n. \tag{1}$$

But, for all $r, s = 1, \ldots, n$,

$$\mu(\mathbf{e}_r, \mathbf{e}_s) = \sum_{i=1}^{n} \sum_{j=1}^{n} a_{ij} x_i y_j,$$

where $x_i = 0$ unless $i = r$, and $x_r = 1$, and $y_j = 0$, unless $j = s$, and $y_s = 1$. Thus, all of the products $x_i y_j$ are zero except when $i = r$ and $j = s$: of course $x_r y_s = 1$. Thus,

$$\mu(\mathbf{e}_r, \mathbf{e}_s) = a_{rs},$$

for all $r, s = 1, \ldots, n$. Equation (1), then implies that

$$a_{rs} = \bar{a}_{sr} \qquad \text{Q.E.D.}$$

In general μ will *not* be positive-definite. The conditions on a_{ij} for μ to be positive-definite are somewhat complicated to formulate. They will be developed in Exercises 6.2.

2.3 Some General Propositions Relating Inner Products and Bases

It is our aim to use inner products as generalizations of our angle and distance measuring functions α and γ of 1.1 and 1.2. We justify this intention in the next section. Here, we show how bases of vector spaces are related to inner products. Essentially, we prove the two statements made in the second paragraph of this chapter.

The following proposition shows that vector-space isomorphisms may be used to "carry" conjugate-bilinear forms from one vector space to another.

Proposition 6.4

Let $F = \mathbf{R}$ or $\mathbf{C}$, let V and W be any vector spaces over F, let $\beta : W \times W \to F$ be any conjugate-bilinear form, and let $T : V \to W$ be an isomorphism. Then, the function $\alpha : V \times V \to F$ defined by

$$\alpha(\mathbf{v}_1, \mathbf{v}_2) = \beta(T(\mathbf{v}_1), T(\mathbf{v}_2)), \quad \text{for all} \quad (\mathbf{v}_1, \mathbf{v}_2) \in V \times V,$$

is a conjugate-bilinear form on $V \times V$. Moreover, α is conjugate-symmetric if *and only if β is, and α is positive-definite if and only if β is. Thus, α is an inner product if and only if β is.*

Proof

The proof that α is conjugate-bilinear is an analog of the proof of the result stated in Exercises 6.1.7. We leave this to the reader.

To prove the next two statements, first note that for any $(\mathbf{w}_1, \mathbf{w}_2) \in W \times W$ there is a unique pair $(\mathbf{v}_1, \mathbf{v}_2) \in V$ such that $T^{-1}(\mathbf{w}_1) = \mathbf{v}_1$ and $T^{-1}(\mathbf{w}_2) = \mathbf{v}_2$. This follows from the fact that T is an isomorphism. Thus,

$$\beta(\mathbf{w}_1, \mathbf{w}_2) = \beta(T(T^{-1}(\mathbf{w}_1)), T(T^{-1}(\mathbf{w}_2))) = \beta(T(\mathbf{v}_1), T(\mathbf{v}_2)) = \alpha(\mathbf{v}_1, \mathbf{v}_2)$$

Now suppose that β is conjugate-symmetric. Choose any $(\mathbf{v}_1', \mathbf{v}_2') \in V \times V$:

$$\alpha(\mathbf{v}_1', \mathbf{v}_2') = \beta(T(\mathbf{v}_1'), T(\mathbf{v}_2')) = \overline{\beta(T(\mathbf{v}_2'), T(\mathbf{v}_1'))} = \overline{\alpha(\mathbf{v}_2', \mathbf{v}_1')}.$$

Therefore, α is conjugate-symmetric.

On the other hand, if α is conjugate-symmetric, then choose any $(\mathbf{w}_1, \mathbf{w}_2) \in W \times W$, and let $T^{-1}(\mathbf{w}_1) = \mathbf{v}_1$ and $T^{-1}(\mathbf{w}_2) = \mathbf{v}_2$. Then, by the equation obtained sbove,

$$\beta(\mathbf{w}_1, \mathbf{w}_2) = \alpha(\mathbf{v}_1, \mathbf{v}_2) = \overline{\alpha(\mathbf{v}_2, \mathbf{v}_1)} = \overline{\beta(\mathbf{w}_2, \mathbf{w}_1)}$$

Therefore, β is conjugate-symmetric.

Next, suppose that β is positive-definite. Choose any $\mathbf{v}' \in V$. Then,

$$\alpha(\mathbf{v}', \mathbf{v}') = \beta(T(\mathbf{v}'), T(\mathbf{v}')) \geqq 0$$

Moreover, if $\mathbf{v}' \neq \mathbf{0}$, then because T is an isomorphism, $T(\mathbf{v}') \neq \mathbf{0}$, and so

$$\alpha(\mathbf{v}', \mathbf{v}') = \beta(T(\mathbf{v}'), T(\mathbf{v}')) > 0$$

Therefore, α is positive-definite.

If, on the other hand α is positive-definite, choose any $\mathbf{w} \in W$ and let $\mathbf{v} = T^{-1}(\mathbf{w})$. Then

$$\beta(\mathbf{w}, \mathbf{w}) = \alpha(\mathbf{v}, \mathbf{v}) \geqq 0$$

Moreover, if $\mathbf{w} \neq \mathbf{0}$, then $\mathbf{v} \neq \mathbf{0}$, for the same reason as above, and so, in this case, $\beta(\mathbf{w}, \mathbf{w}) = \alpha(\mathbf{v}, \mathbf{v}) > 0$. Therefore, β is positive-definite. Q.E.D.

We next "carry" some of the concrete examples of conjugate-bilinear forms to arbitrary finite-dimensional vector spaces. As before the scalar field F is **R** or **C**.

Proposition 6.5

Let V be a vector space over F, and let $\{\mathbf{v}_1, \ldots, \mathbf{v}_n\}$ be a basis of V. Given any scalars a_{ij}, $i = 1, \ldots, n$ and $j = 1, \ldots, n$, there is a unique conjugate-bilinear form δ on V satisfying

$$\delta(\mathbf{v}_i, \mathbf{v}_j) = a_{ij}, \; i = 1, \ldots, n, j = 1, \ldots, n$$

Moreover, δ is conjugate-symmetric if and only if $a_{ij} = \bar{a}_{ji}$.

Proof

Let μ be the conjugate-bilinear form of example (g) in 2.2. Define $T \in \text{Trans}(V, F^n)$ by specifying that $T(\mathbf{v}_i) = \mathbf{e}_i$, $i = 1, \ldots, n$, where $\mathbf{e}_1, \ldots, \mathbf{e}_n$ is the standard basis of F^n. Let $\delta : V \times V \to F$ be given by

$$\delta(\mathbf{v}, \mathbf{v}') = \mu(T(\mathbf{v}), T(\mathbf{v}')),$$

for all $(\mathbf{v}_1, \mathbf{v}_2) \in V \times V$. By Proposition 6.4, δ is conjugate-bilinear. Moreover, it is conjugate-symmetric if and only if μ is, and μ is conjugate-symmetric if and only if $a_{ij} = \bar{a}_{ji}$. Also,

$$\delta(\mathbf{v}_i, \mathbf{v}_j) = \mu(T(\mathbf{v}_i), T(\mathbf{v}_j)) = \mu(\mathbf{e}_i, \mathbf{e}_j) = a_{ij}$$

Finally, suppose that some conjugate-bilinear form $\delta' : V \times V \to F$ satisfies $\delta'(\mathbf{v}_i, \mathbf{v}_j) = a_{ij}$, for all $i, j = 1, \ldots, n$. Then, for any $\mathbf{v} = x_1\mathbf{v}_1 + \cdots + x_n\mathbf{v}_n$ and $\mathbf{w} = y_1\mathbf{v}_2 + \cdots + y_n\mathbf{v}_n$, we expand $\delta'(\mathbf{v}, \mathbf{w})$, using the conjugate-bilinearity of δ', obtaining,

$$\delta'(\mathbf{v}, \mathbf{w}) = \sum_{i=1}^{n} \sum_{j=1}^{n} a_{ij} x_i \bar{y}_j = \delta(\mathbf{v}, \mathbf{w}),$$

so that δ is uniquely determined by the a_{ij}. Q.E.D.

Remark: The formula at the end of the above proof,

$$\delta(\mathbf{v}, \mathbf{w}) = \sum_{i=1}^{n} \sum_{j=1}^{n} a_{ij} x_i \bar{y}_j$$

(which the reader should verify for himself) shows that δ really is a replica of μ.

Indeed, every conjugate-bilinear form on $V \times V$ is given by a formula similar to the one above. For, given any such form, say γ, we can evaluate $\gamma(\mathbf{v}_i, \mathbf{v}_j)$, say $\gamma(\mathbf{v}_i, \mathbf{v}_j) = b_{ij}$. Then, according to the above result, there is one and only one conjugate-bilinear form with these values on the given basis vectors. This form, of course, is γ; but it is also μ' "carried" over by T, where μ' is as in Example (g) of 2.2, with scalars b_{ij} instead of a_{ij}. Therefore, for any $\mathbf{v}, \mathbf{w}$ as in the proof above,

$$\gamma(\mathbf{v}, \mathbf{w}) = \mu'(T(\mathbf{v}), T(\mathbf{w})) = \mu'((x_1, \ldots, x_n), (y_1, \ldots, y_n)) = \sum_{i=1}^{n} \sum_{j=1}^{n} b_{ij} x_i \bar{y}_j$$

To return to our main interest: We seek to introduce into V a method of "angle" and "distance" measurement with respect to which the basis vectors $\mathbf{v}_1, \mathbf{v}_2, \ldots, \mathbf{v}_n$ are in some sense mutually "perpendicular" and of unit length.

For perpendicularity we shall use a concept suggested by 1.1(c), property (iv). This concept will actually reduce to ordinary perpendicularity in the case that $V = \mathbf{R}^2$ or $V = \mathbf{R}^3$. In other cases (e.g., V is a vector space over $\mathbf{C}$) there is no obvious geometric interpretation of the concept. Nevertheless, it has as useful an algebraic role to play in the complex case as in the real case.

Definition 6.2

Let $F = \mathbf{R}$ or $\mathbf{C}$, and let V be any vector space over F, with $\gamma : V \times V \to F$ an inner product.

(1) *We say that two vectors $\mathbf{v}$ and $\mathbf{w}$ in V are orthogonal with respect to γ or γ-orthogonal if and only if $\gamma(\mathbf{v}, \mathbf{w}) = 0$.*

(Intuitively, *nonzero* orthogonal vectors should be thought of as being, in some sense, perpendicular.)

(2) *If $\mathbf{v}$ is any vector in V satisfying $\gamma(\mathbf{v}, \mathbf{v}) = 1$, then we say that $\mathbf{v}$ is a unit vector with respect to γ, or that $\mathbf{v}$ is a γ-unit vector, or that $\mathbf{v}$ has unit length with respect to γ.*

Every nonzero vector $\mathbf{v}$ has a multiple $a\mathbf{v}$ that is a unit vector. Simply choose

$$a = \frac{1}{\sqrt{\gamma(\mathbf{v}, \mathbf{v})}}$$

This unit vector $a\mathbf{v}$ is called the *γ-normalization* of $\mathbf{v}$. A set consisting of unit vectors is called a *γ-normal set of vectors.* Given an arbitrary set S of vectors, the set of all γ-normalizations of vectors in S is called the *γ-normalization of S.* It is, of course, a γ-normal set.

A γ-normal set of mutually γ-orthogonal vectors of V is called *γ-orthonormal.*

Corollary to Proposition 6.5

Given any basis of X of the finite-dimensional vector space V over $F (= \mathbf{R}$ or $\mathbf{C})$, there exists one and only one inner product γ on V such that X is γ-orthonormal.

Proof

Let $X = \{\mathbf{v}_1, \ldots, \mathbf{v}_n\}$ as in Proposition 6.5, and choose $a_{ij} = 0$, if $i \neq j$, and $a_{ij} = 1$, if $i = j$, where i and j range between 1 and n. Then, there exists one and only one conjugate-bilinear form $\gamma : V \times V \to F$ such that

$$\gamma(\mathbf{v}_i, \mathbf{v}_j) = a_{ij} = \begin{cases} 0, & \text{if } i \neq j \\ 1, & \text{if } i = j \end{cases}$$

If we can show that γ is an inner product, then we are finished, since the above equations show that X is γ-orthonormal.

Clearly, $a_{ij} = \bar{a}_{ji}$, so that γ is conjugate-symmetric.

To prove that γ is positive-definite, choose any $\mathbf{v} = z_1\mathbf{v}_1 + \cdots + z_n\mathbf{v}_n$. We may write each z_k as $x_k + y_k i$ (if $F = \mathbf{R}$, then all the z's are real and so all the y's are zero).

Then,

$$\gamma(\mathbf{v}, \mathbf{v}) = \sum_{k=1}^{n} \sum_{j=1}^{n} a_{kj} z_k \bar{z}_j = z_1\bar{z}_1 + \cdots + z_n\bar{z}_n$$
$$= (x_1^2 + y_1^2) + \cdots + (x_n^2 + y_n^2) \geqq 0$$

The second equality holds because all terms, $a_{kj}z_k\bar{z}_j$, for which $k \neq j$ drop out (since $a_{kj} = 0$) and all terms for which $k = j$ reduce to $z_k\bar{z}_k$ (since $a_{kk} = 1$).

Now, the sum

$$(x_1^2 + y_1^2) + \cdots + (x_n^2 + y_n^2)$$

is zero if and only if all x_k and y_k are zero. But this happens if and only if $\mathbf{v} = \mathbf{0}$. Thus, γ is positive-definite, and so it is an inner-product on V. Q.E.D.

We now prove the main result of this section: the converse of the above corollary. Indeed, we do better. But first, we need some terminology.

Definition 6.3

Let V be any vector space over a field F, let $\mathbf{x}_1, \mathbf{x}_2, \mathbf{x}_3, \ldots$ and $\mathbf{y}_1, \mathbf{y}_2, \mathbf{y}_3, \ldots$ be two sequences of vectors in V. Assume that either both sequences consist of n terms, for some given positive integer n, or both sequences have countably many terms. We shall say that the two sequences are similar if, for every positive integer k ($k \leqq n$, if the sequences are finite, k arbitrary, otherwise)

$$\operatorname{span}_V(\{\mathbf{x}_1, \ldots, \mathbf{x}_k\}) = \operatorname{span}_V(\{\mathbf{y}_1, \ldots, \mathbf{y}_k\})$$

Lemma

(1) *If $\mathbf{x}_1, \mathbf{x}_2, \mathbf{x}_3, \ldots$ and $\mathbf{y}_1, \mathbf{y}_2, \mathbf{y}_3, \ldots$ are similar, then for any positive integer k ($k \leqq n$,* if the sequences consist of n terms, k arbitrary, otherwise), *$\mathbf{x}_1, \mathbf{x}_2, \ldots, \mathbf{x}_k$ and $\mathbf{y}_1, \mathbf{y}_2, \ldots, \mathbf{y}_k$ are similar.*

(2) *If $\mathbf{x}_1, \mathbf{x}_2, \mathbf{x}_3, \ldots,$ and $\mathbf{y}_1, \mathbf{y}_2, \mathbf{y}_3, \ldots$ are equinumerous sequences of vectors of V such that for every positive integer k ($k \leqq n$, if the sequences consist of n terms, k arbitrary, otherwise), $\mathbf{x}_1, \mathbf{x}_2, \ldots, \mathbf{x}_k$ and $\mathbf{y}_1, \mathbf{y}_2, \ldots, \mathbf{y}_k$ are similar, then $\mathbf{x}_1, \mathbf{x}_2, \mathbf{x}_3, \ldots$* and *$\mathbf{y}_1, \mathbf{y}_2; \mathbf{y}_3, \ldots$ are similar.*

(3) *If $\mathbf{x}_1, \mathbf{x}_2, \ldots, \mathbf{x}_k$ and $\mathbf{y}_1, \mathbf{y}_2, \ldots, \mathbf{y}_k$ are similar, and if $\mathbf{x}_{k+1}$ and $\mathbf{y}_{k+1}$ are vectors such that*

$$\mathbf{x}_{k+1} \in \operatorname{span}_V(\mathbf{y}_1, \mathbf{y}_2, \ldots, \mathbf{y}_k, \mathbf{y}_{k+1})$$

and

$$\mathbf{y}_{k+1} \in \operatorname{span}_V(\{\mathbf{x}_1, \mathbf{x}_2, \ldots, \mathbf{x}_k, \mathbf{x}_{k+1}\})$$

then $\mathbf{x}_1, \mathbf{x}_2, \ldots, \mathbf{x}_{k+1}$ and $\mathbf{y}_1, \mathbf{y}_2, \ldots, \mathbf{y}_{k+1}$ are similar.

Proof

(1) Choose any k as stated. We must prove that for every $i \leqq k$,

$$\operatorname{span}_V(\mathbf{x}_1, \ldots, \mathbf{x}_i) = \operatorname{span}_V(\mathbf{y}_1, \ldots, \mathbf{y}_i)$$

But this follows from the fact that $\mathbf{x}_1, \mathbf{x}_2, \mathbf{x}_3, \ldots$ and $\mathbf{y}_1, \mathbf{y}_2, \mathbf{y}_3, \ldots$ are similar.

(2) Choose any positive integer ℓ ($\ell \leqq n$, if the sequences consist of n terms, ℓ arbitrary, otherwise). We must show that

$$\operatorname{span}_V(\{\mathbf{x}_1, \ldots, \mathbf{x}_\ell\}) = \operatorname{span}_V(\{\mathbf{y}_1, \ldots, \mathbf{y}_\ell\})$$

Choose any integer $k \geqq \ell$ ($k \leqq n$, if the sequences consist of n terms, k arbitrary, otherwise). By hypothesis, $\mathbf{x}_1, \ldots, \mathbf{x}_k$ and $\mathbf{y}_1, \ldots, \mathbf{y}_k$ are similar. Thus, the above equality holds, by definition of similarity.

(3) Let $\mathbf{x}_1, \ldots, \mathbf{x}_k, \mathbf{x}_{k+1}$ and $\mathbf{y}_1, \ldots, \mathbf{y}_k, \mathbf{y}_{k+1}$ be as stated. We must show that for any $\ell \leqq k+1$

$$\text{span}_V(\{\mathbf{x}_1, \ldots, \mathbf{x}_\ell\}) = \text{span}_V(\{\mathbf{y}_1, \ldots, \mathbf{y}_\ell\})$$

For $\ell \leqq k$, the above equality follows from the postulated similarity of $\mathbf{x}_1, \ldots, \mathbf{x}_k$ and $\mathbf{y}_1, \ldots, \mathbf{y}_k$. Assume then that $\ell = k+1$. We have

$$\begin{aligned}\{\mathbf{x}_1, \ldots, \mathbf{x}_k\} \subset \text{span}_V(\{\mathbf{x}_1, \ldots, \mathbf{x}_k\}) &= \text{span}_V(\{\mathbf{y}_1, \ldots, \mathbf{y}_k\}) \\ &\subset \text{span}_V(\{\mathbf{y}_1, \ldots, \mathbf{y}_{k+1}\})\end{aligned}$$

and

$$\mathbf{x}_{k+1} \in \text{span}_V(\{\mathbf{y}_1, \ldots, \mathbf{y}_{k+1}\}),$$

so that

$$\{\mathbf{x}_1, \ldots, \mathbf{x}_{k+1}\} \subset \text{span}_V(\{\mathbf{y}_1, \ldots, \mathbf{y}_{k+1}\}),$$

whence

$$\begin{aligned}\text{span}_V(\{\mathbf{x}_1, \ldots, \mathbf{x}_{k+1}\}) &\subset \text{span}_V(\text{span}_V(\{\mathbf{y}_1, \ldots, \mathbf{y}_{k+1}\})) \\ &= \text{span}_V(\{\mathbf{y}_1, \ldots, \mathbf{y}_{k+1}\})\end{aligned}$$

The reverse inclusion follows from the same argument with $\mathbf{x}$'s and $\mathbf{y}$'s exchanged. Q.E.D.

Proposition 6.6

Let V be a vector space over F ($= \mathbf{R}$ or $\mathbf{C}$) of finite or countable dimension, let γ be an inner product on V, and let $X = \{\mathbf{x}_1, \mathbf{x}_2, \mathbf{x}_3, \ldots\}$ be a basis of V.

Then, V has a basis $Y = \{\mathbf{y}_1, \mathbf{y}_2, \mathbf{y}_3, \ldots\}$ such that $\mathbf{x}_1, \mathbf{x}_2, \mathbf{x}_3, \ldots$ and $\mathbf{y}_1, \mathbf{y}_2, \mathbf{y}_3, \ldots$ are similar, and such that Y is γ-orthonormal.

Remark: This proposition implies that for every vector space over F of finite or countable dimension and for any inner product on the vector space, there is a basis of the vector space that is orthonormal with respect to the inner product.

This result is not true, in general, for spaces of higher dimension.

Proof

We define $\mathbf{y}_1, \mathbf{y}_2, \mathbf{y}_3, \ldots,$ inductively such that, for every positive integer k ($k \leqq n$, if X consists of n members, k arbitrary, otherwise).

$$\mathbf{x}_1, \ldots, \mathbf{x}_k, \quad \text{and} \quad \mathbf{y}_1, \ldots, \mathbf{y}_k$$

are similar and $\mathbf{y}_1, \ldots, \mathbf{y}_k$ is γ-orthonormal. From this, the desired result will follow easily.

Let $\mathbf{y}_1$ be the γ-normalization of $\mathbf{x}_1$. That is,

$$\mathbf{y}_1 = \left(\frac{1}{\sqrt{\gamma(\mathbf{x}_1, \mathbf{x}_1)}}\right)\mathbf{x}_1 \tag{1}$$

Suppose, next, that $\mathbf{y}_1, \ldots, \mathbf{y}_i$ have been defined so that

$$\mathbf{x}_1, \ldots, \mathbf{x}_i \quad \text{and} \quad \mathbf{y}_1, \ldots, \mathbf{y}_i$$

are similar and $\mathbf{y}_1, \ldots, \mathbf{y}_i$ is γ-orthonormal. If $i =$ number of x's, we are finished. If not, define $\mathbf{y}_{i+1}$ as follows. First, define $\mathbf{y}'_{i+1}$ by,

$$\mathbf{y}'_{i+1} = \mathbf{x}_{i+1} + a_1\mathbf{y}_1 + \cdots + a_i\mathbf{y}_i, \tag{2}$$

where a_ℓ is chosen so that $\mathbf{y}'_{i+1}$ is γ-orthogonal to $\mathbf{y}_\ell$, $\ell = 1, \ldots, i$. The proper choice of a_ℓ is

$$a_\ell = -\gamma(\mathbf{x}_{i+1}, \mathbf{y}_\ell) \tag{3}$$

Note that since $\mathbf{y}_1, \ldots, \mathbf{y}_i$ are assumed to be defined, and since $\mathbf{x}_{i+1}$ is given at the outset, a_ℓ is meaningfully defined by (3) for all $\ell = 1, \ldots, i$. We then define $\mathbf{y}_{i+1}$ to be the normalization of $\mathbf{y}'_{i+1}$**

$$\mathbf{y}_{i+1} = a\mathbf{y}'_{i+1}, \tag{4}$$

where $a = [\gamma(\mathbf{y}'_{i+1}, \mathbf{y}'_{i+1})]^{-1/2}$.

Suppose, now, that $\mathbf{y}'_{i+1} = \mathbf{0}$. Then, by (2), $\mathbf{x}_{i+1}$ would be a linear combination of $\mathbf{y}_1, \ldots, \mathbf{y}_i$. Since

$$\text{span}(\{\mathbf{y}_1, \ldots, \mathbf{y}_i\}) = \text{span}(\{\mathbf{x}_1, \ldots, \mathbf{x}_i\}),$$

this means that $\mathbf{x}_{i+1}$ is a linear combination of $\mathbf{x}_1, \ldots, \mathbf{x}_i$, contradicting the hypothesis that X is a basis of V. Therefore, $\mathbf{y}'_{i+1} \neq \mathbf{0}$.

Next, we evaluate $\gamma(\mathbf{y}'_{i+1}, \mathbf{y}_\ell)$, for all $\ell = 1, \ldots, i$.

$$\begin{aligned}\gamma(\mathbf{y}'_{i+1}, \mathbf{y}_\ell) &= \gamma(\mathbf{x}_{i+1} + a_1\mathbf{y}_1 + \cdots + a_i\mathbf{y}_i, \mathbf{y}_\ell)\\ &= \gamma(\mathbf{x}_{i+1}, \mathbf{y}_\ell) + a_1\gamma(\mathbf{y}_1, \mathbf{y}_\ell) + \cdots + a_\ell\gamma(\mathbf{y}_\ell, \mathbf{y}_\ell) + \cdots + a_i\gamma(\mathbf{y}_i, \mathbf{y}_\ell)\\ &= \gamma(\mathbf{x}_{i+1}, \mathbf{y}_\ell) + a_\ell = 0\end{aligned}$$

The second equation follows from the fact that γ is linear in its first variable, the third from the fact that $\{\mathbf{y}_1, \ldots, \mathbf{y}_i\}$ is γ-orthonormal, and the last from the definition of a_ℓ [see equation (3), above].

Finally,

$$\gamma(\mathbf{y}_{i+1}, \mathbf{y}_\ell) = \gamma(a\mathbf{y}'_{i+1}, \mathbf{y}_\ell) = a\gamma(\mathbf{y}'_{i+1}, \mathbf{y}_\ell) = 0,$$

for all $\ell = 1, \ldots, i$. Thus, $\mathbf{y}_1, \ldots, \mathbf{y}_i, \mathbf{y}_{i+1}$ are mutually γ-orthogonal, γ-unit vectors. That is, $\mathbf{y}_1, \ldots, \mathbf{y}_{i+1}$ is γ-orthonormal.

** Of course, it must be verified that $\mathbf{y}'_{i+1} \neq \mathbf{0}$. This we shall do.

We now show that $\mathbf{x}_1, \ldots, \mathbf{x}_{i+1}$ and $\mathbf{y}_1, \ldots, \mathbf{y}_{i+1}$ are similar. By part (3) of the preceding lemma, and by the inductive assumption that $\mathbf{x}_1, \ldots, \mathbf{x}_i$ and $\mathbf{y}_1, \ldots, \mathbf{y}_i$ are similar, it suffices to prove that

$$\mathbf{x}_{i+1} \in \operatorname{span}(\{\mathbf{y}_1, \ldots, \mathbf{y}_{i+1}\}) \quad \text{and} \quad \mathbf{y}_{i+1} \in \operatorname{span}(\{\mathbf{x}_1, \ldots, \mathbf{x}_{i+1}\})$$

First note that $\mathbf{y}'_{i+1} = (1/a)\mathbf{y}_{i+1}$. Replace $\mathbf{y}'_{i+1}$ in (2) by this multiple of $\mathbf{y}_{i+1}$, and solve for $\mathbf{x}_{i+1}$. This proves the first of the above two membership relations. For the second, note that since

$$\operatorname{span}\{(\mathbf{x}_1, \ldots, \mathbf{x}_i\}) = \operatorname{span}(\{\mathbf{y}_1, \ldots, \mathbf{y}_i\})$$

it follows that

$$\operatorname{span}(\{\mathbf{x}_1, \ldots, \mathbf{x}_{i+1}\}) = \operatorname{span}(\{\mathbf{y}_1, \ldots, \mathbf{y}_i, \mathbf{x}_{i+1}\})$$

By (2), $\mathbf{y}'_{i+1}$ belongs to the span on the right. Hence, so does $\mathbf{y}_{i+1} = a\mathbf{y}'_{i+1}$, and, therefore, $\mathbf{y}_{i+1}$ belongs to the span on the left, as desired.

Thus, $\mathbf{x}_1, \ldots, \mathbf{x}_{i+1}$ and $\mathbf{y}_1, \ldots, \mathbf{y}_{i+1}$ are similar, and $\mathbf{y}_1, \ldots, \mathbf{y}_{i+1}$ is γ-orthonormal. The procedure can then be repeated.

Either it stops after n steps (if X has n members), or it continues without stopping, so that a countable number of $\mathbf{y}$'s are defined. In any case, all the $\mathbf{y}$'s are mutually γ-orthogonal and γ-unit vectors, so that $Y = \{\mathbf{y}_1, \mathbf{y}_2, \mathbf{y}_3, \ldots\}$ is γ-orthogonal. Moreover, by construction, $\mathbf{x}_1, \mathbf{x}_2, \ldots, \mathbf{x}_k$ and $\mathbf{y}_1, \mathbf{y}_2, \ldots, \mathbf{y}_k$ are similar for all positive integers k ($k \leqq n$ if X has n members, k arbitrary, otherwise), so that by part (2) of the lemma, $\mathbf{x}_1, \mathbf{x}_2, \ldots,$ and $\mathbf{y}_1, \mathbf{y}_2, \ldots,$ are similar. We leave to the reader the task of showing that Y is a basis of V. Q.E.D.

The process outlined above for obtaining the orthonormal basis Y equivalent to X is called the *Gram-Schmidt* orthogonalization process.

Remarks: 1. Let $\mathbf{v} = x_1\mathbf{y}_1 + \cdots + x_k\mathbf{y}_k$ and $\mathbf{w} = z_1\mathbf{y}_1 + \cdots + z_k\mathbf{y}_k$ be any vectors of V, where $\mathbf{y}_1, \ldots, \mathbf{y}_k$, are the vectors constructed above. Then,

$$\gamma(\mathbf{v}, \mathbf{w}) = \sum_{i=1}^{k} \sum_{j=1}^{k} x_i \bar{z}_j \gamma(\mathbf{y}_i, \mathbf{y}_j) = x_1\bar{z}_1 + \cdots + x_k\bar{z}_k,$$

the second quality following from the fact that

$$\gamma(\mathbf{y}_i, \mathbf{y}_j) = \begin{cases} 0, & \text{if } i \neq j \\ 1, & \text{if } i = j \end{cases}$$

Thus, the inner product γ is merely a replica of the standard inner product β on F^n described in 2.2, Example (b).

The coefficients a_{ij} of a given conjugate-bilinear form $\delta : V \times V \to F$ (see Proposition 6.5) can be thought of as forming an $n \times n$ matrix (a_{ij}) (if $\dim V = n$). These coefficients, and, hence, the matrix, are obtained by evaluating the given form on pairs of basis vectors, for some particular basis of V. Change the basis and you, most likely, will change the coefficients, and, hence, the matrix.

The above proposition implies that if the form is an inner product, then the basis of V can be so changed that the resulting matrix (b_{ij}) satisfies $b_{ii} = 1$, for all $i = 1, \ldots, n$, and $b_{ij} = 0$ for $i \neq j$. This, of course, is a very simple matrix. The question arises, then, as to how simple a matrix can be so obtained for an arbitrary conjugate-bilinear form on V. The answer, in general, is not easy to give. It turns out, however, that for any conjugate-symmetric, conjugate-bilinear form from $V \times V$ to F, there is a basis such that the matrix of the form with respect to this basis, say (b_{ij}), satisfies, $b_{ii} = 1, 0$, or -1, for $i = 1, \ldots, n$ and $b_{ij} = 0$, for $i \neq j$. We develop this result in later exercises.

2. Another aspect of the significance of the above result resides in the usefulness of orthonormal bases. We indicate how they are useful in a proposition below. The preceding proposition tells us that for any inner product γ, γ-orthonormal bases abound (provided that V has finite or countable dimension).

Proposition 6.7

Let V be a vector space over F ($= \mathbf{R}$ or $\mathbf{C}$), γ an inner product on V, and X a γ-orthonormal basis of V. Choose any $\mathbf{v} \in V$ and suppose that $\mathbf{v} = a_1\mathbf{x}_1 + \cdots + a_n\mathbf{x}_n$, where $a_i \in F$ and $\mathbf{x}_i \in X$, $i = 1, \ldots, n$. Then:

(1) $a_i = \gamma(\mathbf{v}, \mathbf{x}_i)$, $i = 1, \ldots, n$;
(2) $\gamma(\mathbf{v}, \mathbf{v}) = a_1\bar{a}_1 + a_2\bar{a}_2 + \cdots + a_n\bar{a}_n$.

Proof

(1)

$$\begin{aligned}\gamma(\mathbf{v}, \mathbf{x}_i) &= \gamma(a_1\mathbf{x}_1 + \cdots + a_n\mathbf{x}_n, \mathbf{x}_i)\\ &= a_1\gamma(\mathbf{x}_1, \mathbf{x}_i) + \cdots + a_i\gamma(\mathbf{x}_i, \mathbf{x}_i) + \cdots + a_n\gamma(\mathbf{x}_n, \mathbf{x}_i)\\ &= a_1 \cdot 0 + \cdots + a_{i-1} \cdot 0 + a_i \cdot 1 + a_{i+1} \cdot 0 + \cdots + a_n \cdot 0 = a_i\end{aligned}$$

(2)

$$\gamma(\mathbf{v}, \mathbf{v}) = \sum_{i=1}^{n} \sum_{j=1}^{n} a_i\bar{a}_j\gamma(\mathbf{x}_i, \mathbf{x}_j) = a_1\bar{a}_1 + \cdots + a_n\bar{a}_n \qquad \text{Q.E.D.}$$

Remark: 1. Using (1) and the fact that γ is conjugate-symmetric, (2) becomes

$$\gamma(\mathbf{v}, \mathbf{v}) = \gamma(\mathbf{v}, \mathbf{x}_1)\gamma(\mathbf{x}_1, \mathbf{v}) + \cdots + \gamma(\mathbf{v}, \mathbf{x}_n)\gamma(\mathbf{x}_n, \mathbf{v})$$

2. Note that if $\mathbf{x} \in X$ is any vector that does not appear in the above linear combination of vectors of X with value $\mathbf{v}$ (i.e., if $\mathbf{x} \neq \mathbf{x}_i$, for all $i = 1, \ldots, n$), then

$$\gamma(\mathbf{v}, \mathbf{x}) = \gamma(a_1\mathbf{x}_1 + \cdots + a_n\mathbf{x}_n, \mathbf{x}) = a_1\gamma(\mathbf{x}_1, \mathbf{x}) + \cdots + a_n\gamma(\mathbf{x}_n, \mathbf{x}) = 0$$

since $\mathbf{x}$ is orthogonal to $\mathbf{x}_1, \ldots, \mathbf{x}_n$ (X being orthonormal).

Thus, for any $\mathbf{v} \in V$, the products $\gamma(\mathbf{v}, \mathbf{x})$, as $\mathbf{x}$ ranges over X, are zero for all but a finite number of basis vectors $\mathbf{x}$.

For completeness, we state and prove a simple but important result which, by now, should be no surprise to the reader.

Proposition 6.8

Let V be any vector space over $F(= \mathbf{R}$ or $\mathbf{C})$ and let γ be any inner product on V. A set of mutually γ-orthogonal, nonzero vectors is linearly independent.

Proof

Suppose that X is the set of vectors in question, and

$$a_1\mathbf{x}_1 + \cdots + a_n\mathbf{x}_n = \mathbf{0},$$

for some $\mathbf{x}_1, \ldots, \mathbf{x}_n$ in X. Then,

$$\begin{aligned} 0 = \gamma(\mathbf{0}, \mathbf{x}_i) &= \gamma(a_1\mathbf{x}_1 + \cdots + a_n\mathbf{x}_n, \mathbf{x}_i) = a_1\gamma(\mathbf{x}_1, \mathbf{x}_i) + \cdots + a_n\gamma(\mathbf{x}_n, \mathbf{x}_i) \\ &= a_1 \cdot 0 + \cdots + a_{i-1} \cdot 0 + a_i\gamma(\mathbf{x}_i, \mathbf{x}_i) + a_{i+1} \cdot 0 + \cdots + a_n \cdot 0 \\ &= a_i \cdot \gamma(\mathbf{x}_i, \mathbf{x}_i) \end{aligned}$$

for $i = 1, \ldots, n$. Since $\mathbf{x}_i \neq 0$ and γ is positive-definite, $\gamma(\mathbf{x}_i, \mathbf{x}_i) \neq 0$, so that $a_i = 0$, for all $i = 1, \ldots, n$. Thus, the combination is trivial. Since this applies to every linear combination of vectors of X with value zero, X is linearly independent. Q.E.D.

We close this section with some examples of orthonormal sets of vectors. F will always denote either $\mathbf{R}$ or $\mathbf{C}$.

(a) In F^n, the standard basis is orthonormal with respect to the standard inner product on F^n [see 2.2 Example (b)].

In $\mathbf{R}^2$ and $\mathbf{R}^3$, of course, this is just the standard fact that the standard basis vectors have unit length and are mutually perpendicular.

(b) Consider the bilinear form $\delta : \mathbf{R}^2 \times \mathbf{R}^2 \to \mathbf{R}$ given by

$$\delta(\mathbf{x}, \mathbf{y}) = 2x_1y_1 - 3(x_1y_2 + x_2y_1) + 5x_2y_2$$

The reader should verify that this bilinear form is positive-definite and symmetric. Thus, it is an inner product on $\mathbf{R}^2$. Let $\mathbf{e}_1 = (1, 0)$ and $\mathbf{e}_2 = (0, 1)$, as usual. We construct a δ-orthonormal basis of $\mathbf{R}^2$ similar to $\{\mathbf{e}_1, \mathbf{e}_2\}$.

First, let $\mathbf{y}_1$ be the δ-normalization of $\mathbf{e}_1$. That is,

$$\mathbf{y}_1 = \frac{1}{\sqrt{\delta(\mathbf{e}_1, \mathbf{e}_1)}}\mathbf{e}_1$$

But $\delta(\mathbf{e}_1, \mathbf{e}_1) = 2 \cdot 1 \cdot 1 - 3(1 \cdot 0 + 0 \cdot 1) + 5 \cdot 0 \cdot 0 = 2$. Thus, $\mathbf{y}_1 = (1/\sqrt{2})\mathbf{e}_1$. Next, following the Gram-Schmidt process of orthogonalization, let

$$\mathbf{y}_2' = \mathbf{e}_2 + a_1\mathbf{y}_1$$

According to the proof of Proposition 6.6, a_1 should equal

$$-\delta(\mathbf{e}_2, \mathbf{y}_1) = \delta\left((0, 1), \frac{1}{\sqrt{2}}(1, 0)\right) = 2 \cdot 0 \cdot \frac{1}{\sqrt{2}} - 3\left(0 \cdot 0 + \frac{1}{\sqrt{2}} \cdot 1\right) + 5 \cdot 1 \cdot 0$$

$$= -\frac{3}{\sqrt{2}}$$

Thus,

$$\mathbf{y}_2' = \mathbf{e}_2 - \frac{3}{\sqrt{2}}\mathbf{y}_1 = (0, 1) - \frac{3}{\sqrt{2}} \cdot \frac{1}{\sqrt{2}}(1, 0) = (-3/2, 1)$$

Now, normalize $\mathbf{y}_2'$ to obtain $\mathbf{y}_2$. Thus,

$$\mathbf{y}_1 = \left(\frac{1}{\sqrt{2}}, 0\right)$$

$$\mathbf{y}_2 = \sqrt{\frac{2}{37}}(-3/2, 1)$$

The reader should check that $\{\mathbf{y}_1, \mathbf{y}_2\}$ is δ-orthonormal. It is easily seen to be similar to $\{\mathbf{x}_1, \mathbf{x}_2\}$.

(c) On the vector space V of all continuous F-valued functions on the closed interval $[0, 2\pi]$ ($F = \mathbf{R}$ or $\mathbf{C}$), let γ be as in Example (c) of 2.2. That is, for any f, g in V

$$\gamma(f, g) = \int_0^{2\pi} f(x)\overline{g(x)}\, dx$$

γ is an inner product on V. The reader should verify that the set

$$\{\sin sx, \cos rx \mid r, s \in \mathbf{N} = \text{natural numbers}\}$$

is γ-orthogonal. Show that

$$\gamma(\sin sx, \sin sx) = \gamma(\cos rx, \cos rx) = \pi,$$

for all positive integers r and s.

On the other hand, let W be the vector space of all continuous real-valued functions defined on $(0, \pi)$, and let

$$\delta(f, g) = \frac{2}{\pi}\int_0^{\pi} f(x)g(x)\, dx,$$

for all f, g in W. Just as γ is an inner product on V, so is δ an inner product on W. Show that the set of functions given above [with domains now restricted to $(0, \pi)$, of course] is not δ-orthonormal, but that the sets

$$\{\sin sx \mid s \in \mathbf{N}\} \quad \text{and} \quad \{\cos rx \mid r \in \mathbf{N}\}$$

are δ-orthonormal.

EXERCISES / 6.2

1. Which of the following functions $\beta : V \times V \to F$ (V a vector space over $F = \mathbf{R}$ or $\mathbf{C}$) is **i.** conjugate-bilinear, **ii.** conjugate-symmetric, **iii.** positive-definite?
   a. $V = \mathbf{R}$, $F = \mathbf{R}$, $\beta(x, y) = 0$, for all $(x, y) \in \mathbf{R} \times \mathbf{R}$
   b. $V = \mathbf{C}$, $F = \mathbf{R}$, $\beta(w, z) = wz$, for all $(w, z) \in \mathbf{C} \times \mathbf{C}$
   c. $V = \mathbf{C}$, $F = \mathbf{C}$, $\beta(w, z) = 4w\bar{z}$, for all $(w, z) \in \mathbf{C} \times \mathbf{C}$
   d. $V = \mathbf{C}^2$, $F = \mathbf{C}$, $\beta((w_1, w_2), (z_1, z_2)) = w_1 z_1 + w_2 z_2$, for all $((w_1, w_2), (z_1, z_2)) \in \mathbf{C}^2 \times \mathbf{C}^2$
   e. $V = \mathbf{R}^2$, $F = \mathbf{R}$, $\beta((x_1, x_2), (y_1, y_2)) = x_1 y_1 - 3(x_1 y_2 + x_2 y_1) + x_2 y_2$

2. The following will all define conjugate-bilinear forms on $F^n \times F^n$ where $F = \mathbf{R}$ or $\mathbf{C}$ and $n = 1, 2$, or 3. Express their function values at $((x_1, \ldots, x_n), (y_1, \ldots y_n))$ in the standard form

$$\beta((x_1, \ldots, x_n), (y_1, \ldots, y_n)) = \sum_{i=1}^{n} \sum_{j=1}^{n} a_{ij} x_i \bar{y}_j$$

   (*Example:* $\beta((x_1, x_2), (y_1, y_2)) = 3x_1(y_2 - 3y_1) + y_1(x_1 + 4x_2)$ should be rewritten as: $\beta((x_1, x_2), (y_1, y_2)) = -8x_1 y_1 + 3x_1 y_2 + 4x_2 y_1 + 0 \cdot x_2 y_2$.)
   a. $\beta((x_1, x_2, x_3), (y_1, y_2, y_3)) = x_1(y_1 - 2y_3 + y_2) - x_2(y_3 + y_1) + x_3 y_2$
   b. $\beta((x_1, x_2), (y_1, y_2)) = x_1 y_1 + 4(x_1 y_2 + x_2(y_1 + y_2))y_1$
   c. $\beta((x_1, x_2)(y_1, y_2)) = (x_1 - x_2)(y_1 - y_2)$
   d. $\beta(x, y) = 0$

3.* Let V, W, and Z be vector spaces over $\mathbf{C}$. We denote by $V_{\mathbf{R}}$, $W_{\mathbf{R}}$, and $Z_{\mathbf{R}}$ the vector spaces over $\mathbf{R}$ with *underlying sets* V, W, *and* Z, respectively, with the same addition operations as those of V, W, and Z, respectively, and with real multiplications obtained from the complex multiplications of V, W, and Z, respectively, by restricting to real numbers only. If $S : V \to W$ and $T : W \to Z$ are conjugate-linear transformations, then Proposition 6.2 asserts that the functions $S : V_{\mathbf{R}} \to W_{\mathbf{R}}$ and $T : W_{\mathbf{R}} \to Z_{\mathbf{R}}$ (remember, the underlying sets of V and $V_{\mathbf{R}}$ are the same, and similarly for W and $W_{\mathbf{R}}$ and Z and $Z_{\mathbf{R}}$, so that S and T are defined as functions on $V_{\mathbf{R}}$ and $W_{\mathbf{R}}$, respectively) are linear transformations of vector spaces over $\mathbf{R}$.

   Let us denote by $\bar{\mathscr{N}}_S$ the set of all $\mathbf{v} \in V$ such that $S : V \to W$ takes $\mathbf{v}$ to $\bar{\mathbf{0}} \in W$. Let us denote by $\mathscr{N}_S$ the usual null space of $S : V_{\mathbf{R}} \to W_{\mathbf{R}}$. Let $\mathscr{R}_S$ denote the range of S.
   a. Let $\bar{\mathbf{0}}$ be the $+$-identity of W (considered as a vector space over $\mathbf{C}$), and let $\mathbf{0}$ be the $+$-identity of $W_{\mathbf{R}}$. Prove that $\bar{\mathbf{0}} = \mathbf{0}$.
   b. Prove that $\mathscr{N}_S = \bar{\mathscr{N}}_S$.
   c. Prove that S is 1–1 if and only if $\bar{\mathscr{N}}_S = \mathbf{0}$.
   d. Prove that $\bar{\mathscr{N}}_S$ is closed under vector addition and complex scalar multiplication (i.e., it is a vector subspace of V over $\mathbf{C}$).

e. Prove that $\mathcal{R}_S$ is closed under vector addition and complex scalar multiplication.

f. Let U be any complement of $\overline{\mathcal{N}}_S$ in V. Prove that U and $\mathcal{R}_S$ are isomorphic (as vector spaces over **C**). (*Hint:* Choose any basis X of U, show that $S \mid X$ is 1–1 and that $S(X)$ is a basis of R_S, and then define a *linear* transformation from U to $\mathcal{R}_S$ that sends $\mathbf{x}$ to $S(\mathbf{x})$, for every $\mathbf{x} \in X$, and show that it is an isomorphism.)

g. Use **e** to prove that, if V is finite-dimensional, then

$$\dim V = \dim \mathcal{R}_S + \dim \overline{\mathcal{N}}_S$$

h. Show that if $\dim V = \dim W$, then S is 1–1 if and only if it is onto.

i. Prove that $T \circ S$ is a *linear* transformation (over **C**).

j. If $S : V \to W$ is a conjugate-linear transformation that is 1–1 and onto, then we say that S is a *conjugate-isomorphism* (of vector spaces over **C**). Prove that if S is a conjugate-isomorphism, then so is S^{-1}.

4. Let V be any vector space over **C**, and let X be a basis of V. Define a function $i_X : V \to V$ as follows:

$$i_X(a_1\mathbf{x}_1 + \cdots + a_n\mathbf{x}_n) = \bar{a}_1\mathbf{x}_1 + \cdots + \bar{a}_n\mathbf{x}_n$$

a. Prove that $i_X \circ i_X = I_V$, the identity transformation of V. Thus, i_X is 1–1 and onto V and $i_X = i_X^{-1}$.

b. Prove that i_X is a conjugate-linear transformation.

c. Let U_0 be the set of all $\mathbf{v} \in V$ such that $i_X(\mathbf{v}) = \mathbf{v}$. Prove that U_0 is a vector subspace of $V_{\mathbf{R}}$ (see **3**, above, for the definition of $V_{\mathbf{R}}$).**

d. Let U_1 be the set of all $\mathbf{u} \in V$ such that $\mathbf{u} = i\mathbf{v}$, for some $\mathbf{v} \in U_0$. (That is, U_1 is obtained from U_0 by multiplying all $\mathbf{v} \in U_0$ by i.) Prove that U_1 is a vector subspace of $V_{\mathbf{R}}$.

e. Prove that $U_0 \oplus U_1 = V_{\mathbf{R}}$.

f. Show that X is a basis of U_0 (as a vector space over **R**). Prove that every basis of U_0 is a basis of V (as a vector space over **C**)!

Thus, if V is finite-dimensional (over **C**), then U_0 is finite-dimensional (over **R**), and

$$\dim U_0 \text{ (over } \mathbf{R}) = \dim V \text{ (over } \mathbf{C})$$

g. Go through **a**–**f** in case $V = \mathbf{C}$ and $X = \{1\}$.

5. Let U and V be vector spaces over **C**, let X be a basis of V, and let $i_X : V \to V$ be the conjugate isomorphism defined in **4**. Finally, let $\overline{\text{Trans}(U, V)}$ be the set of all conjugate-linear transformations from U to V.

a. Given any $T \in \text{Trans}(U, V)$, prove that $i_X \circ T \in \overline{\text{Trans}(U, V)}$.

b. Given any $S \in \overline{\text{Trans}(U, V)}$, prove that $i_X \circ S \in \text{Trans}(U, V)$.

c. Define a function

$$i^* : \text{Trans}(U, V) \to \overline{\text{Trans}(U, V)}$$

** $V_{\mathbf{R}}$ is a vector space over **R**; thus, we are requesting that the reader prove that U_0 is a vector subspace over **R**.

by the equation $i^*(T) = i_X \circ T$. Similarly, define a function

$$j^* : \overline{\text{Trans}(U, V)} \to \text{Trans}(U, V)$$

by the equation $j^*(S) = i_X \circ S$.

Prove that i^* and j^* are 1–1 correspondences and that $i^* = (j^*)^{-1}$.

d. Prove that $\overline{\text{Trans}(U, V)}$ is a vector space over **C** with respect to ordinary addition and complex multiplication of functions.

e. Prove that i^* is a conjugate-isomorphism. (See **3.j**, for the definition of conjugate-isomorphism.)

6. a. Let V be a vector space over **R** with basis $\{\mathbf{x}_1, \ldots, \mathbf{x}_n\} = X$, W a vector space over **R** with basis $\{\mathbf{y}_1, \ldots, \mathbf{y}_n\} = Y$. Let $T : V \to W$ be an isomorphism with matrix $\mathscr{A}_{X,Y}(T) = {}_n(t_{ij})_n$, and let $\beta : W \times W \to F$ be a bilinear form such that

$$\beta(\mathbf{y}_i, \mathbf{y}_j) = b_{ij}, \qquad i = 1, \ldots, n, \qquad j = 1, \ldots, n$$

The matrix ${}_n(b_{ij})_n$ is called the matrix of β with respect to Y.

Let $\alpha : V \times V \to F$ be the bilinear form on $V \times V$ satisfying $\alpha(\mathbf{v}_1, \mathbf{v}_2) = \beta(T(\mathbf{v}_1), T(\mathbf{v}_2))$, for all $(\mathbf{v}_1, \mathbf{v}_2) \in V \times V$, and let ${}_n(a_{rs})_n$ be the matrix of α with respect to X. Show that

$$a_{rs} = \sum_{i=1}^{n} \sum_{j=1}^{n} b_{ij} t_{ir} t_{js}$$

b. Restate the above problem **a** in case V and W are vector spaces over **C** (replacing "bilinear" by "conjugate-bilinear" leaving "linear" the same). Prove the restated result.

7. Let $F = \mathbf{R}$ or **C**, let γ be an inner product on a vector space V over F, and let $\{\mathbf{x}_1, \mathbf{x}_2, \mathbf{x}_3, \ldots\}$ and $\{\mathbf{y}_1, \mathbf{y}_2, \mathbf{y}_3, \ldots\}$ be similar, γ-orthonormal sets of vectors in V. Prove that for all $j = 1, 2, \ldots,$

$$\mathbf{x}_j = c_j \mathbf{y}_j,$$

where $c_j, j = 1, 2, \ldots,$ are scalars in F of length 1 (i.e., $c_j \bar{c}_j = 1, j = 1, 2, \ldots$). Such scalars are called unit scalars.

This result shows that the basis $\{\mathbf{y}_1, \mathbf{y}_2, \ldots\}$ obtained in Proposition 6.6 is unique "up to multiples of unit scalars"—that is, any other γ orthonormal basis $\{\mathbf{z}_1, \mathbf{z}_2, \ldots\}$ of V similar to X would have to be similar to Y, too, and so $\mathbf{z}_j = c_j \mathbf{y}_j$, where $c_j \bar{c}_j = 1$.

8. a. Let V be any vector space over R with basis $\{\mathbf{x}_1, \ldots, \mathbf{x}_n\}$, and let $\beta: V \times V \to \mathbf{R}$ be a bilinear form. Let (b_{ij}) be the matrix of β with respect to X. Now, choose any other basis $\{\mathbf{y}_1, \ldots, \mathbf{y}_n\}$ of V, and suppose that

$$\mathbf{y}_j = t_{1j}\mathbf{x}_1 + t_{2j}\mathbf{x}_2 + \cdots + t_{nj}\mathbf{x}_n,$$

for all $j = 1, \ldots, n$. Take these coefficients, put them in *columns*. They form the matrix ${}_n(t_{ij})_n$. (The matrix ${}_n(t_{ij})_n$ may also be defined to be $\mathscr{A}_{X,X}(T)$, where $T : V \to V$ is the unique linear transformation satisfying $T(\mathbf{x}_j) = \mathbf{y}_j$ for all $j = 1, \ldots, n$. The reader should show this.) Finally let ${}_n(a_{ij})_n$ be the matrix of β with respect to Y. Prove that (a_{ij}) is given by the matrix product

$$(a_{ij}) = (t_{ij})^t \cdot (b_{ij}) \cdot (t_{ij}), \tag{1}$$

where $(t_{ij})^t$ is the *transpose* of (t_{ij}), which, the reader will recall, is obtained from (t_{ij}) by exchanging rows with columns.

Equation (1) is a *change-of-basis formula* for bilinear forms. It shows how the coefficients in a summation expression for a bilinear form change when the basis is changed.

b. Prove that if V is a complex vector space, and if β is conjugate-bilinear, (1) becomes

$$(a_{ij}) = (\overline{t_{ij}})^t \cdot (b_{ij}) \cdot (t_{ij}) \tag{2}$$

The Gram-Schmidt orthogonalization process (Proposition 6.6) shows us that if β is an inner product, then there is a basis of V such that the matrix of β with respect to this basis is a unit matrix (i.e., $a_{ij} = 1$, if $i = j$, $a_{ij} = 0$, if $i \neq j$). This is just another way of looking at orthonormality. We have denoted the $n \times n$ unit matrix by $(1)_n$. Thus,

$$(1)_n = (\overline{t_{ij}})^t \cdot (b_{ij}) \cdot (t_{ij}),$$

for appropriate choice of t_{ij} (i.e., appropriate change of basis).

9. Let V be a vector space over $F (= \mathbf{R}$ or $\mathbf{C})$ with ordered basis $X = \{\mathbf{x}_1, \ldots, \mathbf{x}_n\}$.

a. Show that the sum of two conjugate-bilinear forms on $V \times V$ is a conjugate bilinear form on $V \times V$.

b. Show that any scalar multiple of a conjugate-bilinear form on $V \times V$ is a conjugate-bilinear form on $V \times V$.

Call the set of all conjugate-bilinear forms on V, B. B is a subset of the vector space of all functions from $V \times V$ to F. Exercises **a** and **b** show that B is closed with respect to the operations of this vector space. Thus, B is a vector subspace of $F^{V \times V}$, and, hence, it is a vector space over F, in its own right.

c. Recall that $\mathfrak{M}(n, n)$ is the vector space of $n \times n$ matrices over F. Define a function

$$M_X : B \to \mathfrak{M}(n, n)$$

as follows: $M_X(\beta) = {}_n(a_{ij})_n$ if and only if (a_{ij}) is the matrix of β with respect to X (i.e., $a_{ij} = \beta(\mathbf{x}_i, \mathbf{x}_j)$, for all $i, j = 1, \ldots, n$).

Prove that M_X is an isomorphism of vector spaces.

d. Let γ be the inner product on V with respect to which X is γ-orthonormal. (Proposition 6.5 assures us that a unique such γ exists.) Let $T : V \to V$ be any linear transformation, and suppose that $\mathscr{A}_{X,X}(T) = {}_n(t_{ij})_n \in \mathfrak{M}(n, n)$.

Define a function $\alpha_T : V \times V \to F$ by the formula

$$\alpha_T(\mathbf{v}_1, \mathbf{v}_2) = \gamma(T(\mathbf{v}_1), \mathbf{v}_2),$$

for all $(\mathbf{v}_1, \mathbf{v}_2) \in V \times V$. Prove that α_T is conjugate bilinear, and prove that

$$M_X(\alpha_T) = {}_n(t_{ij})_n \quad [= \mathscr{A}_{X,X}(T)]$$

e. Define a function $\alpha : \mathrm{Trans}(V, V) \to B$ by the formula $\alpha(T) = \alpha_T$. Prove that α is an isomorphism of vector spaces. (*Hint:* Use **d** to show that $\alpha = M_X{}^{-1} \circ \mathscr{A}_{X,X}$.)

10. Let V be as in **9**, and let β be any positive-definite conjugate-symmetric, conjugate-bilinear form on $V \times V$. Define

$$d : V \to \mathbf{C}$$

as follows: $d(\mathbf{v}) = \sqrt{\beta(\mathbf{v}, \mathbf{v})}$. Prove that

$$\beta(\mathbf{v}, \mathbf{w}) = (1/4)([d(\mathbf{v} + \mathbf{w})]^2 - [d(\mathbf{v} - \mathbf{w})]^2 + i[d(\mathbf{v} + i\mathbf{w})]^2 - i[d(\mathbf{v} - i\mathbf{w})]_2)$$

This is the *polarization equality*, a special case of which was presented in Exercises 6.1.**11**.

11. Let $\mathscr{P}$ be the vector space of polynomials in one indeterminate with real coefficients. We suppose that the indeterminate x ranges over **R**. Define a function $\gamma : \mathscr{P} \times \mathscr{P} \to \mathbf{R}$ as follows: for all $(p(x), g(x)) \in \mathscr{P} \times \mathscr{P}$

$$\gamma(p(x), g(x)) - \int_0^\infty e^{-x} p(x) g(x)\, dx + \int_{-\infty}^0 e^x p(x) g(x)\, dx$$

a. Assume that the quantity on the right is always a well-defined real number (or prove it, if you can). Using the standard properties of integrals, prove that γ is an inner product on $\mathscr{P}$.

b. Construct the first four members of a γ-orthonormal basis of $\mathscr{P}$ similar to $\{1 = x^0, x = x^1, x^2, x^3, x^4, \ldots\}$.

12. Let $\mathscr{P}$ be as in **11**, and define $\beta : \mathscr{P} \times \mathscr{P} \to \mathbf{R}$ as follows:

$$\beta(p(x), g(x)) = \int_0^1 p(x) g(x)\, dx,$$

for all $(p(x), g(x)) \in \mathscr{P}$.

a. Prove that β is an inner product on $\mathscr{P}$.

b. Construct the first four members of a β-orthonormal basis of P similar to $\{1, x, x^2, x^3, \ldots\}$.

13. **a.** Let F be any field, V any vector space over F, X any basis of V, and $b : X \times X \to F$ any function. (Assume that $X \neq \varnothing$.) Show that there exists one and only one bilinear function $\beta : V \times V \to F$ such that $\beta \mid X \times X = b$.

b. Let $F = \mathbf{C}$, and let V, X, and b be as above. Show that there exists one and only one conjugate-bilinear function $\gamma : V \times V \to F$ such that $\gamma \mid X \times X = b$.

c. Use **a** and **b** to show that for *any* vector space V over **R** or **C** with given basis X there is an inner product $\gamma : V \times V \to \mathbf{R}$ or **C** with respect to which X is γ-orthonormal.

Compare this result to Corollary to Proposition 6.5.

14. Let V be any vector space over **R** of finite dimension $n \geqq 1$, let $X = \{\mathbf{x}_1, \ldots, \mathbf{x}_n\}$ be a basis of V, and let $\beta : V \times V \to \mathbf{R}$ be an inner product on V. Suppose that ${}_n(a_{ij})_n$ is the matrix of β with respect to X [i.e., $a_{ij} = \beta(\mathbf{x}_i, \mathbf{x}_j)$].

A principal submatrix of (a_{ij}) of order k is a $k \times k$ matrix obtained from (a_{ij}) by deleting $n - k$ rows and the "same" columns. That is, if rows $r_1, \ldots, r_{n-k}$ are deleted, then so are columns $r_1, \ldots, r_{n-k}$. A principal minor of (a_{ij}) is the determinant of a principal submatrix of (a_{ij}).

If ${}_k(b_{ij})_k$ is the principal submatrix of (a_{ij}) obtained by deleting all rows and columns of (a_{ij}) except rows $s_1, \ldots, s_k$ and columns $s_1, \ldots, s_k$, then we write

$$ {}_k(b_{ij})_k = (a_{ij})_{s_1,\ldots,s_k} $$

Of course, then $(a_{ij}) = (a_{ij})_{1,2,\ldots,n}$.

a. For any integers $s_1, \ldots, s_k$ between 1 and n, let $V_{s_1,\ldots,s_k} = \text{span}\{(\mathbf{x}_{s_1}, \ldots, \mathbf{x}_{s_k}\})$, and let $X_{s_1,\ldots,s_k} = \{\mathbf{x}_{s_1}, \ldots, \mathbf{x}_{s_k}\}$. Clearly, $X_{s_1,\ldots,s_k}$ is a basis of $V_{s_1,\ldots,s_k}$.
Verify that $\beta \mid V_{s_1,\ldots,s_k}$ is an inner product on $V_{s_1,\ldots,s_k}$ and that the matrix of $\beta \mid V_{s_1,\ldots,s_k}$ with respect to $X_{s_1,\ldots,s_k}$ is $(a_{ij})_{s_1,\ldots,s_k}$.

b. Consider the following statement: *All the principal minors of ${}_n(a_{ij})_n$ are positive.*

i. Prove that the result is true for $n = 1$.

ii. Assume that the result is true for all matrices of inner products on vector spaces over **R** of dimension $\leqq k$. Suppose that $n = k + 1$. Use the assumption to prove that all minors of ${}_n(a_{ij})_n$ of order $\leqq k$ are positive; **a** will be useful here.

iii. Of course, ${}_n(a_{ij})_n$ has only one principal submatrix of order n. Use the Gram-Schmidt orthogonalization result, together with equation (2) and the following discussion in **8**, above, to show that $det(a_{ij}) > 0$. (Recall that $det\ \mathfrak{a} = det\ \mathfrak{a}^t$.) Combine this result with that of **ii** to show that all principal minors of ${}_n(a_{ij})_n$ are positive when $n = k + 1$.

Thus, conclude, by the Axiom of Induction that if ${}_n(a_{ij})_n$ is the matrix of an inner product (over **R**), then all the principal minors of (a_{ij}) are positive.

A similar result holds when the scalar field $F = \mathbf{C}$.

Moreover, the converse also holds. More precisely: if β is a conjugate-bilinear, conjugate-symmetric form on a finite-dimensional vector space V over $F (= \mathbf{R}$ or $\mathbf{C})$, then β is positive-definite (i.e., it is an inner product) if, for any matrix (a_{ij}) of β, the principal minors of (a_{ij}) are positive.

We shall not prove this converse.

2.4 Some Geometric Properties of Inner Products

In this section we show that inner products, in general, have many of the properties that our concrete angle-distance measuring functions α and γ of 1.1 and 1.2 have. This will constitute our justification for considering inner products as *valid* generalizations of the concrete functions. This will also justify our use of the words "length," "perpendicular," and so on, in the general situation. Throughout this section γ will denote a fixed inner product on a (not necessarily finite dimensional) vector space V over $F (= \mathbf{R}$ or $\mathbf{C})$.

(a) *The Pythagorean theorem*

If $\mathbf{v}_1, \mathbf{v}_2, \ldots, \mathbf{v}_n$ are mutually γ-orthogonal (i.e., "perpendicular") vectors in V, then the sum of the squares of their γ-lengths equals the square of the γ-length of their sum [where the γ-length of a vector $\mathbf{w} \in V$ is $\gamma(\mathbf{w}, \mathbf{w})^{1/2}$—this is a nonnegative real number because γ is positive-definite]:

Let $\mathbf{v}$ be the sum $\mathbf{v}_1 + \cdots + \mathbf{v}_n$. Then

$$\gamma(\mathbf{v}, \mathbf{v}) = \gamma(\mathbf{v}_1, \mathbf{v}_1) + \cdots + \gamma(\mathbf{v}_n, \mathbf{v}_n) \tag{1}$$

The proof of this fact amounts to a simple evaluation of $\gamma(\mathbf{v}, \mathbf{v})$:

$$\gamma(\mathbf{v}, \mathbf{v}) = \gamma\left(\sum_{i=1}^{n} \mathbf{v}_i, \sum_{j=1}^{n} \mathbf{v}_j\right) = \sum_{i=1}^{n} \sum_{j=1}^{n} \gamma(\mathbf{v}_i, \mathbf{v}_j) = \sum_{i=1}^{n} \gamma(\mathbf{v}_i, \mathbf{v}_i),$$

the last equality holding because $\gamma(\mathbf{v}_i, \mathbf{v}_j) = 0$ if $i \neq j$. The reader should compare this result with Proposition 6.7.

(b) *Schwarz's inequality*

We refer the reader to 1.1(c)(vii) and 1.2(d)(vi). The proper generalization of these inequations is as follows: For any $(\mathbf{v}, \mathbf{w})$ in $V \times V$

$$\gamma(\mathbf{v}, \mathbf{w})\overline{\gamma(\mathbf{v}, \mathbf{w})} \leqq \gamma(\mathbf{v}, \mathbf{v})\gamma(\mathbf{w}, \mathbf{w}) \tag{2}$$

Notice that if $F = \mathbf{R}$, the left-hand side becomes $\gamma(\mathbf{v}, \mathbf{w})^2$, as in 1.1(c)(vii). Notice also that $\gamma(\mathbf{w}, \mathbf{v}) = \overline{\gamma(\mathbf{v}, \mathbf{w})}$ so that (2) may be written as

$$\gamma(\mathbf{v}, \mathbf{w})\gamma(\mathbf{w}, \mathbf{v}) \leqq \gamma(\mathbf{v}, \mathbf{v})\gamma(\mathbf{w}, \mathbf{w}) \tag{2'}$$

Finally, we remind the reader that the left-hand side of (2) (and of (2')) is a nonnegative real number because it is the product of a complex number and its conjugate.

In addition to proving (2), *we shall show that equality holds in* (2), *if and only if* $\mathbf{v} = \mathbf{w}$ *or* $\{\mathbf{v}, \mathbf{w}\}$ *is dependent*. Equation (2) is known as Schwarz's inequality.

Proof

(1) We first prove that (2) holds for all $(\mathbf{v}, \mathbf{w}) \in V \times V$. If either $\mathbf{v} = \mathbf{0}$ or $\mathbf{w} = \mathbf{0}$, then (2) is obvious, both sides reducing to 0. Thus, we are left with the case $\mathbf{v} \neq \mathbf{0}$ and $\mathbf{w} \neq \mathbf{0}$. Clearly, in this case, $\gamma(\mathbf{v}, \mathbf{v}) \neq 0$.

Let $c = \gamma(\mathbf{v}, \mathbf{w})$, and consider $\gamma(\bar{c}\mathbf{v} + r\mathbf{w}, \bar{c}\mathbf{v} + r\mathbf{w})$, for any scalar r. Since γ is positive-definite, this number is not less than 0. Thus, using the conjugate-bilinearity and conjugate-symmetry of γ, and the fact that $\bar{\bar{c}} = c$,

$$\begin{aligned} 0 \leqq \gamma(\bar{c}\mathbf{v} + r\mathbf{w}, \bar{c}\mathbf{v} + r\mathbf{w}) &= \bar{c}c\gamma(\mathbf{v}, \mathbf{v}) + \overline{rc}\gamma(\mathbf{v}, \mathbf{w}) + rc\gamma(\mathbf{w}, \mathbf{v}) + r\bar{r}\gamma(\mathbf{w}, \mathbf{w}) \\ &= \bar{c}c\gamma(\mathbf{v}, \mathbf{v}) + \overline{rc}c + rc\bar{c} + r\bar{r}\gamma(\mathbf{w}, \mathbf{w}) \end{aligned}$$

Now, let $r = -\gamma(\mathbf{v}, \mathbf{v})$. This is a real number, so that $r = \bar{r}$. Thus,

$$0 \leqq -r\bar{c}c + r\bar{c}c + rc\bar{c} + r^2\gamma(\mathbf{w}, \mathbf{w}),$$

and so

$$-rc\bar{c} \leqq r^2\gamma(\mathbf{w}, \mathbf{w})$$

Since γ is positive-definite, $r = -\gamma(\mathbf{v}, \mathbf{v})$ is negative, so that $-r > 0$. Thus, we may divide the above inequality by $-r$ and obtain

$$c\bar{c} \leqq -r\gamma(\mathbf{w}, \mathbf{w}) \tag{2''}$$

If we replace c by $\gamma(\mathbf{v}, \mathbf{w})$ and r by $-\gamma(\mathbf{v}, \mathbf{v})$, then we obtain (2).

(2) We now show that equality holds in (2) if and only if $\mathbf{v} = \mathbf{w}$ or $\{\mathbf{v}, \mathbf{w}\}$ is linearly dependent.

If $\mathbf{v} = \mathbf{w}$, then a glance at (2) or (2′) shows that equality must hold. Suppose, then, that $\{\mathbf{v}, \mathbf{w}\}$ is dependent. If $\mathbf{v} = \mathbf{0}$ or $\mathbf{w} = \mathbf{0}$, then, again, it is obvious that equality holds in (2), both sides reducing to zero. Suppose then that $\mathbf{v} \neq \mathbf{0}$ and $\mathbf{w} \neq \mathbf{0}$. Since $\{\mathbf{v}, \mathbf{w}\}$ is dependent, we must have a nontrivial linear combination $a\mathbf{v} + b\mathbf{w} = \mathbf{0}$, where, say, $a \neq 0$. Therefore, $\mathbf{v} = -(b/a)\mathbf{w}$. Let $d = -b/a$. Then, $\mathbf{v} = d\mathbf{w}$. Thus,

$$\gamma(\mathbf{v}, \mathbf{w})\overline{\gamma(\mathbf{v}, \mathbf{w})} = \gamma(\mathbf{v}, 1/d\mathbf{v})\overline{\gamma(d\mathbf{w}, \mathbf{w})} = \frac{\bar{1}}{d}\,\gamma(\mathbf{v}, \mathbf{v})\bar{d}\gamma(\mathbf{w}, \mathbf{w}) = \gamma(\mathbf{v}, \mathbf{v})\gamma(\mathbf{w}, \mathbf{w}),$$

so that equality holds in this case.

Now assume that equality holds in (2). Rewrite (2) in the form (2″), by letting $c = \gamma(\mathbf{v}, \mathbf{w})$ and $r = -\gamma(\mathbf{v}, \mathbf{v})$, and proceed backwards through the steps of part 1 of this proof. All the steps are reversible. The result will be the equation

$$0 = \gamma(\bar{c}\mathbf{v} + r\mathbf{w}, \bar{c}\mathbf{v} + r\mathbf{w})$$

Since γ is positive-definite, this equation means that

$$\bar{c}\mathbf{v} + r\mathbf{w} = \mathbf{0}$$

Now, either $\mathbf{v} = \mathbf{w}$, one of the desired conclusions, or $\mathbf{v}$ and $\mathbf{w}$ are distinct vectors. It remains to show that if $\mathbf{v}$ and $\mathbf{w}$ are distinct, then they are linearly dependent. If $\mathbf{v} = \mathbf{0}$, then $\mathbf{v}$ and $\mathbf{w}$ are dependent, since any set of vectors containing $\mathbf{0}$ is dependent. Thus, suppose $\mathbf{v} \neq \mathbf{0}$. In this case $\gamma(\mathbf{v}, \mathbf{v}) \neq 0$, so that $-r \neq 0$ and, hence, $r \neq 0$. In this case, then, the above equation is a nontrivial linear combination of distinct vectors $\mathbf{v}$ and $\mathbf{w}$ with value $\mathbf{0}$. Thus, $\{\mathbf{v}, \mathbf{w}\}$ is dependent. Q.E.D.

(c) *The triangle inequality*

In plane geometry it is proved that the sum of the lengths of two sides of a triangle is greater than or equal to the length of the third side. In terms of the inner product γ, this becomes: For any $\mathbf{v}$, $\mathbf{w}$ in V

$$\gamma(\mathbf{v} + \mathbf{w}, \mathbf{v} + \mathbf{w})^{1/2} \leqq \gamma(\mathbf{v}, \mathbf{v})^{1/2} + \gamma(\mathbf{w}, \mathbf{w})^{1/2} \tag{3}$$

Figure 42 illustrates the situation.

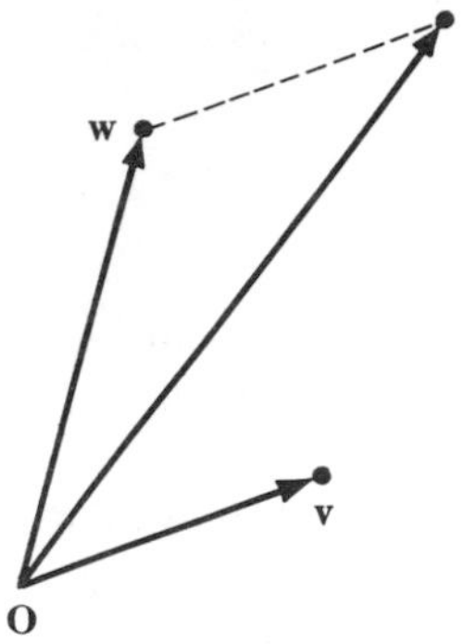

FIGURE 42

We prove (3) by squaring the right-hand side:

$$[\gamma(\mathbf{v}, \mathbf{v})^{1/2} + \gamma(\mathbf{w}, \mathbf{w})^{1/2}]^2 = \gamma(\mathbf{v}, \mathbf{v}) + \gamma(\mathbf{w}, \mathbf{w}) + 2\gamma(\mathbf{v}, \mathbf{v})^{1/2}\gamma(\mathbf{w}, \mathbf{w})^{1/2}$$

We then apply Schwarz's equality to the last term on the right:

$$[\gamma(\mathbf{v}, \mathbf{v})^{1/2} + \gamma(\mathbf{w}, \mathbf{w})^{1/2}]^2 \geqq \gamma(\mathbf{v}, \mathbf{v}) + \gamma(\mathbf{w}, \mathbf{w}) + 2[\gamma(\mathbf{v}, \mathbf{w})\overline{\gamma(\mathbf{v}, \mathbf{w})}]^{1/2}$$

Now, let $\gamma(\mathbf{v}, \mathbf{w}) = a + bi$. Then,

$$\gamma(\mathbf{v}, \mathbf{w})\overline{\gamma(\mathbf{v}, \mathbf{w})} = a^2 + b^2, \quad \text{and} \quad \gamma(\mathbf{v}, \mathbf{w}) + \overline{\gamma(\mathbf{v}, \mathbf{w})} = 2a$$

Clearly $2\sqrt{a^2 + b^2} \geqq 2\sqrt{a^2} \geqq 2a$, so that

$$2[\gamma(\mathbf{v}, \mathbf{w})\overline{\gamma(\mathbf{v}, \mathbf{w})}]^{1/2} \geqq \gamma(\mathbf{v}, \mathbf{w}) + \overline{\gamma(\mathbf{v}, \mathbf{w})}$$

Substituting the right-hand side in the preceding inequality, we get,

$$\begin{aligned}[\gamma(\mathbf{v}, \mathbf{v})^{1/2} + \gamma(\mathbf{w}, \mathbf{w})^{1/2}]^2 &\geqq \gamma(\mathbf{v}, \mathbf{v}) + \gamma(\mathbf{w}, \mathbf{w}) + \gamma(\mathbf{v}, \mathbf{w}) + \overline{\gamma(\mathbf{v}, \mathbf{w})} \\ &= \gamma(\mathbf{v} + \mathbf{w}, \mathbf{v} + \mathbf{w})\end{aligned}$$

The result now follows by taking the square root of both sides.

(d) *The parallelogram equality*

In Exercises 6.1.3, the reader showed that the sum of the squares of the lengths of the diagonals of a parallelogram in $\mathbf{R}^2$ equals the sum of the squares of the lengths of (all four of) its sides. In terms of γ, this equality becomes the following: For any $(\mathbf{v}, \mathbf{w}) \in V \times V$,

$$\gamma(\mathbf{v} + \mathbf{w}, \mathbf{v} + \mathbf{w}) + \gamma(\mathbf{v} - \mathbf{w}, \mathbf{v} - \mathbf{w}) = 2\gamma(\mathbf{v}, \mathbf{v}) + 2\gamma(\mathbf{w}, \mathbf{w}) \tag{4}$$

The reader may easily verify (4) for himself.

EXERCISES / 6.3

1. Recall that $\mathscr{C}[a, b]$, is the vector space of real-valued continuous functions on $[a, b]$. Define $\gamma : \mathscr{C}[a, b] \times \mathscr{C}[a, b] \to \mathbf{R}$ by the equation

$$\gamma(f, g) = \int_a^b f(x)g(x)\, dx,$$

[cf. 2.2. Example (c)]. Verify that γ is an inner product on $\mathscr{C}[a, b]$.
Prove that

$$\left(\int_a^b f(x)g(x)\, dx\right)^2 \leqq \left(\int_a^b f^2(x)\, dx\right)\left(\int_a^b g^2(x)\, dx\right),$$

for all f, g in $\mathscr{C}[a, b]$.

2. Given any complex numbers $a_1, \ldots, a_n, b_1, \ldots, b_n$, prove that

$$\left(\sum_{i=1}^n a_i\bar{b}_i\right)\left(\sum_{i=1}^n \bar{a}_i b_i\right) \leqq \left(\sum_{i=1}^n a_i\bar{a}_i\right)\left(\sum_{i=1}^n b_i\bar{b}_i\right)$$

3. Let V be a vector space over $F(=\mathbf{R}$ or $\mathbf{C})$ with an inner product γ, and suppose that $X = \{\mathbf{x}_1, \mathbf{x}_2, \mathbf{x}_3, \ldots\}$ is a countable orthonormal subset of V.

a. Prove that for any $\mathbf{v} \in V$ and any natural number n,

$$\gamma(\mathbf{v}, \mathbf{v}) \geqq \sum_{i=1}^n \gamma(\mathbf{v}, \mathbf{v}_i)\overline{\gamma(\mathbf{v}, \mathbf{v}_i)}$$

[*Hint:* Let $a_i = \gamma(\mathbf{v}, \mathbf{v}_i)$. For any n, let $\mathbf{w}_n = a_1\mathbf{v}_1 + \cdots + a_n\mathbf{v}_n$. Expand $\gamma(\mathbf{v} - \mathbf{w}_n, \mathbf{v} - \mathbf{w}_n)$.]

b. Prove that for any $\varepsilon > 0$, there is a natural number N_ε such that if $i > N_\varepsilon$ then

$$\gamma(\mathbf{v}, \mathbf{v}_i)\overline{\gamma(\mathbf{v}, \mathbf{v}_i)} < \varepsilon$$

Thus, $\lim_{i\to\infty}[\gamma(\mathbf{v}, \mathbf{v}_i)\overline{\gamma(\mathbf{v}, \mathbf{v}_i)}] = 0.$

c. Apply **a** to Example **c** of the previous section to show that for any $f \in \mathscr{C}[0, \pi]$,

$$\int_0^\pi f^2(x)\, dx \geqq \frac{2}{\pi}\sum_{k=1}^n \left(\int_0^\pi f(x)\sin kx\, dx\right)^2$$

4. Let V be a vector space over $F(=\mathbf{R}$ or $\mathbf{C})$, let γ be an inner product on V, and let $U_1, \ldots, U_k$ be vector subspaces of V such that $U_1 + \cdots + U_k = V$. Finally, suppose that V has finite or countable dimension and that $U_1, \ldots, U_{k-1}$ are finite-dimensional. Prove that V has a γ-orthonormal basis X which breaks up into disjoint subsets $X_1, X_2, \ldots, X_k$ (i.e., $X = X_1 \cup \cdots \cup X_k$, $X_i \cap X_j = \varnothing$, if $i \neq j$) such that X_i is a basis of U_i, $i = 1, \ldots, k$.

5. a. Let V and γ be as in Exercises 3 or 4, above, let $X = \{\mathbf{x}_1, \mathbf{x}_2, \ldots\}$ be a countable or finite γ-orthonormal subset of V, and let $\mathbf{v}$ be any vector in V. Consider $\gamma(\mathbf{v} - (a_1\mathbf{x}_1 + \cdots + a_k\mathbf{x}_k), \mathbf{v} - (a_1\mathbf{x}_1 + \cdots + a_k\mathbf{x}_k))$ [i.e., the square of the γ-length of $\mathbf{v} - (a_1\mathbf{x}_1 + \cdots + a_k\mathbf{x}_k)$], for all linear combinations $a_1\mathbf{x}_1 + \cdots + a_k\mathbf{x}_k$ of $\mathbf{x}_1, \ldots, \mathbf{x}_k$ (k fixed). Show that the linear combination of $\mathbf{x}_1, \ldots, \mathbf{x}_k$ for which the γ-length is the smallest is $a_1\mathbf{x}_1 + \cdots + a_k\mathbf{x}_k$, where $a_i = \gamma(\mathbf{v}, \mathbf{x}_i)$, $i = 1, \ldots, k$ (cf. Exercises 6.1.**10**).

The numbers $a_1, a_2, a_3, \ldots$ are called the *Fourier coefficients* of $\mathbf{v}$ with respect to (γ and) $\{\mathbf{x}_1, \mathbf{x}_2, \mathbf{x}_3, \ldots\}$. These play an important role in advanced analysis.

b. Use **3.a** to show that

$$\gamma(\mathbf{v}, \mathbf{v}) \geqq \sum_{i=1}^{n} a_i\bar{a}_i$$

(and, thus, that the series $\sum_{i=1}^{\infty} a_i\bar{a}_i$ converges).

c. Let $V = C[0, \pi]$, $\mathbf{v} = \bar{1}$, $X = \{\sin x, \sin 2x, \sin 3x, \ldots\}$ and $\gamma = \delta$ of Example **c** of the previous section. Calculate the a_i in this case.

d. Let $V = \mathbf{R}^n$, $X = \{\mathbf{x}_1, \ldots, \mathbf{x}_k\}$, any orthonormal subset of V with respect to the standard inner product β on V (see Section 2.2, Example **b** for the definition of the standard inner product on V), and let $\mathbf{v}$ be any vector in V. Assume that $\dim[\operatorname{span}_V(X)] < n$ and that $\mathbf{v} \notin \operatorname{span}_V(X)$. Show that $\mathbf{v} - (a_1\mathbf{x}_1 + \cdots + a_k\mathbf{x}_k)$ is β-orthogonal to $\operatorname{span}_V(X)$ (where $a_1, \ldots, a_k$ are the Fourier coefficients of $\mathbf{v}$ with respect to β and $\mathbf{x}_1, \ldots, \mathbf{x}_k$). Show that $a_1\mathbf{x}_1 + \cdots + a_k\mathbf{x}_k$ is the vector in span_V (X) closest to $\mathbf{v}$ (See Exercises 6.1.**10**.).

Thus, the shortest distance between $\mathbf{v}$ and points of $\operatorname{span}_V(X)$ is the length of the perpendicular dropped from $\mathbf{v}$ to $\operatorname{span}_V(X)$.

3 / INNER PRODUCT SPACES

3.1 Definitions and Basic Properties

Definition 6.4

An inner product space is a vector space V over $F(= \mathbf{R}$ or $\mathbf{C})$ together with a fixed inner product γ on V. We shall, generally, omit explicit reference to γ. Thus, such terms as "γ-orthonormal," "γ-orthogonal," and so on, will become, simply, "orthonormal," "orthogonal," and so on. Moreover, we shall refer to the inner product space as V, again omitting explicit reference to γ. If we wish to refer to only the vector-space structure of V, and not to the additional inner product structure, then we shall refer to it as the underlying vector space of the inner product space V. Finally, it will be useful to replace the symbol "γ" by the following notation:

For any $\mathbf{v}, \mathbf{w} \in V$, denote $\gamma(\mathbf{v}, \mathbf{w})$ by $[\mathbf{v}, \mathbf{w}]$ and let $\gamma(\mathbf{v}, \mathbf{v})^{1/2} = \|\mathbf{v}\|$.

(Sometimes we shall affix a subscript "V" to these symbols to indicate their dependence on V.)

The usual vector-space terminology will apply to inner product spaces. Thus, for example, a *subspace* U of an inner product space V is a vector subspace of the underlying vector space of V *together with* the inner product of V restricted to $U \times U$. This restriction, it is easy to see, is an inner product on U. Therefore, a subspace of an inner product space is an inner product space.

Also, if $V_1, \ldots, V_n$ are inner product spaces (over the same field), then, define a function on $(V_1 \times \cdots \times V_n) \times (V_1 \times \cdots \times V_n)$ to F as follows:

$$[(\mathbf{v}_1, \ldots, \mathbf{v}_n), (\mathbf{v}'_1, \ldots, \mathbf{v}'_n)]_{V_1 \times \cdots \times V_n} = [\mathbf{v}_1, \mathbf{v}'_1]_{V_1} + \cdots + [\mathbf{v}_n, \mathbf{v}'_n]_{V_n}$$

The reader should verify that $[\ ,\ ]_{V_1 \times \cdots \times V_n}$ is an inner product on $V_1 \times \cdots \times V_n$. The vector space $V_1 \times \cdots \times V_n$ together with this inner product is, therefore, an inner product space, which we call the product of the inner product spaces $V_1, \ldots, V_n$.

We shall say that an inner product space is finite-dimensional, trivial, or nontrivial if the same can be truthfully said about its underlying vector space. All of our previous terminology involving linear spans, linear combinations, linear dependence and independence, bases, and dimension apply here as before.

It is important that the reader appreciate the difference between the viewpoint taken in this section and that taken in the preceding sections of this chapter. Earlier, the objects of our study were vector spaces, and we considered certain functions (inner products), which could serve as analogs of the angle and distance measuring functions of 1.1 and 1.2. Any such inner product would do, and, in general (at least for finite and countable dimensional vector spaces), there were many (infinitely many) that would do. These, however, were all considered to be *extrinsic* to the structure of our main objects of interest, the vector spaces. After all, vector spaces are simply sets, together with certain special operations: No geometric notions are inherent here.

In this section, we focus our attention no longer on mere vector spaces, but on vector spaces intrinsic to which are fixed notions of distance and direction: namely, inner product spaces.

Just as vector spaces are sets together with additional structure (i.e., certain operations)—and, thus, they are thought of in a way quite distinct from the way that sets are thought of—so are inner product spaces vector spaces *together* with additional structure.

Definition 6.5

Let V and W be inner product spaces over F. A linear transformation of the underlying vector spaces

$$T : V \to W$$

is said to preserve the inner product structure of V if, for all $(\mathbf{v}_1, \mathbf{v}_2) \in V \times V$,

$$[\mathbf{v}_1, \mathbf{v}_2]_V = [T(\mathbf{v}_1), T(\mathbf{v}_2)]_W$$

We shall say that a linear transformation whose domain and range are inner product spaces is an inner product transformation if it preserves the inner product structure of its domain.

If V is an inner product space over **R**, *then an inner product transformation $T: V \to V$ is often called orthogonal.*

If V is an inner product space over **C**, *then an inner product transformation $T: V \to V$ is often called unitary.*

*An inner product transformation that is a vector-space isomorphism is called an isometry.*** *If V and W are inner product spaces and $T: V \to W$ is an isometry, then we say that V is isometric to W.* The reader should be able to prove the following analogue of a proposition in Chapter 4.

Proposition 6.9

Let U, V, W be inner product spaces over F, and let $S: U \to V$, $T: V \to W$ be isometries. Then: (1) *$T \circ S$ is an isometry;* (2) *S^{-1} is an isometry:* (3) *I_U is an isometry.*

Thus: (1) *if U is isometric to V, and if V is isometric to W, then U is isometric to W;* (2) *if U is isometric to V, then V is isometric to U;* (3) *U is isometric to itself.*

Thus, inner product spaces may be partitioned into isometry classes, just as vector spaces are partitioned into isomorphism classes.

Proposition 6.10

*Every finite-dimensional vector space over $F(=$***R** *or* **C**$)$ *is the underlying space of an inner product space. If two finite-dimensional inner product spaces have isomorphic underlying vector spaces, then they are isometric.*

Thus, among finite-dimensional vector spaces, there is a 1–1 *correspondence between isomorphism classes of vector spaces and isometry classes of inner product spaces. In particular, all n-dimensional inner product spaces are isometric to F^n endowed with the standard inner product* [see 2.2, *Example* (d)].

Proof

The first statement of the proposition follows immediately from Corollary to Proposition 6.5.

To prove the second statement, suppose that V and W are inner product spaces with isomorphic underlying vector spaces (over F). Thus, they both have the same dimension, say, n. If $n = 0$, the result is obvious. If not, let $\{\mathbf{v}_1, \ldots, \mathbf{v}_n\}$ and $\{\mathbf{w}_1, \ldots, \mathbf{w}_n\}$ be orthonormal bases of V and W, respectively. Define the isomorphism $T: V \to W$ by the equations $T(\mathbf{v}_i) = \mathbf{w}_i$, $i = 1, \ldots, n$. We show that T preserves the inner product structure of V.

** The word "isometry" is used to indicate that the range and domain of the transformation have the same measurement-structure. Isometries of inner product spaces play the same role as isomorphisms of vector spaces.

Choose any $\mathbf{v} = a_1\mathbf{v}_1 + \cdots + a_n\mathbf{v}_n$ and $\mathbf{v}' = a_1'\mathbf{v}_1 + \cdots + a_n'\mathbf{v}_n$ in V. Then,

$$[\mathbf{v}, \mathbf{v}']_V = [a_1\mathbf{v}_1 + \cdots + a_n\mathbf{v}_n, a_1'\mathbf{v}_1 + \cdots + a_n'\mathbf{v}_n]_V = \sum_{i=1}^{n} a_i\bar{a}_i'$$

$$= [a_1\mathbf{w}_1 + \cdots + a_n\mathbf{w}_n, a_1'\mathbf{w}_1 + \cdots + a_n'\mathbf{w}_n]_W = [T(\mathbf{v}), T(\mathbf{v}')]_W$$

Thus, T is an isometry.

The proof of the last statement of the proposition is left to the reader. Q.E.D.

Proposition 6.11

Let V and W be inner product spaces, and let $T: V \to W$ be an inner product transformation. Then, T is 1–1. Thus, an onto inner product transformation is an isometry.

Proof

Suppose that $T(\mathbf{v}) = \mathbf{0}$, for some $\mathbf{v} \in V$. Then,

$$[\mathbf{v}, \mathbf{v}]_V = [T(\mathbf{v}), T(\mathbf{v})]_W = [\mathbf{0}, \mathbf{0}]_W = 0$$

Since $[\ ,\ ]_V$ is positive-definite, $\mathbf{v} = \mathbf{0}$. Thus $\mathcal{N}_T = \{\mathbf{0}\}$, so that T is 1–1. Q.E.D.

Proposition 6.12**

Let V and W be as in the preceding proposition, let $S: V \to W$ be an inner product transformation, $T: V \to W$ a 1–1 linear transformation (of the underlying vector spaces), X an orthonormal set of vectors of V, and Y any orthonormal basis of V (we assume such exists).‡ Then: (1) *$S(X)$ is orthonormal;* (2) *If $T(Y)$ is orthonormal, then T is an inner product transformation.*

Proof

(1) For any $\mathbf{x}$, $\mathbf{x}'$ in X

$$[S(\mathbf{x}), S(\mathbf{x}')]_W = [\mathbf{x}, \mathbf{x}']_V = \begin{cases} 0, & \mathbf{x} \neq \mathbf{x}' \\ 1, & \mathbf{x} = \mathbf{x}', \end{cases}$$

so that $S(X)$ is orthonormal.

(2) For any $\mathbf{v} = a_1\mathbf{y}_1 + \cdots + a_n\mathbf{y}_n$ and $\mathbf{v}' = a_1'\mathbf{y}_1 + \cdots + a_n'\mathbf{y}_n$, where $\mathbf{y}_i \in Y$

$$[T(\mathbf{v}), T(\mathbf{v}')]_W = \sum_{i=1}^{n} \sum_{j=1}^{n} a_i\bar{a}_j'[T(\mathbf{y}_i), T(\mathbf{y}_j)]_W$$

$$= a_1\bar{a}_1' + \cdots + a_n\bar{a}_n'$$

$$= [\mathbf{v}, \mathbf{v}']_V$$

** This proposition explains the common use of the term "orthogonal transformation" for inner product transformation.

‡ For some inner product spaces there are no orthonormal bases. We assume that V is not one of these. Of course, if V has finite or countable dimension, then it has an orthonormal basis, by Proposition 6.6.

This shows that T is an inner product transformation. Q.E.D.

The above proposition has the following consequence. Let V be an inner product space with *finite orthonormal basis* $X = \{\mathbf{x}_1, \ldots, \mathbf{x}_n\}$, and let $T: V \to V$ be a linear transformation. Consider the columns of the $n \times n$ matrix $\mathscr{A}_{X,X}(T) = (a_{ij})$:

$$\begin{pmatrix} a_{11} \\ \vdots \\ a_{n1} \end{pmatrix}, \ldots, \begin{pmatrix} a_{1j} \\ \vdots \\ a_{nj} \end{pmatrix}, \ldots, \begin{pmatrix} a_{1n} \\ \vdots \\ a_{nn} \end{pmatrix}$$

These columns are just the n-tuples of coefficients in the linear combinations of vectors of X with values $T(\mathbf{x}_1), T(\mathbf{x}_2), \ldots, T(\mathbf{x}_n)$, respectively. According to the above proposition, T is an inner product transformation if and only if these vectors form an orthonormal set. Thus, T is an inner product transformation if and only if

$$[T(\mathbf{x}_r), T(\mathbf{x}_s)]_V = \begin{cases} 0, \text{ if } r \neq s \\ 1, \text{ if } r \neq s \end{cases}$$

In terms of the coefficients a_{ij}, this condition becomes

$$\sum_{i=1}^{n} a_{ir}\bar{a}_{is} = \begin{cases} 0, \text{ if } r \neq s, \\ 1, \text{ if } r = s \end{cases} \tag{1}$$

Thus, T is an inner product transformation, if and only if its matrix $\mathscr{A}_{X,X}(T) = (a_{ij})$ satisfies (1). Those $n \times n$ matrices over F satisfying (1) are called *orthogonal matrices*, if $F = \mathbf{R}$, and *unitary matrices*, if $F = \mathbf{C}$.

Now we list the important geometric results of previous sections, translating them into the terminology introduced in this section.

(a) *Gram-Schmidt Orthogonalization Theorem:* Let V be an inner product space of finite or countable dimension. Then, for every basis X of V, there is an orthonormal basis Y of V similar to X. Moreover, Y is uniquely determined up to unit scalar multiples (see Exercises 6.2.7 for this last statement).

(b) Let V be any inner product space and let $\{\mathbf{v}_1, \ldots, \mathbf{v}_n\}$ be any orthonormal set of vectors in V. Then, for every $\mathbf{v} \in \text{span}_V(\{\mathbf{v}_1, \ldots, \mathbf{v}_n\})$,

$$\text{(i)} \quad \mathbf{v} = [\mathbf{v}, \mathbf{v}_1]\mathbf{v}_1 + \cdots + [\mathbf{v}, \mathbf{v}_n]\mathbf{v}_n$$

$$\text{(ii)} \quad \|\mathbf{v}\|^2 = [\mathbf{v}, \mathbf{v}_1]\overline{[\mathbf{v}, \mathbf{v}_1]} + \cdots + [\mathbf{v}, \mathbf{v}_n]\overline{[\mathbf{v}, \mathbf{v}_n]}$$

Bessel's Equality

$$\text{(iii)} \quad \|\mathbf{v}_1 + \cdots + \mathbf{v}_n\|^2 = \|\mathbf{v}_1\|^2 + \cdots + \|\mathbf{v}_n\|^2$$

Pythagorean Theorem

This last equation holds even when $\{\mathbf{v}_1, \ldots, \mathbf{v}_n\}$ is an arbitrary *orthogonal* set, which may or may not be normal.

(c) Let V be any inner product space, and let **v** and **w** be any vectors in V. Then,

(i) $[\mathbf{v}, \mathbf{w}]\overline{[\mathbf{v}, \mathbf{w}]} \leqq \|\mathbf{v}\|^2 \, \|\mathbf{w}\|^2$ *Schwarz's Inequality*

(ii) $\|\mathbf{v} + \mathbf{w}\| \leqq \|\mathbf{v}\| + \|w\|$ *Triangle Inequality*

(iii) $\|\mathbf{v} + \mathbf{w}\|^2 + \|\mathbf{v} - \mathbf{w}\|^2 = 2(\|\mathbf{v}\|^2 + \|w\|^2)$ *Parallelogram Equality*

To complete our description of inner product spaces, we define the important notion of *orthogonal complement.*

Definition 6.6

Let V be an inner product space, and let X be any subset of V. The orthogonal complement of X, written $X^{\perp}$ (sometimes read as "X perp") is the set of all $\mathbf{v} \in V$ such that $\mathbf{v}$ is orthogonal to every $\mathbf{x} \in X$.

Proposition 6.13

Let V and X be as above. Then:

(1) *$X^{\perp}$ is a vector subspace of V.*
(2) *If $X \subset Y$, then $Y^{\perp} \subset X^{\perp}$.*
(3) *$X^{\perp} = [span_V(X)]^{\perp}$.*
(4) *$(X^{\perp})^{\perp} \supset span_V(X)$.*
(5) *$X^{\perp} \cap span_V(X) = \{\mathbf{0}\}$.*
(6) *If $span_V(X)$ is finite-dimensional, then*

$$V = X^{\perp} \oplus span_V(X)$$

(7) *If V is finite-dimensional, then $(X^{\perp})^{\perp} = span_V(X)$.*

Remark: If X is a vector subspace of V, then $X = \text{span}_V(X)$ and some of the above statements assume a simpler form. We let the reader make his own translation.

Proof

Assume, first, that $X \neq \varnothing$.

(1) Clearly $[\mathbf{0}, \mathbf{x}] = 0$, for every $\mathbf{x} \in X$, so that $\mathbf{0} \in X^{\perp}$, which is, therefore, nonempty. Choose any **v**, **w** in $X^{\perp}$ and any $a \in F$. Then, for all $\mathbf{x} \in X$,

$$[\mathbf{v} + \mathbf{w}, \mathbf{x}] = [\mathbf{v}, \mathbf{x}] + [\mathbf{w}, \mathbf{x}] = 0 + 0 = 0$$

and

$$[a\mathbf{v}, \mathbf{x}] = a[\mathbf{v}, \mathbf{x}] = a \cdot 0 = 0,$$

so that $\mathbf{v} + \mathbf{w}$ and $a\mathbf{v}$ are in $X^{\perp}$.

(2) If $X \subset Y$ every vector orthogonal to all **y**'s will be orthogonal to all **x**'s.

(3) Since $X \subset \text{span}_V(X)$, we obtain, from (2), the inclusion

$$[\text{span}_V(X)]^\perp \subset X^\perp.$$

Choose any $\mathbf{w} \in X^\perp$, any $\mathbf{x}_1, \ldots, \mathbf{x}_n$ in X, and any $a_1, \ldots, a_n$ in F. Then,

$$[\mathbf{w}, a_1\mathbf{x}_1 + \cdots + a_n\mathbf{x}_n] = \bar{a}_1[\mathbf{w}, \mathbf{x}_1] + \cdots + \bar{a}_n[\mathbf{w}, \mathbf{x}_n] = \bar{a}_1 \cdot 0 + \cdots + \bar{a}_n \cdot 0 = 0$$

Thus, $\mathbf{w}$ is orthogonal to every member of $\text{span}_V(X)$, or $\mathbf{w} \in [\text{span}_V(X)]^\perp$. This proves that the above inclusion relation may be replaced by an equality.

(4) Choose any $\mathbf{x} \in X$. Every $\mathbf{w} \in X^\perp$ is orthogonal to it. Thus, $\mathbf{x} \in (X^\perp)^\perp$, which proves that $X \subset (X^\perp)^\perp$. Since $(X^\perp)^\perp$ is a vector subspace of V containing X, it follows that $\text{span}_V(X) \subset (X^\perp)^\perp$, as desired.

(5) Choose any $\mathbf{v} \in \text{span}_V(X) \cap X^\perp$. Since $X^\perp = [\text{span}_V(X)]^\perp$, $\mathbf{v} \in \text{span}_V(X)$ and $\mathbf{v} \in [\text{span}_V(X)]^\perp$. Thus, $\mathbf{v}$ is orthogonal to itself, being both in $\text{span}_V(X)$ and orthogonal to *every* member of $\text{span}_V(X)$. That is, $[\mathbf{v}, \mathbf{v}] = 0$. Since an inner product is positive-definite, $\mathbf{v} = \mathbf{0}$.

(6) It suffices, by (5), to show that $X^\perp + \text{span}_V(X) = V$. Since $\text{span}_V(X)$ is a finite-dimensional subspace of an inner product space, it is either trivial or has an orthonormal basis. If it is trivial, then $X = \{\mathbf{0}\}$ (since we are assuming that $X \neq \varnothing$) and, since *every* $\mathbf{v} \in V$ is orthogonal to $\mathbf{0}$, $X^\perp = V$. Thus, in this case, the desired result is true. Suppose it is nontrivial and let $\{\mathbf{y}_1, \ldots, \mathbf{y}_k\}$ be its orthonormal basis.

Choose any $\mathbf{v} \in V$, let $a_i = [\mathbf{v}, \mathbf{y}_i]$, and let $\mathbf{w} = a_1\mathbf{y}_1 + \cdots + a_k\mathbf{y}_k$. Finally, let $\mathbf{u} = \mathbf{v} - \mathbf{w}$. Then,

$$[\mathbf{u}, \mathbf{y}_i] = [\mathbf{v}, \mathbf{y}_i] - [\mathbf{w}, \mathbf{y}_i] = a_i - a_i = 0,$$

$i = 1, \ldots, k$, so that $\mathbf{u} \in \{\mathbf{y}_1, \ldots, \mathbf{y}_k\}^\perp$

$$= \text{span}_V(\{\mathbf{y}_1, \ldots, \mathbf{y}_k\})^\perp, \text{ by (5)},$$
$$= [\text{span}_V(X)]^\perp = X^\perp$$

Thus, $\mathbf{v} = \mathbf{w} + \mathbf{u}$, where $\mathbf{w} \in \text{span}_V(X)$ and $\mathbf{u} \in X^\perp$. Since $\mathbf{v}$ was chosen arbitrarily, this means that

$$V = \text{span}_V(X) + X^\perp$$

(7) If V is finite-dimensional, then so is $\text{span}_V(X)$, so that $X^\perp + \text{span}_V(X) = V$. Thus,

$$\dim X^\perp = \dim V - \dim[\text{span}_V(X)]$$

Substitute $X^\perp$ for X in this equality:

$$\begin{aligned}
\dim(X^\perp)^\perp &= \dim V - \dim[\text{span}_V(X^\perp)] \\
&= \dim V - \dim X^\perp \\
&= \dim V - (\dim V - \dim[\text{span}_V(X)] \\
&= \dim[\text{span}_V(X)]
\end{aligned}$$

The conclusion now follows from this dimension equality and (4).

Suppose now that $X = \varnothing$. Then *every* $\mathbf{v} \in V$ is orthogonal to "every" $\mathbf{x} \in X$, since there are no $\mathbf{x} \in X$ to which $\mathbf{v}$ can fail to be orthogonal. Thus, $X^\perp = V$, which is certainly a vector subspace of V. This proves (1). (2) is proved as before. To prove (3), note that $\text{span}_V(X) = \{\mathbf{0}\}$, and every $\mathbf{v} \in V$ is orthogonal to $\mathbf{0}$. Thus, $X^\perp = V = [\text{span}_V(X)]^\perp$. For (4), note that no nonzero vector can be orthogonal to all $\mathbf{v} \in V = X^\perp$, for then it would have to be orthogonal to itself, which is impossible (inner products being positive-definite). This implies that $(X^\perp)^\perp = V^\perp = \{\mathbf{0}\} = \text{span}_V(X)$, proving (4). To prove (5) note that the intersection on the left is a vector subspace of V, hence containing $\mathbf{0}$. But $\text{span}_V(X) = \{\mathbf{0}\}$, so that equality must hold. (6) and (7) follow trivially. Q.E.D.

To illustrate the notion of orthogonal complement we consider $\mathbf{R}^3$ (with the standard inner product) and $X = \{(0, 0, 1)\}$. Then, $X^\perp = \text{span}((1, 0, 0), (0, 1, 0))$, and $(X^\perp)^\perp = \text{span}(\{(0, 0, 1)\})$. Figure 43 illustrates the example.

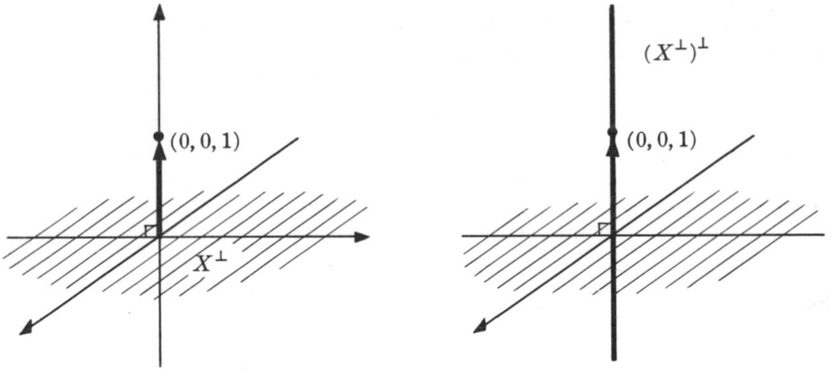

FIGURE 43

EXERCISES / 6.4

1. **a.** Prove that an $n \times n$ matrix (a_{ij}) over $F(= \mathbf{R}$ or $\mathbf{C})$ is orthogonal or unitary if and only if

$$(b_{ij}) \cdot (a_{ij}) = (1)_n,$$

where $b_{ij} = \bar{a}_{ji}$, $i = 1, \ldots, n$ $j = 1, \ldots, m$, and where $(1)_n$ is the $n \times n$ unit matrix (i.e., $(1)_n = (c_{ij})$, where $c_{ij} = 0$ if $i \neq j$, and $c_{ij} = 1$ if $i = j$).

b. Use **a** to prove that (a_{ij}) is orthogonal or unitary if and only if $(b_{ij}) = (a_{ij})^{-1}$, where b_{ij} is as in **a**.

c. Use **b** to show that (a_{ij}) is orthogonal or unitary if and only if

$$(a_{ij}) \cdot (b_{ij}) = (1)_n,$$

where b_{ij} is as in **a**.

d. Use **c** to show that (a_{ij}) is orthogonal or unitary, if and only if

$$\sum_{j=1}^{n} a_{rj}a_{sj} = \begin{cases} 0, & \text{if } r \neq s \\ 1, & \text{if } r = s \end{cases}$$

Contrast this with equation (1) of the text. This equation implies that (a_{ij}) is orthogonal or unitary if and only if its *rows* form an orthonormal subset of n distinct vectors of F^n (with respect to the standard inner product of F^n).

2. Consider $\mathbf{R}^3$ equipped with the standard inner product. Which of the following matrices are orthogonal?

a. $\begin{pmatrix} 0 & 1 & 0 \\ 1 & 0 & 0 \\ 0 & 0 & 1 \end{pmatrix}$

b. $\begin{pmatrix} 1 & 0 & 0 \\ 0 & 1 & 0 \\ 0 & 0 & 1 \end{pmatrix}$

c. $\begin{pmatrix} 1/\sqrt{2} & 0 & 1/\sqrt{2} \\ 0 & 1 & 0 \\ -1/\sqrt{2} & 0 & 1/\sqrt{2} \end{pmatrix}$

d. $\begin{pmatrix} 1 & 0 & -1 \\ 0 & 1 & 0 \\ 1 & 0 & 1 \end{pmatrix}$

e. $\begin{pmatrix} 1/2 & 3/2 & 0 \\ 1/2 & 3/2 & 0 \\ 0 & 0 & 0 \end{pmatrix}$

f. $\begin{pmatrix} \cos\theta & \sin\theta & 0 \\ -\sin\theta & \cos\theta & 0 \\ 0 & 0 & 1 \end{pmatrix}$, for any real number θ.

3.* **a.** Let $\mathbf{R}^2$ be equipped with the standard inner product $\alpha:\mathbf{R}^2 \times \mathbf{R}^2 \to \mathbf{R}$. Let $R_\theta:\mathbf{R}^2 \to \mathbf{R}^2$ be the linear transformation obtained by rotating through the angle θ. Prove that R_θ is an inner product transformation.
What is the matrix of R_θ with respect to the standard basis of $\mathbf{R}^2$?

b. Show (using **1**, above) that if $T:\mathbf{R}^2 \to \mathbf{R}$ is an inner product transformation and if $\det T = 1$, then the matrix of T with respect to the standard basis of $\mathbf{R}^2$ is of the form,

$$\begin{pmatrix} a & -b \\ b & a \end{pmatrix}, \qquad a^2 + b^2 = 1$$

Thus, show that T is a rotation through some angle θ.

4. Let $F = \mathbf{R}$ or $\mathbf{C}$, and let (a_{ij}) be any $n \times n$ matrix over F.

a. Prove that $det(\overline{a_{ij}}) = \overline{det(a_{ij})}$.

b. Recall that $det(a_{ij})^t = det(a_{ij})$, where $(a_{ij})^t$ is the *transpose* of (a_{ij}). The matrix (b_{ij}) of **1.a** above is $(\overline{a_{ij}})^t$, the *conjugate-transpose* of (a_{ij}). Prove that if (a_{ij}) is orthogonal or unitary, then $det(b_{ij})$ equals both $[det(a_{ij})]^{-1}$ and $\overline{det(a_{ij})}$.

c. Let $det(a_{ij}) = c + di$. Prove that if (a_{ij}) is orthogonal or unitary, then $c^2 + d^2 = 1$. (*Hint:* Use **b.**)

Thus, $det\,(a_{ij})$, if complex, is a number on the unit circle around 0 in $\mathbf{C}$, and if real, is ± 1.

5. Consider the vector space over **R** of all continuous real-valued functions on the closed interval [0, 1]: $\mathscr{C}[0, 1]$. Let $\gamma: \mathscr{C}[0, 1] \times \mathscr{C}[0, 1] \to R$ be given by

$$\gamma(f, g) = \int_0^1 f(x)g(x)\, dx$$

γ is an inner product on $\mathscr{C}[0, 1]$. Consider the polynomial functions $f_n: [0, 1] \to \mathbf{R}$ given by $f_n(x) = x^n$, $n = 0, 1, 2, 3, \ldots$. For short, we denote f_n by x^n.

a. Construct a γ-orthonormal set $g_0, g_1\, g_2, \ldots \in \mathscr{C}[0, 1]$ similar to $x^0, x^1, x^2, \ldots$ Give the general expression for g_n.

b. Show that $\text{span}(\{g_0, g_1, \ldots\}) = \text{span}(\{x^0, x^1, x^2, \ldots\})$ = the subset of $\mathscr{C}[0, 1]$ consisting of all polynomial functions from [0, 1] to **R**.

c. Let $f: [0, 1] \to \mathbf{R}$ be defined as follows:

$$f(x) = \begin{cases} x \sin(1/x), & x \neq 0 \\ 0\quad, & x = 0 \end{cases}$$

It can be proved that f is a continuous function on [0, 1]. (The reader should try to prove this if he has the appropriate background.) Thus, $f \in \mathscr{C}[0, 1]$. Why is f *not* in $\text{span}(\{g_0, g_1, \ldots\})$?

This example shows than $\text{span}(\{g_0, g_1, \ldots\}) \neq \mathscr{C}[0, 1]$.

d. Consider the following theorem:

Choose any $h \in \mathscr{C}[0, 1]$. *If* $\int_0^1 h(x)p(x)\, dx = 0$, *for all polynomial functions* $p(x)$ *in* $\mathscr{C}[0, 1]$, *then* $h = \bar{0}$, *the constantly zero function.*

Use this result to show that

$$(\text{span}(\{g_0, g_1, \ldots\}))^\perp = \{\bar{0}\}$$

e. Use **d** to show that $([\text{span}(\{g_0, g_1, \ldots,\})]^\perp)^\perp = \mathscr{C}[0, 1]$.

Thus, combining **c** and **e**, we obtain an example of an inner product space V, a *proper* subspace U such that

$$(U^\perp)^\perp \neq U$$

6. **a.** Let V be any n-dimensional vector space, $n \geqq 1$, over $F(=\mathbf{R}$ or $\mathbf{C})$, and let $\beta: V \times V \to F$ be any conjugate-bilinear, conjugate-symmetric form. Choose any $\mathbf{v} \in V$ and let $U_\mathbf{v} = \{\mathbf{w} \in V \mid \beta(\mathbf{v}, \mathbf{w}) = 0\}$. Prove that U is a vector subspace of V.

b. Prove that if $\beta(\mathbf{v}, \mathbf{v}) = 0$, for all $\mathbf{v} \in V$, then $\beta(\mathbf{v}, \mathbf{w}) = 0$, for all $(\mathbf{v}, \mathbf{w}) \in V \times V$. (*Hint:* Use the "polarization" equality of Exercises 6.2.**10**.)

c. We shall say that β is *trivial* if $\beta(\mathbf{v}, \mathbf{w}) = 0$ for all $(\mathbf{v}, \mathbf{w}) \in V \times V$. Otherwise, it is *nontrivial*. Suppose that β is nontrivial. Show that there is at least one vector $\mathbf{v} \in V$, such that

$$\dim U_\mathbf{v} < \dim V$$

That is, show that for at least one $\mathbf{v} \in V$, $U_\mathbf{v}$ does not contain $\mathbf{v}$ (where $U_\mathbf{v}$ is as in **a**).

d. Let $\mathbf{v}$ be as in **c**. For any $\mathbf{w} \in V$, let $\mathbf{u} = \mathbf{w} - [\beta(\mathbf{v}, \mathbf{w})/\beta(\mathbf{v}, \mathbf{v})]\mathbf{v}$. (Why is $\beta(\mathbf{v}, \mathbf{v}) \neq 0$?) Show that $\mathbf{u} \in U_\mathbf{v}$. Thus $\mathbf{w} = \mathbf{u} + [\beta(\mathbf{v}, \mathbf{w})/\beta(\mathbf{v}, \mathbf{v})]\mathbf{v}$. Conclude from this that

$$\text{span}(\{\mathbf{v}\}) + U_\mathbf{v} = V$$

e. Use **c** and **d** to prove that for **v** as in **c**, dim $U_{\mathbf{v}} = (\dim V) - 1$.
f. Prove that if $\{\mathbf{y}_1, \ldots, \mathbf{y}_k\}$ is any basis of $U_{\mathbf{v}}$, then $\{\mathbf{y}_1, \ldots, \mathbf{y}_k, \mathbf{v}\}$ is a basis of V.

7. This exercise is a sequel to **6**. Here, we use the results of **6** to show that if V and $\beta: V \times V \to F$ are as in **6**, then there is a basis of V, say $\{\mathbf{v}_1, \ldots \mathbf{v}_n\}$, such that

$$\beta(\mathbf{v}_i, \mathbf{v}_j) = \begin{cases} 0, & \text{, if } i \neq j \\ -1, 0, \text{ or } 1, & \text{if } i = j \end{cases}$$

The proof uses the inductive method.

a. Suppose dim $V = 1$. Prove the above result directly.

b. Suppose that the result is true for all vector spaces over F of dimension k and for all conjugate-symmetric, conjugate-bilinear forms defined on these vector spaces. Let V and β be as above, and suppose that dim $V = k + 1$. Show that if β is trivial, then the desired result is immediate. Suppose that β is nontrivial, find a **v** as in **6.c**, and apply the inductive hypothesis to $U_{\mathbf{v}}$ to obtain a basis $\{\mathbf{y}_1, \ldots, \mathbf{y}_k, \mathbf{v}\}$ of V such that $\beta(\mathbf{y}_i, \mathbf{y}_j) = 0$, if $i \neq j$, and $\beta(\mathbf{y}_i, \mathbf{v}) = 0$, for all $i = 1, \ldots, k$.

c. Show that a basis of the desired kind can be obtained from $\{\mathbf{y}_1, \ldots, \mathbf{y}_k, \mathbf{v}\}$ by multiplying these vectors by suitable scalars.

Thus, by the Axiom of Induction, the result holds for all $n \geqq 1$.

d. Show that if $F = \mathbf{C}$, the above result can be improved as follows: There exists a basis $\{\mathbf{v}_1, \ldots, \mathbf{v}_n\}$ of V such that

$$\beta(\mathbf{v}_i, \mathbf{v}_j) = \begin{cases} 0, & \text{if } i \neq j \\ 0 \text{ or } 1, & \text{if } i = j \end{cases}$$

Thus, for every conjugate-symmetric, conjugate-bilinear $\beta: V \times V \to F$, there is a basis $\{\mathbf{v}_1, \ldots, \mathbf{v}_n\}$ such that for any $\mathbf{x} = x_1\mathbf{v}_1 + \cdots + x_n\mathbf{v}_n$ and $\mathbf{y} = y_1\mathbf{v}_1 + \cdots + y_n\mathbf{v}_n$,

$$\beta(\mathbf{x}, \mathbf{y}) = \pm x_{i_1}\bar{y}_{i_1} \pm x_{i_2}\bar{y}_{i_2} \pm \cdots \pm x_{i_r}\bar{y}_{i_r},$$

where $i_1, \ldots, i_r$ are those integers i between and 1 and n for which $\beta(\mathbf{v}_i, \mathbf{v}_i) \neq 0$. This particularly simple form that the summation expression for β takes is known as a *canonical form* for β.** The basis $\{\mathbf{v}_1, \ldots, \mathbf{v}_n\}$ is known as a *canonical basis* for β.

If $F = \mathbf{C}$, then negative signs may be eliminated in the above expression; if $F = \mathbf{R}$, conjugation may be eliminated.

Although there are many canonical bases for the same β, they all have the following in common (for $F = \mathbf{R}$): the number of i for which $\beta(\mathbf{v}_i, \mathbf{v}_i) = 0$, the number of i for which $\beta(\mathbf{v}_i, \mathbf{v}_i) = 1$, and the number of i for which $\beta(\mathbf{v}_1, \mathbf{v}_i) = -1$ are independent of the choice of canonical basis $\{\mathbf{v}_1, \ldots, \mathbf{v}_n\}$. We do not prove this result here, but note only that it is sometimes known as the Law of Inertia. The difference between the number of ones and minus ones is called the *signature* or *index* of β.

** The word "form," here, is meant in its usual sense.

8. Determine canonical bases for each of the following conjugate-symmetric, conjugate-bilinear forms $\beta: \mathbf{R}^3 \times \mathbf{R}^3 \to \mathbf{R}$. Use the methods of **6** and **7** to determine these bases. [Let $\mathbf{x} = (x_1, x_2, x_3)$ and $\mathbf{y} = (y_1, y_2, y_3)$.]

a. $\beta(\mathbf{x}, \mathbf{y}) = 2x_1y_1 - 3x_2y_2 + x_3y_3$
b. $\beta(\mathbf{x}, \mathbf{y}) = x_1(y_1 + y_2 + y_3) + x_2(y_1 - y_2 - y_3) - x_3(y_1 + y_2 + y_3)$
c. $\beta(\mathbf{x}, \mathbf{y}) = x_1y_2$
d. $\beta(\mathbf{x}, \mathbf{y}) = 2x_1y_1 - 3(x_1y_2 - x_2y_1) + 2x_2y_2$
e. $\beta(\mathbf{x}, \mathbf{y}) = x_1y_1 + x_2y_2$

3.2† Conjugate-adjoints

Throughout this section, V will be an inner product space over $F(=\mathbf{R}$ or $\mathbf{C})$, V^* will be the dual of the underlying vector space of V: That is, $V^* = \text{Trans}(V, F)$.

We shall show how every $\mathbf{v}_0 \in V$ can be considered as a linear transformation from V to F. That is, every $\mathbf{v}_0 \in V$ corresponds to a certain member in V^*.

Choose $\mathbf{v}_0$ and hold it fixed. Define $f_{\mathbf{v}_0}: V \to F$ as follows:

$$f_{\mathbf{v}_0}(\mathbf{v}) = [\mathbf{v}, \mathbf{v}_0]_V$$

Since $[\ ,\ ]_V$ is linear in its first variable, $f_{\mathbf{v}_0}$ is a linear transformation. That is, $f_{\mathbf{v}_0} \in V^*$. The association $\mathbf{v}_0 \to f_{\mathbf{v}_0}$ will be called s. That is, for every $\mathbf{v}_0 \in V$,

$$s(\mathbf{v}_0) = f_{\mathbf{v}_0}$$

Thus, $s: V \to V^*$ is a function.

Proposition 6.14

The function $s: V \to V^*$ is a 1–1 conjugate-linear transformation. It is a conjugate-isomorphism if and only if V is finite-dimensional.

Proof

Choose any $\mathbf{v}_0, \mathbf{v}_1 \in V$ and any $a \in F$. Then, $s(\mathbf{v}_0 + \mathbf{v}_1)$ is a linear transformation from V, to F, whose value at any $\mathbf{v} \in V$ is

$$\begin{aligned} s(\mathbf{v}_0 + \mathbf{v}_1)(\mathbf{v}) = f_{\mathbf{v}_0 + \mathbf{v}_1}(\mathbf{v}) &= [\mathbf{v}, \mathbf{v}_0 + \mathbf{v}_1] \\ &= [\mathbf{v}, \mathbf{v}_0] + [\mathbf{v}, \mathbf{v}_1] \\ &= (f_{\mathbf{v}_0} + f_{\mathbf{v}_1})(\mathbf{v}) \\ &= [s(\mathbf{v}_0) + s(\mathbf{v}_1)](\mathbf{v}), \end{aligned}$$

so that $s(\mathbf{v}_0 + \mathbf{v}_1) = s(\mathbf{v}_0) + s(\mathbf{v}_1)$. Similarly,

$$\begin{aligned} s(a\mathbf{v}_0) = f_{a\mathbf{v}_0}(\mathbf{v}) = [\mathbf{v}, a\mathbf{v}_0] &= \bar{a}[\mathbf{v}, \mathbf{v}_0] \\ &= (\bar{a}s(\mathbf{v}_0))(\mathbf{v}), \end{aligned}$$

so that $s(a\mathbf{v}_0) = \bar{a}s(\mathbf{v}_0)$. Therefore, s is a conjugate-linear transformation. To prove that it is 1–1, it suffices to show that $\mathcal{N}_s = \{\mathbf{0}\}$ (see Exercises 6.2.3.**a**).

Suppose then that $s(\mathbf{v}_0)$ is the zero transformation. Then, $(s(\mathbf{v}_0))(\mathbf{v}_0) = 0$. But,

$$s(\mathbf{v}_0)(\mathbf{v}_0) = [\mathbf{v}_0, \mathbf{v}_0] = \|\mathbf{v}_0\|^2$$

Since $\|\mathbf{v}_0\|^2 = 0$ and $[\ ,\ ]_V$ is positive-definite, $\mathbf{v}_0$ must equal $\mathbf{0}$. Therefore, $\mathcal{N}_s = \{\mathbf{0}\}$.

The last statement follows from a comparison of the dimension of V and V^* and is proved in the same way as is the corresponding statement for linear transformations. Q.E.D.

The adjoint $T^* : V^* \to V^*$ of a linear transformation $T : V \to V$ was defined in Chapter 4 as follows: For every $y \in V^* = \text{Trans}(V, F)$, the composition

$$y \circ T$$

is a linear transformation from V to F, and hence, it is a member of V^*. The association $y \to y \circ T$ is, thus, a function from V^* to V^* which we call T^*. More precisely, for every $y \in V^*$,

$$T^*(y) = y \circ T \in V^* = \text{Trans}(V, F)$$

It is easy to verify that T is a linear transformation.

We now assume that V is finite-dimensional, so that $s : V \to V^*$ is a conjugate-isomorphism. We then make the following tentative definition: *The conjugate-adjoint of a linear transformation* $T : V \to V$ *is*

$$s^{-1} \circ T^* \circ s : V \to V \tag{1}$$

and will (tentatively) be denoted by $T^{\#}$. The following proposition gives a complete characterization of T.

Proposition 6.15

Let V be a finite-dimensional inner product space over F, and let $T : V \to V$. The conjugate-adjoint of T, $T^{\#} : V \to V$ is a linear transformation that, for every $(\mathbf{v}_1, \mathbf{v}_2) \in V \times V$, satisfies

$$[\mathbf{v}_1, T^{\#}(\mathbf{v}_2)]_V = [T(\mathbf{v}_1), \mathbf{v}_2] \tag{2}$$

Moreover, it is the only linear transformation to satisfy this relation for all $(\mathbf{v}_1, \mathbf{v}_2) \in V \times V$.

Proof

That $T^{\#}$ is a linear transformation follows from the facts that: (1) the composition of a linear transformation and a conjugate-linear transformation is conjugate linear; (2) the composition of two conjugate-linear transformations is linear; (3) s and s^{-1} are conjugate-linear; (4) T^* is linear. These facts can easily be verified by the reader.

Now, choose any $(\mathbf{v}_1, \mathbf{v}_2) \in V \times V$. Then

$$\begin{aligned}
[\mathbf{v}_1, T^{\#}(\mathbf{v}_2)] &= s(T^{\#}(\mathbf{v}_2))(\mathbf{v}_1), \text{ by definition of } s,\\
&= s((s^{-1} \circ T^* \circ s)(\mathbf{v}_2))(\mathbf{v}_1), \text{ by definition of } T^{\#},\\
&= (s \circ s^{-1})(T^*(s(\mathbf{v}_2)))(\mathbf{v}_1), \text{ since composition is associative},\\
&= T^*(s(\mathbf{v}_2))(\mathbf{v}_1), \text{ because } s \circ s^{-1} = I_{V^*},\\
&= ((s(\mathbf{v}_2)) \circ T)(\mathbf{v}_1), \text{ by definition of } T^*,\\
&= s(\mathbf{v}_2)(T(\mathbf{v}_1))\\
&= [T(\mathbf{v}_1), \mathbf{v}_2], \text{ by definition of } s
\end{aligned}$$

Thus, $T^{\#}$ satisfies (2).

Suppose that $S : V \to V$ satisfies (2) too. That is, for all $(\mathbf{v}_1, \mathbf{v}_2) \in V \times V$

$$[\mathbf{v}_1, S(\mathbf{v}_2)] = [T(\mathbf{v}_1), \mathbf{v}_2]$$

Then, for all $(\mathbf{v}_1, \mathbf{v}_2) \in V \times V$,

$$[\mathbf{v}_1, S(\mathbf{v}_2)] = [\mathbf{v}_1, T^{\#}(\mathbf{v}_2)],$$

so that for all $(\mathbf{v}_1, \mathbf{v}_2) \in V \times V$,

$$[\mathbf{v}_1, (S - T^{\#})(\mathbf{v}_2)] = 0$$

In particular, letting $\mathbf{v}_1 = (S - T^{\#})(\mathbf{v}_2)$,

$$\|(S - T^{\#})(\mathbf{v}_2)\|^2 = 0,$$

so that $(S - T^{\#})(\mathbf{v}_2) = \mathbf{0}$ (inner products being positive-definite). That is,

$$S(\mathbf{v}_2) = T^*(\mathbf{v}_2)$$

Since this holds for all $\mathbf{v}_2 \in V$, $S = T^{\#}$. Q.E.D.

So far, our notation and definitions have been tentative. This is because the standard terminology differs from that which we introduced. Briefly, the difference consists in this: What we have called "conjugate-adjoint" is what is commonly called "adjoint"; what we have called "adjoint" is also commonly called "adjoint"; the notation "T^*" is commonly used in place of our "$T^{\#}$"; our T^* is also commonly denoted by "T^*".

The difference can be explained in this way. In the context of *vector spaces*, our *adjoint* (of T) is the standard *adjoint* (of T); both are denoted by "T^*." In the context of inner product spaces, the common use of the word "adjoint" refers to our "conjugate-adjoint," "T^*" is also commonly used here. In the former case, if $T \in \text{Trans}(V, V)$, then $T^* \in \text{Trans}(V^*, V^*)$. In the latter case, if $T \in \text{Trans}(V, V)$, then $T^* \in \text{Trans}(V, V)$ as well.

We now adopt the standard terminology and notation.

Definition 6.7

Let V be a finite-dimensional inner product space over $F(=\mathbf{R}$ or $\mathbf{C})$, and let $T : V \to V$ be any linear transformation. The adjoint of T is the unique linear *transformation $T^*: V \to V$ satisfying*

$$[\mathbf{v}_1, T^*(\mathbf{v}_2)] = [T(\mathbf{v}_1), \mathbf{v}_2] \tag{3}$$

for all $(\mathbf{v}_1, \mathbf{v}_2) \in V \times V$. A linear transformation $T: V \to V$ is called self-adjoint (sometimes Hermitian, if $F = \mathbf{C}$) if $T = T^*$.

Proposition 6.16

Let V be as above, and let $S, T: V \to V$ be linear transformations. Then, the following statements are equivalent:

(1) $S = T^*$

(2) *For any orthonormal ordered basis X of V the matrix $\mathscr{A}_{X,X}(S)$ is the conjugate-transpose of the matrix $\mathscr{A}_{X,X}(T)$. That is, if $\mathscr{A}_{X,X}(S) = (b_{ij})$ and $\mathscr{A}_{X,X}(T) = (a_{ij})$, then*

$$b_{ij} = \bar{a}_{ji}, \; i = 1, \ldots, n, \; j = 1, \ldots, n.$$

Proof

Suppose, first, that $S = T^*$, that $\mathscr{A}_{X,X}(S) = (b_{ij})$ and $\mathscr{A}_{X,X}(T) = (a_{ij})$. Suppose, also, that $X = \{\mathbf{x}_1, \ldots, \mathbf{x}_n\}$. Then,

$$T^*(\mathbf{x}_j) = b_{1j}\mathbf{x}_1 + \cdots + b_{nj}\mathbf{x}_n,$$

and

$$T(\mathbf{x}_i) = a_{1i}\mathbf{x}_1 + \cdots + a_{ni}\mathbf{x}_n, \text{ for } i, j = 1, \ldots, n.$$

Using Proposition 6.7(1) and equation (3) above,

$$b_{ij} = [T^*(\mathbf{x}_j), \mathbf{x}_i] = \overline{[x_i, T^*(x_j)]} = \overline{[T(x_i), x_j]} = \bar{a}_{ji},$$

for all $i, j = 1, \ldots, n$.

Next, suppose that (2) is true. Then

$$S(\mathbf{x}_j) = b_{1j}\mathbf{x}_1 + \cdots + b_{nj}\mathbf{x}_n$$

and $T(\mathbf{x}_i) = a_{1i}\mathbf{x}_1 + \cdots + a_{ni}\mathbf{x}_n$, and, by Proposition 6.7(1),

$$[\mathbf{x}_i, S(\mathbf{x}_j)] = \overline{[S(\mathbf{x}_j), \mathbf{x}_i]} = \bar{b}_{ij} = \overline{\bar{a}_{ji}} = a_{ji} = [T(\mathbf{x}_i), \mathbf{x}_j] = [\mathbf{x}_i, T^*(\mathbf{x}_j)]$$

for all $i, j = 1, \ldots, n$. Thus,

$$[\mathbf{x}_i, (S - T^*)(\mathbf{x}_j)] = 0$$

for all $i, j = 1, \ldots, n$. This means that

$$\begin{aligned}(S - T^*)(\mathbf{x}_j) \in \{\mathbf{x}_1, \ldots, \mathbf{x}_n\}^\perp &= X^\perp \\ &= [\text{span}(X)]^\perp \\ &= V^\perp = \{\mathbf{0}\},\end{aligned}$$

for all $j = 1, \ldots, n$. Thus, $S = T^*$. Q.E.D.

Corollary to Proposition 6.16

Let $T : V \to V$ be a linear transformation, where V is as above. Then, T is self-adjoint if and only if

$$a_{ij} = \bar{a}_{ji}, \; i, j = 1, \ldots, n,$$

where $(a_{ij}) = \mathscr{A}_{X,X}(T)$, and X is any orthonormal ordered basis of V.

We leave a proof to the reader.

EXERCISES / 6.5

1. The standard inner product on **R** is ordinary multiplication. Consider the inner product space consisting of **R** together with this inner product. Show that *every* linear transformation $T : \mathbf{R} \to \mathbf{R}$ is self-adjoint.

2. The standard inner product on **C** is given by γ of 1.2: $\gamma(w, x) = w\bar{z}$. Consider the inner product space (over **C**) consisting of **C** and γ. Show that a linear transformation $T : \mathbf{C} \to \mathbf{C}$ is self-adjoint if and only if T is multiplication by some real number.

3. Let $c = a + bi$, where $a^2 + b^2 = 1$. Show that M_c is rotation through some angle θ.

4. Use Exercises **2** and **3** to show that every linear transformation from **C** to **C** is the composition of a rotation and a self-adjoint transformation. Show that every linear transformation from **C** to **C** is multiplication by a complex number. Thus, for any complex number c, there is a complex number d, such that $d\,\bar{d} = 1$, and a real number r, so that $M_c = M_r \circ M_d$. Show that this yields the polar coordinate expression for c.

5. Prove that if V is a finite-dimensional inner product space over $F(= \mathbf{R}$ or $\mathbf{C})$, and if $a \in \mathbf{R}$, then $M_a : V \to V$ (multiplication by a) is self-adjoint.

6.* Suppose that V is as in **5**, and that U is a vector subspace of V. Let $T : V \to V$ be a self-adjoint linear transformation such that $T(U) \subset U$. That is, for every $\mathbf{u} \in U$, $T(\mathbf{u}) \in U$. Then, $T \mid U$ is a linear transformation for U to U. That is, $(T \mid U) \in \text{Trans}(U, U)$. Moreover, U is an inner product space with respect to the inner product of V restricted to U.

   Prove that $T \mid U$ is a self-adjoint transformation from U to U.

7. Let V and U be as in **6**, and let $S \in \text{Trans}(V, V)$. We say, as in **6**, that $S(U) \subset U$ if and only if $S(\mathbf{u}) \in U$, for all $\mathbf{u} \in U$. Prove that $S(U) \subset U$ if and only if $S^*(U^\perp) \subset U^\perp$.

8.* Let V be as in **5** and let $X = \{\mathbf{x}_1, \ldots, \mathbf{x}_n\}$ an orthonormal basis of V. Suppose that the linear transformation $T : V \to V$ satisfies:

$$T(\mathbf{x}_i) = \lambda_i \mathbf{x}_i,$$

for some real numbers $\lambda_1, \ldots, \lambda_n$. Show that T is self-adjoint.

In the next chapter we obtain a converse to this result. That is, we show, given any self-adjoint $T: V \to V$, that there is an orthonormal basis $\{\mathbf{x}_1, \ldots, \mathbf{x}_n\}$ such that $T(\mathbf{x}_i) = \lambda_i \mathbf{x}_i$, for all $i = 1, \ldots, n$.

Such $\mathbf{x}_i$ are called characteristic vectors or proper vectors or eigenvectors of T, and λ_i are called characteristic, proper, or eigenvalues of T.

9. Let V be any finite-dimensional vector space over any field F, and let T be any linear transformation. Recall that $M_\lambda: V \to V$ denotes multiplication by λ. Regarding λ is an indeterminate, the quantity

$$\det(T - M_\lambda)$$

becomes a polynomial in powers of λ with coefficients in F. (We called this the characteristic polynomial of T, in Chapter 5, Exercises 5.6.3.)

Prove that $T(\mathbf{v}) = a\mathbf{v}$, for some nonzero $\mathbf{v} \in V$ if and only if a is a zero of $\det(T - M_\lambda)$. (*Hint:* $\det S = 0$ if and only if S is not 1–1 if and only if $\mathcal{N}_S \neq \{\mathbf{0}\}$.)

We call $\mathbf{v}$ an eigenvector, a an eigenvalue, of T (cf. **8**).

10. Let V, X, and T be as in **8**, except that, now, suppose that

$$T(\mathbf{x}_i) = \lambda_i \mathbf{x}_i,$$

$i = 1, \ldots, n$, where the λ_i are scalars in $\mathbf{C}$ of unit length (i.e., $\lambda_i \bar{\lambda}_i = 1$).

Prove that T is an inner product transformation.

In the next chapter, we prove the converse of this result. Namely, we show that, for every inner product transformation T from V to V, there are a basis X and complex numbers λ_i of unit length such that the above equations are satisfied.

The vectors $\mathbf{x}_i$ are eigen-, proper, or characteristic vectors of T; the λ_i are eigen-, proper, or characteristic values of T.

11. In Exercises 6.2.**9.d** and **e**, we defined an isomorphism $\bar{\alpha}: \text{Trans}(V, V) \to B$, where V is an n-dimensional vector space over a field $F(= \mathbf{R}$ or $\mathbf{C})$, $n \geqq 1$, and B is the vector space of all conjugate-bilinear forms from $V \times V$ to F. Briefly, we defined $\bar{\alpha}$ as follows: We chose a fixed inner product γ on V, and, for any $T \in \text{Trans}(V, V)$, we defined $\alpha_T: V \times V \to F$ by the equation

$$\alpha_T(\mathbf{v}_1, \mathbf{v}_2) = \gamma(T(\mathbf{v}_1), \mathbf{v}_2),$$

which must hold for all $(\mathbf{v}_1, \mathbf{v}_2) \in V \times V$. We showed that $\alpha_T \in B$ and let $\alpha(T) = \alpha_T$, for all $T \in \text{Trans}(V, V)$. (Of course $\bar{\alpha}$ depends on the choice of γ.)

Now, suppose that V is an n-dimensional inner product space over F, with inner product $\gamma = [\,,\,]_V$.

Prove that a linear transformation $T \in \text{Trans}(V, V)$ is self-adjoint, if and only if $\bar{\alpha}(T)$ is conjugate-symmetric.

12.* Let V be a finite-dimensional inner product space. Prove that $T \in \text{Trans}(V, V)$ is an inner product transformation if and only if $T^* = T^{-1}$.

CHAPTER 7 CANONICAL FORMS

Throughout this chapter V will be an n-dimensional vector space over a field F, where $n \geqq 1$. In certain sections we impose other restrictions on F and V.

Let X be any given basis of V, where the basis members are given in a fixed order: Say, $X = \{\mathbf{x}_1, \mathbf{x}_2, \ldots, \mathbf{x}_n\}$. Then, we defined an isomorphism

$$\text{Trans}(V, V) \xrightarrow{\mathscr{A}_{X,X}} \mathfrak{M}(n, n),$$

by letting $\mathscr{A}_{X,X}(T)$ be the matrix of T with respect to the ordered basis X. Of course, if we choose a different basis or if we write the elements of X in a different order, then the matrix of T with respect to the new ordered basis will be different.

In this chapter we study, first, just how different the two matrices are from one another. Then—and this is our main aim—we show that, given $T \in \text{Trans}(V, V)$, under certain circumstances we can find a basis of V (perhaps even an orthonormal basis, if V is an inner product space) such that the matrix of T with respect to that basis has a very simple form. The various general forms that these matrices take will be called (informally) canonical forms.

Now, the reader should note that, given T as above, we have, in general, defined $\mathscr{A}_{X,Y}(T)$, for bases X and Y of V, to be the matrix obtained by writing out $T(\mathbf{x}_1), \ldots, T(\mathbf{x}_n)$ in terms of the $\mathbf{y}$'s and placing the resulting coefficients in columns. If we allow X and Y to vary independently, then it is no trick at all to find a very simple matrix for T. We outline the procedure in the exercises. This matrix, however, tells us almost nothing about T. Indeed, all it tells us is the dimension of $\mathcal{N}_T$ and $\mathcal{R}_T$. Any isomorphism $S : A \to V$ can be given a very simple matrix with respect to the bases X and $S(X)$: It is just the unit matrix—that is, it equals $_n(a_{ij})_n$, where $a_{ij} = 1$ if $i = j$ and $a_{ij} = 0$, if $i \neq j$. (See Exercises 7.1.7.)

It is clear that if the matrix of T is to describe the extent to which T "transforms" V, then we must use fixed measuring rods. We must measure the transforms of $\mathbf{x}_1, \ldots, \mathbf{x}_n$, namely, $T(\mathbf{x}_1), \ldots, T(\mathbf{x}_n)$, against the original $\mathbf{x}_1, \ldots, \mathbf{x}_n$. Thus, for $T \in \text{Trans}(V, V)$ the question of how simple $\mathcal{A}_{X,Y}(T)$ can be is only significant if one imposes the restriction $Y = X$ (with the same order).

Our interest in these simple matrices of T is both practical and theoretical. Let us give an example. The *main diagonal* of an $n \times n$ matrix (a_{ij}), the reader will recall, consists of all entries a_{ii}, $i = 1, \ldots, n$. Figure 44 indicates the main

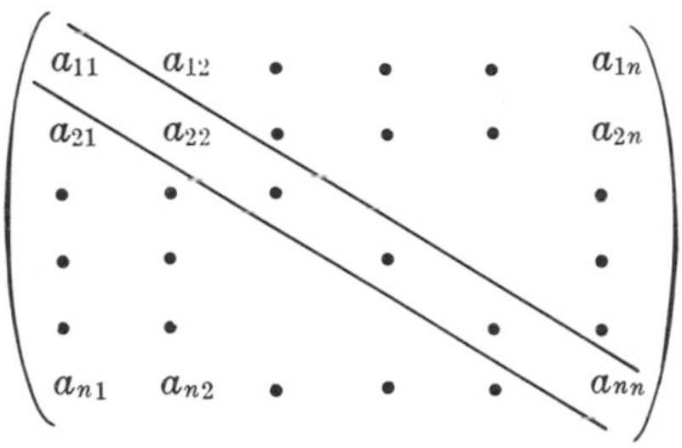

FIGURE 44

diagonal enclosed in heavy lines. A diagonal matrix is one in which all terms *not* on the main diagonal are zero. Suppose now that $\mathcal{A}_{X,X}(T)$ is a diagonal matrix. Then, by definition,

$$T(\mathbf{x}_j) = a_{jj}\mathbf{x}_j, \; j = 1, \ldots, n$$

T, therefore, can be described as follows: It transforms V by multiplying the basis vectors $\mathbf{x}_1, \ldots, \mathbf{x}_n$ by certain scalars $a_{11}, \ldots, a_{nn}$, respectively. In concrete cases, this gives a very precise geometric picture of the behavior of T.

Now, in many problems of practical interest, certain linear transformations will be defined by the conditions of the problem. Generally, complicated matrices of these transformations will be presented, with respect to certain standard bases. If we could find bases with respect to which the matrices are diagonal, then we will have simplified the problem greatly. Often, the basis vectors yielding the simple matrix will have concrete physical interpretations. We shall present an example of this at the end of the chapter.

1 / THE EFFECT OF A BASIS CHANGE

Let V be as stated in the Introduction, let $X = \{\mathbf{x}_1, \ldots, \mathbf{x}_n\}$ be an ordered basis of V, choose any $T \in \text{Trans}(V, V)$, and let $\mathcal{A}_{X,X}(T) = (a_{ij})$. That is,

$$T(\mathbf{x}_j) = a_{1j}\mathbf{x}_1 + \cdots + a_{nj}\mathbf{x}_n, \; j = 1, \ldots, n \tag{1}$$

Let $Y = \{\mathbf{y}_1, \ldots, \mathbf{y}_n\}$ be any ordered basis of V, and let $S : V \to V$ be the isomorphism determined by

$$S(\mathbf{x}_j) = \mathbf{y}_j, \; j = 1, \ldots, n \tag{2}$$

Finally, let $(c_{ij}) = \mathscr{A}_{X,X}(S)$ and $(b_{ij}) = \mathscr{A}_{Y,Y}(T)$.

$$S(\mathbf{x}_j) = \mathbf{y}_j = c_{1j}\mathbf{x}_1 + \cdots + c_{nj}\mathbf{x}_n, \; j = 1, \ldots, n \tag{3}$$

and

$$T(\mathbf{y}_j) = b_{1j}\mathbf{y}_1 + \cdots + b_{nj}\mathbf{y}_n, \; j = 1, \ldots, n \tag{4}$$

Proposition 7.1

$\mathscr{A}_{Y,Y}(T) = (\mathscr{A}_{X,X}(S))^{-1} \cdot \mathscr{A}_{X,X}(T) \cdot \mathscr{A}_{X,X}(S).$

Proof

By results of Chapter 4,

$$(\mathscr{A}_{X,X}(S))^{-1} \cdot \mathscr{A}_{X,X}(T) \cdot \mathscr{A}_{X,X}(S) = \mathscr{A}_{X,X}(S^{-1} \circ T \circ S)$$

Thus, it suffices to prove that $\mathscr{A}_{Y,Y}(T) = \mathscr{A}_{X,X}(S^{-1} \circ T \circ S)$.

We evaluate $T(\mathbf{y}_j)$ in terms of the $\mathbf{y}$'s and $(S^{-1} \circ T \circ S)(\mathbf{x}_j)$ in terms of the $\mathbf{x}$'s:

$$T(\mathbf{y}_j) = b_{1j}\mathbf{y}_1 + \cdots + b_{nj}\mathbf{y}_n,$$

by (4) above, whereas

$$\begin{aligned}(S^{-1} \circ T \circ S)(\mathbf{x}_j) &= S^{-1}(T(S(\mathbf{x}_j))) \\ &= S^{-1}(T(\mathbf{y}_j)) = S^{-1}(b_{1j}\mathbf{y}_1 + \cdots + b_{nj}\mathbf{y}_n) \\ &= b_{1j}S^{-1}(\mathbf{y}_1) + \cdots + b_{nj}S^{-1}(\mathbf{y}_n) \\ &= b_{1j}\mathbf{x}_1 + \cdots + b_{nj}\mathbf{x}_n,\end{aligned}$$

the last equation following from the fact that $S^{-1}(\mathbf{y}_i) = \mathbf{x}_i$, which follows from (2), above.

Therefore, the linear combination of the $\mathbf{y}$'s with value $T(\mathbf{y}_j)$ has the same coefficients as does the linear combination of the $\mathbf{x}$'s with value

$$(S^{-1} \circ T \circ S)(\mathbf{x}_j)$$

Thus, the jth column of $\mathscr{A}_{Y,Y}(T)$ equals the jth column of $\mathscr{A}_{X,X}(S^{-1} \circ T \circ S)$. Since this holds for all $j = 1, \ldots, n$, the two matrices are equal. Q.E.D.

Corollary to Proposition 7.1

$$(b_{ij}) = (c_{ij})^{-1} \cdot (a_{ij}) \cdot (c_{ij})$$

The proof of this fact is obvious.

Example

Let $F = \mathbf{R}$, $V = \mathbf{R}^2$, and, as usual, let $X = \{(1, 0), (0, 1)\}$, the standard basis of $\mathbf{R}^2$. Define $T : \mathbf{R}^2 \to \mathbf{R}^2$ as follows:

$$T(x_1, x_2) = (3x_1 - 2x_2, x_1 + x_2)$$

Finally, let $Y = \{(-3, 0), (1, 2)\}$.

Then, to compute $\mathscr{A}_{X,X}(T)$, we evaluate $T(1, 0)$ and $T(0, 1)$:

$$T(1, 0) = (3, 1), T(0, 1) = (-2, 1);$$

hence,

$$\mathscr{A}_{X,X}(T) = \begin{pmatrix} 3 & -2 \\ 1 & 1 \end{pmatrix}$$

To compute $\mathscr{A}_{Y,Y}(T)$, we evaluate $T(-3, 0)$, $T(1, 2)$ (in terms of $\{(-3, 0)$ and $(1, 2)\}$):

$$T(-3, 0) = (-9, -3) = 5/2(-3, 0) - 3/2(1, 2),$$
$$T(1, 2) = (-1, 3) = 5/6(-3, 0) + 3/2(1, 2),$$

so that

$$\mathscr{A}_{Y,Y}(T) = \begin{pmatrix} 5/2 & 5/6 \\ -3/2 & 3/2 \end{pmatrix}$$

Next, we verify that the equation in the above proposition is true.

We have

$$S(1, 0) = \mathbf{y}_1 = (-3, 0) = -3(1, 0)$$

and

$$S(0, 1) = \mathbf{y}_2 = (1, 2) = (1, 0) + 2(0, 1),$$

so that

$$\mathscr{A}_{X,X}(S) = \begin{pmatrix} -3 & 1 \\ 0 & 2 \end{pmatrix}$$

Note that

$$det\begin{pmatrix} -3 & 1 \\ 0 & 2 \end{pmatrix} = -6$$

We compute $(\mathscr{A}_{X,X}(S))^{-1}$ by the technique described in Chapter 5 in our discussion of Cramer's Rule. First, we compute the minors M_{11}, M_{12}, M_{21}, M_{22} of $\mathscr{A}_{X,X}(S)$: $M_{11} = 2$, $M_{12} = 0$, $M_{21} = 1$, $M_{22} = -3$. Then,

$$(\mathscr{A}_{X,X}(S))^{-1} = -\frac{1}{6}\begin{pmatrix} M_{11} & -M_{21} \\ -M_{12} & M_{22} \end{pmatrix} = -\frac{1}{6}\begin{pmatrix} 2 & -1 \\ 0 & -3 \end{pmatrix}$$

Therefore,

$$(\mathscr{A}_{X,X}(S))^{-1}\cdot\mathscr{A}_{X,X}(T)\cdot\mathscr{A}_{X,X}(S) = -\frac{1}{6}\begin{pmatrix}2 & -1\\ 0 & -3\end{pmatrix}\cdot\begin{pmatrix}3 & -2\\ 1 & 1\end{pmatrix}\cdot\begin{pmatrix}-3 & 1\\ 0 & 2\end{pmatrix}$$

$$= -\frac{1}{6}\begin{pmatrix}5 & -5\\ -3 & -3\end{pmatrix}\cdot\begin{pmatrix}-3 & 1\\ 0 & 2\end{pmatrix}$$

$$= -\frac{1}{6}\begin{pmatrix}-15 & -5\\ 9 & -9\end{pmatrix}$$

$$= \begin{pmatrix}5/2 & 5/6\\ -3/2 & 3/2\end{pmatrix} = \mathscr{A}_{Y,Y}(T)$$

Note that the matrix (c_{ij}) of the corollary (i.e., the matrix $\mathscr{A}_{X,X}(S)$) can be thought of as the matrix obtained by expressing the new basis $\{\mathbf{y}_1, \ldots, \mathbf{y}_n\}$ in terms of the original $\{\mathbf{x}_1, \ldots, \mathbf{x}_n\}$ and writing the coefficients in columns.

EXERCISES / 7.1

1. Let $V = \mathbf{R}^3$, $X = \{(0, 1, 2), (-1, 0, 1), (0, 0, 3)\}$, and let $Y = \{(1, 4, 2), (2, 0, 0), (0, 1, 0)\}$.
   a. Express the $\mathbf{y}$'s as linear combinations of the $\mathbf{x}$'s. (*Hint:* This will require solving three systems of three linear equations each involving three indeterminates.)
   b. Let the matrix of T with respect to X be

$$\begin{pmatrix}1 & -3 & 5\\ 0 & 4 & 1\\ 2 & -2 & 1\end{pmatrix}$$

   Compute the matrix of T with respect to Y.

2. Let V, F, T be as in Proposition 7.1. Recall that $det(r_{ij}) = \sum_{\sigma} \text{sgn}(\sigma) r_{\sigma}$, and that

$$det((r_{ij})\cdot(s_{ij})) = (det(r_{ij}))\cdot(det(s_{ij})),$$

   for any $n \times n$ matrices (r_{ij}) and (s_{ij}) over F. Use these facts and Proposition 7.1 (or the subsequent corollary) to conclude that

$$det(\mathscr{A}_{Y,Y}(T)) = det(\mathscr{A}_{X,X}(T))$$

   Of course, we deduced this by other means in Chapter 5.

3. Let V, F, and X be as in Proposition 7.1, and suppose that Y is another ordered basis of V. Let S and T be linear transformations from V to V such that

$$\mathscr{A}_{X,X}(S) = \mathscr{A}_{Y,Y}(T)$$

Prove that there is an isomorphism $R: V \to V$ such that

$$S = R^{-1} \circ T \circ R$$

4. Suppose that V is an inner product space over F (**R** or **C**), and suppose that $X = \{\mathbf{x}_1, \ldots, \mathbf{x}_n\}$ and $Y = \{\mathbf{y}_1, \mathbf{y}_2, \ldots, \mathbf{y}_n\}$ are orthonormal bases of V. Let $T: V \to V$ be any linear transformation, and suppose that $\mathscr{A}_{X,X}(T) = (a_{ij})$, $\mathscr{A}_{Y,Y}(T) = (b_{ij})$. Show that there is an orthogonal or unitary matrix (c_{ij}) such that

$$(b_{ij}) = (\bar{c}_{ij})^t \cdot (a_{ij}) \cdot (c_{ij})$$

Compare this result to the result of Exercises 6.2.8.

5. Let V, F, X be as above, let $T: V \to V$ be any linear transformation, and let $(a_{ij}) = \mathscr{A}_{X,X}(T)$. Suppose that (c_{ij}) is an invertible $n \times n$ matrix. Let

$$(b_{ij}) = (c_{ij})^{-1} \cdot (a_{ij}) \cdot (c_{ij})$$

Show that there is an ordered basis Y of V such that $\mathscr{A}_{Y,Y}(T) = (b_{ij})$. Express Y in terms of X.

6. Let V, F, X, Y, S, and T be as in Proposition 7.1. Use the proposition to prove that

$$\mathscr{A}_{X,X}(S) = \mathscr{A}_{Y,Y}(S)$$

Then, verify the result directly.

7. Let $T: V \to V$ be any nonzero linear transformation, and let $X = \{\mathbf{x}_1, \ldots, \mathbf{x}_n\}$ be any ordered basis of V. Consider the vectors

$$T(\mathbf{x}_1), T(\mathbf{x}_2), \ldots, T(\mathbf{x}_n)$$

Choose from among them a maximal linearly independent set $\{\mathbf{y}_1, \ldots, \mathbf{y}_k\}$, and extend it to a basis $Y = \{\mathbf{y}_1, \ldots, \mathbf{y}_n\}$ of V.

a. Show that $\mathscr{A}_{X,Y}(T)$ is of the form

$$\begin{pmatrix} A \\ B \end{pmatrix}$$

where B is the $(n - k) \times n$ matrix with only zero entries and A has the following properties: **i.** A is a $k \times n$ matrix, **ii.** A has k columns which are the standard-basis k-tuples of F^k, occurring in the standard order from left to right; **iii.** interspersed among these are $n - k$ other columns, each of which is a linear combination of the standard-basis columns preceding it.

b. Show that X can be reordered, to yield X', so that $\mathscr{A}_{X',Y}(T)$ has the form

$$\begin{pmatrix} C & D \\ E & F \end{pmatrix}$$

where E and F are zero matrices, C is the $k \times k$ unit matrix (i.e., the $k \times k$ diagonal matrix with only 1's on the main diagonal), and D consists of $n - k$ columns each of which is a linear combination of those of C.

c. Let $X' = \{\mathbf{x}_1', \ldots, \mathbf{x}_k', \mathbf{x}_{k+1}', \ldots, \mathbf{x}_n'\}$.
Perform an elementary basis transformation on X', obtaining X''. Show that the matrix $\mathscr{A}_{X'',Y}(T)$ can be obtained from $\mathscr{A}_{X',Y}(T)$ by performing an operation of the same type on the *columns* of $\mathscr{A}_{X',Y}(T)$.

d. Use **b** and **c** to show how elementary basis transformations of X', etc., can be used to *eliminate* nonzero columns from among last $n-k$ columns of $\mathscr{A}_{X',Y}(T)$. Thus, conclude that there is a basis Z of V such that $\mathscr{A}_{Z,Y}(T)$ has the form

$$\begin{pmatrix} G & H \\ I & J \end{pmatrix}$$

where H, I, J are zero matrices and G is the $k \times k$ unit matrix.

e. Prove that $k = \dim \mathscr{R}_T$ and $n-k = \dim \mathscr{N}_T$.

2 / INVARIANT SUBSPACES

One way to simplify the study of a linear transformation $T: V \to V$ is to restrict it to low-dimensional subspaces of V and try to piece together information about T from these restrictions. Of course, even these restrictions might be complicated, since their ranges could be any one of many different subspaces of V. It is desirable, therefore, to find restrictions of T to subspaces of V such that the ranges of the restrictions are contained in the very same subspaces. These restrictions, then, are linear transformations from a vector space to itself, just as is T. In this section we define the relevant concepts. In subsequent sections we show that under certain circumstances suitable restrictions can be found. These results, as the reader will see, can be interpreted in terms of matrices to yield the simple or "canonical" forms desired.

Definition 7.1

Let V be any vector space over a field F, and let $T: V \to V$ be any linear transformation. A vector subspace $U \subset V$ is called T-invariant if and only if $T(U) \subset U$ (i.e., $T(\mathbf{u}) \in U$, for all $\mathbf{u} \in U$).

A one-dimensional T-invariant subspace is called an eigenray of T. Nonzero members of an eigenray of T are called eigenvectors of T.

Proposition 7.2

Let V and T be as in the definition above. A nonzero vector $\mathbf{v} \in V$ is an eigenvector of T if and only if $T(\mathbf{v}) = \lambda \mathbf{v}$, for some $\lambda \in F$.

Proof

Let $\mathbf{v}$ be an eigenvector of T. Then, there is an eigenray $U \subset V$ such that $\mathbf{v} \in U$. Since, by definition, U is one-dimensional and $\mathbf{v} \neq \mathbf{0}$, it follows that $\{\mathbf{v}\}$ is a basis of U. Therefore, since $T(\mathbf{v}) \in U$, we have $T(\mathbf{v}) = \lambda \mathbf{v}$, for some $\lambda \in F$.

On the other hand, suppose that $T(\mathbf{v}) = \lambda\mathbf{v}$, for some $\lambda \in F$, and let $U = \text{span}_V(\{\mathbf{v}\})$. Choose any vector $\mathbf{u} \in U$. By definition of U, $\mathbf{u} = a\mathbf{v}$, for some $a \in F$. Therefore, $T(\mathbf{u}) = T(a\mathbf{v}) = aT(\mathbf{v}) = a(\lambda\mathbf{v}) = (a\lambda)\mathbf{v} \in U$, so that $T(U) \subset U$. Moreover, U is clearly one-dimensional, so that it is an eigenray of T. Since $\mathbf{v} \in U$, then, $\mathbf{v}$ is an eigenvector of T. Q.E.D.

Definition 7.2

Let V be as in Definition 7.1, *and let T be any linear transformation from V to V. For any $\lambda \in F$, let $U_\lambda = \{\mathbf{v} \in V \mid T(\mathbf{v}) = \lambda\mathbf{v}\}$. The reader should be able to show that U_λ is precisely the null space of $T - \lambda I_V$. Thus, U_λ is a vector subspace of V. If nontrivial, it is called an eigenspace of T, or the eigenspace of T corresponding to λ. If U_λ is nontrivial, then we call λ an eigenvalue of T.***

Let T and V be as above, and let x be any indeterminate scalar. The determinant $\det(T - xI_V)$, when evaluated in any of the standard ways described in Chapter 5, is a polynomial function of x, which we have called the characteristic polynomial of T.‡

Proposition 7.3

Let T and V be as above, and let λ be any scalar. Then, λ is an eigenvalue of T, if and only if it is a zero of the characteristic polynomial of T.

Proof

$U_\lambda \neq \{\mathbf{0}\}$ if and only if $T - \lambda I_V$ is not 1–1, if and only if $\det(T - \lambda I_V) = 0$, if and only if λ is a zero of $\det(T - xI_V)$. Q.E.D.

Thus, the question of whether or not T has any eigenvalues (hence, eigenspaces and eigenvectors) reduces to the question of whether or not $\det(T - xI_V)$ has any zeros in F. In general, it is *not* true that a polynomial with coefficients in F need have zeros in F. Indeed, the polynomial $x^2 + 1$ has no zeros in $\mathbf{R}$, and the polynomial $x^2 - 2$, although having coefficients in $\mathbf{Q}$, has no zeros in $\mathbf{Q}$.

A field F for which all polynomials (in one indeterminate) with coefficients in F have zeros in F is called *algebraically closed*. The *Fundamental Theorem of Algebra states that* $\mathbf{C}$ *is algebraically closed.*

Corollary to Proposition 7.3

Let F be any algebraically closed field (e.g., $F = \mathbf{C}$), and let V and T be as above. Then, T has eigenvalues (in F). Thus, T has eigenspaces, eigenvectors, eigenrays.

We leave the proof to the reader.

** Sometimes the words "proper" or "characteristic" are used instead of "eigen."

‡ To see that it is a polynomial function of x, take any matrix of $T - xI_V$, and write out the summation expression of its determinant. Powers of x will occur. Collect terms with the same power of x as factor.

Proposition 7.4

Let $T: V \to V$ be a linear transformation, where V is any vector space over any field F. The following subspaces of V are T-invariant: $\{\mathbf{0}\}$, V, $\mathcal{N}_T$, $\mathcal{R}_T$, any eigenspace of T, any eigenray of T.

Proof

The last on the list is T-invariant by definition. Since $T(\mathbf{0}) = \mathbf{0}$, $\{\mathbf{0}\}$ is T-invariant, and since $T(V) \subset V$, V is T-invariant. Since $T(\mathbf{v}) = \mathbf{0}$ for all $\mathbf{v} \in \mathcal{N}_T$, $T(\mathcal{N}_T) = \{\mathbf{0}\} \subset \mathcal{N}_T$, so that $\mathcal{N}_T$ is T-invariant. Since, $\mathcal{R}_T \subset V$, we have $T(\mathcal{R}_T) \subset T(V) = \mathcal{R}_T$, so that $\mathcal{R}_T$ is T-invariant.

Now, suppose that U_λ is an eigenspace of T. Choose any $\mathbf{v} \in U_\lambda$. If $\mathbf{v} = \mathbf{0}$, then $T(\mathbf{v}) = T(\mathbf{0}) = \mathbf{0} = \lambda \cdot \mathbf{0} = \lambda\mathbf{v}$. If $\mathbf{v} \neq \mathbf{0}$, then $\mathbf{v}$ is an eigenvector of T which, by definition, satisfies $T(\mathbf{v}) = \lambda\mathbf{v}$. In either case, then $T(\mathbf{v}) = \lambda\mathbf{v}$, which belongs to U_λ since U_λ is closed with respect to scalar multiplication (being a vector subspace of V). Thus, $T(U_\lambda) \subset U_\lambda$. Q.E.D.

Remark: The preceding results show that if V is any finite-dimensional vector space over an algebraically closed field F, then any linear transformation $T \in \text{Trans}(V, V)$ has nontrivial T-invariant subspaces: any eigenspace or eigenray of T.

We use this fact in the next section.

EXERCISES / 7.2

1. Let V be any vector space over any field F, and let T be a linear transformation which has an eigenspace U_λ equal to V. Show that T is just multiplication by λ.

2. Show that if $T: \mathbf{R}^2 \to \mathbf{R}^2$ is a rotation through a nonzero angle θ, then the only T-invariant subspaces of $\mathbf{R}^2$ are $\mathbf{R}^2$ and $\{\mathbf{0}\}$.

3.*Let $T: \mathbf{R}^2 \to \mathbf{R}^2$ have matrix

$$\begin{pmatrix} a & b \\ b & c \end{pmatrix}$$

with respect to the standard basis of $\mathbf{R}^2$.

a. Show that $1/2(a + c + \sqrt{(a-c)^2 + 4b^2})$ and $1/2(a + c - \sqrt{(a-c)^2 + 4b^2})$ are eigenvalues of T.

b. Let

$$\begin{pmatrix} e & f \\ g & h \end{pmatrix}$$

be the matrix of T with respect to some other basis of $\mathbf{R}^2$, $\{\mathbf{y}_1, \mathbf{y}_2\}$, where $\mathbf{y}_1 = r_1\mathbf{e}_1 + r_2\mathbf{e}_2$ and $\mathbf{y}_2 = s_1\mathbf{e}_1 + s_2\mathbf{e}_2$ ($\{\mathbf{e}_1, \mathbf{e}_2\}$ = standard basis of $\mathbf{R}^2$). Calculate

e, f, g, h in terms of $a, b, c, r_1, r_2, s_1, s_2$. Show directly that

$$\{1/2(e+h+\sqrt{(e-h)^2+4fg}),\ 1/2(e+h-\sqrt{(e-h)^2+4fg})\}$$

equals

$$\{1/2(a+c+\sqrt{(a-c)^2+4b^2}),\ 1/2(a+c-\sqrt{(a-c)^2+4b^2})\}$$

c. Let $\lambda = 1/2(a+c+\sqrt{(a-c)^2+4b^2})$. Solve the homogeneous system of equations.

$$(a-\lambda)x_1 + bx_2 = 0$$

$$bx_1 + (c-\lambda)x_2 = 0$$

and show that the nonzero solution (c_1, c_2) is an eigenvector of T satisfying $T(c_1, c_2) = \lambda(c_1, c_2)$.

4. Show that 0 is an eigenvalue of a linear transformation $T: V \to V$, if and only if T is not 1–1.

5. Suppose that $T: V \to V$ is a linear transformation with eigenvalues $\lambda_1, \lambda_2, \ldots, \lambda_r$. Suppose that the eigenspace U_{λ_i} has dimension k_i, $i = 1, \ldots, r$, and that

$$U_{\lambda_1} \oplus \cdots \oplus U_{\lambda_r} = V$$

Let X_i be a basis of U_{λ_i}, $i = 1, \ldots, r$, and let $X = X_1 \cup \cdots \cup X_r$. Then, X is a basis of V. Order it so that X_1 comes first, X_2 second, etc.

Show that $\mathscr{A}_{X,X}(T)$ is a diagonal matrix with k_1 λ_1's, k_2 λ_2's, $\ldots$, and k_r λ_r's appearing on the main diagonal, in that order (reading from upper left to lower right).

3 / TRIANGULAR FORM

Let V be a vector space over F, and let V^* be the dual of V, namely, $V^* = \text{Trans}(V, F)$. Given any vector subspace $U \subset V$, recall that the annihilator of U, U^0, consists of all linear transformations $f: V \to F$, such that $f \mid U$ is identically zero. U^0 is a vector subspace of V^*. If V is finite-dimensional, then

$$\dim U + \dim U^0 = \dim V = \dim V^*$$

These facts were established in Chapter 4. To make use of them, we remind the reader of the notion of *adjoint* of a linear transformation $T: V \to V$.** Given T, the adjoint of T, $T^*: V^* \to V^*$, is defined by the equation

$$T^*(f) = f \circ T,$$

for all $f \in V^*$.

** This should not be confused with the notion of adjoint used in connection with inner product spaces (see Chapter 6).

Proposition 7.5

Let U, V, T, and T^* be as above. Then U is T-invariant if and only if U^0 is T^*-invariant.

Proof

Suppose that U is T-invariant and that $f \in U^0$. Then, for any $\mathbf{u} \in U$, $T(\mathbf{u})$ belongs to U, so that

$$(T^*(f))(\mathbf{u}) = (f \circ T)(\mathbf{u}) = f(T(\mathbf{u})) = 0$$

Thus, $T^*(f) \mid U$ is identically zero, so that $T^*(f) \in U^0$. Therefore, U^0 is T^*-invariant.

Next suppose that U^0 is T^*-invariant and that $\mathbf{u} \in U$. Then, for any $f \in U^0$, $T^*(f)$ belongs to U^0, so that

$$f(T(\mathbf{u})) = (T^*(f))(\mathbf{u}) = 0$$

Let $T(U) = W$. The above equation shows that every $f \in U^0$ belongs to W^0, since $f \mid T(U)$ is identically zero. Thus, $U^0 \subset W^0$. In Chapter 4, we proved that $W \subset U$ if and only if $U^0 \subset W^0$. Thus, we conclude that

$$T(U) = W \subset U,$$

and, hence, that U is T-invariant. Q.E.D.

Lemma

Let V be any vector space, and let f be any member of V^*. Suppose that $U = \mathcal{N}_f$. Then, $U^0 = \text{span}_{V^*}(\{f\})$.

Proof

Clearly, $f \mid \mathcal{N}_f$ is identically zero, so that $f \in U^0$. Since U^0 is a vector subspace of V^*, it is closed with respect to scalar multiplication; thus $\text{span}(\{f\}) \subset U^0$.

On the other hand, suppose that $g \in U^0$. Then, $g \mid U = g \mid \mathcal{N}_f$ is constantly zero. This means that $\mathcal{N}_f \subset \mathcal{N}_g$. In Chapter 4 (Exercises 4.4.3.**d**) we showed that this implies that g is a multiple of f: that is, $g \in \text{span}_{V^*}(\{f\})$. Thus, $U^0 \subset \text{span}_{V^*}(\{f\})$.

The two inclusions imply that $U^0 = \text{span}_{V^*}(\{f\})$. Q.E.D.

Proposition 7.6

*Let F be an algebraically closed field,** let V be an n-dimensional vector space over F, and let $T: V \to V$ be any linear transformation. Then, there exist T-invariant subspaces of V, $U_0, U_1, \ldots, U_n$ satisfying:*

(1) $U_0 \subset U_1 \subset U_2 \subset \cdots \subset U_n$
(2) $\dim(U_i) = i$, $i = 1, 2, \ldots, n$.

** See Section 2, above Corollary to Proposition 7.3.

Proof

We proceed by induction on n. If $n = 0$ or 1, the result is obvious. We leave verification, here, to the reader.

Suppose that the result holds for $n = k$, and suppose that $\dim V = k + 1$.

Then, $\dim V^* = k + 1$. According to Corollary to Proposition 7.3, $T^*: V^* \to V^*$ has eigenvectors. Let $f \in V^*$ be such an eigenvector, and let $W = \text{span}_{V^*}(\{f\})$, the eigenray of T^* containing f. By Proposition 7.4, W is T^*-invariant.

Now, let $U = \mathcal{N}_f$. Then $U^0 = W$, by the above lemma. Thus, U^0 is T^*-invariant, so that by Proposition 7.5, U is T-invariant.

Moreover,

$$\dim U + \dim W = \dim V^* = k + 1,$$

so that, since $\dim W = 1$, we have

$$\dim U = k$$

Since $T(U) \subset U$, $T \mid U$ is a linear transformation from U to U. Thus, since U is k-dimensional, we may apply the result to $T \mid U$ and U: there is a sequence $U_0 \subset U_1 \subset \cdots \subset U_k = U$ of $(T \mid U)$-invariant subspaces of U, such that $\dim U_i = i$, $i = 0, 1, \ldots, k$.

Now, we show that U_i is T-invariant, for $i = 0, 1, \ldots, k$. To see this, choose any $\mathbf{u} \in U_i$, and note that $(T \mid U)(\mathbf{u}) \in U_i$. Thus,

$$T(\mathbf{u}) = (T \mid U)(\mathbf{u}) \in U_i,$$

so that $T(U_i) \subset U_i$, as desired.

We now set $U_{k+1} = V$, and we have our sequence $U_0 \subset U_1 \subset \cdots \subset U_k \subset U_{k+1}$ of T-invariant subspaces of V as desired. Thus, the result holds for $n = k + 1$.

Applying the Principle of Induction, we conclude that the result holds for all n. Q.E.D.

Corollary to Proposition 7.6

Let V be an n-dimensional vector space over an algebraically closed field F, and let T be any linear transformation from V to V. Then, there is an ordered basis of X of V such that $\mathcal{A}_{X,X}(T)$ has only zero entries below the main diagonal. That is,

$$\mathcal{A}_{X,X}(T) = \begin{pmatrix} a_{11} & a_{12} & \cdots & & a_{1n} \\ 0 & a_{22} & \cdots & & a_{2n} \\ 0 & 0 & \cdot & & \cdot \\ \vdots & \vdots & & \cdot & \vdots \\ 0 & 0 & \cdots & 0 & a_{nn} \end{pmatrix}$$

Proof

Let $U_0 \subset U_1 \subset \cdots \subset U_n$ be a sequence of T-invariant vector subspaces of V satisfying $\dim U_i = i$, $i = 1, \ldots, n$.

Choose any nonzero $\mathbf{x}_1$ in U_1, choose any $\mathbf{x}_2$ in U_2 not in U_1, and, in general, let $\mathbf{x}_i$ be any vector in U_i but not in U_{i-1} for $i = 1, \ldots, n$. This can be done because each U_i is one dimension higher than the preceding U_{i-1}. The reader should be able to show that $\{\mathbf{x}_1, \ldots, \mathbf{x}_i\}$ is a basis of U_i, for all $i = 1, \ldots, n$. In particular, $X = \{\mathbf{x}_1, \ldots, \mathbf{x}_n\}$ is a basis of $U_n = V$.

Since $T(U_j) \subset U_j$, each $T(\mathbf{x}_j)$ is a linear combination of $\mathbf{x}_1, \ldots, \mathbf{x}_j$: say,

$$T(\mathbf{x}_j) = a_{1j}\mathbf{x}_1 + \cdots + a_{jj}\mathbf{x}_j = a_{1j}\mathbf{x}_1 + \cdots + a_{jj}\mathbf{x}_j + 0\mathbf{x}_{j+1} + \cdots + 0\mathbf{x}_n$$

Writing these coefficients in columns, to obtain $\mathscr{A}_{X,X}(T)$ we see that $\mathscr{A}_{X,X}(T)$ has the form described. Q.E.D.

A matrix ${}_n(b_{ij})_n$ with only zeros below the main diagonal is called *triangular*. The above proposition and corollary show that linear transformations $T: V \to V$ have triangular matrices, with respect to suitably chosen bases, provided that the scalar field is algebraically closed. This last condition is necessary, as we now shall show. (Note: Of course, we used the condition in our proof of the above results; it is conceivable, however, that there is a proof of these results that does not use the condition and, hence, that the condition is not necessary. We show that this is false.)

Note that the determinant of a triangular matrix equals the product of the terms on its main diagonal. This is obvious when the matrix is 1×1. For $n > 1$, expand by minors, with respect to the first column:

$$\begin{vmatrix} b_{11} & b_{12} & \cdots & b_{1n} \\ 0 & b_{22} & \cdots & b_{2n} \\ 0 & 0 & & \cdot \\ \vdots & \vdots & & \vdots \\ 0 & 0 & 0 & b_{nn} \end{vmatrix} = b_{11} \cdot \begin{vmatrix} b_{22} & \cdots & \cdot & b_{2n} \\ 0 & & & \cdot \\ \vdots & & & \vdots \\ 0 & \cdots & 0 & b_{nn} \end{vmatrix}.$$

The second determinant (on the right) has order $n - 1$. We assume, inductively, that the result is true for $(n-1) \times (n-1)$ matrices. Thus,

$$det(b_{ij}) = b_{11}(b_{22} \ldots b_{nn}) = b_{11}b_{22} \ldots b_{nn}$$

Therefore, if the result holds for $(n-1) \times (n-1)$ matrices, then it holds for $n \times n$ matrices, so that by the Principle of Induction, it holds for all n.

Now, let $T: V \to V$ be a linear transformation such that $\mathscr{A}_{X,X}(T) = (a_{ij})$ is triangular for some ordered basis $X = \{\mathbf{x}_1, \ldots, \mathbf{x}_n\}$. Then, for any indeterminate scalar x,

$$\begin{aligned}(T - xI_V)(\mathbf{x}_j) &= (a_{1j}\mathbf{x}_1 + \cdots + a_{jj}\mathbf{x}_j) - x \cdot \mathbf{x}_j \\ &= a_{1j}\mathbf{x}_1 + \cdots + a_{1,j-1}\mathbf{x}_{j-1} + (a_{jj} - x)\mathbf{x}_j,\end{aligned}$$

so that $\mathscr{A}_{X,X}(T - xI_V) =$

$$\begin{pmatrix} (a_{11} - x) & a_{12} & \cdots & & a_{1n} \\ 0 & (a_{22} - x) & a_{23} & \cdots & a_{2n} \\ 0 & 0 & & & \vdots \\ \vdots & \vdots & & & a_{n-1,n} \\ 0 & 0 & \cdots & 0 & (a_{nn} - x) \end{pmatrix}$$

and, therefore, $\det(T - xI_V) = (a_{11} - x)(a_{22} - x) \cdots (a_{nn} - x)$. This means that the zeros of this polynomial are precisely $a_{11}, a_{22}, \ldots, a_{nn}$. *That is, $a_{11}, a_{22}, \ldots, a_{nn}$ are the eigenvalues of T.* Since these are entries in the matrix (over F), this means that *all the eigenvalues of T belong to F.* In general, this can happen for all $T \in \text{Trans}(V, V)$ and all V over F only if F is algebraically closed. To see this, choose any polynomial $a_k x^k + a_{k-1}x^{k-1} + \cdots a_1 x + a_0$, $a_k \neq 0$, with coefficients in F. Choose any vector space V over F with finite dimension equal to $k + 1$. Let X be any basis of V, and let $T: V \to V$ be the unique linear transformation with matrix

$$\mathscr{A}_{X,X}(T) = \begin{pmatrix} 0 & 1 & 0 & 0 & \cdots & 0 \\ 0 & 0 & 1 & 0 & \cdots & 0 \\ \vdots & \vdots & & & & \vdots \\ & & & & & 0 \\ 0 & 0 & & \cdots & 0 & 1 \\ -b_0 & -b_1 & & \cdots & -b_{k-1} & 0 \end{pmatrix}$$

where $b_i = a_i/a_k$, $i = 0, 1, \ldots, k - 1$.

Then,

$$\mathscr{A}_{X,X}(T - xI_V) = \begin{pmatrix} -x & 1 & 0 & \cdots & & 0 \\ 0 & -x & 1 & \cdots & & \vdots \\ 0 & 0 & & & & \vdots \\ \vdots & \vdots & & & & 0 \\ 0 & 0 & & 0 & -x & 1 \\ -b_0 & -b_1 & & & -b_{k-1} & -x \end{pmatrix}$$

It is not hard to show (Exercises 7.3.7) that

$$\begin{aligned} \det(T - xI_V) &= (-1)^{k+1}(x^k + b_{k-1}x^{k-1} + \cdots + b_1 x + b_0) \\ &= (-1)^{k+1} \frac{1}{a_k} (a_k x^k + a_{k-1}x^{k-1} + \cdots + a_1 x + a_0) \end{aligned}$$

That is, $\det(T - xI_V)$ is a nonzero scalar multiple of the given polynomial $a_k x^k + a_{k-1}x^{k-1} + \cdots + a_1 x + a_0$. Therefore, $\det(T - xI_V)$ has the same zeros as the given polynomial. Since these zeros are the eigenvalues of T, they belong to F. Thus, the zeros of any polynomial with coefficients in F belong to F, so that F is algebraically closed.

Thus, we have shown that if all the eigenvalues of all $T \in \text{Trans}(V, V)$, for all finite-dimensional V over F, belong to F, then F is algebraically closed. Therefore, by the discussion above, if every $T \in \text{Trans}(V, V)$ has a triangular matrix, for all finite-dimensional V over F, then F must be algebraically closed. The corollary to Proposition 7.6 can then be rephrased as follows:

A field F is algebraically closed if and only if for every finite-dimensional V over F and every $T \in \text{Trans}(V, V)$, there is a basis X such that $\mathscr{A}_{X,X}(T)$ is triangular.

EXERCISES / 7.3

1. The field of complex numbers $\mathbf{C}$ is algebraically closed. Let $T : \mathbf{C}^2 \to \mathbf{C}^2$ be a linear transformation, and let $X = \{(1, 0), (0, 1)\}$, the standard ordered basis of $\mathbf{C}^2$. Suppose that

$$\mathscr{A}_{X,X}(T) = \begin{pmatrix} a & b \\ c & d \end{pmatrix}$$

where a, b, c, d are complex numbers.

Determine an ordered basis $Y = \{\mathbf{y}_1, \mathbf{y}_2\}$ (in terms of a, b, c, d) such that $\mathscr{A}_{Y,Y}$ is triangular.

2. Let F be algebraically closed, let V be an n-dimensional vector space over F, $n \geqq 1$, let $T \in \text{Trans}(V, V)$ be a linear transformation with only zero eigenvalues.
   a. Show that there is a basis $X = \{\mathbf{x}_1, \mathbf{x}_2, \ldots, \mathbf{x}_n\}$ of V such that $T(\mathbf{x}_1) = \mathbf{0}$ and

$$T(\mathbf{x}_i) \in \text{span}_V(\{\mathbf{x}_1, \mathbf{x}_2, \ldots, \mathbf{x}_{i-1}\}),$$

   for $i = 2, 3 \ldots, n$.
   b. Show that $T(\text{span}(\{\mathbf{x}_1, \ldots, \mathbf{x}_i\}) \subset \text{span}(\{\mathbf{x}_1, \ldots, \mathbf{x}_{i-1}\})$, for $i = 2, 3, \ldots, n$.
   c. Let T^i be the i-fold composition of T with itself. Show that

$$T^i(\text{span}(\{\mathbf{x}_1, \ldots, \mathbf{x}_i\})) = \{\mathbf{0}\}$$

   d. Show that $T^n = \bar{\mathbf{0}}$, the zero transformation.

3. Show that the product of two triangular matrices is triangular.

4. Show that the set of all triangular matrices over F is a vector subspace of $\mathfrak{M}(n, n)$. What is its dimension?

5. Let $T: \mathbf{C}^3 \to \mathbf{C}^3$ have the matrix

$$\begin{pmatrix} 0 & 5 & 0 \\ 2 & 0 & -3 \\ 0 & 3 & 0 \end{pmatrix}$$

with respect to the standard basis of $\mathbf{C}^3$.

a. What is the matrix of the adjoint $T^*: (\mathbf{C}^3)^* \to (\mathbf{C}^3)^*$ with respect to the basis of $(\mathbf{C}^3)^*$ dual to the standard basis of $\mathbf{C}^3$?

b. Calculate the eigenvalues of T^*.

c. Determine one eigenvector of T^*.

d. Determine its null space, and a basis for this null space consisting of one eigenvector of T.

e. Determine a basis of $\mathbf{C}^3$ with respect to which T's matrix is triangular.

6. Let $T: \mathbf{R}^3 \to \mathbf{R}^3$ have the following matrix with respect to the standard basis of $\mathbf{R}^3$:

$$\begin{pmatrix} 1 & 1 & 2 \\ 0 & 1 & 3 \\ 0 & 0 & 2 \end{pmatrix}$$

a. Determine the eigenvectors of T. That is, solve the equation systems

$$\begin{aligned} x_1 + x_2 + 2x_3 &= x_1 \\ x_2 + 3x_3 &= x_2 \\ 2x_3 &= x_3 \end{aligned} \qquad \text{and} \qquad \begin{aligned} x_1 + x_2 + 2x_3 &= 2x_1 \\ x_2 + 3x_3 &= 2x_2 \\ 2x_3 &= 2x_3 \end{aligned}$$

b. Show that the sum of the eigenspaces of T does *not* equal all of $\mathbf{R}^3$. That is, the eigenvectors of T do *not* generate $\mathbf{R}^3$. This example is credited to Bernard Friedman in *Principles and Techniques of Applied Mathematics* (John Wiley & Sons, Inc., New York, 1956).

7. Show that

$$\begin{vmatrix} -x & 1 & 0 & 0 & \cdot & \cdot & 0 \\ 0 & -x & 1 & 0 & \cdot & \cdot & 0 \\ 0 & 0 & -x & \cdot & \cdot & & \cdot \\ \cdot & \cdot & \cdot & \cdot & \cdot & & \cdot \\ \cdot & \cdot & \cdot & \cdot & \cdot & 1 & 0 \\ \cdot & \cdot & & & 0 & -x & 1 \\ -b_0 & -b_1 & \cdot & \cdot & \cdot & -b_{k-1} & -x \end{vmatrix}$$

$$= (-1)^{k+1}(x^k + b_{k-1}x^{k-1} + \cdots + b_1 x + b_0)$$

(*Hint:* Expand by minors with respect to the last row.)

4† / POLYNOMIALS AND INVARIANT SUBSPACES

In this section, we make use of the notions developed in Chapter 4, Section 4.3. The relevance of the study of polynomials to the goals of this chapter is contained in the results of the previous two sections. We are interested in invariant subspaces of linear transformations. Eigenspaces are such subspaces. However, if the scalar field is not algebraically closed, a linear transformation need not have eigenvectors: The zeros of the characteristic polynomial of the transformation need not belong to the scalar field—or, to put it another way, the characteristic polynomial may have no scalar zeros. This corresponds to the standard fact that the characteristic polynomial may have no first degree factors (with coefficients in the scalar field). Thus, in general, when F is not algebraically closed (e.g., when $F = \mathbf{R}$ or $\mathbf{Q}$), we may not be able to find any invariant subspaces of $T: V \to V$ other than $\{\mathbf{0}\}$ or $\mathbf{V}$.

Now, although a polynomial of degree k may have no factors of first degree, it may still have nontrivial factors of degree $<k$. It would be interesting to determine invariant subspaces that correspond to these factors in the way that eigenspaces correspond to first degree factors. This procedure will lead to another canonical form for matrices of linear transformations.

Let F be any field, and let $\mathscr{P}_F$ be the algebra of polynomials in the indeterminate x with coefficients in F. Recall that if A is any algebra over F and if $\mathbf{t}$ is any element of A, then there exists one and only one homomorphism of algebras

$$\mathscr{E}_{\mathbf{t}}: \mathscr{P}_F \to A$$

satisfying $\mathscr{E}_{\mathbf{t}}(x) = \mathbf{t}$. The homomorphism is defined by the equation

$$\mathscr{E}_{\mathbf{t}}(a_k x^k + a_{k-1}x^{k-1} + \cdots + a_1 x + a_0) = a_k \mathbf{t}^k + a_{k-1}\mathbf{t}^{k-1} + \cdots + a_1\mathbf{t} + a_0 \cdot \mathbf{1},$$

where $\mathbf{1} \in A$ is the multiplicative identity. Thus, $\mathscr{E}_{\mathbf{t}}$ amounts to substituting $\mathbf{t}$ for x.

We now adopt some convenient (and familiar) terminology. Let $p(x)$ be any polynomial in $\mathscr{P}_F$, and let $\mathbf{t}$ be any member of A. Then, let

$$p(\mathbf{t}) = \mathscr{E}_{\mathbf{t}}(p(x)).$$

Proposition 7.7

Let V be any vector space over F, T any linear transformation from V to V, U any T-invariant subspace of V, and $p(x)$ any polynomial in $\mathscr{P}_F$. Then, U is $p(T)$-invariant.

Proof

If $p(x)$ is the zero polynomial, then $p(T)$ is the zero transformation, so that

$$(p(T))(U) = \{\mathbf{0}\} \subset U$$

If $p(x) = ax^k$, then $p(T) = a \cdot T^k$, so that

$$\begin{aligned}(p(T))(U) &= (a \cdot T^k)(U)\\ &= (a \cdot T^{k-1})(T(U))\\ &\subset (a \cdot T^{k-1})(U)\end{aligned}$$

If $k = 1$, then $T^{k-1} = T^0 = I_V$, and, clearly $a \cdot I_V(U)$ is contained in U. If we assume that $(aT^{k-1})(U) \subset U$, for k as above, then the above inclusion shows that $(aT^k)(U) \subset U$. Thus, by the Principle of Induction, if $p(x)$ is any power of x (times a scalar factor), $p(T)(U) \subset U$.

Finally, suppose that

$$p(x) = q_1(x) + \cdots + q_r(x),$$

and that $(q_i(T))(U) \subset U$, for $i = 1, \ldots, r$. Then,

$$\begin{aligned}(p(T))(U) &= (q_1(T) + \cdots + q_r(T))(U)\\ &= (q_1(T))(U) + \cdots + (q_r(T))(U)\\ &\subset (U + \cdots + U) = U\end{aligned}$$

Since every $p(x)$ in $\mathscr{P}_F$ is the sum of scalar multiples of powers of x and a constant term, the above results can be combined to yield

$$(p(T))(U) \subset U,$$

for any $p(x) \in \mathscr{P}_F$. Q.E.D.

Proposition 7.8

Let F, V, T, and p be as in the preceding proposition. Then:

$$\mathscr{N}_{p(T)} \quad \text{and} \quad \mathscr{R}_{p(T)}$$

are T-invariant.

Proof

The proof is based on the fact that

$$xp(x) = p(x)x$$

and the consequence that $T \circ p(T) = p(T) \circ T$. More precisely, if $p(x) = a_k x^k + a_{k-1}x^{k-1} + \cdots + a_1 x + a_0$, we have

$$\begin{aligned}T \circ p(T) &= T \circ (a_k T^k + a_{k-1}T^{k-1} + \cdots + a_1 T + a_0 I_V)\\ &= a_k T^{k+1} + a_{k-1}T^k + \cdots + a_1 T^2 + a_0 T\\ &= (a_k T^k + a_{k-1}T^{k-1} + \cdots + a_1 T + a_0 I_V) \circ T\\ &= p(T) \circ T\end{aligned}$$

Choose any $\mathbf{v} \in \mathcal{N}_{p(T)}$. Then,

$$\begin{aligned}(p(T))(T(\mathbf{v})) &= (p(T) \circ T)(\mathbf{v}) \\ &= (T \circ p(T))(\mathbf{v}) \\ &= T(p(T)(\mathbf{v})) = T(\mathbf{0}) = \mathbf{0},\end{aligned}$$

so that $T(\mathbf{v}) \in \mathcal{N}_{p(T)}$. Thus, $T(\mathcal{N}_{p(T)}) \subset \mathcal{N}_{p(T)}$.

Next choose any $\mathbf{w} \in \mathcal{R}_{p(T)}$. By definition, $\mathbf{w} = (p(T))(\mathbf{v})$, for some $\mathbf{v} \in V$. Therefore,

$$T(\mathbf{w}) = T((p(\mathbf{T}))(\mathbf{v})) = (p(T))(T(\mathbf{v})) \in \mathcal{R}_{p(T)},$$

so that $T(\mathcal{R}_{p(T)}) \subset \mathcal{R}_{p(T)}$. Q.E.D.

Before we can develop our main result, we need some basic facts about divisibility properties of polynomials in $\mathcal{P}_F$. We remind the reader that the degree of a polynomial is the largest integer k such that x^k has a nonzero coefficient in the polynomial. The zero polynomial, $\bar{0}$, will be thought of as having no degree.

Proposition 7.9

Let $p(x)$ and $d(x)$ be any polynomials in $\mathcal{P}_F$, $d(x) \neq \bar{0}$ (the zero polynomial). Then, there exist polynomials $q(x)$ and $r(x)$ satisfying:

(1) $p(x) = q(x)d(x) + r(x)$;
(2) either $r(x) = \bar{0}$ or degree $r(x) <$ degree $d(x)$.

Remark: This result is known as the *division algorithm for polynomials.* The reader should think of $d(x)$ as the divisor, $q(x)$ as the quotient, and $r(x)$ as the remainder

Proof

First, suppose that $p(x) = \bar{0}$. Then

$$p(x) = \dot{0} \cdot d(x) + \bar{0},$$

so that the desired result is obtained.

Next, suppose that degree $p(x) = 0$. If degree $d(x) = 0$, then $d(x)$ is a nonzero constant polynomial $\bar{c}$. $p(x)$ is a (possibly zero) constant $\bar{b}$. Thus,

$$p(x) = \frac{\bar{b}}{c}\, d(x) + \bar{0},$$

where $\bar{b}/c$ is the constant polynomial with constant term b/c.

Now, suppose that the result holds for all polynomials $p(x)$ of degree $\leqq k$, where $k \geqq 0$, and suppose that we are given $p(x)$ and $d(x)$, where degree

$p(x) = k + 1$. If degree $d(x) = 0$, then $d(x)$ is a nonzero constant polynomial, $\bar{c}$, so that

$$p(x) = \left[\frac{1}{c}\, p(x)\right] d(x) + \bar{0},$$

as desired.

Now, suppose that degree $d(x) = \ell > 0$. If $\ell > k + 1$, we have

$$p(x) = 0 \cdot d(x) + p(x),$$

again the desired result. If $\ell \leqq k + 1$, let b_ℓ be the coefficient of x^ℓ in $d(x)$ and a_{k+1} the coefficient of x^{k+1} in $p(x)$. Let

$$s(x) = p(x) - \left(\frac{a_{k+1}}{b_\ell}\, x^{k+1-\ell}\right) d(x)$$

The highest power of x in $p(x)$ cancels with the highest power of x in $((a_{k+1}/b_\ell)x^{k+1-\ell})\, d(x)$. Thus,

$$\text{degree } s(x) \leqq k,$$

so that the induction hypothesis applies:

$$s(x) = q'(x)\, d(x) + r(x),$$

or

$$p(x) - \left(\frac{a_{k+1}}{b_\ell}\, x^{k+1-\ell}\right) d(x) = q'(x)\, d(x) + r(x),$$

so that

$$p(x) = \left[\frac{a_{k+1}}{b_\ell}\, x^{k+1-\ell} + q'(x)\right] d(x) + r(x),$$

where $r(x) = \bar{0}$ or degree $r(x) <$ degree $d(x)$.

Thus, in every case, the desired relation holds for polynomials of degree $\leqq k + 1$. Applying the induction principle, we conclude that it holds for all polynomials. Q.E.D.

We shall say that a nonzero polynomial $q(x)$ *divides* $p(x)$, also nonzero, written $q(x) \mid p(x)$ if and only if $p(x) = q(x)t(x)$, for some $t(x) \in \mathscr{P}_F$. In this case, we may also say that $p(x)$ *is divisible by* $q(x)$.

Suppose that $p_1(x), \ldots, p_k(x) \in \mathscr{P}_F$ are given and nonzero. We say that $q(x)$ is a *greatest common divisor* of $p_1(x), \ldots, p_k(x)$ if and only if $q(x)$ is a common divisor of (i.e., divides) $p_1(x), \ldots, p_k(x)$ and $q(x)$ is divisible by every common divisor of $p_1(x), \ldots, p_k(x)$.

If $q_1(x)$ and $q_2(x)$ are greatest common divisors of $p_1(x), \ldots, p_k(x)$, then $q_1(x) \mid q_2(x)$ and $q_2(x) \mid q_1(x)$: that is,

$$q_2(x) = q_1(x)t_1(x), \quad \text{and} \quad q_1(x) = q_2(x)t_2(x),$$

for some $t_1(x)$ and $t_2(x)$ in $\mathscr{P}_F$. Therefore,

$$q_2(x) = q_2(x)t_2(x)t_1(x)$$

Since the degree of the product of two polynomials equals the sum of their degrees, we have

$$\text{degree } q_2(x) = \text{degree } q_2(x) + \text{degree } t_2(x) + \text{degree } t_1(x),$$

so that degree $t_2(x) =$ degree $t_1(x) = 0$. Thus, $t_1(x)$ and $t_2(x)$ are nonzero constant polynomials (if $t_1(x) = \bar{0}$, then $q_2(x) = \bar{0}$, which is contrary to assumption—similarly $t_2(x) \neq \bar{0}$).

Thus, $q_1(x)$ and $q_2(x)$ differ by a nonzero constant multiple. Clearly, any nonzero constant multiple of $q_1(x)$ or $q_2(x)$ is also a greatest common divisor of $p_1(x), \ldots, p_k(x)$.

Now, given a polynomial of degree ℓ there is precisely one polynomial that is a nonzero multiple of it and has 1 as a coefficient of x^ℓ. To obtain it, multiply the given polynomial by the reciprocal of the coefficient of x^ℓ. *A polynomial whose highest coefficient is* 1 *is called monic.*

Given nonzero polynomials $p_1(x), \ldots, p_k(x)$, therefore, there is *at most* one monic greatest common divisor of these polynomials. If it exists, we call it *the* greatest common divisor of $p_1(x), \ldots, p_k(x)$, written g.c.d.$(p_1(x), \ldots, p_k(x))$.

Proposition 7.10

Let $p_1(x), \ldots, p_k(x)$ be nonzero polynomials in $\mathscr{P}_F$, where F is any field. Then, g.c.d.$(p_1(x), \ldots, p_k(x))$ *exists. Moreover, there are polynomials $t_1(x), \ldots, t_k(x)$ such that*

$$t_1(x)p_1(x) + t_2(x)p_2(x) + \cdots + t_k(x)p_k(x) = \text{g.c.d.}[p_1(x), p_2(x), \ldots, p_k(x)]$$

Proof

Consider all polynomials of the form

$$s_1(x)p_1(x) + s_2(x)p_2(x) + \cdots + s_k(x)p_k(x), \tag{1}$$

where $s_1(x), s_2(x), \ldots, s_k(x)$ range over $\mathscr{P}_F$. Aside from the zero polynomial, all polynomials of the form of (1) have degrees. If one of them has degree zero, choose it. If not, let S be the set of all degrees of polynomials of the form of (1). S consists of natural numbers, and so it has a smallest member d. Choose a polynomial of the form of (1) with degree d. In either case, we have a polynomial

$$t_1'(x)p_1(x) + t_2'(x)p_2(x) + \cdots + t_k'(x)p_k(x) = d(x) \tag{2}$$

which has minimal degree among all polynomials of the form of (1).

First, we show that $d(x) \mid p_i(x)$, $i = 1, \ldots, k$. Choose any i between 1 and k. By Proposition 7.9,

$$p_i(x) = q(x)\, d(x) + r(x) \tag{3}$$

where $r(x) = \bar{0}$ or degree $r(x) <$ degree $d(x)$. Now, solve (3) for $r(x)$ and substitute for $d(x)$ the left-hand side of (2).

Then,

$$\begin{aligned} r(x) &= -q(x)[t_1'(x)p_1(x) + \cdots + t_i'(x)p_i(x) + \cdots + t_k'(x)p_k(x)] + p_i(x) \\ &= [-q(x)t_1'(x)]p_1(x) + \cdots + [-q(x)t_i'(x) + 1]p_i(x) \\ &\quad + \cdots + [-q(x)t_k'(x)]p_k(x), \end{aligned}$$

so that $r(x)$ is of the form of (1). Since $d(x)$ has minimal degree among all those polynomials of the form of (1), it is impossible that degree $r(x) <$ degree $d(x)$. Therefore, the only alternative is $r(x) = \bar{0}$, so that (3) becomes

$$p_i(x) = q(x)\, d(x), \tag{4}$$

and, hence, $d(x) \mid p_i(x)$, as claimed. Thus, $d(x)$ is a common divisor of $p_1(x), \ldots, p_k(x)$.

Suppose that $d'(x)$ is also a common divisor of $p_1(x), \ldots, p_k(x)$. That is,

$$p_i(x) = q_i(x)\, d'(x), \qquad i = 1, \ldots, k$$

Then, by (2),

$$d(x) = [t_1'(x)q_1(x) + \cdots + t_k'(x)q_k(x)]\, d'(x),$$

so that $d'(x) \mid d(x)$. Therefore, $d(x)$ is a greatest common divisor of $p_1(x), \ldots, p_k(x)$.

There exists a nonzero constant c such that $cd(x)$ is monic. Therefore,

$$\begin{aligned} \text{g.c.d.}[p_1(x), \ldots, p_k(x)] &= cd(x) \\ &= (ct_1'(x))p_1(x) + \cdots + (ct_k'(x))p_k(x) \\ &= t_1(x)p_1(x) + \cdots + t_k(x)p_k(x), \end{aligned}$$

where $t_i(x) = ct_i'(x)$, $i = 1, \ldots, k$. Q.E.D.

If g.c.d. $[p_1(x), \ldots, p_k(x)] = \bar{1}$ (the constant polynomial with constant term 1), then we say that $p_1(x), \ldots, p_k(x)$ are *relatively prime*. Clearly, in this case,

$$t_1(x)p_1(x) + \cdots + t_k(x)p_k(x) = \bar{1}, \tag{5}$$

for some $t_1(x), \ldots, t_k(x)$ in $\mathscr{P}_F$. Moreover, if polynomials $p_1(x), \ldots, p_k(x)$ satisfy (5) [for some $t_1(x), \ldots, t_k(x)$], then they are relatively prime. For, in this case, $\bar{1}$ is clearly a polynomial of minimal degree of the appropriate form (it has degree zero), and it is monic.

Recall that we say that $T \in \text{Trans}(V, V)$ is a zero of $p(x) \in \mathscr{P}_F$ if $p(T) = \bar{0}$, the constantly zero transformation.

Proposition 7.11

Let V be any vector space over any field F, let $p(x)$ be any (nonzero) polynomial in $\mathscr{P}_F$, and let $T \in \text{Trans}(V, V)$ be any zero of $p(x)$. Moreover, suppose that $g_1(x)$ and $g_2(x)$ are relatively prime polynomials in $\mathscr{P}_F$ satisfying $p(x) = g_1(x)g_2(x)$. Let $U_i = \mathscr{N}_{g_i(T)}$, $i = 1, 2$. Then, U_1 and U_2 are T-invariant and

$$U_1 \oplus U_2 = V$$

Proof

Let $V_i = \mathscr{R}_{g_i(T)}$. Choose any $\mathbf{w} \in V_2$. Then $\mathbf{w} = g_2(T)(\mathbf{v})$, for some $\mathbf{v} \in V$. Now,

$$\begin{aligned} g_1(T)(\mathbf{w}) = g_1(T)[g_2(T)(\mathbf{v})] &= [g_1(T) \circ g_2(T)](\mathbf{v}) \\ &= [p(T)](\mathbf{v}) \\ &= \bar{0}(\mathbf{v}) = \mathbf{0}, \end{aligned}$$

the second to last equation following from the fact that T is a zero of $p(x)$. Therefore $\mathbf{w} \in \mathscr{N}_{g_1(T)} = U_1$. Since this holds for all $\mathbf{w} \in V_2$, it follows that

$$V_2 \subset U_1$$

Next, note that polynomial multiplication is commutative. Thus, $p(T) = \mathscr{E}_T(p(x)) = \mathscr{E}_T(g_1(x)g_2(x)) = \mathscr{E}_T(g_2(x)g_1(x)) = g_2(T) \circ g_1(T)$.

Now, apply the argument of the preceding paragraph, with 1 and 2 exchanged, using the above equation. The result will be:

$$V_1 \subset U_2$$

Since $g_1(x)$ and $g_2(x)$ are relatively prime, there are polynomials $t_1(x)$ and $t_2(x)$ satisfying

$$t_1(x)g_1(x) + t_2(x)g_2(x) = \bar{1},$$

to which we apply $\mathscr{E}_T : \mathscr{P}_F \to \text{Trans}(V, V)$, obtaining,

$$\begin{aligned} t_1(T) \circ g_1(T) + t_2(T) \circ g_2(T) &= I_V; \\ g_1(T) \circ t_1(T) + g_2(T) \circ t_2(T) &= I_V, \end{aligned}$$

by the commutativity of polynomial multiplication, as above.

Choose any $\mathbf{v} \in V$. Then,

$$\mathbf{v} = I_V(\mathbf{v}) = g_1(T)(t_1(T)(\mathbf{v})) + g_2(T)(t_2(T)(\mathbf{v})).$$

Since $g_1(T)(t_1(T)(\mathbf{v})) \in \mathscr{R}_{g_1(T)} = V_1$, and $g_2(T)(t_2(T)(\mathbf{v})) \in \mathscr{R}_{g_2(T)} = V_2$ we have $\mathbf{v} \in V_1 + V_2$.

Thus, since $\mathbf{v}$ is any vector in V, it follows that

$$V = V_1 + V_2$$

On the other hand, since $U_1 \supset V_2$ and $U_2 \supset V_1$, we have

$$V = U_1 + U_2$$

We now prove that $U_1 \cap U_2 = \{\mathbf{0}\}$. Choose $\mathbf{w} \in U_1 \cap U_2$. Then,

$$\begin{aligned} \mathbf{w} = I_V(\mathbf{w}) &= t_1(T) \circ g_1(T)(\mathbf{w}) + t_2(T) \circ g_2(T)(\mathbf{w}) \\ &= t_1(T)(\mathbf{0}) + t_2(T)(\mathbf{0}) = \mathbf{0} + \mathbf{0} = \mathbf{0}, \end{aligned}$$

which proves the desired equality.

Therefore, $U_1 \oplus U_2 = V$, as asserted. That U_1 and U_2 are T-invariant follows from Proposition 7.8. Q.E.D.

Remark: Note that since $V_1 \subset U_2$ and $V_2 \subset U_1$, we have $V_1 \cap V_2 \subset U_2 \cap U_1 = \{\mathbf{0}\}$. Thus,

$$V_1 \oplus V_2 = V$$

Moreover, by Proposition 7.8, both V_1 and V_2 are T-invariant.

We now extend this result to the case of more than two factors. We shall say that polynomials $g_1(x), \ldots, g_k(x)$ are *pairwise prime* if any pair of them are relatively prime. The reader should be able to show that if $g_1(x), \ldots, g_k(x)$ are pairwise prime, then they are relatively prime, but not necessarily conversely (unless $k = 2$).

Corollary to Proposition 7.11

Let F, V, $p(x)$ and T be as in the first sentence of Proposition 7.11. *Suppose that $g_1(x), \ldots, g_k(x)$ are pairwise prime polynomials such that $p(x) = g_1(x) \cdot \cdots \cdot g_k(x)$. Then, there are T-invariant subspaces of V, $U_1, \ldots, U_k$ satisfying:*

(1) $U_1 \oplus \cdots \oplus U_k = V$
(2) $U_i = \mathcal{N}_{g_i(T)} \cap \mathcal{N}_{T_i}, \quad i = 1, \ldots, k,$
where $T_i = g_i(T) \circ g_{i+1}(T) \circ \cdots \circ g_k(T)$.

Proof

If $k = 2$, then the above result is the same as that of Proposition 7.11. For, then, $T_1 = g_1(T) \circ g_2(T) = p(T) = \bar{\mathbf{0}}$, to that $\mathcal{N}_{T_1} = V$, and $T_2 = g_2(T)$, so that $\mathcal{N}_{T_2} = \mathcal{N}_{g_2(T)}$. Thus, $U_1 = \mathcal{N}_{g_1(T)} \cap V = \mathcal{N}_{g_1(T)}$ and $U_2 = \mathcal{N}_{g_2(T)}$, as in Proposition 7.11.

Assume that the result holds for $k = \ell$, and suppose that $p(x) = g_1(x)g_2(x) \ldots g_{\ell+1}(x)$, where the $g_i(x)$ are pairwise prime. Let

$$g(x) = g_2(x) \cdots g_{\ell+1}(x)$$

Since

$$g_1(x), g_2(x), \ldots, g_{\ell+1}(x) \text{ are pairwise prime,}$$

$$s_2(x)g_1(x) + t_2(x)g_2(x) = \bar{1}$$

$$s_3(x)g_1(x) + t_3(x)g_3(x) = \bar{1}$$

$$\vdots$$

$$s_{\ell+1}(x)g_1(x) + t_{\ell+1}(x)g_{\ell+1}(x) = \bar{1},$$

or

$$t_2(x)g_2(x) = \bar{1} - s_2(x)g_1(x)$$

$$t_3(x)g_3(x) = \bar{1} - s_3(x)g_1(x)$$

$$\vdots$$

$$t_{\ell+1}(x)g_{\ell+1}(x) = \bar{1} - s_{\ell+1}(x)g_1(x)$$

Multiply all these equations together. The result is an equation of the form

$$t(x)g(x) = \bar{1} - s(x)g_1(x),$$

where $t(x) = t_2(x) \ldots t_{\ell+1}(x)$, and $s(x)$ is the polynomial obtained from the product of the right-hand sides of the above equations by collecting all terms with a factor $g_1(x)$, factoring out $g_1(x)$, and (if necessary) changing the sign to get a minus sign in front. The reader should examine some simple examples to confirm the fact that the above equation has the correct form.

Thus,

$$t(x)g(x) + s(x)g_1(x) = \bar{1},$$

so that $g_1(x)$ and $g(x)$ are relatively prime. Let $U_1 = \mathcal{N}_{g_1(T)}$ and $U_2' = \mathcal{N}_{g(T)} = \mathcal{N}_{T_i}$.

Then, by Proposition 7.11,

$$V = U_1 \oplus U_2',$$

and U_1 and U_2' are T-invariant.

Next, consider $T \mid U_2'$. This is a linear transformation from U_2' to U_2'. Since $U_2' = \mathcal{N}_{g(T)}$, $T \mid U_2'$ is a zero of $g(x)$. (For, choose any $\mathbf{v} \in U_2$. Then $g(T)(\mathbf{v}) = \mathbf{0}$. Moreover, $g(T \mid U_2') = g(T) \mid U_2'$: both have U_2' as domain and have the same values thereon.) Note that $g(x) = g_2(x) \ldots g_{\ell+1}(x)$, and $g_2(x), \ldots, g_{\ell+1}(x)$ are ℓ pairwise prime polynomials. Thus, the induction hypothesis applies to U_2', $T \mid U_2'$, and $g_2(x), \ldots, g_{\ell+1}(x)$.

That is, there are $(T \mid U_2')$-invariant subspaces of U_2', $U_2, U_3, \ldots, U_{\ell+1}$, satisfying

1. $U_2 \oplus U_3 \oplus \cdots \oplus U_1 = U_2'$
2. $U_i = \mathcal{N}_{g_i(T)} \cap \mathcal{N}_{g_i(T) \circ \cdots \circ g_{\ell+1}(T)}, i = 2, \ldots, \ell + 1.$

Note that since U_i is $(T \mid U_2')$-invariant, it is T-invariant (since $U_i \subset U_2'$, $i = 2, \ldots, \ell + 1$.) To see this, choose any $\mathbf{v} \in U_i$, $i \geqq 2$. This $\mathbf{v}$, then, also belongs to U_2'. Therefore,

$$T(\mathbf{v}) = (T \mid U_2')(\mathbf{v}) \in U_i,$$

so that $T(U_i) \subset U_i$.

Note also that

$$U_1 \oplus (U_2 \oplus \cdots \oplus U_{\ell+1}) = U_1 \oplus U_2 \oplus \cdots \oplus U_{\ell+1},$$

because both subspaces are the smallest subspaces containing $U_1, \ldots, U_{\ell+1}$, and any two sums of different U's have only $\mathbf{0}$ in common.

Finally, note that $V = \mathcal{N}_{\bar{0}} = \mathcal{N}_{p(T)} = \mathcal{N}_{g_1(T) \circ \cdots \circ g_{\ell+1}(T)}$, so that $U_1 = \mathcal{N}_{g_1(T)} \cap \mathcal{N}_{T_1}$.

Therefore, $U_1, U_2, \ldots, U_{\ell+1}$ are the desired subspaces. Q.E.D.

This has a nice interpretation in terms of matrices. Let X_i be a basis of U_i,

$i = 1, \ldots, k$ (supposing V to be finite-dimensional), and let $X = X_1 \cup X_2 \cup \cdots \cup X_k$. Then, X is a basis of V, and, for T as above, if

$$\mathscr{A}_{X_i,X_i}(T \mid U_i) = \mathfrak{a}_i, \qquad i = 1, \ldots, k,$$

then

$$\mathscr{A}_{X,X}(T) = \begin{pmatrix} \mathfrak{a}_1 & 0 & \cdot & \cdot & \cdot & \cdot & 0 \\ 0 & \mathfrak{a}_2 & \cdot & & & & \cdot \\ 0 & 0 & \cdot & \cdot & & & \cdot \\ \cdot & & \cdot & \cdot & \cdot & & \cdot \\ \cdot & & & \cdot & \cdot & \cdot & \cdot \\ \cdot & & & & \cdot & \cdot & 0 \\ 0 & \cdot & \cdot & \cdot & \cdot & 0 & \mathfrak{a}_k \end{pmatrix}$$

That is, the matrix of T (with respect to X) consists of (matrix) blocks, corresponding to the matrices of the restrictions of T to the invariant subspaces U_i. These blocks are arranged so that their main diagonals are superimposed onto that of the matrix of T. Zeros occur elsewhere.

The reader is invited to verify this interpretation.

This result is *sometimes useful* because:

1. It applies to vector spaces over *any* field F.
2. If V is finite dimensional, then we have shown that every $T \in \text{Trans}(V, V)$ is the zero of some polynomial in $\mathscr{P}_F$ (Chapter 4).
3. Although the polynomial may not have scalar zeros, it may have pairwise prime factors for which the U_i have low dimension, so that T will have a matrix in very simple form.

The result is *sometimes useless*, because it may happen that the polynomial p does not have factors other than constants or constant multiples of itself. Thus, it may happen that all $U_i = \{\mathbf{0}\}$ except one of them which equals V. In this case, all the $\mathfrak{a}_i$ but one disappear from the above matrix, and the matrix is just an ordinary (perhaps very complicated) matrix.

In the next section, we show that when $F = \mathbf{R}$ or $\mathbf{C}$, very simple matrix forms can be obtained.

EXERCISES / 7.4

1. Let V be a finite-dimensional vector space over a field F, let X be an ordered basis of V, and let T be any member of Trans(V, V).

Prove that T is a zero of a polynomial $p(x) \in \mathscr{P}_F$, if and only if $\mathscr{A}_{X,X}(T)$ is a zero of $p(x)$. [*Hint:* Show that $p(\mathscr{A}_{X,X}(T)) = \mathscr{A}_{X,X}(p(T))$.]

2. Let $\mathfrak{a} = {}_n(a_{ij})_n$ be any triangular matrix over F, and let $p(x)$ be any polynomial in $\mathscr{P}_F$. Prove that $p(\mathfrak{a})$ is a triangular matrix, and that the terms on its main diagonal are (reading from upper left to lower right) $p(a_1), p(a_{22}), \ldots, p(a_{nn})$.

3. Let V be an n-dimensional vector space, $n \geqq 1$, over an algebraically closed field F, and let $T: V \to V$ be a linear transformation. Let $p(x) = \det(T - xI_V)$.

a. Use the hint in **1** and the result of **2**, as well as material in Section 3, to show that there is an ordered basis X of V such that $\mathscr{A}_{X,X}(p(T))$ is a triangular matrix with zeros on its main diagonal. Thus, conclude that the eigenvalues of $p(T)$ are zero.

b. Use Exercises 7.3.2 to show that $(p(T))^n = \bar{\mathbf{0}}$ (where $(p(T))^n$ is the n-fold composition of $p(T)$ with itself).

4. Let F be any field, V an n-dimensional vector space over F and $T \in \text{Trans}(V, V)$. Let $p(x) \in \mathscr{P}_F$ be any nonzero polynomial of which T is a zero. Suppose also that $g_1(x), \ldots, g_k(x)$ are (nonzero) polynomials such that $p(x) = g_1(x) \ldots g_k(x)$. Let U_1 be the null space of $g_1(T)$. For $i \geqq 2$, let U_i be the null space of $g_1(T) \circ \cdots \circ g_i(T)$.

a. Prove that $U_1 \subset U_2 \subset \cdots \subset U_k = V$.

b. Prove that U_i is T-invariant.

c. Suppose that $p(x)$ has minimal degree among all polynomials of which T is a zero [i.e., $p(x)$ is a minimal polynomial of T]. Prove that $g_i(T)$ is not 1–1 for every $i = 1, 2, \ldots, k$.

d. Suppose that $p(x)$ is a minimal polynomial of T and that $g_1(x)$ has degree one. That is, $g_1(x) = bx + a$, for some $a, b \in F$, $b \neq 0$. Prove that $-b/a$ is an eigenvalue of T.

e. Suppose that $p(x)$ is a minimal polynomial for T and that $p(x) = g_1(x) \ldots g_k(x)$, where $g_1(x), \ldots, g_k(x)$ are all polynomials of positive degree. Let $U_1, \ldots, U_k$ be as above. Prove that if $U_i = U_{i+1}$, for some i between 1 and k, then,

$$g_1(x) \cdots g_i(x) g_{i+2}(x) \cdots g_k(x) = g(x)$$

has T as a zero. [*Hint:* Note that if $(g_{i+2}(T) \circ \cdots \circ g_k(T))(\mathbf{v}) \in U_{i+1}$, then it belongs to U_i.] But degree $g(x) =$ degree $p(x) -$ degree $g_{i+1}(x) <$ degree $p(x)$, contradicting the minimality of degree $p(x)$.

This proves that $U_i \neq U_{i+1}$, for all i, and, hence, that in the sequence

$$U_1 \subset U_2 \subset \cdots \subset U_k = V,$$

the dimensions of the successive subspaces are strictly increasing.

f. If F is algebraically closed, and if V is n-dimensional, then T has a monic minimal polynomial of the form

$$p(x) = (x - \lambda_1)^{v_1} (x - \lambda_2)^{v_2} \ldots (x - \lambda_j)^{v_j},$$

where $\lambda_1, \lambda_2, \ldots, \lambda_k$ are (distinct) eigenvalues of T. Let

$$g_i(x) = \begin{cases} x - \lambda_1, \text{ for } i = 1, \ldots, v_1 \\ x - \lambda_j, j > 1, \text{ for } i = (v_1 + \cdots + v_{j-1} + 1), \ldots, (v_1 + \cdots + v_j) \end{cases}$$

Let U_i be as above. Choose a basis X_1 of U_1, enlarge it to a basis X_2 of U_2, and thence to a basis X_3 of U_3 and so on, obtaining, finally, a basis $X_k = X$ of V, where $k = v_1 + \cdots + v_j$. Show that

$$\mathscr{A}_{X,X}(T) \text{ is triangular.}$$

(We assume that the basis vectors are ordered so that those in U_i come before those not in U_i, $i = 1, \ldots, k$.)

5. Let V be any finite-dimensional vector space, and consider the homomorphism of algebras

$$\mathscr{E}_T : \mathscr{P}_F \in \mathrm{Trans}(V, V),$$

where $T \in \mathrm{Trans}(V, V)$. $\mathscr{E}_T$ is, among other things, a linear transformation. We have shown that $\mathscr{N}_{\mathscr{E}_T} \neq \{\bar{0}\}$.

a. Show that if $p(x) \in \mathscr{N}_{\mathscr{E}_T}$ and if $g(x) \in \mathscr{P}_F$, then $g(x)p(x) \in \mathscr{N}_{\mathscr{E}_T}$.

b. Let $p(x)$ be a polynomial of *minimal degree* among those in $\mathscr{N}_{\mathscr{E}_T}$. Choose any $g(x) \in \mathscr{N}_{\mathscr{E}_T}$. Use Proposition 7.9 to show that $g(x)$ is a polynomial multiple of $p(x)$.

c. Let $h(x)$ be any polynomial in $\mathscr{P}_F$, and let $\mathbf{v} \in V$ be an eigenvector of T. Say $T(\mathbf{v}) = \lambda\mathbf{v}$, for some $\lambda \in F$ Show that

$$[h(T)](\mathbf{v}) = h(\lambda)\mathbf{v}$$

d. Let $p(x)$ be as in **b**. Show that a scalar a is an eigenvalue of T, if and only if a is a zero of $p(x)$

Thus, $p(x)$ and $\det(T - xI_V)$ have precisely the same zeros.

e. Show that any two minimal polynomials for T differ only by a nonzero constant multiple and, hence, that there is only one *monic* minimal polynomial of T (which we call *the* minimal polynomial of T).

6. Let V, F, and T be as in **3** and **4.f**. Note that U_{v_1} in **4.f** equals the null space of $(T - \lambda_1 I_V)^{v_1}$. Since λ_1 is an eigenvalue of T, it is a zero of $\det(T - xI_V)$.

a. Think of x as a scalar indeterminate Show that U_{v_1} is $(T - xI_V)$-invariant.

b. Choose any basis for U_{v_1} and extend it to a basis X of V. Assume X ordered so that basis vectors in U_{v_1} precede those not in U_{v_1}. Show that $\mathscr{A}_{X,X,}(T - xI_V)$ is of the form

$$\begin{pmatrix} A & B \\ 0 & C \end{pmatrix}$$

where A is the matrix of $(T - xI_V)|U_{v_1}$ with respect to that part of X that is a basis of U_{v_1}. Show that $\det(T - xI_V) = (\det A)(\det C)$.

c. Choose a basis of Y of U_{v_1} so that the matrix $\mathscr{A}_{Y,Y}(T)|U_{v_1})$ is triangular. Let Y be extended to the basis X in **b**, letting $A = \mathscr{A}_{Y,Y}((T - xI_V)|U_{v_1})$. Use **b** to show that

$$\det(T - xI_V) = (x - \lambda_1)^{\ell} h(x),$$

where $h(x)$ is some polynomial in F, and $\ell =$ dimension U_{v_1}.

d. Use **4.e** to show that $\ell \geq v_1$.

The results of this exercise show that if $(x - \lambda_1)^{v_1}$ is the highest power of $x - \lambda_1$ dividing $p(x)$ a minimal polynomial of T, then $(x - \lambda_1)^{v_1}$ divides the characteristic polynomial of T, $\det(T - xI_V)$.

Thus, not only do $p(x)$ and $\det(T - xI_V)$ have the same zeros, but $p(x)$ divides $\det(T - xI_V)$. (The reader should prove this.)

This implies that T is a zero of $\det(T - xI_V)$. Since $\det(T - xI_V)$ is computable, this gives us some hold on the polynomials of which T is a zero.

We formulate this result as follows:

Let V be a finite-dimensional vector space over an algebraically closed field. Then every member of Trans(V, V) is a zero of its characteristic polynomial.

The result actually holds for any scalar field, but we shall not prove this here. The general case is known as the *Hamilton-Cayley Theorem*.

7. Let $T: \mathbf{R}^3 \to \mathbf{R}^3$ have matrix

$$\begin{pmatrix} -1 & 2 & 1 \\ -3 & 4 & 7 \\ 0 & 0 & 2 \end{pmatrix}$$

with respect to the standard basis of $\mathbf{R}^3$.

a. Determine the characteristic and minimal polynomials of T.

b. Determine a matrix of T in triangular form, using the method of Exercise 4.

5† / DIAGONAL FORMS—THE SPECTRAL THEOREM

In this section we apply some of the previous results to obtain, for certain kinds of transformations, diagonal matrices.

We shall be dealing exclusively with *inner product spaces* over **R** or **C**. The results for spaces over **C** are analogous to those for spaces over **R**, but because **C** is algebraically closed and **R** is not,** the methods of proof differ in the two cases.

First, we present the (simpler) case of inner product spaces over **C**.

5.1 The Complex Spectral Theorem

In this portion of our presentation V will always be an n-dimensional inner product space over **C**, $n \geqq 1$. Our main result will be stated first. Its proof will occupy the rest of 5.1.

Proposition 7.12

Let $T: V \to V$ be a linear transformation satisfying either (a) T is self-adjoint or (b) T is an inner product transformation (i.e., T is unitary). Then, there is an orthonormal basis $\{\mathbf{x}_1, \mathbf{x}_2, \ldots, \mathbf{x}_n\}$ of V consisting entirely of eigenvectors of T.

** e.g., the polynomial $x^2 + 1$ is in $\mathscr{P}_{\mathbf{R}}$ but its zeros are not real.

Corollary to Proposition 7.12

Let V and T be as above. Then, there exists an orthonormal basis X of V such that $\mathscr{A}_{X,X}(T)$ is a diagonal matrix.

Indeed, the basis X, furnished by Proposition 7.12, consisting entirely of eigenvectors of T, has the required property. For since $T(\mathbf{x}_j) = \lambda_j \mathbf{x}_j$, for $j = 1, \ldots, n$, $\mathscr{A}_{X,X}(T)$ is, by definition, the diagonal matrix with $\lambda_1, \lambda_2, \ldots, \lambda_n$ on its main diagonal (in that order, from upper left to lower right).

The following propositions are ingredients in the proof of Proposition 7.12.

Proposition 7.13

*Let $S : V \to V$ be any linear transformation, let Y be a basis of V for which $\mathscr{A}_{Y,Y}(S)$ is triangular, and let Z be a basis of V similar to Y.** Then, $\mathscr{A}_{Z,Z}(S)$ is triangular.*

Proof

For any basis $W = \{\mathbf{w}_1, \ldots, \mathbf{w}_n\}$ of V, $\mathscr{A}_{W,W}(S)$ is triangular if and only if

$$S(\text{span}(\{\mathbf{w}_1, \ldots, \mathbf{w}_i\})) \subset \text{span}(\{\mathbf{w}_1, \ldots, \mathbf{w}_i\}),$$

$i = 1, \ldots, n$. This follows immediately from the definitions of $\mathscr{A}_{W,W}(S)$ and "triangular."

Thus, since Z and Y are similar, and since $\mathscr{A}_{Y,Y}(S)$ is triangular,

$$\begin{aligned} S(\text{span}(\{\mathbf{z}_1, \ldots, \mathbf{z}_i\})) &= S(\text{span}(\{\mathbf{y}_1, \ldots, \mathbf{y}_i\})) \\ &\subset \text{span}(\{\mathbf{y}_1, \ldots, \mathbf{y}_i\}) = \text{span}(\{\mathbf{z}_1, \ldots, \mathbf{z}_i\}), \end{aligned}$$

$i = 1, 2, \ldots, n$. Therefore, $\mathscr{A}_{Z,Z}(S)$ is triangular. Q.E.D.

Corollary to Proposition 7.13

If $S : V \to V$ is any linear transformation, then there exists an orthonormal basis Z of V such that $\mathscr{A}_{Z,Z}(S)$ is triangular.

Proof

According to Proposition 7.6 (or its corollary), there is a basis Y of V such that $\mathscr{A}_{Y,Y}(S)$ is triangular (since $\mathbf{C}$ is algebraically closed). According to the Gram-Schmidt orthogonalization theorem, there is an orthonormal basis Z of V similar to Y. Thus, $\mathscr{A}_{Z,Z}(S)$ is triangular. Q.E.D.

Proposition 7.14

Let $S : V \to V$ be an isomorphism, and let Y be a basis of V such that $\mathscr{A}_{Y,Y}(S)$ is triangular. Then, $\mathscr{A}_{Y,Y}(S^{-1})$ is triangular.

** $Z = \{\mathbf{z}_1, \ldots, \mathbf{z}_n\}$ is *similar* to $Y = \{\mathbf{y}_1, \ldots, \mathbf{y}_n\}$ if and only if $\text{span}(\{\mathbf{z}_i, \ldots, \mathbf{z}_i\}) = \text{span}(\{\mathbf{y}_i, \ldots, \mathbf{y}_i\})$, $i = 1, \ldots, n$.

Proof

By the remark made at the beginning of the proof of Proposition 7.13,

$$S(\mathrm{span}(\{\mathbf{y}_1, \ldots, \mathbf{y}_i\})) \subset \mathrm{span}(\{\mathbf{y}_1, \ldots, \mathbf{y}_i\}),$$

for $i = 1, \ldots, n$. Let $U_i = \mathrm{span}(\{\mathbf{y}_1, \ldots, \mathbf{y}_i\})$. Since S is an isomorphism, it is 1–1, so that $S \mid U_i$ is 1–1, for all $i = 1, \ldots, n$. $S \mid U_i$ is, therefore, a 1–1 linear transformation from U_i to U_i, and so, since U_i is finite-dimensional, $S \mid U_i$ takes U_i *onto* U_i. That is, $S(U_i) = \mathscr{R}_{S \mid U_i} = U_i$, $i = 1, \ldots, n$.

Now, consider any $\mathbf{w} \in S^{-1}(U_i)$. By definition, $\mathbf{w} = S^{-1}(\mathbf{u})$, for some $\mathbf{u} \in U_i$, so that $S(\mathbf{w}) = \mathbf{u} \in U_i$. Since $S(U_i) = U_i$, there is a $\mathbf{v} \in U_i$ satisfying $S(\mathbf{v}) = \mathbf{u}$, so that

$$S(\mathbf{v} - \mathbf{w}) = \mathbf{u} - \mathbf{u} = \mathbf{0}$$

Because S is 1–1, $\mathscr{N}_S = \{\mathbf{0}\}$, so that $\mathbf{w} = \mathbf{v} \in U_i$. Thus, $S^{-1}(U_i) \subset U_i$, for all $i = 1, \ldots, n$. Again, by the remark made at the beginning of the proof of Proposition 7.13, this implies that $\mathscr{A}_{Y,Y}(S^{-1})$ is triangular. Q.E.D.

We shall say that a matrix is *transpose-triangular* if and only if it is the transpose of a triangular matrix (i.e., obtained from some triangular matrix by interchanging its rows with its columns). Another, equivalent, definition of a transpose-triangular matrix is that it is a square matrix with only zeros *above* the main diagonal.

Clearly, a matrix is both triangular and transpose-triangular (simultaneously) if and only if it is a diagonal matrix.

Proposition 7.15

*Let $T : V \to V$ be a linear transformation, and let Y be an orthonormal basis of V such that $\mathscr{A}_{Y,Y}(T)$ is triangular. Then, $\mathscr{A}_{Y,Y}(T^*)$ is transpose-triangular.***

Proof

Let $\mathscr{A}_{Y,Y}(T) = (a_{ij})$ and $\mathscr{A}_{Y,Y}(T^*) = (b_{ij})$. Then, by definition,

$$T(\mathbf{y}_j) = a_{1j}\mathbf{y}_1 + \cdots + a_{nj}\mathbf{y}_n$$

$$T^*(\mathbf{y}_j) = b_{1j}\mathbf{y}_1 + \cdots + b_{nj}\mathbf{y}_n$$

According to Proposition 6.7(1),

$$a_{ij} = [T(\mathbf{y}_j), \mathbf{y}_i]_V$$

and

$$b_{ij} = [T^*(\mathbf{y}_j), \mathbf{y}_i]_V$$

** T^* is the adjoint of T in the context of inner product spaces. See definition 6.6.

By definition of T^*,

$$\begin{aligned} a_{ij} = [T(\mathbf{y}_j), \mathbf{y}_i]_V &= [\mathbf{y}_j, T^*(\mathbf{y}_i)]_V \\ &= \overline{[T^*(\mathbf{y}_i), \mathbf{y}_j]_V} \\ &= \overline{b_{ji}} \end{aligned}$$

Since (a_{ij}) is triangular, $a_{ij} = 0$, for $i > j$. Therefore, $\overline{b_{ji}} = 0$, for $i > j$, which is equivalent to the equation, $b_{ji} = 0$, for $i > j$. This means that all b's above the main diagonal are zero, so that (b_{ij}) is transpose-triangular. Q.E.D.

Proof of Proposition 7.12

(1) *T is self-adjoint.*

According to Corollary to Proposition 7.13, there is an orthonormal basis X of V such that $\mathscr{A}_{X,X}(T)$ is triangular. Therefore, by Proposition 7.15, $\mathscr{A}_{X,X}(T^*)$ is transpose-triangular. But, since T is self-adjoint (i.e., $T = T^*$), $\mathscr{A}_{X,X}(T) = \mathscr{A}_{X,X}(T^*)$. Thus, $\mathscr{A}_{X,X}(T)$ is both triangular and transpose-triangular. Therefore, it is a diagonal matrix, or, equivalently, the basis vectors are eigenvectors of T.

(2) *T is unitary.*

According to Corollary to Proposition 7.13, V has an orthonormal basis such that $\mathscr{A}_{X,X}(T)$ is triangular. Therefore, $\mathscr{A}_{X,X}(T^{-1})$ is triangular, and $\mathscr{A}_{X,X}(T^*)$ is transpose-triangular. But, according to Exercises 6.6.**12**, $T^{-1} = T^*$ (because T is unitary), so that $\mathscr{A}_{X,X}(T^{-1})$ is both triangular and transpose-triangular, and, hence, it is diagonal. Thus, $X = \{\mathbf{x}_1, \ldots, \mathbf{x}_n\}$ consists of eigenvectors of T^{-1}. That is, $T^{-1}(\mathbf{x}_i) = a_i\mathbf{x}_i$, $i = 1, \ldots, n$. Note that since T^{-1} is 1–1, none of the a_i is zero. Apply T to both sides of the equation $T^{-1}(\mathbf{x}_i) = a_i\mathbf{x}_i$, and divide by a_i, obtaining $T(\mathbf{x}_i) = 1/a_i\mathbf{x}_i$. This means that X consists of eigenvectors of T. Q.E.D.

5.2 The Spectral Theorem for Real, Self-Adjoint Linear Transformations

Again, we state the main result first and then develop the material needed for its proof. Throughout 5.2, V is an n-dimensional inner product space over **R**.

Proposition 7.16

Let $T: V \to V$ be a self-adjoint linear transformation. Then, there is an orthonormal basis X of V consisting entirely of eigenvectors of T (or, equivalently, $\mathscr{A}_{X,X}(T)$ is diagonal).

We need three subsidiary results.

Proposition 7.17

Let $T: V \to V$ be a self-adjoint linear transformation. If U is an S-invariant subspace of V, then $U^{\perp}$, the orthogonal complement of U, is S^*-invariant.

Proof

Let S and U be as proposed. To show that $U^{\perp}$ is S^*-invariant choose any $\mathbf{v} \in U^{\perp}$. By definition, $[\mathbf{u}, \mathbf{v}]_V = 0$, for all $\mathbf{u} \in U$. We must show that $[\mathbf{u}, S^*(\mathbf{v})] = 0$, for all $\mathbf{u} \in U$. Now by definition of S^*,

$$[\mathbf{u}, S^*(\mathbf{v})]_V = [S(\mathbf{u}), \mathbf{v}]_V$$

Since U is S-invariant, $S(\mathbf{u}) \in U$, so that $[S(\mathbf{u}), \mathbf{v}]_V = 0$. Thus,

$$[\mathbf{u}, S^*(\mathbf{v})]_V = 0,$$

for all $\mathbf{u} \in U$. Q.E.D.

Proposition 7.18

Let $S: V \to V$ be any self-adjoint linear transformation, and let $U \subset V$ be any S-invariant subspace of V. Then, $S \mid U$ is a self-adjoint linear transformation in Trans(U, U).

Proof

First, recall that U is an inner product space with respect to the inner product of V restricted to U. Next, recall that any linear transformation in Trans(U, U) has an adjoint; in particular, $S \mid U$ has an adjoint, $(S \mid U)^*$, which is the unique member R of Trans(U, U) satisfying

$$[(S \mid U)(\mathbf{u}), \mathbf{v}]_U = [\mathbf{u}, R(\mathbf{v})]_U \tag{$*$}$$

for all $(\mathbf{u}, \mathbf{v}) \in U \times U$.

But S is self-adjoint, $(S \mid U)(\mathbf{u}) = S(\mathbf{u})$, and $[\ ,\ ]_U = [\ ,\ ]_V \mid U \times U$. Therefore, $[(S \mid U)(\mathbf{u}), \mathbf{v}]_U = [S(\mathbf{u}), \mathbf{v}]_V = [\mathbf{u}, S(\mathbf{v})]_V = [\mathbf{u}, (S \mid U)(\mathbf{v})]_U$, for all $(\mathbf{u}, \mathbf{v}) U \times U$. Thus, $S \mid U$ satisfies $(*)$—taking the place of R—so that since there is only one R satisfying $(*)$ (by definition, $(S \mid U)^*$), it follows that $(S \mid U)^* = S \mid U$. That is, $S \mid U$ is self-adjoint. Q.E.D.

Proposition 7.19

Let $S: V \to V$ be any self-adjoint linear transformation, and let $p(x) = x^2 + ax + b \in \mathscr{P}_R$ be any monic, second-degree polynomial of which S is a zero. Then, there are real numbers λ_1 and λ_2 (perhaps equal) such that $p(x) = (x - \lambda_1)(x - \lambda_2)$.

Proof

Determine the (perhaps complex) zeros of $p(x)$ by the usual formula:

$$\lambda_1 = -(1/2)a + 1/2\sqrt{a^2 - 4b}$$

$$\lambda_2 = -(1/2)a - 1/2\sqrt{a^2 - 4b}$$

Clearly, $p(x) = (x - \lambda_1)(x - \lambda_2)$. It remains only to show that λ_1 and λ_2 are real numbers. For this, it is necessary and sufficient to show that $a^2 \geqq 4b$.

We rewrite $p(x)$ as follows:

$$p(x) = \left(x + \frac{a}{2}\right)^2 + \left(b - \frac{a^2}{4}\right)$$

Since $p(S) = \bar{\mathbf{0}}$, we have

$$\left(S + \frac{aI_V}{2}\right) \circ \left(S + \frac{aI_V}{2}\right) = \left(\frac{a^2}{4} - b\right)I_V$$

Now, since S is self-adjoint, so is $S + (a/2)I_V$ (see Exercises 7.5.7). Therefore, for any $\mathbf{v} \in V$, letting

$$\mathbf{w} = \left(S + \frac{aI_V}{2}\right)(\mathbf{v}),$$

$$\left[\left(S + \frac{aI_V}{2}\right)(\mathbf{w}), \mathbf{v}\right] = \left[\mathbf{w}, \left(S + \frac{aI_V}{2}\right)(\mathbf{v})\right]$$

$$= [\mathbf{w}, \mathbf{w}] \geqq 0$$

On the other hand,

$$\left(S + \frac{aI_V}{2}\right)(\mathbf{w}) = \left(S + \frac{aI_V}{2}\right) \circ \left(S + \frac{aI_V}{2}\right)(\mathbf{v})$$

$$= \left(\frac{a^2}{4} - b\right)I_V(\mathbf{v}) = \left(\frac{a^2}{4} - b\right)\mathbf{v},$$

so that

$$\left[\left(S + \frac{aI_V}{2}\right)(\mathbf{w}), \mathbf{v}\right] = \left[\left(\frac{a^2}{4} - b\right)\mathbf{v}, \mathbf{v}\right] = \left(\frac{a^2}{4} - b\right)[\mathbf{v}, \mathbf{v}],$$

and, hence,

$$\left(\frac{a^2}{4} - b\right)[\mathbf{v}, \mathbf{v}] = [\mathbf{w}, \mathbf{w}] \geqq 0$$

This holds for all $\mathbf{v} \in V$. Since $\dim V = n \geqq 1$, there is at least one $\mathbf{v} \in V$ that is nonzero, so that $[\mathbf{v}, \mathbf{v}] > 0$. Since for this $\mathbf{v}$, the above inequality holds, it is impossible for $a^2/4 - b$ to be <0. Thus, $a^2/4 - b \geqq 0$, or $a^2 \geqq 4b$. Q.E.D.

Proof of Proposition 7.16

We proceed inductively according to the dimension of V.

If $\dim V = 1$, the result is obvious because every 1×1 matrix is a diagonal matrix. Assume that the result holds for all inner product spaces (over $\mathbf{R}$) of dimension k, and suppose that $\dim V = k + 1$.

We show, first, that T has an eigenvector. That is, we show that there exist a nonzero vector $\mathbf{v} \in V$ and a real number λ_0 such that $T(\mathbf{v}_0) = \lambda_0 \mathbf{v}_0$.

Let $g(x)$ be the minimal polynomial of T. That is $g(x)$ is the monic polynomial of least degree among all those polynomials of which T is a zero (cf. Exercises 7.4.5). If $g(x)$ has degree one, then $g(x) = x - a$, so that $\bar{\mathbf{0}} = T - aI_V$, or $T = aI_V$. Every vector $\mathbf{v} \in V$ is, then, an eigenvector of T. If degree $g(x) \geqq 2$, then $g(x)$ has a factor of degree one or two.** If it has a factor of degree one, say $x - a$, then according to Exercises 7.4.**4.d** a is an eigenvalue of T, so that $T(\mathbf{v}) = a\mathbf{v}$ for some $\mathbf{v} \in V$.

Finally, suppose that $p(x)$ is a factor of $g(x)$ of degree two, say $p(x) = x^2 + ax + b$. We shall show that $p(x) = (x - \lambda_1)(x - \lambda_2)$, for some λ_1, λ_2 in $\mathbf{R}$. Let $U = \mathcal{N}_{p(T)}$. U is T-invariant, and, by Proposition 7.18, $T \mid U$ is a self-adjoint transformation from U to U. Moreover, $T \mid U$ is a zero of $p(x)$, because $U = \mathcal{N}_{p(T)}$ and $\dim U \neq O$, by Exercises 7.4.**4**. **c**. Thus, by Proposition 7.19, $p(x) = (x - \lambda_1)(x - \lambda_2)$, as desired.

Therefore, $x - \lambda_1$ is a factor of $g(x)$ of degree one, so that λ_1 is an eigenvalue of T, and $T(\mathbf{v}) = \lambda_1 \mathbf{v}$, for some $\mathbf{v} \in V$.

Thus, T has an eigenvector $\mathbf{v}_0 \in V$. Let $W = \text{span}_V(\{\mathbf{v}_0\})$, the eigenray containing $\mathbf{v}_0$. W is T-invariant. Therefore, by Proposition 7.17, $W^\perp$ is T^*-invariant. Since $T = T^*$, this means that $W^\perp$ is T-invariant. Now by Proposition 7.18, $T \mid W^\perp$ is self-adjoint. Moreover, by Proposition 6.13, (5) and (6),

$$W \oplus W^\perp = V$$

so that $\dim W^\perp = \dim V - \dim W = (k + 1) - 1 = k$. Therefore, the inductive assumption applies to $W^\perp$ and $T \mid W^\perp$. That is, $W^\perp$ has an orthonormal basis $\{\mathbf{v}_2, \mathbf{v}_3, \ldots, \mathbf{v}_{k+1}\}$ consisting of eigenvectors of $T \mid W^\perp$.

Let $\mathbf{v}_1$ be the normalization of $\mathbf{v}_0$. Then, we claim *that* $\{\mathbf{v}_1, \mathbf{v}_2, \ldots, \mathbf{v}_{k+1}\}$ *is an orthonormal basis of V consisting of eigenvectors of T.*

To see this, note first that $\{\mathbf{v}_1, \mathbf{v}_2, \ldots, \mathbf{v}_{k+1}\}$ is an orthonormal subset of V. In particular, the $\mathbf{v}_i$ are nonzero and mutually orthogonal. Thus, they are linearly independent. Since there are $k + 1$ of them and $\dim V = k + 1$, $\{\mathbf{v}_1, \mathbf{v}_2, \ldots, \mathbf{v}_{k+1}\}$ is an orthonormal basis of V. Next, since $\mathbf{v}_1$ is the normalization of the eigenvector $\mathbf{v}_0$, $\mathbf{v}_1$ is a multiple of $\mathbf{v}_0$. Therefore, it, too, is an eigenvector of T. Finally, for any i between 2 and $k + 1$, $\mathbf{v}_i$ is an eigenvector of $T \mid W^\perp$, so that

$$T(\mathbf{v}_i) = (T \mid W^\perp)(\mathbf{v}_i) = \lambda_i \mathbf{v}_i$$

for some $\lambda_i \in \mathbf{R}$. Therefore, $\mathbf{v}_i$ is an eigenvector of T. Q.E.D.

** Every polynomial with real coefficients is the product of polynomials in $\mathscr{P}_{\mathbf{R}}$ of degree one or two. This fact is proved in advanced algebra high school courses.

The reader will note that the real and complex cases are the same for self-adjoint transformations. For inner product transformations, however, the real and complex results differ. In general, there are real inner product transformations with no eigenvalues.

For example, let $T:\mathbf{R}^2 \to \mathbf{R}^2$ have the following matrix with respect to the standard basis of $\mathbf{R}^2$:

$$\begin{pmatrix} 1/2 & -\sqrt{3}/2 \\ \sqrt{3}/2 & 1/2 \end{pmatrix}$$

The reader should verify that T is an inner product transformation, with respect to the standard inner product on $\mathbf{R}^2$.

Now,

$$\det(T - xI_V) = \begin{pmatrix} 1/2 - x & -\sqrt{3}/2 \\ \sqrt{3}/2 & 1/2 - x \end{pmatrix}$$
$$= (1/2 - x)^2 + 3/4 = x^2 - x + 1$$

This polynomial has *strictly complex* zeros $1/2(1 \pm i\sqrt{3})$. Therefore T has no eigenvectors.

Another way to see that T has no eigenvectors is to observe that T is just rotation through 60° ($= \pi/3$ radians). Thus, no vector is taken by T into a multiple of itself [except (0, 0)].

Although the spectral theorem does not hold for real inner product transformations, however, something almost as good does hold. It can be shown that any real inner product transformation has a matrix, with respect to some orthonormal basis, of the form

$$\begin{pmatrix} \mathfrak{a}_1 & & & & \\ & \mathfrak{a}_2 & & O & \\ & & \cdot & & \\ & & & \cdot & \\ & O & & & \cdot \\ & & & & \mathfrak{a}_k \end{pmatrix}$$

where $\mathfrak{a}_i$ is either a 1×1 matrix whose lone entry is 1 or -1, or a 2×2 orthogonal matrix—that is, a matrix of the form

$$\begin{pmatrix} a & c \\ b & d \end{pmatrix}$$

where $a^2 + b^2 = c^2 + d^2 = 1$ and $ac + bd = 0$. This result will be developed and elaborated on in the exercises.

In 5.3, examples and some applications of the foregoing results will be presented.

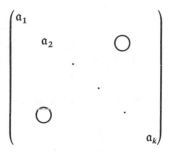

EXERCISES / 7.5

1. Let $T: V \to V$ be any linear transformation, where V is any vector space over any field F. Let $\mathbf{v}_1, \mathbf{v}_2, \ldots, \mathbf{v}_k$ be eigenvectors of T, each corresponding to a different eigenvalue of T: say $T(\mathbf{v}_i) = \lambda_i \mathbf{v}_i$, where $\lambda_j \neq \lambda_i$ if $j \neq i$, $i, j = 1, 2, 3, \ldots, k$.
   Suppose that $\{\mathbf{v}_1, \ldots, \mathbf{v}_k\}$ is dependent. Then, some one of these is a linear combination of preceding vectors (i.e., of vectors with smaller subscripts). Let $\mathbf{v}_{i+1}$ be the vector with smallest subscript for which this is true. That is,
   $$\mathbf{v}_{i+1} = a_1\mathbf{v}_1 + \cdots + a_i\mathbf{v}_i$$
   and, for no $j < i + 1$ is $\mathbf{v}_j \in \operatorname{span}_V(\{\mathbf{v}_1, \ldots, \mathbf{v}_{j-1}\})$.
   Apply T to both sides, and obtain a contradiction.
   Thus, $\{\mathbf{v}_1, \ldots, \mathbf{v}_k\}$ is linearly independent.

2. Let V be an inner product space, and let $T: V \to V$ be a self-adjoint linear transformation or an inner product transformation.
   Prove that if $\mathbf{v}_1$ and $\mathbf{v}_2$ are eigenvectors of T, corresponding, respectively, to eigenvalues of T, λ_1 and λ_2, where $\lambda_1 \neq \lambda_2$, then $[\mathbf{v}_1, \mathbf{v}_2]_V = 0$. That is, $\mathbf{v}_1$ is orthogonal to $\mathbf{v}_2$.

3. Let V be a finite-dimensional inner product space, and let $S: V \to V$ be a linear transformation.
   a. Prove that $(S^*)^* = S$.
   b. Prove that $(\mathscr{R}_S)^\perp = \mathscr{N}_{S^*}$. (*Hint*: Show that $(\mathscr{R}_S)^\perp \subset \mathscr{N}_{S^*}$ by choosing any $\mathbf{v} \in (\mathscr{R}_S)^\perp$ and showing that $[S^*(\mathbf{v}), S^*(\mathbf{v})] = 0$. Then, show that
   $$\dim(\mathscr{R}_S)^\perp = \dim \mathscr{N}_{S^*})$$
   c. Prove that $(\mathscr{R}_{S^*})^\perp = \mathscr{N}_S$. (*Hint*: Combine **a** and **b**.)
   d. Use **b** and **c**, together with Proposition 6.13, (7), to show that $\mathscr{R}_{S^*} = (\mathscr{N}_S)^\perp$ and $\mathscr{R}_S = (\mathscr{N}_{S^*})^\perp$.

4. Let V and S be as in Exercise **3**, and assume that $S \circ S^* = S^* \circ S$. (We call such an S *normal*.)
   a. Show that for any $\mathbf{v} \in V$,
   $$[S(\mathbf{v}), S(\mathbf{v})]_V = [S^*(\mathbf{v}), S^*(\mathbf{v})]_V$$
   b. Use **a** to show that $\mathscr{N}_S = \mathscr{N}_{S^*}$.
   c. Use **b** and **3d** to conclude that
   $$\mathscr{R}_S \cap \mathscr{N}_S = 0$$
   Thus, for any $\mathbf{v} \in V$, if $S[S(\mathbf{v})] = \mathbf{0}$, then $S(\mathbf{v}) = \mathbf{0}$.
   d. Prove that for every scalar a,
   $$(S - aI_V)^* \circ (S - aI_V) = (S - aI_V) \circ (S - aI_V)^*$$

e. Prove that if $(S - aI_V)^2 \mid U$ is identically $\mathbf{0}$, for some subspace $U \subset V$, then $S - aI_V \mid U$ is identically $\mathbf{0}$.

f. Let $p(x)$ be the minimal polynomial of S, and suppose that $p(x) = (x - a)^2 g(x)$. Show that S is a zero of $(x - a)g(x)$, thus contradicting the minimality of degree of $p(x)$. (*Hint*: Let $U = \mathscr{R}_{g(S)}$ and apply **4.e.**)

Thus, the minimal polynomial of S does not have repeated first degree factors.

5. Let V be an n-dimensional inner product space, $n \geqq 1$, and let $S: V \to V$ be an inner product transformation. Suppose that S is a zero of the polynomial $p(x) = x^2 + ax + b$.

a. Show that there are nonzero vectors $\mathbf{v}$ and $\mathbf{w}$ in V such that $S(\mathbf{v}) = c\mathbf{v} + d\mathbf{w}$ and $S(\mathbf{w}) = e\mathbf{v} + f\mathbf{w}$, for some scalars c, d, e, f. [*Hint*: Choose any nonzero $\mathbf{v}$, and let $\mathbf{w} = S(\mathbf{v})$.]

b. Show that either S has an eigenvector or there are orthonormal vectors $\mathbf{v}_1$ and $\mathbf{v}_2$ such that span$(\{\mathbf{v}_1, \mathbf{v}_2\})$ is S-invariant.

c. Let S, $\mathbf{v}_1$, and $\mathbf{v}_2$ be as in **b**, and let $U = \text{span}(\{\mathbf{v}_1, \mathbf{v}_2\})$. Show that there is a real number θ such that the matrix of $S|U$ with respect to $\{\mathbf{v}_1, \mathbf{v}_2\}$ is

$$\begin{pmatrix} \cos\theta & -\sin\theta \\ \sin\theta & \cos\theta \end{pmatrix} \quad \text{or} \quad \begin{pmatrix} \cos\theta & \sin\theta \\ \sin\theta & -\cos\theta \end{pmatrix}$$

6*. Let V be any n-dimensional inner product space over $\mathbf{R}$, $n \geqq 1$, and let $S: V \to V$ be any inner product transformation.

a. If λ is an eigenvalue of S, then $\lambda = \pm 1$. Prove this. (*Hint*: Consider $\|S(\mathbf{v})\|^2$, for any eigenvector $\mathbf{v}$ of S.)

b. Let $p(x)$ be the minimal polynomial of S. Show that if $p(x)$ has degree one, then $S = \pm I_V$.

c. Suppose that degree $p(x) \geqq 2$, and let $g(x) = x^2 + ax + b$ be a factor of $p(x)$. Show that $g(S)$ is not 1–1. [*Hint*: $p(x) = g(x)h(x)$, so that $\bar{\mathbf{0}} = g(S) \circ h(S)$; moreover $p(x)$ is the *minimal* polynomial of S.]

d. Show that there is an S-invariant subspace $U \subset V$, such that dim $S = 1$ or 2. (*Hint*: Consider $S \mid \mathscr{N}_{g(S)}$, and apply the results of **5**, above.) Show that if dim $U = 1$, then $S \mid U$ has a 1×1 matrix (± 1), and if dim $U = 2$, then S $\mid U$ has a matrix of the type exhibited in **5c**, above.

e. Show that if W is an S-invariant subspace of V, then so is $W^\perp$.

f. Show that V has an orthonormal basis X such that

$$\mathscr{A}_{X,X}(S) = \begin{pmatrix} \alpha_1 & & & & \\ & \alpha_2 & & \bigcirc & \\ & & \cdot & & \\ & & & \cdot & \\ & \bigcirc & & & \cdot \\ & & & & \alpha_k \end{pmatrix}$$

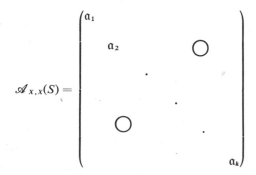

where $\mathfrak{a}_i = (\pm 1)$ or

$$\begin{pmatrix} \cos\theta & -\sin\theta \\ \sin\theta & \cos\theta \end{pmatrix} \quad \text{or}$$

$$\begin{pmatrix} \cos\theta & \sin\theta \\ \sin\theta & -\cos\theta \end{pmatrix} \quad \text{(for some } \theta\text{, depending on } i\text{)}$$

(*Hint*: "Break up" V into a direct sum of 1 or 2 dimensional S-invariant subspaces.)

7. Let V be any finite-dimensional inner product space and $T: V \to V$ any linear transformation. Prove that for any polynomial $p(x) \in \mathscr{P}_F$, $[p(T)]^* = p(T^*)$. Conclude that if T is self-adjoint, then so is $p(T)$.

5.3 Applications and Examples

We present one theoretical application.

Proposition 7.20

Let V be any finite-dimensional inner product space, and let $T: V \to V$ be an isomorphism. Then, there exist one and only one self-adjoint transformation with positive eigenvalues A and one and only one inner product transformation S such that

$$T = A \circ S.$$

Proof

First we show that A and S exist. Then we show that they are unique.

(1) Let $B = T \circ T^*$, where T^* is the adjoint of T. Note that, for all $(\mathbf{v}, \mathbf{w}) \in V \times V$,

$$\begin{aligned}[B(\mathbf{v}), \mathbf{w}] &= [T(T^*(\mathbf{v})), \mathbf{w}] \\ &= [T^*(\mathbf{v}), T^*(\mathbf{w})] = [\mathbf{v}, T(T^*(\mathbf{w}))] \\ &= [\mathbf{v}, B(\mathbf{w})]\end{aligned}$$

Thus, by definition of B^*, $B = B^*$. That is, B is self-adjoint. Therefore, there is a basis $X = \{\mathbf{x}_1, \ldots, \mathbf{x}_n\}$ of V that is orthonormal and consists entirely of eigenvectors of B. Note that $[B(\mathbf{v}), \mathbf{v}] = [T^*(\mathbf{v}), T^*(\mathbf{v})] \geqq 0$, for all $\mathbf{v} \in V$. Therefore, $0 \leqq [B(\mathbf{x}_i), \mathbf{x}_i] = [\lambda_i \mathbf{x}_i, \mathbf{x}_i] = [\lambda_i \mathbf{x}_i, \mathbf{x}_i]$, for all $i = 1, \ldots, n$. Since $\mathbf{x}_i \neq \mathbf{0}$, $[\mathbf{x}_i, \mathbf{x}_i] > 0$, so that $\lambda_i \geqq 0$. Moreover, since T is an isomorphism, it is easy to show that T^* is an isomorphism, and, therefore, $B = T \circ T^*$ is an isomorphism. Thus, $\lambda_i \neq 0$. That is, all $\lambda_i > 0$, $i = 1, \ldots, n$ (where λ_i is the eigenvalue corresponding to the eigenvector $\mathbf{x}_i$).

Define $A \in \text{Trans}(V, V)$ as follows: It is the unique linear transformation from V to V satisfying $A(\mathbf{x}_i) = (\sqrt{\lambda_i})\mathbf{x}_i$, $i = 1, \ldots, n$. Clearly the $\mathbf{x}_i$ are eigenvectors of A corresponding to the eigenvalues $\sqrt{\lambda_i}$, respectively. The matrix $\mathscr{A}_{X,X}(A)$ is a diagonal matrix with $\sqrt{\lambda_1}, \sqrt{\lambda_2}, \ldots, \sqrt{\lambda_n}$ on the main diagonal. Thus, $\det A = \sqrt{\lambda_1 \lambda_2 \ldots \lambda_n} \neq 0$, so that A is an isomorphism. A is self-adjoint, since its matrix with respect to X is its own conjugate-transpose. Let $S = A^{-1} \circ T$. Then, $T = A \circ S$, so that it remains to show that S is an inner product transformation. Note that $A^2(\mathbf{x}_i) = A(A(\mathbf{x}_i)) = \lambda_i \mathbf{x}_i$, $i = 1, \ldots, n$ so that $A^2 = B$.

We now make use of the following equalities relating the adjoint to composition and inverse of transformations:

$$\text{(i) } (T_1 \circ T_2)^* = T_2^* \circ T_1^* \qquad \text{(ii) } (T_1^{-1})^* = (T_1^*)^{-1}.$$

We outline proofs of these relations in subsequent exercises. Now, consider the following:

$$\begin{aligned} S^* \circ S &= (A^{-1} \circ T)^* \circ (A^{-1} \circ T) \\ &= T^* \circ (A^{-1})^* \circ A^{-1} \circ T \\ &= T^* \circ (A^*)^{-1} \circ A^{-1} \circ T = T^* \circ (A^2)^{-1} \circ T \\ &= T^* \circ B^{-1} \circ T \\ &= T^* \circ (T \circ T^*)^{-1} \circ T \\ &= (T^* \circ (T^*)^{-1}) \circ (T^{-1} \circ T) \\ &= I_V, \end{aligned}$$

so that $S^* = S^{-1}$. This means that S is an inner product transformation.**

(2) Suppose that A_1 is a self-adjoint linear transformation from V to V, with positive eigenvalues, and that $S_1 : V \to V$ is an inner product transformation, such that $T = A_1 \circ S_1$. Then,

$$\begin{aligned} A^2 = B = T \circ T^* &= (A_1 \circ S_1) \circ (A_1 \circ S_1)^* \\ &= A_1 \circ (S_1 \circ S_1^*) \circ A_1^* \\ &= A_1 \circ (S_1 \circ S_1^{-1}) \circ A_1 = A_1^2 \end{aligned}$$

We shall show, first, that every eigenvector of A is an eigenvector of A_1. Then, we show that $A = A_1$ and $S = S_1$.

Suppose that $\mathbf{v}$ is an eigenvector of A, and let $\{\mathbf{v}_1, \mathbf{v}_2, \ldots, \mathbf{v}_n\}$ be an orthonormal basis consisting of eigenvectors of A_1. Then, we may write

$$\mathbf{v} = a_1\mathbf{v}_1 + \cdots + a_n\mathbf{v}_n$$

Let $\lambda, \lambda_1, \ldots, \lambda_n$ be such that $A(\mathbf{v}) = \lambda\mathbf{v}$ and $A_1(\mathbf{v}_i) = \lambda_i v_i$, $i = 1, \ldots, n$. Apply $A^2 = A_1^2$ to both sides of the above equation. We get

$$\lambda^2\mathbf{v} = a_1\lambda_1^2\mathbf{v}_1 + \cdots + a_n\lambda_n^2\mathbf{v}_n$$

** See Exercises 6.5.**12**.

On the other hand, multiply the first equation by λ^2, and subtract from the second:

$$\mathbf{0} = a_1(\lambda_1{}^2 - \lambda^2)\mathbf{v}_1 + \cdots + a_n(\lambda_n{}^2 - \lambda^2)\mathbf{v}_n$$

Since $\{\mathbf{v}_1, \ldots, \mathbf{v}_n\}$ is linearly independent, the coefficients of this combination are zero. That is,

$$a_i(\lambda_i{}^2 - \lambda^2) = 0,$$

so that either $a_i = 0$ or $\lambda_i{}^2 = \lambda^2$. Since both λ_i and λ are positive, we conclude that either $a_i = 0$ or $\lambda_i = \lambda$. Thus, in the combination

$$\mathbf{v} = a_1\mathbf{v}_1 + \cdots + a_n\mathbf{v}_n,$$

the only $\mathbf{v}_i$ that appear with nonzero coefficients are those corresponding to the eigenvalue λ of A_1. That is, $\mathbf{v}$ is a linear combination of eigenvectors of A_1 corresponding to the fixed eigenvalue λ. These vectors belong to the eigenspace U_λ of A_1, which is a vector subspace of V. Hence, so do all their combinations: $\mathbf{v} \in U_\lambda$, or $A_1(\mathbf{v}) = \lambda\mathbf{v}$.

Thus, every eigenvector of A is an eigenvector of A_1. Indeed, in the process of proving this assertion, we showed that if $A(\mathbf{v}) = \lambda\mathbf{v}$, then $A_1(\mathbf{v}) = \lambda\mathbf{v}$.

Now, let $\mathbf{x}_1, \ldots, \mathbf{x}_n$ be a basis of V consisting of eigenvectors of A. Then it is also a basis of V consisting of eigenvectors of A_1. Indeed, if $A(\mathbf{x}_i) = \lambda_i\mathbf{x}_i$, for some scalar λ_i, then $A_1(x_i) = \lambda_i\mathbf{x}_i$. Thus,

$$A(\mathbf{x}_i) = A_1(\mathbf{x}_i)$$

for all $i = 1, \ldots, n$, so that $A = A_1$.

Therefore, since

$$A \circ S = A_1 \circ S_1,$$

we have $S = A^{-1} \circ A_1 \circ S_1 = S_1$. Q.E.D.

This result has a nice interpretation in case $V = \mathbf{R}^2$. First, note that if $A: \mathbf{R}^2 \to \mathbf{R}^2$ is self-adjoint (with respect to the standard inner product of $\mathbf{R}^2$), then, there exist mutually perpendicular vectors of unit length, $\mathbf{v}_1$ and $\mathbf{v}_2$, such that $A(\mathbf{v}_1) = \lambda_1\mathbf{v}_1$ and $A(\mathbf{v}_2) = \lambda_2\mathbf{v}_2$, for real numbers λ_1 and λ_2. If $\lambda_1 > 0$ and $\lambda_2 > 0$, we may describe the effect of A on $\mathbf{v}_1$ and $\mathbf{v}_2$ by saying that A "stretches" $\mathbf{v}_1$ and $\mathbf{v}_2$ in the ratios $\lambda_1 : 1$ and $\lambda_2 : 1$, respectively. (Of course, if $0 < \lambda_1 < 1$ or $0 < \lambda_2 < 1$, then A does not really stretch the vectors but "contracts" them. Nevertheless, we can think of *contraction* as *stretching in a ratio less than one*.) Thus, it is reasonable to call every self-adjoint linear transformation from $\mathbf{R}^2$ to $\mathbf{R}^2$ with positive eigenvalues a *stretching* (in certain mutually perpendicular directions). Moreover, by Exercises 7.5.**5c**, every inner product transformation $S: R^2 \to R^2$, *with positive determinant* has a matrix of the form

$$\begin{pmatrix} \cos\theta & -\sin\theta \\ \sin 0 & \cos\theta \end{pmatrix},$$

for some θ (with respect to the standard basis of $\mathbf{R}^2$). That is, S is a *rotation* through the angle θ.

Therefore, the above proposition tells us that *every orientation-preserving isomorphism from* $\mathbf{R}^2$ *to* $\mathbf{R}^2$ (i.e., every isomorphism with positive determinant —so that it takes positively oriented parallelograms to positively oriented ones, and negatively oriented ones to negatively oriented ones) *is the composition of a rotation and a stretching*. This gives a pretty good picture of the nature of isomorphisms from $\mathbf{R}^2$ to $\mathbf{R}^2$. The case of isomorphisms with negative determinants is described in the exercises. An analogous interpretation can be constructed for higher dimensional inner product spaces over $\mathbf{R}$ or for inner product spaces over $\mathbf{C}$.

One fact should be emphasized, however. (And it is this fact that leads to enormous complications in advanced linear algebra.) Although every self-adjoint transformation has a nice (diagonal) matrix and every inner product transformation has a nice (diagonal, if $F = \mathbf{C}$, close to diagonal, if $F = \mathbf{R}$) matrix, in general, these matrices are obtained with respect to different bases, depending on the transformation in question. That is, in general, it is *not* possible to find a basis X of V such that $\mathscr{A}_{X,X}(A)$ *and* $\mathscr{A}_{X,X}(S)$ *are both diagonal*, where A and S are given self-adjoint and inner product transformations, respectively. Thus, in general, it is not possible to obtain a diagonal matrix for a given isomorphism.

Most concrete applications of the results of this section actually involve infinite-dimensional analogues of these results. The infinite-dimensional analogs are much harder to state and prove and are beyond the scope of this text. Nevertheless, as the following will show, there are useful applications for the finite-dimensional results as well.

Let (a_{ij}) be an $n \times n$ matrix of real numbers satisfying $a_{ij} = a_{ji}$, and suppose that $u_1, u_2, \ldots, u_n$ are real-valued functions of a real variable x, such that

$$\frac{d}{dx} u_j(x) = a_{1j}u_1(x) + \cdots + a_{nj}u_n(x), j = 1, \ldots, n$$

Define $u: \mathbf{R} \to \mathbf{R}^n$ by the equation

$$u(x) = (u_1(x), \ldots, u_n(x)),$$

and let $A: \mathbf{R}^n \to \mathbf{R}^n$ be the linear transformation whose matrix with respect to the standard basis of $\mathbf{R}^n$ is (a_{ij}).** Then, the above differential equations become

$$\frac{d}{dx}(u(x)) = A(u(x))$$

To solve this system of equations, determine an orthonormal basis of eigenvectors of A, $\{\mathbf{v}_1, \mathbf{v}_2, \ldots, \mathbf{v}_n\} \subset \mathbf{R}^n$. Then, we may write, for every $x \in \mathbf{R}$,

$$u(x) = f_1(x)\mathbf{v}_1 + \cdots + f_n(x)\mathbf{v}_n$$

** A is self-adjoint, with respect to the standard inner product of $\mathbf{R}^n$.

The above equation then becomes:

$$\frac{d}{dx}f_1(x)\mathbf{v}_1 + \cdots + \frac{d}{dx}f_n(x)\mathbf{v}_n = \lambda_1 f_1(x)\mathbf{v}_1 + \cdots + \lambda_n f_n(x)\mathbf{v}_n,$$

where $\lambda_1, \ldots, \lambda_n$ are the eigenvalues of A. This equation breaks up into the equations

$$\frac{d}{dx}f_i(x) = \lambda_i f_i(x),$$

$i = 1, \ldots, n$, which, it is well known, have as their solutions all functions of the form

$$f_i(x) = C_i e^{\lambda_i x},$$

where C_i is any real constant. Thus,

$$u(x) = C_1 e^{\lambda_1 x}\mathbf{v}_1 + \cdots + C_n e^{\lambda_n x}\mathbf{v}_n,$$

where $C_1, \ldots, C_n$ are any real constants. Thus, to solve the original equation $(d/dx)(u(x)) = A(u(x))$, it is only necessary to find the eigenvalues and eigenbasis (i.e., orthonormal basis consisting of eigenvectors) of A.

Infinite-dimensional analogs of this technique are carried out in almost the same way, only instead of finite linear combinations, infinite (series) combinations or integrals (which, after all, can be thought of as "infinite sums") are used. The interested student should consult the substantially more advanced book, *Principles and Techniques of Applied Mathematics* by Bernard Friedman (John Wiley & Sons, Inc., New York, 1956).

Finally, we present an example of an isomorphism $T: \mathbf{C}^2 \to \mathbf{C}^2$ and its expression as a composition of an inner product transformation and a self-adjoint transformation with positive eigenvalues. Let T have the following matrix with respect to the stadard basis of $\mathbf{C}^2$:

$$\begin{pmatrix} -2i & 4 \\ 3 & -1 \end{pmatrix}$$

Then, the corresponding matrix of T^* is

$$\begin{pmatrix} 2i & 3 \\ 4 & -1 \end{pmatrix}$$

and that of $T \circ T^*$ is

$$\begin{pmatrix} 20 & -4-6i \\ -4+6i & 10 \end{pmatrix}$$

Let

$$p(x) = \begin{vmatrix} 20 - x & -4 - 6i \\ -4 + 6i & 10 - x \end{vmatrix}$$

$$= (20 - x)(10 - x) - (-4 + 6i)(-4 - 6i)$$

$$= x^2 - 30x + 148$$

The zeros of $p(x)$ are $\lambda_1 = 15 + \sqrt{67}$ and $\lambda_2 = 15 - \sqrt{67}$. These are the eigenvalues of $T \circ T^*$. We now determine its eigenvectors. These are the solutions (c_1, c_2) to the two systems of equations

$$20x_1 + (-4 - 6i)x_2 = \lambda_1 x_1$$
$$(-4 + 6i)x_1 + 10x_2 = \lambda_1 x_2$$

and

$$20x_1 + (-4 - 6i)x_2 = \lambda_2 x_1$$
$$(-4 + 6i)x_1 + 10x_2 = \lambda_2 x_2$$

The pair $-1/52((5 + \sqrt{67})(4 + 6i), 1)$ is a solution to the first system, whereas the pair $-1/52(1, (-4 + 6i)(5 + \sqrt{67}))$ is a solution to the second system. The reader should verify that these two pairs are mutually orthogonal. Call the normalization of the first $\mathbf{v}_1$ and the normalization of the second $\mathbf{v}_2$. Define $A: \mathbf{C}^2 \to \mathbf{C}^2$ by the equations $A(\mathbf{v}_1) = \sqrt{\lambda_1}\mathbf{v}_1$ and $A(v_2) = \sqrt{\lambda_2}\mathbf{v}_2$, and let

$$S = A^{-1} \circ T$$

To determine the matrix of S with respect to the standard basis of $\mathbf{C}^2$, determine that of A^{-1}. To do this, note that the matrix of A^{-1} with respect to $\{\mathbf{v}_1, \mathbf{v}_2\}$ is

$$\begin{pmatrix} \frac{1}{\sqrt{\lambda_1}} & 0 \\ 0 & \frac{1}{\sqrt{\lambda_2}} \end{pmatrix}$$

Then, use the standard change-of basis formula to determine the matrix of A^{-1} (see Section 1 of this chapter).

EXERCISES / 7.6

1. Let V be a finite-dimensional inner product space, and let S and $T: V \to V$ be linear transformations. Prove that for all $(\mathbf{v}, \mathbf{w}) \in V \times V$,

$$[(S \circ T)(\mathbf{v}), \mathbf{w}] = [\mathbf{v}, (T^* \circ S^*)(\mathbf{w})]$$

Thus, conclude that $(S \circ T)^* = T^* \circ S^*$

2. Let V and T be as in 1, and assume that T is an isomorphism. Show that for every $(\mathbf{v}, \mathbf{w}) \in V \times V$,

$$[T^{-1}(\mathbf{v}), \mathbf{w}] = [\mathbf{v}, (T^*)^{-1}(\mathbf{w})]$$

This, conclude that $(T^{-1})^* = (T^*)^{-1}$.

3. Prove that if V is any vector space and $A: V \to V$ and $B: V \to V$ are any linear transformations satisfying $A \circ B = B \circ A$, then $\mathscr{R}_A$ and $\mathscr{N}_A$ are B-invariant and $\mathscr{R}_B$ and $\mathscr{N}_B$ are A-invariant.

4. Solve the following system of differential equations

$$\frac{df}{dx}(x) = f(x) + 3g(x)$$

$$\frac{dg}{dx}(x) = 3f(x) + g(x),$$

where f and g are real-valued functions of a real variable.

5. Prove that for every $c \in \mathbf{C}$, if $c \neq 0$, then there exists a positive real number r and another real number θ, so that

$$c = r(\cos\theta + i\sin\theta)$$

(*Hint*: Apply Proposition 7.20 to the isomorphisms from $\mathbf{C}$ to $\mathbf{C}$.)

6. Let V be a finite-dimensional inner product space. Prove that $I_V: V \to V$ is the only isomorphism of V that is both self-adjoint and an inner product transformation.

7. Let $\mathscr{D}^\infty[0, 1]$ be the vector space of all real-valued functions on $[0, 1]$ that possess all derivatives of all orders in $\mathscr{C}[0, 1]$. $\mathscr{C}[0, 1]$ is the vector space of all real-valued continuous functions on $[0, 1]$. We consider $\mathscr{C}[0, 1]$ to be an inner product space with respect to the inner product $[\ ,\ ]$ defined by

$$[f, g] = \int_0^1 f(x)g(x)\,dx,$$

for all f, g in $\mathscr{C}[0, 1]$. $\mathscr{D}^\infty[0, 1]$ is a vector subspace of $\mathscr{C}[0, 1]$, and, thus, is an inner product space with respect to $[\ ,\ ]$. Let U be the subset of $\mathscr{D}^\infty[0, 1]$ consisting of all functions h such that $h(0) = h(1)$ and $\frac{dh}{dx}(0) = \frac{dh}{dx}(1)$.

a. Show that U is a vector subspace of $\mathscr{D}^\infty[0, 1]$.

Now, consider U as an inner product space with respect to $[\ ,\ ]$, as defined above. Let $D: U \to U$ be the linear transformation satisfying

$$D(h) = \frac{dh}{dx}$$

b. Prove that $[D(f), g] = [f, D(g)]$, for all $(f, g) \in U \times U$.

Thus, if D has an adjoint D^*, then $D = D^*$.

c. Consider $D = d/dx$ as a linear transformation from $\mathscr{D}^\infty[0, 1]$ to $\mathscr{D}^\infty[0, 1]$. Show that the only eigenvectors of D are the functions h given by

$$h(x) = Ce^{\lambda x},$$

for any real numbers $C \neq 0$ and λ. (Thus, any real number λ is an eigenvalue of D.)

Therefore, conclude that $D \mid U$ has no eigenvectors.

8. a. Let $S: \mathbf{R}^2 \to \mathbf{R}^2$ be an inner product transformation (with respect to the standard inner product of $\mathbf{R}^2$), with negative determinant. Show that there is a real number θ such that the matrix of S with respect to the standard basis of $\mathbf{R}^2$ is

$$\begin{pmatrix} \cos\theta & \sin\theta \\ \sin\theta & -\cos\theta \end{pmatrix}$$

b. Let $T: \mathbf{R}^2 \to \mathbf{R}^2$ be the rotation of $\mathbf{R}^2$ through the angle θ. Let $R: \mathbf{R}^2 \to \mathbf{R}^2$ be the linear transformation whose matrix with respect to the standard basis is:

$$\begin{pmatrix} 1 & 0 \\ 0 & -1 \end{pmatrix}$$

Show that $T \circ R = S$.

The transformation R keeps the standard basis vector $\mathbf{e}_1$ fixed and sends $\mathbf{e}_2$ to $-\mathbf{e}_2$. Thus, R takes the ordered pair (x, y) to the ordered pair $(x, -y)$. This transformation is sometimes called, *reflection through the X-axis.*

This result shows that every inner product transformation from $\mathbf{R}^2$ to $\mathbf{R}^2$ with negative determinant is the composition of a rotation and reflection through the X-axis.

Thus, every isomorphism from $\mathbf{R}^2$ to $\mathbf{R}^2$ can be expressed uniquely in the form $A \circ S \circ B$, where A is a stretching, S is a rotation, and $B = I_{\mathbf{R}^2}$ if the determinant of the isomorphism is positive, or $B = R$ if the determinant is negative.

9. Consider the inner product space $\mathscr{D}^\infty[0, 1]$ of **7** and the linear transformation $D: \mathscr{D}^\infty[0, 1] \to \mathscr{D}^\infty[0, 1]$ given by

$$D(f) = \frac{df}{dx},$$

for every $f \in \mathscr{D}^\infty[0, 1]$.

a. Prove that $\mathscr{N}_D$ consists of all constant functions and, hence, that $\mathscr{N}_D$ has dimension 1.

b. Prove, by the inductive method, that $\mathscr{N}_{D^k}$ has dimension k, for all integers $k \geqq 1$ (where D^k is the usual k-fold composition of D with itself).

c. Let S and T be any members of Trans(V, V), for any vector space V.

i. Prove that $S(\mathscr{N}_{T \circ S}) \subset \mathscr{N}_T$ and $\mathscr{N}_S \subset \mathscr{N}_{T \circ S}$.

ii. Prove that $\mathscr{N}_{S \mid \mathscr{N}_{T \circ S}} = \mathscr{N}_S$.

iii. Assume that $\mathscr{N}_T$ and $\mathscr{N}_S$ are finite-dimensional. Prove that

$$\dim \mathscr{N}_{T \circ S} \leqq \dim \mathscr{N}_T + \dim \mathscr{N}_S$$

(*Hint*: Consider $S \mid \mathscr{N}_{T \circ S}$ and note that, by **i**, $\mathscr{R}_{S \mid \mathscr{N}_{T \circ S}} \subset \mathscr{N}_T$.)

d. Let $p(x)$ be any polynomial of $\mathscr{P}_{\mathbf{R}}$ of degree n. Suppose, furthermore, that all the zeros of $p(x)$ are real. Prove inductively that $\dim \mathscr{N}_{p(D)} \leqq n$.

(*Hint*: Prove the result directly for $n = 1$. Then express $p(x) = (x - a)g(x)$, consider $p(D)$, and apply **c.**)

e. Let $p(x) = a_n x^n + a_{n-1}x^{n-1} + \cdots + a_1 x + a_0$. Then, the equation

$$\overline{0} = p(D)(h) = a_n D^n(h) + a_{n-1}D^{n-1}(h) + \cdots + a_1 D(h) + a_0 h,$$

where h is an indeterminate function in $\mathscr{D}^\infty[0, 1]$, is known as an nth *order homogeneous linear differential equation with constant coefficients.* In **d** it is shown that there are no more than n linearly independent solutions to such an equation, or, in other words, that the solution set is not more than n-dimensional.** Indeed, its dimension is precisely n.

Prove that if λ is a zero of $p(x)$, then any eigenvector of D corresponding to λ is a solution to the above equation. Show that $e^{\lambda t}$ is such an eigenvector (where t is a real variable ranging over $[0, 1]$). Show that if $\lambda_0 \neq \lambda_1$, then the functions f_0 and f_1 given by $f_0(t) = e^{\lambda_0 t}$ and $f_1(t) = e^{\lambda_1 t}$ are linearly independent as vectors in the vector space $\mathscr{D}^\infty[0, 1]$ over $\mathbf{R}$.

f. Suppose that $p(x) = a_n(x - \lambda_1)^{r_1} \ldots (x - \lambda_k)^{r_k}$, where $r_i \geqq 1$. Show that the functions

$$e^{\lambda_1 t}, te^{\lambda_1 t}, \ldots, t^{r_1 - 1}e^{\lambda_1 t}$$
$$e^{\lambda_2 t}, te^{\lambda_2 t}, \ldots, t^{r_2 - 1}e^{\lambda_2 t}$$
$$e^{\lambda_k t}, te^{\lambda_k t}, \ldots, t^{r_k - 1}e^{\lambda_k t}$$

form a basis of $\mathscr{N}_{p(D)}$. Call it X. Recall that $\mathscr{N}_{p(D)}$ is D-invariant. Show that

$$\mathscr{A}_{X,X}(D \mid \mathscr{N}_{p(D)})$$

is triangular.

** Provided that the zeros of $p(x)$ are real, which we assume.

Index

MAJOR SYMBOL

First Appearance